ORGANIC CHEMISTRY

By the same author

GENERAL AND INORGANIC CHEMISTRY

By P. J. Durrant and B. Durrant

INTRODUCTION TO ADVANCED INORGANIC CHEMISTRY

ORGANIC
CHEMISTRY

BY

P. J. DURRANT, M.A., Ph.D.

FELLOW AND LECTURER IN CHEMISTRY,
SELWYN COLLEGE, CAMBRIDGE

WITH DIAGRAMS

LONGMANS

LONGMANS, GREEN AND CO LTD
48 Grosvenor Street, London, W.1.

*Associated companies, branches and representatives
throughout the world*

First Published 1950
Second Impression 1952
Third Impression, with minor corrections, 1954
Fourth Impression 1956
Fifth Impression 1957
Sixth Impression 1958
Seventh Impression 1959
Eighth Impression 1961
Ninth Impression 1963

PRINTED IN GREAT BRITAIN BY ROBERT MACLEHOSE AND CO. LTD
THE UNIVERSITY PRESS GLASGOW

PREFACE

THIS book is intended for students reading for such examinations as the General Certificate in Education, Entrance Scholarships Examinations to universities and colleges, and examinations in organic chemistry which form part of pre-clinical medical courses and other preliminary university examinations.

Chapter I contains a summary of the current view of atomic structure. The treatment, which is necessarily elementary, describes an atom as a system of particles, in which the electrons describe geometrical orbits about a positive nucleus. It is so written, however, that the ideas presented can be translated into the more abstract concepts of the wave-mechanical theory without confusion or contradiction. The account of atomic structure is followed by an account of the modes of combination by which atoms are bonded together in molecules. The emphasis throughout is laid on carbon and the other elements which are met with most frequently in organic chemistry. The theory of resonance is described shortly in order to furnish an explanation of the properties of benzene. The electronic theory of organic reactions is touched on, but it is recognised that the general use of such a theory would bewilder rather than assist the reader, and the few examples given in the book are chiefly intended to indicate the present outlook on the mechanism of chemical reactions in organic chemistry.

In the experience of the author, many students who begin a course on organic chemistry by learning the preparations and properties of the commoner types of compounds are hindered in their progress by failure to appreciate where the study is leading; it is often a long time before they gain any panoramic view of the subject. Chapter II is included to meet this difficulty. It shows what organic chemistry is about, and provides a background for the more detailed accounts of particular compounds contained in Chapters V to XXVIII. Chapter XXIX draws together in a generalised study the principal chemical reactions that have been mentioned elsewhere in the book; Chapter XXX does the same for technical processes. These two Chapters introduce the reader to a broader survey of organic chemistry than is possible in earlier Chapters.

Chapters III and IV describe the general laboratory procedure which has been evolved for the study of organic compounds. The procedure is described in terms of physical chemistry, but it has been found possible to omit detailed accounts of methods (such as methods for the determination of molecular weights) which are to be found in the standard text-books of physical chemistry. The practical details of the preparations of the more important compounds are inserted in the Chapters in which these compounds are described. These detailed accounts of laboratory preparations are neither intended to be rigorously learnt, nor to serve as guides for practical work. They are included to emphasize that organic chemistry is not a form of algebra governing the manipulation of the symbols C, H, O and N, but a practical science directed in the end to the fabrication and use of certain classes of compounds. The descriptions of many of these experiments are based on the carefully prepared instructions in *Practical Organic Chemistry* by F. G. Mann and B. C. Saunders. I am greatly indebted to Dr. Mann and Dr. Saunders for permission to make use of their material which has enabled me to describe practical experiments with precision and consistency. It also ensures that students who learn their theoretical work from the present book will be able to use the book of Drs. Mann and Saunders on the bench without meeting contradictions in points of detail.

Most students master the concrete more easily than the abstract, and they can learn about a particular compound more readily than a class of compounds. For this reason the descriptions of the preparations and properties of the principal classes of organic compounds are made as direct and concrete as possible. The preparation and reactions of a typical member of each class are first dealt with fully, and any distinctions between other members of the class and the typical member are then pointed out. In certain cases this method of approach requires that the order in which members of a class are described differs from their order in the homologous series ; for example acetic acid (not formic acid) is the first member of the fatty acids to be discussed, and ethyl bromide (not methyl chloride) is chosen as the typical member of the alkyl halides.

My warmest thanks are due to my many friends in Cambridge who by their readiness to place their knowledge and experience at my service have assisted me in the preparation of this book, and in particular to Dr. F. Wild, Fellow of Downing College, who read the whole of the galley proof and suggested many modifications and additions of great value, and to Dr. R. C. Evans, Fellow of St. Catharine's College, University Lecturer in Mineralogy and Petrology, who made the drawings of the crystals illustrating the section on optical isomerism (Figs. 53–56).

Acknowledgments are due to the Cambridge University Press Syndicate, the Oxford Local Examinations Delegacy, the University of Cambridge Local Examinations Syndicate, the Oxford and Cambridge Schools Examinations Board, the Joint Matriculation Board, and to the Universities of London, Bombay,* Calcutta, Cape Town, Melbourne, and Sydney, for permission to include questions set in various examinations.

P. J. DURRANT.

SELWYN COLLEGE,
CAMBRIDGE.
February, 1950

* The copyright of questions set in examinations held by the University of Bombay is vested in that University.

CONTENTS

ix

x

CONTENTS

Part III.   Aromatic Compounds

Part IV.

ATOMIC WEIGHTS OF CERTAIN ELEMENTS

	Symbol	At. wt.		Symbol	At. wt.
Aluminium	Al	26·97	Manganese	Mn	54·93
Barium	Ba	137·36	Mercury	Hg	200·61
Bromine	Br	79·92	Nickel	Ni	58·69
Calcium	Ca	40·08	Nitrogen	N	14·008
Carbon	C	12·01	Oxygen	O	16·000
Chlorine	Cl	35·46	Phosphorus	P	30·98
Chromium	Cr	52·01	Platinum	Pt	195·23
Copper	Cu	63·57	Potassium	K	39·10
Fluorine	F	19·00	Silicon	Si	28·06
Gold	Au	197·2	Silver	Ag	107·88
Hydrogen	H	1·008	Sodium	Na	23·00
Iodine	I	126·92	Strontium	Sr	87·63
Iron	Fe	55·84	Sulphur	S	32·06
Lead	Pb	207·21	Tin	Sn	118·7
Magnesium	Mg	24·32	Zinc	Zn	65·38

NOTE

Temperatures are expressed in degrees centigrade, and the "C." which designates this temperature scale is not printed after the numerical value of the temperature. For example, 15° means 15 degrees centigrade.

Pressures are expressed as millimetres of mercury printed thus: 760 mm.

The Ångstrom unit of length, symbol Å, is 1×10^{-8} cm.

CHAPTER I

THE ULTIMATE STRUCTURE OF ELEMENTS AND COMPOUNDS

I. THE CONSTITUENT PARTICLES

IT is the aim of chemistry, by a study of the physical and chemical properties of elements and compounds, to conceive an ultimate structure of matter, in terms of which observed properties may be explained, and by which the existence of unsuspected properties may be predicted. At the present day, matter is assumed to be composed of very small particles of several types, which by their interaction and combination give rise to the complexity and diversity of matter as ordinarily observed. The particles are assumed to possess mass, velocity, certain wave properties, and in some cases electric charge. For an elementary study of chemistry the velocities and wave properties are disregarded, and attention is concentrated on the positions occupied by the particles with respect to one another.

The particles with which the science of chemistry is chiefly concerned are the molecule and the atom. The **molecule** is defined as *the smallest particle of a gas which moves about as a whole.* Any perceptible volume of a gas is constituted of a large number of molecules ; there are $6 \cdot 023 \times 10^{23}$ molecules in $22 \cdot 4$ litres of a gas at N.T.P. These molecules are in agitated motion, and in frequent collision, but they are otherwise independent of one another. When the gas is liquefied the molecules come closer together and their motion is diminished, and when the liquid crystallises the molecules take up fixed positions in the geometrical array which is characteristic of the crystalline state. The molecule is a very important unit in organic chemistry, and the elucidation of the structures of molecules of organic compounds is one of the chief tasks of the organic chemist.

Molecules are constituted of atoms. An **atom** is defined as *the smallest particle of an element which can enter into, or be expelled from, chemical combination.* Experimental evidence has led to the assumption that atoms are constructed of three sub-atomic particles, the electron, the neutron and the proton. Modern research has indicated the existence of two other sub-atomic particles, the

A

positron and the mesotron, but in the present state of our knowledge these are of more interest to the physicist than to the chemist.

The atom of any element consists of (i) a positively charged nucleus, known as the *positive nucleus*, and (ii) a number of electrons known as the *planetary electrons* which move in fixed orbits about the positive nucleus. The positive charge on the nucleus is exactly neutralised by the aggregate negative charge of the planetary electrons. The electron is a simple particle : the positive nucleus of the hydrogen atom is a single proton ; the positive nucleus of any other atom consists of protons and neutrons.

The electron. The electron is a particle of mass $9 \cdot 11 \times 10^{-28}$ gm. which is equal to 1/1834 of that of the hydrogen atom. It carries a charge of negative electricity of magnitude $1 \cdot 602 \times 10^{-19}$ coulombs, or $4 \cdot 8024 \times 10^{-10}$ e.s.u. The cathode rays produced during an electric discharge in a gas at very low pressure (at pressures of the order of 0·01 mm. of mercury) consist of electrons free from association with other forms of matter. Electrons are also emitted by metals when heated or when illuminated by ultra-violet light, and by certain substances undergoing radioactive disintegration.

The neutron. The neutron is a particle of mass 1·0090 (on a scale on which the mass of the oxygen atom is 16), and diameter of the order of 10^{-13} cm. It has no electrical charge. Neutrons are emitted when certain elements, for example beryllium, are bombarded by α-particles, also when deuterium (heavy hydrogen) is irradiated with X-rays of very short wave-length, and when the atomic nucleus breaks down in the disintegration of the isotope of uranium, U^{235}, used in the atomic bomb.

The proton. The proton is a particle of mass 1·0081 (O = 16), which mass is identical with that of the hydrogen atom. It carries a positive electrical charge equal in magnitude to the negative charge of the electron. Its diameter is of the order of 10^{-13} cm.

The positive nucleus. The hydrogen nucleus is a single proton ; nuclei of other atoms contain neutrons as well as protons. The manner in which the protons and neutrons are bonded together is unknown. The nucleus carries a positive charge numerically equal to the atomic number of the element, that is, the number which represents the position of the element in the periodic classification. Each unit of charge corresponds to the presence of one proton in the nucleus, and therefore the number of protons in the nucleus is equal to the atomic number of the element. The mass of the nucleus is very nearly, but not exactly, equal to the sum of the masses of the protons and neutrons it contains. The number of neutrons in the positive nucleus is, therefore, the nearest whole number to the difference between the mass of the atom (O = 16) and the atomic number. Since the mass of an electron is very small compared with that of a proton or neutron, the mass of the atom may be taken as that of the nucleus. The diameter of the positive nucleus, even in atoms of elements of high atomic number, appears to be of the same order as the diameter of a proton or neutron.

The planetary electrons. The positive charge of the nucleus of the atom is neutralised by the aggregate charge of the planetary electrons which surround it. Since the atom as a whole is electrically neutral, the number of planetary electrons in the atom must be equal to the number of protons in the positive nucleus. These electrons are in motion in definite orbits about the nucleus. The name " planetary electrons " was chosen because their motion about the nucleus was once thought to resemble in some degree the motion of the planets about the sun.

TABLE I

COMPARISON OF THE CONSTANTS OF CERTAIN PARTICLES

Particle	Mass on a scale on which the mass of the oxygen atom is 16 units	Diameter	Electrical charge	
			Sign	Magnitude
Electron	1/1834 of the mass of the hydrogen atom		negative	$4 \cdot 8024 \times 10^{-10}$ e.s.u.
Proton	1·0081	of the order of 10^{-13} cm.	positive	$4 \cdot 8024 \times 10^{-10}$ e.s.u.
Neutron	1·0090	of the order of 10^{-13} cm..	neutral	zero
Positive nucleus of hydrogen	The positive nucleus of hydrogen is a single proton			
Hydrogen atom	1·0081	$0 \cdot 6 \times 10^{-8}$ cm.*	neutral	zero
Carbon atom	12·000	$1 \cdot 54 \times 10^{-8}$ cm.*	neutral	zero

* From measurements made on the distances separating atomic nuclei in hydrocarbons of the paraffin series (p. 32).

Atomic number. The characteristic property of an atom, which distinguishes the atoms of one element from those of another, is its atomic number. The atomic number of an element primarily represents its position in the periodic table. It is pointed out above that the atomic number of a given element also represents (i) the number of protons in the nucleus, and (ii) the number of planetary electrons in the atom.

The hydrogen atom. The simplest atom is the hydrogen atom ; the positive nucleus is a single proton, and there is one planetary electron. The diameter of the hydrogen atom is of the order of 10^{-8} cm. ; the diameter of the proton is of the order 10^{-13} cm. The volume swept out by the planetary electron, which corresponds to the volume of the hydrogen atom, therefore, is one million million times that of the positive nucleus.

The planetary electron in the hydrogen atom is in motion in an orbit about the positive nucleus. It has been found that the laws and equations of Newtonian dynamics, which successfully interpret the motions of astronomical bodies and of familiar objects such as golf balls and rifle bullets, cannot be applied to the motion of planetary electrons within the atom. On the classical theory the rapidly moving electrons would be expected to radiate energy as light. As the radiant eyergy was emitted the electrons would describe smaller and smaller orbits with ever-increasing speed, and finally fall into the nucleus. In place of the Newtonian laws a specially devised system of mechanics, known as quantum mechanics, must be used. It is assumed by this quantum theory that a planetary electron describing an orbit about the positive nucleus neither gains nor radiates any energy ; the electron exhibits perpetual motion. The planetary electron in the hydrogen atom, however, is not restricted to one orbit ; there are a number of possible orbits which it may describe, and in jumping from one orbit to another it may either emit or absorb energy, according to whether it jumps towards, or away from, the nucleus. For example, the hydrogen atom absorbs energy when an electric spark is passed through hydrogen gas. This energy is stored in the atom by the elevation of the planetary electron from one orbit to another in which it possesses more energy. When the atom passes out of the influence of the electric spark, the planetary electron returns again to its original orbit, and the energy which it had absorbed is emitted as light of a single definite wave-length. If numerous hydrogen atoms are energised by the electric spark, they do not all gain equal quantities of energy, and consequently their planetary electrons are elevated to different orbits, and the atoms in regaining their normal condition then radiate several wave-lengths, thus producing the spark spectrum of hydrogen. By a careful study of the wave-lengths of the light of the hydrogen spectrum the differences in the amounts of energy possessed by the planetary electron in various orbits have been calculated.

The hydrogen atom may, therefore, be conceived as the positive nucleus, consisting of a proton, surrounded by a system of definite orbits for the planetary electron. The electron may describe any one of these orbits without losing or gaining energy, but when it jumps from one orbit to another, energy may be either radiated or absorbed.

A crude mechanical parallel may serve to help in the understanding of this model, and to emphasise the difference between the outlooks of the classical and the quantum theories. Suppose the positive nucleus of the hydrogen atom is a small town set in a hollow, and that the electronic orbits are a series of ring-roads reaching further and further into the countryside, each successive road being higher up the surrounding hillside (Fig. 1).

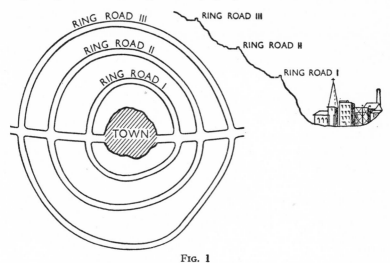

FIG. 1

Suppose also that the single planetary electron of the hydrogen atom is a cyclist on a frictionless bicycle who may travel on any given ring-road without expenditure of energy. To move from one ring-road to another further away from the town he must climb up-hill, and the work he is forced to do he retains as potential energy by virtue of his increased height above sea-level. Once having gained the higher road he can free-wheel along it for an indefinite period without either gaining or losing energy. If, however, he desires to return to a ring-road nearer the town, he must go down-hill with his brakes applied. The difference between the potential energy which he possessed at the high road level, and that which he will still possess at the lower road level, will then be radiated as heat from his wheel rims and brake-blocks.

The electronic orbits of the hydrogen atom fall into types. A particular type of orbit in the hydrogen atom may be specified by assigning numerical values to each of the two terms known as **quantum numbers.** The quantum numbers are :

> (a) *the* **principal quantum number,** *n, which may be any integer from* 1 *to* 7 :
> (b) *the* **angular quantum number,** *l, which for a given value of n may have any value from zero to n* – 1.

The number of orbits of any particular type may be designated as μ. μ is governed by the angular quantum number of the orbits, and is given by the relation

$$\mu = 2l + 1.$$

The state of lowest energy of an atom is the *ground state.* When the hydrogen atom is in the ground state, the planetary electron is describing an orbit of the type specified by the lowest possible value of the principal quantum number, namely, $n = 1$. There is only one such orbit, since $l = 0$ and

$$\mu = 2l + 1 = 2 \times 0 + 1 = 1.$$

If the atom of hydrogen is made to absorb energy, the planetary electron is forced into an orbit of higher energy level. The orbit of next higher energy level is characterised by $n = 2$. There are two types of orbit for which $n = 2$, since in this case the angular quantum number, l, may be either 0 or 1 ; the two types of orbit may be described as $n2,l0$ and $n2,l1$ orbits. There is only one $n2,l0$ orbit, since

$$\mu = 2l + 1 = 2 \times 0 + 1 = 1,$$

but there are three $n2,l1$ orbits, since

$$\mu = 2l + 1 = 2 \times 1 + 1 = 3.$$

Any orbit for which the angular quantum number $l = 0$ is known as an *s-orbit*, and any orbit for which $l = 1$ is known as a *p-orbit*. The planetary electron of the hydrogen atom in the ground state is in the s-orbit of the type characterised by $n = 1$, or shortly in a 1s orbit. In the next higher energy state of the hydrogen atom the planetary electron is in one of the types of orbit for which $n = 2$. The first of these types of orbits is specified by the quantum numbers $n2,l0$. There is only one such orbit which is an s-orbit, and it is described shortly as a 2s orbit. The second type of orbit is specified by the quantum numbers $n2,l1$. There are three such orbits which are p-orbits described by the symbol 2p. The three p-orbits are differentiated * by means of the magnetic quantum number, m, which may have one of the values 1, 0 or -1.

Similarly, when $n = 3$ there are the three types of orbits, $n3,l0$, $n3,l1$ and $n3,l2$ which are shortly described as 3s,3p and 3d orbits respectively. There are five d-orbits ($\mu = 2 \times 2 + 1$) which are differentiated by the magnetic quantum m, which has the possible values 2, 1, 0, -1, -2. The first few orbits of low energy level in the hydrogen atom are shown in Table II below.

TABLE II

ELECTRONIC ORBITS OF LOW ENERGY LEVEL IN THE HYDROGEN ATOM

State of hydrogen atom	Principal quantum number, n (n may be any integer from 1 to 7)	Angular quantum number, l (l may have any value from zero to n − 1)	Type of orbit	Number of orbits $\mu = 2l + 1$	Magnetic quantum number, m
Ground state	1	0	1s	1	0
First activated state	2 2	0 1	2s 2p	1 3	0 1, 0, −1
Second activated state	3 3 3	0 1 2	3s 3p 3d	1 3 5	0 1, 0, −1 2, 1, 0, −1, −2

* For the hydrogen atom under ordinary conditions the energy of a given electronic orbit depends only on the principal quantum number n, and hence, under ordinary conditions, the energy levels of the three p-orbits are identical. If the atom is placed in a magnetic field, however, the energy levels of the three p-orbits differ ; in these conditions each p-orbit acquires a different energy level which is dependent on m, its magnetic quantum number. Each of the three p-orbits is therefore distinguished by the appropriate value of the magnetic quantum number.

For other atoms under ordinary conditions the energy of a given orbit is mainly dependent on the value of the principal quantum number n ; it is also dependent to a much smaller degree on the value of the angular quantum number l. The greater the value of l, the higher is the energy level of the orbit.

Much progress has been made in the deduction, from observations on spectra, of the number and types of electronic orbits in atoms which are more complex than that of hydrogen *by assuming that the configuration of electronic orbits in all other atoms is similar to the configuration of orbits in the hydrogen atom.*

The specification of the particular orbit which an electron is describing does not give a complete account of the behaviour of the electron. The rotation of an electron about its own axis while it is describing the orbit must also be considered. The rotation of an electron about its own axis is known as *spin.* It has been deduced that a planetary electron is capable of two directions of spin. These are designated by assigning the values $\frac{1}{2}$ and $-\frac{1}{2}$ to a fourth quantum number s.* The condition of a planetary electron in an atom is completely defined by assigning numerical values to the principal quantum number n, the angular quantum number l, and the magnetic quantum number m, which together define the orbit which the electron is occupying, and to the spin quantum number s, which defines the direction of spin.

The maximum number of electrons which can be present in any given orbit is decided by **Pauli's exclusion principle,** which states that *no two electrons in any atom may have identical values for the three quantum numbers n, l, and s.* This means that a single orbit can contain no more than two electrons, one with the spin quantum number $s = +\frac{1}{2}$, and the other with $s = -\frac{1}{2}$. The maximum number of electrons which can be present in any given orbit is 2.

On the assumptions that the atoms of all elements possess configurations of electronic orbits which are similar to that of the hydrogen atom, and that the maximum number of electrons which may be present in any electronic orbit is two, it is possible to deduce how the electrons are distributed in an atom of any given element. Table III shows the types of orbit arranged in order of increasing energy level. These types are identical with those given in column 4 of Table II. Column 4 of Table III shows the maximum number of orbits of any given type which can be found in an atom, and column 5 shows the maximum number of electrons which may occupy this number of orbits.

---

* The reader will note that the symbol s is used to denote (i) a type of orbit, (ii) the spin quantum number. Although this notation is confusing, it has become so well established in the literature of atomic structure that the use of any other in the present chapter would be undesirable.

TABLE III

THE SIMPLER ELECTRONIC ORBITS OF THE ORBITAL CONFIGURATION
GENERALLY APPLICABLE TO THE ATOMS OF ALL ELEMENTS

Types of orbit	Principal quantum number n	Angular quantum number l	Maximum number of orbits, μ, of each type. $\mu = 2l + 1$	Maximum number of electrons in the maximum number of orbits of each type
1s	1	0	1	2
2s	2	0	1	2
2p	2	1	3	6
3s	3	0	1	2
3p	3	1	3	6
3d	3	2	5	10

In order to see how the planetary electrons of the atoms of the elements are distributed among the orbits of the general orbital configuration which is possessed by all atoms, the first ten elements in the periodic table may be considered. The atom of hydrogen contains 1 electron and, for the atom in the ground state, this occupies the orbit of lowest energy level which is a 1s orbit. The element next following hydrogen in the periodic table is helium, with two planetary electrons in the atom. Both these electrons can be placed in the 1s orbit, since this orbit may contain two electrons if their spin quantum numbers are different. The 1s orbit is then full. The next element, lithium has three planetary electrons in the atom. Two of these fill the 1s orbit, and the remaining one is in a 2s orbit. Similarly, of the four electrons of beryllium, two occupy the 1s orbit, and two the 2s orbit. The boron atom contains five electrons. Of these two are in the 1s orbit, two are in the 2s orbit, and one is in the first 2p orbit. The carbon atom contains six electrons of which five are disposed in the same way as in the atom of boron. It can be shown that the energy of the system of electrons in the p-orbits is lowest when the electron spins are in the same direction. Since by Pauli's exclusion principle (p. 8) two electrons with the same spin cannot be accommodated in one orbit, the sixth carbon electron must occupy the second p-orbit. By similar arguments it is possible to construct Table IV which shows the electronic configurations of the atoms of elements in the first two periods of the periodic table.

TABLE IV

ELECTRONIC CONFIGURATIONS OF ELEMENTS OF
ATOMIC NUMBER 1–10

Period	Atomic number	Element	Number of electrons in orbit				
			K shell	L shell			
			1s orbit	2s orbit	2p orbits		
I	1	H	1				
	2	He	2				
II	3	Li	2	1			
	4	Be	2	2			
	5	B	2	2	1		
	6	C	2	2	1	1	
	7	N	2	2	1	1	1
	8	O	2	2	2	1	1
	9	F	2	2	2	2	1
	10	Ne	2	2	2	2	2

When describing the electronic configuration of an atom it is not always necessary to enumerate in detail all the occupied orbits. For many purposes it is sufficient to group together all the orbits of the same principal quantum number ; each group is then known as a **quantum shell.** Planetary electrons in orbits of principal quantum number 1 are said to be in the K quantum shell, those of principal quantum number 2 in the L quantum shell, and so on. Table IV shows how this nomenclature applies to orbits of principal quantum numbers 1 and 2.

Consideration of Table IV shows that the filling of all orbits of principal quantum number 1 corresponds with the completion of Period I of the periodic classification, and the filling of all orbits of principal quantum number 2 corresponds with the completion of Period II. The relation between the capacities of the electronic orbits and the periods of the periodic table becomes less simple in Period IV and the following periods, but for our present purpose the discussion need not be carried further.

The electron configurations of the inert gases are of importance in the theory of chemical combination which is described in Section II below. It is evident that the inert gases, which are monatomic and do not enter into chemical combination, must possess atomic structures of the highest stability. Table V summarises the distribution of electrons in the atoms of each of the inert gases, and shows the total numbers of electrons in each quantum shell ; the distribution of the electrons among the various types of orbits constituting each quantum shell is not given, as its consideration is unnecessary for the present purpose.

TABLE V

ELECTRONIC CONFIGURATIONS OF THE INERT GASES

Inert gas			Number of electrons in quantum shell					
Atomic number	Name	Symbol	K $(n=1)$	L $(n=2)$	M $(n=3)$	N $(n=4)$	O $(n=5)$	P $(n=6)$
2	Helium	He	2					
10	Neon	Ne	2	8				
18	Argon	A	2	8	8			
36	Krypton	Kr	2	8	18	8		
54	Xenon	Xe	2	8	18	18	8	
86	Radon	Rn	2	8	18	32	18	8

The characteristics of the atomic structures of the inert gases are :

(i) with the exception of helium, the number of electrons in the external quantum shell is 8 ;

(ii) the internal quantum shells contain 2, 8, 18 or 32 electrons. The configurations of the quantum shells of the atoms of an inert gas must possess such stability that the atom cannot use any electrons to effect combination with other atoms.

II. CHEMICAL COMBINATION

The present view of chemical combination is based both on consideration of the properties and reactions of chemical substances, and also on the results of experiments in physics bearing on the structure of matter.   It involves the assumptions that :

(i) an atom entering into chemical combination changes the number of electrons in its external quantum shell ;

(ii) an atom of an element other than an inert gas, tends, by chemical combination with other atoms, to adjust the number of electrons in its external quantum shell, so that it may attain the electron configuration of the inert gas at the beginning or end of the period of the periodic classification in which the element occurs ;

(iii) atoms of elements in Period III and Period IV of the periodic classification may also attain stable electronic configurations by increasing the number of electrons in their external quantum shells to 12, and elements in Period V and higher periods may increase the number to 16.

There are two primary modes by which an atom can combine with other atoms, and so effect a change in the number of electrons in its external quantum shell, namely, by the formation of (i) an ionic bond, and (ii) a covalent bond.

The ionic bond. Certain atoms may attain the electronic configuration of an inert gas by the loss or gain of one or more electrons. For example, from Table IV (p. 10) it may be seen that the lithium atom may attain the configuration of the helium atom by the loss of one electron, and the fluorine atom may attain the configuration of the neon atom by the gain of one electron. When lithium and fluorine combine to form lithium fluoride, one electron is transferred from each lithium atom to a fluorine atom. This change may be represented diagrammatically by means of an equation in which the electrons in the external quantum shells of each atom are shown beside its symbol, thus :

$$\text{Li} \circ \; + \; \cdot \overset{\bullet\bullet}{\underset{\bullet\bullet}{\text{F}}} \colon \; = \; \left[\text{Li}\right]^{+} \; \left[\overset{\bullet\bullet}{\underset{\bullet\bullet}{\circ \; \text{F} \; \bullet}}\right]^{-}$$

The modified atoms, indicated by the square brackets, are called **ions.** The lithium ion, Li⁺, is positively charged, and the fluorine ion, F⁻, is negatively charged. These charges are produced by the loss or gain of one electron, and therefore they are equal in magnitude. Lithium and fluorine in lithium fluoride are held together by the electrostatic attraction between the two ions, and an ionic bond is thus established between the atoms of lithium and fluorine.

It is possible for more than one ionic bond to be established between a pair of atoms. The calcium atom has 2 electrons in its external quantum shell, and the oxygen atom has 6. By transference of the 2 electrons from the calcium atom to the oxygen atom, two ions are formed, each of which carries a double charge and has the configuration of an inert gas :

$$\text{Ca} \; {\overset{\circ}{\underset{\circ}{}}} \; + \; \overset{\bullet\bullet}{\underset{\bullet\bullet}{\text{O}}} \colon \; = \; \left[\text{Ca}\right]^{++} \left[\overset{\bullet\bullet}{\underset{\bullet\bullet}{\circ \; \text{O} \; \bullet}}\right]^{--}$$

The calcium and oxygen atoms in calcium oxide are linked by two ionic bonds.

An ion does not necessarily consist of a single atom. The ammonium ion is the group NH_4 carrying one positive charge, and the sulphate ion is the group SO_4 carrying two negative charges. Ammonium sulphate contains two ammonium ions linked by ionic bonds to a sulphate ion :

$$[NH_4]^+ \; [SO_4]^{--} \; [NH_4]^+.$$

The ionic bond may be defined as *a link between two atoms, or groups of atoms, which is dependent on the electrostatic attraction between a positive ion derived from one atom or group, and a negative ion derived from the other, by the loss or gain respectively of one electron.* As the force which holds the ions together in an ionic bond is simple electrostatic attraction, there is no intimate structural link between the ions. Consequently atoms linked by ionic bonds have no fixed orientation to one another, and crystals of ionic substances are assemblies of ions in geometrical arrangements which permit of the closest packing. The presence of an ionic bond in a compound diminishes its volatility, and its solubility in such solvents as benzene and ether. When an ionic compound dissolves in water, the ions fall apart ; in dilute aqueous solution the ions exist independently of one another. Aqueous solutions of ionic compounds, therefore, conduct electricity. Although ionic compounds are usually chemically reactive, and undergo dissociation in aqueous solution, compounds which contain only ionic bonds are not decomposed by being heated to high temperatures. The vapour of sodium chloride, which boils at 1490°, is undecomposed when heated to 2000°.

The highly electropositive metals sodium, potassium and calcium enter into chemical combination only by means of ionic bonds, and therefore the sodium, potassium and calcium salts of organic acids consist of ions; sodium acetate for example has the constitution $Na^+(CH_3COO)^-$. For the same reason sodium derivatives of organic compounds, such as sodium methyl $Na^+(CH_3)^-$, sodium benzyl $Na^+(CH_2.C_6H_5)^-$, sodium ethoxide $Na^+(C_2H_5O)^-$, sodium phenate $Na^+(C_6H_5O)^-$ and the sodium derivative of ethyl acetoacetate $Na^+(CH_3CO.CHCOO.C_2H_5)^-$ must also consist of ions. Organic compounds are not usually salt-like substances, however, and the ionic bond in organic chemistry is not common.

The covalent bond. Elements with atoms containing 1, 2, 3, or 4 electrons less than the number in the atom of the inert gas next following in the periodic classification, are able to attain the atomic structure of the inert gas by mutually sharing the appropriate numbers of electrons in their outer quantum shells. For example, the L quantum shell of the fluorine atom contains 7 electrons. If two fluorine atoms each contribute one electron from this quantum shell to be held in common, the following configuration is attained :

The dotted circles enclose the electrons which are controlled by each nucleus. This is the fluorine molecule, F_2. Each of the two atoms, by holding two electrons in common with the other atom, controls 8 electrons. The electron pair held in common establishes a covalent bond between the two atoms.

In the molecule of hydrogen, H_2, each atom contributes its single planetary electron to form a pair held in common :

$$H^{\circ} \; + \; {}_{\bullet}H \quad \longrightarrow \quad (H \; {}^{\circ}_{\bullet} \; H)$$

Each hydrogen atom thus acquires 2 electrons, thus simulating the electron configuration of helium, and the two atoms in the molecule are linked together by a single covalent bond.

In the hydrogen fluoride molecule, HF, the hydrogen atom and the fluorine atom each contributes one electron to the shared pair :

$$H^{\circ} \; + \; {}_{\bullet} \, F \! : \quad \longrightarrow \quad (H \; {}^{\circ}_{\bullet} \; F \, {}^{\bullet}_{\bullet})$$

the arrangement of electrons in the hydrogen atom then resembles the arrangement in the helium atom, and the arrangement in the fluorine atom that of neon.

The oxygen atom has 6 electrons in the L shell ; it needs to acquire 2 more to attain the octet which is present in the atom of neon. It has been explained on p. 12 how the oxygen atom may acquire additional electrons by establishing two ionic bonds with an electropositive element such as calcium. Oxygen may also increase the number of electrons in its external quantum shell by forming two covalent bonds with another element. For example, the atom of oxygen combines covalently with two atoms of hydrogen to form a molecule of water, thus :

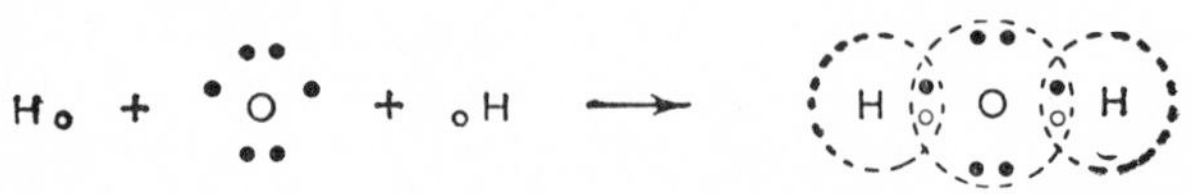

$$H_{\circ} \; + \; {}^{\bullet}_{\bullet} \, O \, {}^{\bullet}_{\bullet} \; + \; {}_{\circ}H \quad \longrightarrow \quad (H \; {}^{\circ}_{\circ} \; O \; {}^{\circ}_{\circ} \; H)$$

Similarly, the atom of nitrogen attains the stable octet present in the atom of neon by combining with three atoms of hydrogen to form a molecule of ammonia :

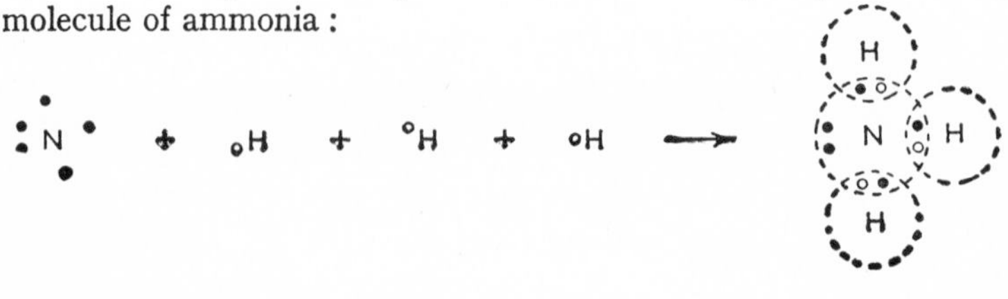

$$ {}^{\bullet}_{\bullet} N \, {}^{\bullet} \; + \; {}_{\circ}H \; + \; {}^{\circ}H \; + \; {}_{\circ}H \quad \longrightarrow \quad \begin{pmatrix} H \\ N \; {}^{\circ}_{\circ} \; H \\ H \end{pmatrix}$$

and the atom of carbon combines with four atoms of hydrogen to form the very stable molecule of methane :

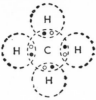

An element is described as mono-covalent, bi-covalent, tri-covalent or quadri-covalent, according to the number of covalencies which its atom can exert. Hydrogen and fluorine are mono-covalent, oxygen and sulphur are di-covalent, nitrogen is tri-covalent, and carbon is quadri-covalent. From Table IV (p. 10), and from the examples quoted above, it is clear that the maximum covalency which the atom of an element can display is equal to the difference between the number of electrons in its external quantum shell, and the number in the external quantum shell of the next following inert gas.

An atom of a polycovalent element may combine with an atom of another element in such a way that more than one shared electron pair is held in common. Examples of this mode of combination are provided by the carbon and oxygen atoms in the molecule of carbon dioxide :

and by the atoms of carbon and nitrogen in the molecule of hydrogen cyanide :

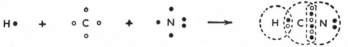

In the molecule of ethylene two carbon atoms are linked by two shared electron pairs, and in the molecule of acetylene two carbon atoms are linked by three shared electron pairs :

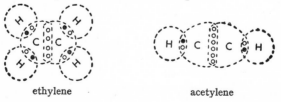

ethylene   acetylene

The **covalent bond** may be defined as *a link between two atoms formed by the sharing of a pair of electrons, one of which is contributed by each atom.*

In contradistinction to the ionic bond, by which an ion-pair is held together merely by electrostatic attraction, a covalent bond is an intimate structural link between two atoms. The atoms can neither change their respective positions in the molecule without its chemical decomposition, nor do they fall apart when the molecule is in aqueous solution. Two or more covalent bonds exerted by the same atom make definite angles with one another which can be measured. In consequence of these properties, molecules which contain covalently linked atoms have definite shapes, which influence the symmetry of the crystals they form.

In organic chemistry the covalent bond is predominant. Kekulé in 1858 first pointed out that the structures of molecules of organic compounds could be consistently explained on the assumption that the valencies of carbon, nitrogen and oxygen were four, three, and two respectively, and that the valencies of hydrogen, chlorine, bromine and iodine were one. He interpreted valency as a structural bond which he represented by a stroke joining the atoms linked together. He wrote the following simple molecules thus :

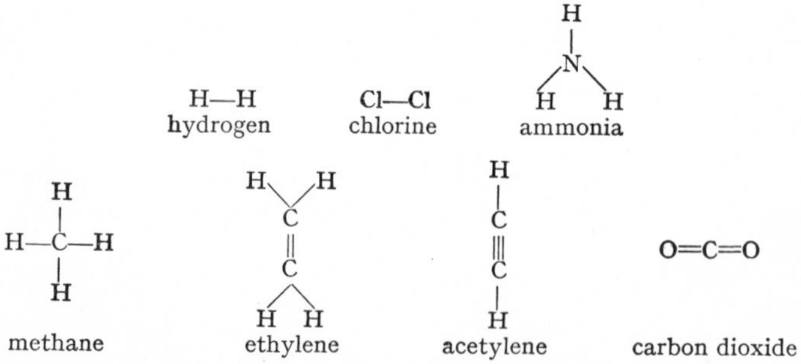

The Kekulé bond is now recognised as a symbol for a covalent bond ; each Kekulé stroke represents a shared electron pair. This very convenient representation is likely to be permanently retained.

Rules for determining the probable type of bond in a given compound

The electronic configuration, say, of the oxygen atom, K_2L_6, shows that the oxygen atom tends to enter into combination with other atoms in order to gain two electrons and attain the neon configuration K_2L_8. It may gain these electrons by forming either an ionic bond or a covalent bond. The conditions deciding which type of bond will be established in the formation of a particular compound are set out in the following rules.

The given compound (whatever may be its actual structure) is first assumed to contain an ionic bond. Then the assumed ionic bond must be replaced by a covalent bond

(i) if the charge on either of the ions is large, whether positive or negative,

(ii) if the volume of the cation (positive) is small,

(iii) if the volume of the anion (negative) is large,

(iv) if either, or both, of the ions has not attained the electron configuration of an inert gas.

The charge on the carbon ion, C^{----}, which might be formed by the addition of 4 electrons to the neutral carbon atom, is -4, which is large, and this decides that in the majority of its compounds carbon is covalent, even though the radius of the carbon atom in combination (0·77 Å units) is only slightly greater than that of the atom of fluorine (0·6 Å units). No compounds are known in which carbon is present in the form of the simple ions C^{++++} or C^{----}. Only when the carbon atom has gained three additional electrons by exerting covalencies does it accept one more electron to form an ionic valency in which the carbon atom is part of a negative ion. For example, if two carbon atoms are linked together by three covalencies the pair may become a negative ion carrying a double negative charge. This ion is present in such compounds as the carbides of sodium and calcium :

$$Na^+(C{\equiv}C)^{--}Na^+ \qquad Ca^{++}(C{\equiv}C)^{--}.$$

For highly electropositive elements, such as the metals sodium, potassium and calcium, the ionic state, in which the atoms have discarded the electrons in the external quantum shell, appears to be a condition of great chemical stability. It is well known that the free elements are difficult to prepare and preserve because of their strong tendency to combine with other elements, that is, to pass into the ionic state. Atoms of elements which tend to be electronegative, such as carbon, nitrogen, oxygen and the halogens, usually enter into chemical combination by increasing the number of electrons in their external quantum shells. The compounds of these elements which display the greatest chemical stability are those in which all the electrons in the external quantum shell of the element in question are shared with other atoms. It will be seen from the diagrams of the electronic configurations of the molecules of hydrogen fluoride, water, and ammonia on p. 14 that the sharing of electrons is not necessarily complete when the atoms are linked by simple covalent bonds ; for example, in the molecule of hydrogen fluoride the fluorine atom contains six electrons which are not shared with the hydrogen atom. The sharing of electrons is complete in the methane molecule, and this goes far to explain the exceptional stability of methane. In some molecules the maximum degree of electron sharing is attained by the development of a double bond consisting of an ionic bond and a covalent bond. This mixed double bond is the co-ionic bond which is described below.

The co-ionic bond. Many instances are known in which atoms are linked by a double bond consisting of one ionic bond and one covalent bond. This mixed double bond is the co-ionic bond. A simple example of the co-ionic bond is found in the molecule of carbon monoxide. Its structure may be pictured thus. First, a double covalent bond is established between the carbon atom and the oxygen atom, leaving two unshared electrons on the carbon atom, and four on the oxygen atom :

This molecular structure, which assigns eight electrons to the oxygen atom, but only six electrons to the carbon atom, is not compatible with the chemical inactivity of carbon monoxide. Some further rearrangement of the electrons is therefore required. A highly symmetrical electronic configuration in which each nucleus controls eight electrons is at once obtained for the molecule, if it is assumed that the atoms are linked by a co-ionic bond in addition to the covalent double bond shown in the above diagram.

The development of the co-ionic bond may be envisaged as follows. One electron is transferred from the oxygen atom to the carbon atom, thus establishing an ionic bond between them :

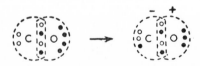

Each atom then carries an electrical charge and contains three unshared electrons. A third covalent bond between the atoms is now formed by the sharing of one of the three unshared electrons on each atom :

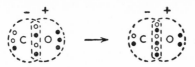

Using the Kekulé symbol, the molecule may be written

$$\bar{C}\overset{+}{\equiv}O.$$

There are four bonds linking the carbon atom to the oxygen atom, of which three are covalent and one is ionic. In this molecule each nucleus controls eight electrons, and the maximum degree of electron sharing is attained.

Another example of the co-ionic bond is found in the link between one of the oxygen atoms and the nitrogen atom in the nitro group, NO_2, present in nitromethane, $CH_3.NO_2$. The nitrogen atom has five electrons in the L quantum shell. By establishing a covalent bond with the methyl group, CH_3, the nitrogen atom increases the number of electrons in the L shell to 6 :

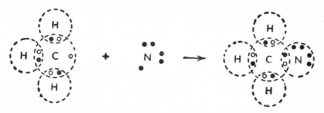

Two of the 4 unshared electrons in the L quantum shell of the nitrogen atom are used to establish a double covalent bond with an oxygen atom

leaving the nitrogen atom with one unshared electron pair. It is not possible for the nitrogen atom in this state to form any more simple covalent bonds, because it could not do so without increasing the number of electrons in the L quantum shell beyond 8. It can, however, form a co-ionic bond with another oxygen atom according

to the following mechanism. One of the unshared electrons is transferred to the oxygen atom to establish an ionic bond, thus:

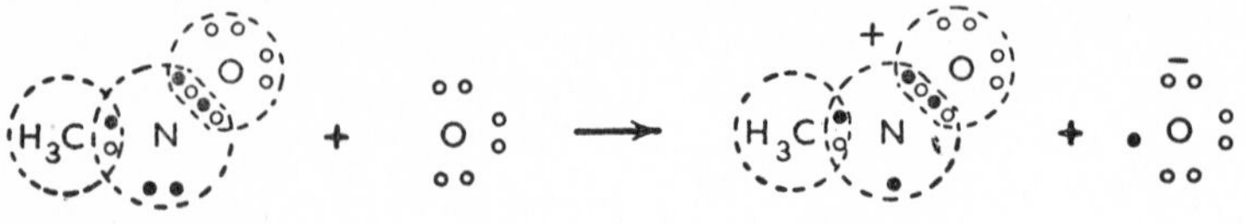

and the nitrogen and oxygen atoms then enter into a covalent bond
by sharing the single electrons which the ionic bond has made
available:

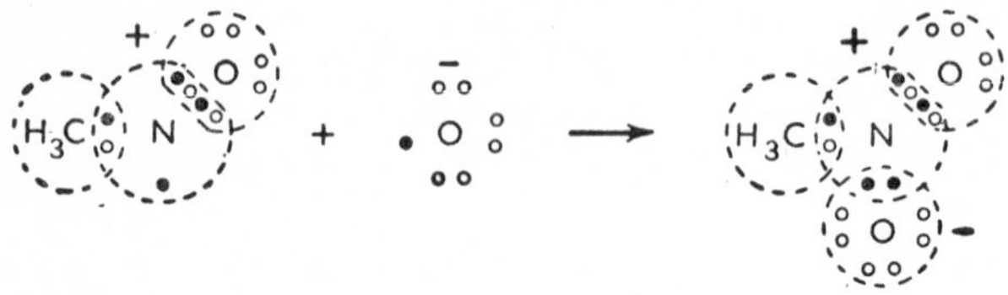

It should be noted that the nitrogen atom carries a unit positive
charge, and the oxygen atom joined to it by the co-ionic bond carries
a unit negative charge. If the Kekulé bond symbol is used to denote
a single covalent bond, the molecule of nitromethane may be written

$$H_3C—\overset{+}{N}\underset{O^-}{\overset{O}{\diagup}}.$$

The two oppositely charged parts of a molecule containing a co-ionic
link may be regarded as " bound ions ", in contrast to the " free
ions " of an ionic compound such as sodium chloride.

The **co-ionic bond** may be defined as *a double link between two
atoms, one of the two bonds being ionic and the other covalent.* In order
that a co-ionic bond may be established between two atoms the external quantum shell of one must contain a pair of unshared electrons,
and that of the other must be at least two electrons short of the
configuration of an inert gas. The common types of organic compounds whose molecules contain co-ionic bonds are the nitro-
compounds, e.g. nitromethane:

$$H_3C—\overset{+}{N}\underset{O^-}{\overset{O}{\diagup}},$$

the isocyanides, e.g. methyl isocyanide $H_3C—\overset{+}{N}\equiv\overset{-}{C}$, and the
cyanates, e.g. methyl cyanate $H_3C—C\equiv\overset{+}{N}—\overset{-}{O}$.

The co-ionic bond has all the properties of the covalent bond ; the
relative positions of atoms joined by the co-ionic bond are fixed.

and cannot be changed without chemical decomposition of the molecule. Each of the atoms carries an electric charge, but the presence of the covalent bond prevents the electrolytic dissociation of the two charged atoms when the molecule containing the co-ionic bond is dissolved in water. The volatility of a compound constituted of molecules containing a co-ionic bond is usually depressed.

Electric moments. In the establishment of an ionic bond between, say, an atom of sodium and an atom of fluorine, an electron is transferred from the sodium atom to the fluorine atom. The sodium atom thus acquires a positive charge, and the fluorine atom a negative charge, leading to the formation of an ion-pair of sodium fluoride, Na^+F^-. When a co-ionic bond is formed, say, in the molecule of nitromethane, it has been shown above that the nitrogen atom acquires a positive charge and the oxygen atom a negative charge :

$$H_3C-\overset{+}{N}\underset{O^-}{\overset{O}{\diagdown}}$$

The presence of electrical charges of opposite sign on different atoms in a molecule produces an electric moment. The electric moment of two equal and opposite charges is the product of one of the charges into the distance between them. The distance between two atoms in a molecule is of the order of 1×10^{-8} cm. and the charge on an electron is $4 \cdot 8 \times 10^{-10}$ e.s.u., and hence the electric moment produced by the transference of an electron from one atom in a molecule to a neighbouring atom is of the order

$$4 \cdot 8 \times 10^{-10} \times 10^{-8} = 4 \cdot 8 \times 10^{-18} \text{ e.s.u.} \times \text{cm.}$$

Molecules which possess an electric moment exert an external electrical field and are said to be *polar*. Polar molecules tend to attract one another, and to induce polarity in molecules of other compounds with which they are brought into contact. Polar compounds, therefore, are less volatile than otherwise similar non-polar compounds, and tend to enter into chemical reactions more readily.

In a molecule composed of two atoms of the same element united by a covalent bond there is no resultant displacement of electrons, and therefore molecules of such substances as hydrogen H—H, or chlorine Cl—Cl, are non-polar. It is observed, however, that molecules composed of atoms of different elements joined by a covalent bond are frequently polar ; the electric moment of hydrogen chloride, H—Cl, for example, is $1 \cdot 03 \times 10^{-18}$ units. The electric moments of some common compounds are given in Table VI.

TABLE VI

ELECTRIC MOMENTS

Compound	Formula	Moment × 10^{-18} e.s.u. × cm.
Hydrogen chloride	HCl	1·03
Hydrogen bromide	HBr	0·78
Hydrogen iodide	HI	0·38
Water	H_2O	1·8
Carbon dioxide	CO_2	0
Ammonia	NH_3	1·5
Methane	CH_4	0
Ethylene	C_2H_4	0
Ethyl alcohol	C_2H_5OH	1·74
Diethyl ether	$C_2H_5OC_2H_5$	1·12
Methyl chloride	CH_3Cl	1·89
Nitromethane	CH_3NO_2	3·8
Methyl cyanide	CH_3CN	3·5
Methylamine	CH_3NH_2	1·3
Benzene	C_6H_6	0
Chlorobenzene	C_6H_5Cl	1·53
Nitrobenzene	$C_6H_5NO_2$	3·8
Aniline	$C_6H_5NH_2$	1·55
Phenol	C_6H_5OH	1·71

The exhibition of polarity by covalent compounds must mean that the electron-pair, which is held in common by two atoms of different kinds, is not situated at equal distances from the two atomic nuclei. The molecule of hydrogen chloride may be represented diagram-

matically showing that the pair of shared electrons is displaced away from the hydrogen nucleus towards the chlorine nucleus. Thus, in effect, the chlorine atom acquires a negative charge and the hydrogen atom a positive charge. If the displacement proceeded until the hydrogen nucleus lost all control of the pair of electrons originally shared, two separate ions would be produced, H⁺ and Cl⁻. From this point of view an ionic bond may be regarded as a covalency which has been distorted to such an extent that one of the two linked atoms has gained complete control of the shared electron-pair, and the other atom has lost control altogether.

Polarity and organic reactions. The existence of polarity in molecules of organic compounds is the basis of modern theories of the mechanism of their chemical reactivity. A compound such as methane which is non-polar is inert. Reactive compounds are those such as acetaldehyde which consists of polar molecules $CH_3.\overrightarrow{HC=O}$, or ethylene, $H_2C=CH_2$, of which the molecules, although non-polar, can readily assume the polar state $\overrightarrow{H_2C=CH_2}$.*

The two following examples illustrate the principles of current theories.

(i) The addition of hydrogen cyanide to acetaldehyde (p. 203). The reaction takes place in two stages. In the first the cyanogen ion, CN^-, is attracted to the positively charged carbon atom in acetaldehyde

$$CH_3.\overrightarrow{HC=O} \;+\; CN^- + H^+ \;=\; \begin{matrix} CH_3.\overrightarrow{HC=O} \\ CN^- \end{matrix} \;+\; H^+.$$

In the second stage, by a redistribution of electrons, a covalent link is established between the two carbon atoms, and the double link in the carbonyl group becomes a single link. The oxygen atom of the carbonyl group now carries eight valency electrons, whereas the number controlled by an oxygen atom forming one covalent link should be seven. The extra electron in the oxygen atom is used to neutralise the charge on the hydrogen atom which was originally part of the hydrogen cyanide molecule, and the hydrogen atom thus formed becomes covalently linked to the oxygen atom. The molecule of acetaldehyde cyanhydrin, $CH_3.HC{\Large<}^{OH}_{CN}$ is thus obtained.

(ii) The addition of bromine to ethylene (p. 119). Bromine and ethylene react only in the presence of a polar material such as glass. It is assumed that in the electric field of the polar material both the bromine molecules and the ethylene molecules become polar, and the positive end of the bromine dipole becomes attracted to the negative end of the ethylene dipole, thus

$$\begin{matrix} \overrightarrow{H_2C=CH_2} \\ \overrightarrow{Br—Br} \end{matrix}$$

---

* The arrow above a bond in a molecule is used here to indicate the direction of the drift of electrons which gives rise to polarity ; the atom at the arrow head, to which the electrons have drifted, becomes negatively charged with respect to the atom at the tail of the arrow. The drift is only small, and it by no means corresponds to the complete transference of an electron from one atom to the other which would result in the ionisation of the bond. For an authoritative account of the influence of polarity on organic reactions, see the Faraday Lecture, 1947, given before the Chemical Society by Sir Robert Robinson. *J.C.S.*, 1947, p. 1288.

A covalent link is then established between the adjacent carbon and bromine atoms, and the second bromine atom is released as an ion,

Br^-. The two ions $\overset{H}{\underset{H}{>}}C-\overset{\overset{H}{|}}{\underset{\underset{Br}{|}}{C}}-H$ and Br^-, thus formed at this intermediate stage of the reaction, then unite to give $H-\overset{\overset{H}{|}}{\underset{\underset{Br}{|}}{C}}-\overset{\overset{H}{|}}{\underset{\underset{Br}{|}}{C}}-H$.

Support is given to this interpretation of the reaction by the observation that if a more electronegative ion than Br^-, for instance Cl^-, is present during the reaction, it links with the positively charged carbon atom in the final stage to give $CH_2Cl.CH_2Br$, and bromine ions are set free.

Resonance. The molecules of many organic compounds contain atoms linked to one another by covalent bonds only ; molecules of a few organic compounds also contain an ionic or a co-ionic bond. These three modes of atomic linkage, however, have not provided an adequate basis for the interpretation of the properties of many well-known compounds which appear at first sight to be of simple constitution. In these cases the observed properties of the compounds differ from those which would be expected from consideration of the simple covalent or co-ionic formula, and it is found that :

(i) the chemical stability of the compound is greater than that which would be deduced from the simple formula ;

(ii) the compound fails to exhibit many of the chemical actions which would be predicted from the simple formula ;

(iii) the distances between the atoms in the molecule of the compound are either greater or less than the distances normally found when the atoms are covalently or co-ionically linked ;

(iv) the heat of formation of the compound is greater than that calculated from the simple formula.

The concept of resonance has been put forward to explain these anomalies. In order to give an account of resonance the properties and constitution of carbon dioxide will be discussed. The molecule of carbon dioxide consists of a carbon atom joined to two oxygen atoms so that all three atoms are in the same straight line. For many purposes it is sufficient to assume that each oxygen atom is joined to the carbon atom by a double covalent bond, giving the molecular structure, $O{=}C{=}O$.

The group consisting of an oxygen atom doubly linked to a carbon atom, the carbonyl group $>C{=}O$, is frequently found in organic compounds, for example, in the class of compounds known as the aldehydes, of which a typical member is acetaldehyde,

$$\begin{array}{c} H_3C \\ \diagdown \\ H \diagup \end{array} C{=}O.$$

This compound is extremely reactive. It is easily reduced to methyl alcohol by the action of sodium amalgam and water, and it readily combines with hydrogen cyanide, ammonia, and sodium bisulphite. These reactions, and many others described on p. 203 are additive in character, and are represented by equations of the type

$$\begin{array}{c} H_3C \\ \diagdown \\ H \diagup \end{array} C{=}O \ + \ HCN \ = \ \begin{array}{c} H_3C \quad OH \\ \diagdown \diagup \\ C \\ \diagup \diagdown \\ H \quad CN \end{array}$$

Carbon dioxide, however, is a very stable substance towards oxidising and reducing agents ; only very small quantities of carbon dioxide are reduced to formaldehyde when it is exposed to the action of water and amalgamated magnesium for several days. Its principal chemical reactions are its combination with water to form carbonic acid, and with bases to form carbonates. It does not undergo any of the additive reactions displayed by acetaldehyde. The distance apart of the two atomic nuclei in the group C=O in acetaldehyde is 1·24 Å units, and it might be expected that the length of the molecule of carbon dioxide would be twice this, namely, 2·48 Å units. The length determined experimentally is 2·32 Å units. The heat of formation from free atoms of carbon and oxygen of the molecule O=C=O has been calculated from data obtained from experiments on aldehydes to be 340 Cal. per gram-molecule ; the corresponding heat of formation of carbon dioxide determined experimentally is 380 Cal. per gram-molecule.

The structure O=C=O is, therefore, an inadequate representation of the molecule of carbon dioxide, and it is necessary to enquire whether there are other possible ways of writing a molecular structure for carbon dioxide in which

(i) the three atoms are in one and the same straight line, and

(ii) each atom contains eight electrons in the external quantum shell.

The theory of resonance attempts to solve this problem in the following manner. The electronic configurations of the uncombined atoms are

:O   C   O:

A   B

Suppose that an ionic bond is formed by the transference of one electron from the oxygen atom A to the carbon atom

and that another ionic bond is formed by the transference of an electron from the carbon atom to the oxygen atom B

Three covalent bonds may now be developed between the oxygen atom A and the carbon atom, and one between the carbon atom and the oxygen atom B giving the structure

If the above scheme is carried out starting with the transference of one electron from the oxygen atom B to the carbon atom, a similar but reversed structure is obtained

$$\overset{-}{O}\text{—}C\equiv\overset{+}{O}$$
$$\quad A \qquad B$$

It is thus possible to write three distinct molecular structures for carbon dioxide, each representing a different mode in which the same three atoms may be linked together :

$$O\text{=}C\text{=}O \quad , \quad \overset{-}{O}\text{—}C\text{≡}\overset{+}{O} \quad , \quad \overset{+}{O}\text{≡}C\text{—}\overset{-}{O}$$

The theory of resonance assumes that the actual molecule of carbon dioxide consists not of any one of these forms, but of all three in resonance. In general, resonance may be expected if it is possible to write more than one molecular formula for a compound, using ionic or covalent bonds, in such a manner that

(i) the relative positions of the positive nuclei of the atoms are unchanged, and

(ii) the electronic configurations of the external quantum shells of the atoms correspond to those of inert gases.

The concept of resonance is difficult because it does not lead to a model of a molecule which can be imagined or expressed in terms of a mechanical structure. There is only one structure for the molecule

TABLE VII

STRUCTURES EXHIBITING RESONANCE

Compound	Simple formula	Alternative formulae	Difference between calculated and observed heats of formation in Cals. per gram.-mol.
Carbon dioxide	$O{=}C{=}O$	$\overset{-}{O}{-}C{\equiv}\overset{+}{O}$ $\overset{+}{O}{\equiv}C{-}\overset{-}{O}$	40
Carbonate ion	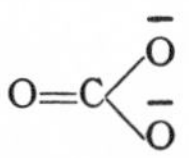 $O{=}C\big\langle{}^{\overset{-}{O}}_{O}$	$\overset{-}{O}{-}C\big\langle{}^{\overset{-}{O}}_{O}$ $\overset{-}{O}{-}C\big\langle{}^{O}_{O}$	44
Organic acid	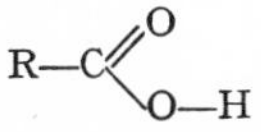 $R{-}C\big\langle{}^{O}_{O{-}H}$	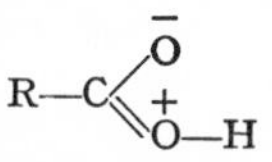 $R{-}C\big\langle{}^{\overset{-}{O}}_{\overset{+}{O}{-}H}$	28
Esters	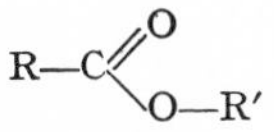 $R{-}C\big\langle{}^{O}_{O{-}R'}$	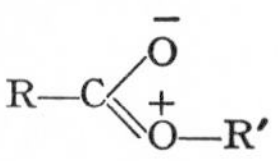 $R{-}C\big\langle{}^{\overset{-}{O}}_{\overset{+}{O}{-}R'}$	28
Organic acid ions	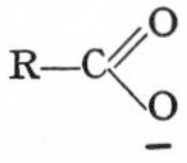 $R{-}C\big\langle{}^{O}_{\overset{-}{O}}$	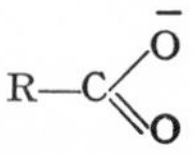 $R{-}C\big\langle{}^{\overset{-}{O}}_{O}$	28
Urea	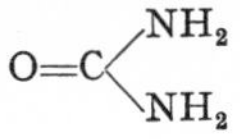 $O{=}C\big\langle{}^{NH_2}_{NH_2}$	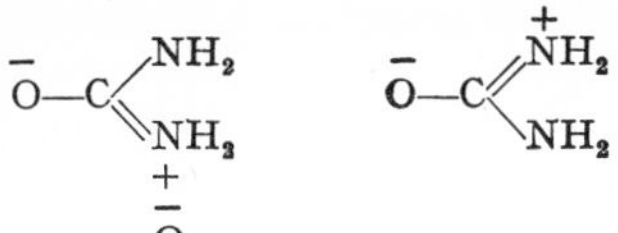 $\overset{-}{O}{-}C\big\langle{}^{NH_2}_{\overset{+}{NH_2}}$ $\overset{-}{O}{-}C\big\langle{}^{\overset{+}{NH_2}}_{NH_2}$	37
Amides	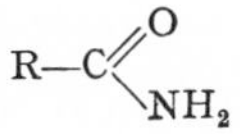 $R{-}C\big\langle{}^{O}_{NH_2}$	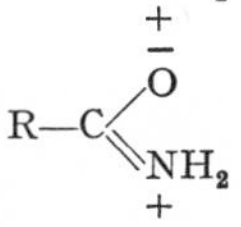 $R{-}C\big\langle{}^{\overset{-}{O}}_{\overset{+}{NH_2}}$	21
Benzene		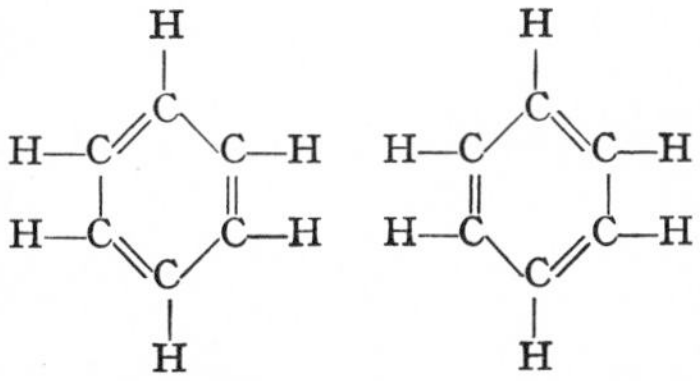 (benzene resonance structures)	36

of carbon dioxide, but it is not represented by any of the structures given above ; carbon dioxide is not a mixture of these three forms, nor should it be regarded as consisting of molecules which change from one form to another in finite intervals of time.   A rough illustration of the effect of resonance can be given in terms of colour. If, say, the letter A is printed in blue ink and then over-printed in yellow ink, the effect produced is neither blue nor yellow, but an

entirely new colour, green.* Similarly the effect of resonance between
the three possible forms of the carbon dioxide molecule is to produce
a new type of molecule which unfortunately cannot be described in
terms of the electron considered as a particle.   The principal types
of compounds in which resonance occurs are set out in Table
VII.†

For the purpose of descriptive chemistry the molecular structures
of most of these compounds can be taken as those in Column 2 of
Table VII.   Benzene is an exception.   It has always been realised
that the structure

for benzene is not satisfactory, and although this formula is retained
for writing chemical equations, the unique and striking properties
of benzenoid compounds can be adequately explained only in terms
of resonance.   An account of the chemical and physical evidence
leading to the accepted structure for benzene is given on p. 367.

---

* W. G. Palmer, *Valency* (Cambridge University Press), 1944, p. 120.

† Most of the information in Table VII is reproduced from W. G. Palmer,
Valency, p. 211 ; it is based originally on data of Pauling and Sherman.

CHAPTER II

THE SCOPE OF ORGANIC CHEMISTRY

ORGANIC chemistry is the study of the chemical compounds of carbon. Carbon is unique among the elements because

(i) the number of compounds it forms is greater than the number formed by any other element ;

(ii) the bodies of all living organisms, both plants and animals, are built up of carbon compounds ; the chemical changes resulting in the formation and decomposition of carbon compounds are the basis of growth, movement, and all other activities of plants and animals.

It was thought at one time that organic compounds could be produced only through the activity of a " vital force " which resided in living organisms. Numerous organic compounds, however, can be prepared from mineral sources without the aid of any living substance ; for example, methane can be made by passing a spark between carbon poles in an atmosphere of hydrogen, and acetaldehyde, acetic acid and many other compounds are obtained from acetylene made by the action of water on calcium carbide. The possibility of these and other syntheses does not logically dispose of the concept of " vital force ", because it can be argued that the carbon which the reagents must always contain may have acquired the " vital force " at some previous period in its history when it was part of a living organism. Nevertheless, there is overwhelming evidence that identical principles apply both to the chemistry of carbon and the chemistry of other elements. The concept of " vital force ", therefore, is of no assistance in elucidating the chemistry of organic substances, and it has been rejected as superfluous. It must be remembered, however, that the concepts and theories of chemistry and physics have so far failed to provide an explanation of the essential difference between dead and living matter.

The exceptionally large number of stable carbon compounds is accounted for by the following three properties of the carbon atom.

(i) The affinity of carbon for the electropositive element hydrogen is of the same order as its affinity for electronegative elements such as oxygen or chlorine. Hence carbon forms equally stable compounds with hydrogen and with oxygen, sulphur or the halogens.

(ii) It is possible for large numbers of carbon atoms to be linked to one another by covalent bonds ; chains, rings and networks of carbon atoms furnish the basic molecular structures of all organic compounds. Atoms of certain other elements such as silicon, nitrogen and sulphur possess this property to a limited extent, but whereas molecules containing more than 60 carbon atoms linked together are well known, it is unusual for more than three or four atoms of any other element to be linked together in a molecule.

(iii) The electronic configuration of the external quantum shell of a carbon atom exerting four covalent bonds consists of four pairs of electrons, all of which are shared with other atoms. A molecule is unlikely to break up spontaneously, or to be eager to enter into chemical combination, if the atoms in it are in this condition of very great stability. Moreover, since elements in Period I and Period II of the periodic classification cannot increase the number of electrons in the external quantum shell beyond 8, the external shell of the carbon atom (carbon is in Period II) is completely filled when the atom is exerting four covalent bonds. The expansion of the octet of electrons in the external shells of certain atoms, which is possible for elements in Period III and in higher periods, is the first step in the mechanism of many of the chemical reactions of their compounds. The impossibility of the expansion of the octet in a carbon atom which is exerting four covalencies precludes this type of chemical reaction, and thus enhances the stability of carbon compounds.

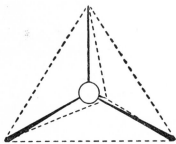

FIG. 2. The tetra-covalent carbon atom at the centre of a regular circumscribed tetrahedron. In this figure, and in subsequent figures depicting molecular structure, bonds represented by lines of uniform thickness lie in the plane of the paper ; bonds represented by lines of non-uniform thickness do not lie in the plane of the paper. The thick end of a line of varying thickness is to be regarded as nearer than the thin end to the eye of the reader.

The four covalent bonds of the carbon atom subtend equal angles with one another. If the carbon atom is imagined to be situated at the centre of a regular tetrahedron, a covalent bond is directed towards each of the four corners, as shown in Fig. 2.

The magnitude of the angle between two bonds of the carbon atom is 109·5° ; it is sometimes spoken of as the *tetrahedral angle*.

It has been shown by X-ray analysis that in the crystal of diamond each carbon atom is linked with four neighbouring carbon atoms ; if one carbon atom be taken as the centre of a regular

tetrahedron its four neighbours are situated at the four corners.
Fig. 3 shows the relative positions of carbon atoms in the diamond
crystal ; each full line in the diagram represents a covalent bond.

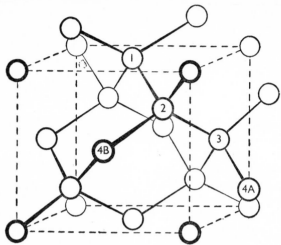

FIG. 3.   The crystal structure of diamond.

The crystal of graphite, another allotropic form of carbon, consists
of sheets of carbon atoms disposed in hexagonal rings, Fig. 4.   Each

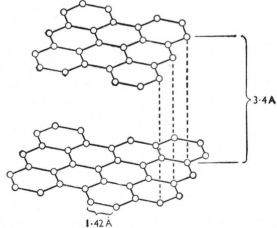

FIG. 4.   The crystal structure of graphite.

carbon atom is linked by covalent bonds to its **three neighbours in**
the sheet, but the adjacent layers are held together only by the **forces**

of general atomic attraction, and are not linked to one another by chemical bonds. This structure explains the soft flaky nature of graphite, and accounts for its properties as a lubricant. It is not possible at present to give a complete account of the electronic configuration of the carbon atoms in graphite. The covalent linking of carbon atoms in hexagonal rings leaves each atom with 7 electrons in the external quantum shell, of which 6 are shared. The unshared electrons must be disposed in such a way that the external quantum shell of every carbon atom in a sheet effectively contains 8 electrons, which retain sufficient freedom to account for the electrical conductivity of graphite.

The compounds of carbon fall into two main divisions, the *aliphatic* division and the *aromatic*. The aliphatic compounds have molecular structures in which the arrangement of the carbon atoms is similar to that in diamond. The aromatic compounds have molecular structures based on a hexagonal ring of carbon atoms known as the *benzene ring*. It is tempting to suggest that the condition of the carbon atom in the benzene ring is similar to that of the carbon atom in graphite. The elucidation of the precise nature of the linkages between the planes of carbon atoms in graphite, however, is not yet sufficiently advanced to enable this suggestion to be confirmed.

The aliphatic division of organic compounds is composed of a number of classes of which some of the principal are the paraffins, the olefines, the acetylenes, the halogen derivatives of the paraffins, the alcohols, the ethers, the aldehydes, the ketones, the carboxylic acids, the esters, the amides and the amines. The paraffins, the olefines and the acetylenes consist of carbon and hydrogen only. Members of these classes of compounds, together with benzene and its homologues naphthalene and anthracene, which are in the aromatic division, and which also contain only carbon and hydrogen, are therefore described as *hydrocarbons*.

The paraffins. The first member of the paraffins is methane, CH_4, in the molecule of which one carbon atom is covalently linked to four hydrogen atoms, arranged in such a way that if the carbon atom is imagined to be at the centre of a regular tetrahedron, one hydrogen atom will be situated at each corner. A molecule of methane may be derived theoretically from the diamond by removing a single atom from the crystal structure, for instance the carbon atom labelled 1 in Fig. 3, p. 31, and linking each of the four freed covalent bonds with a hydrogen atom. The second member of the paraffin series is ethane, C_2H_6. The molecule of ethane may be derived theoretically from the diamond by removing two adjacent carbon atoms from the crystal, for instance, the carbon atoms labelled 1 and 2 in Fig. 3, p. 31, without disturbing the covalent bond between them : each of the three free covalent bonds on each carbon atom is then linked to a hydrogen atom. The structures of the molecules of methane and ethane are shown in Fig. 5.

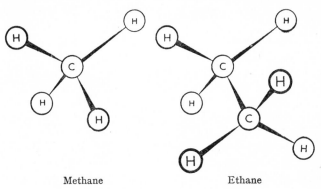

Methane   Ethane

Fig. 5.   The structures of methane and ethane.

The molecule of propane, C_3H_8, the third member of the paraffin series, may be similarly derived by separating a chain of three carbon atoms from the diamond crystal, for instance the carbon atoms labelled 1, 2 and 3 in Fig. 3, p. 31, and linking each of the eight free covalent bonds to a hydrogen atom.

Not more than one structure can be obtained by the imaginary removal of a single carbon atom, or of two or three linked carbon atoms, from the diamond crystal. The structure of a paraffin molecule derived by the separation of more than three linked carbon atoms from the diamond crystal depends, however, on the shape of the group of carbon atoms detached. For example, two differently shaped groups of four carbon atoms may be detached from the diamond crystal shown in Fig. 3, p. 31 : (*a*) the group of atoms labelled 1, 2, 3, 4A, and (*b*) the group labelled 1, 2, 3, 4B. If the free valencies of the detached groups are linked to hydrogen atoms, the molecular structures of normal butane,* Fig. 6, and iso-butane, Fig. 7, are respectively obtained. Similarly five linked carbon atoms with their free bonds joined to hydrogen atoms may be arranged to

---

* The prefix " normal " applied to the name of a paraffin indicates that the molecule contains an unbranched chain of carbon atoms. The prefix " normal " is frequently abbreviated to " *n-* ", and the prefix " iso " to " *i-* ".

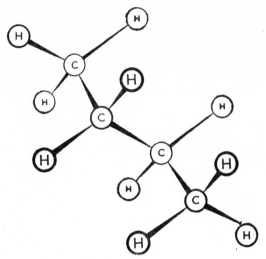

FIG. 6.   The structure of normal butane.

give the three compounds normal pentane, iso-pentane and tetra-methyl methane.

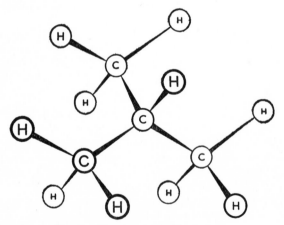

FIG. 7.   The structure of iso-butane.

Isomerism.   Chemical compounds which have identical molec-ular formulae but different molecular structures are said to be *isomeric* ;   substances which are isomeric with one another are known **as** *isomers* or *isomerides :*   the phenomenon is known as *isomerism.* The brief outline of the molecular structures of the simpler paraffins shows that the members of the series having molecular weights greater than that of propane, C_3H_8, display isomerism. There are two isomerides having the molecular formula C_4H_{10}, and three having the molecular formula C_5H_{12}. The number of isomerides increases rapidly with the number of carbon atoms in the paraffin molecule. Theoretically there are 18 isomerides with the molecular formula C_8H_{18}, 802 with the formula $C_{13}H_{28}$, and 115,000 with the formula $C_{20}H_{42}$.*

Formulae of organic compounds. The graphical formulae † which have been used in Figs. 5, 6 and 7, for molecules of paraffins are clearly too cumbersome for general use. It is usual to employ conventional graphical formulae in which :

(i) the real chain of carbon atoms consisting of successive linkages inclined at 109° 28′ is represented by a *straight chain*, and

(ii) the spatial atomic arrangement in the molecule is projected on a *single plane*.

On this system graphical formulae for butane, Fig. 6, and iso-butane, Fig. 7, are written thus :

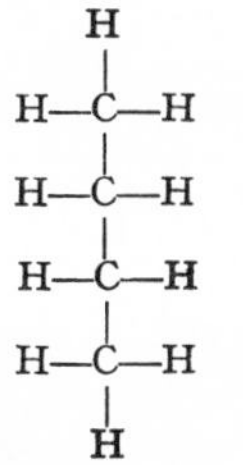

normal butane 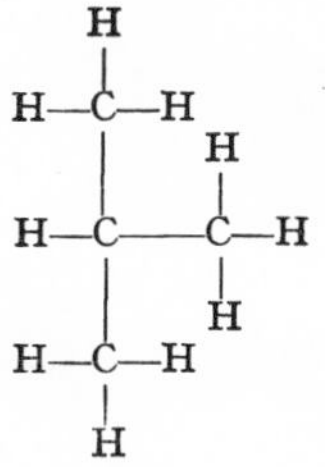   iso-butane

* These numbers refer to structural isomerides only. If optical isomerides (p. 303) are also included, the total number of theoretically possible isomers of $C_{20}H_{42}$ is nearly 3,400,000.

† Four types of formula are used for describing an organic compound :

the *empirical formula*, which indicates the *proportions* in which the constituent atoms are present in the molecule,

the *molecular formula*, which indicates the *actual numbers* of the constituent atoms in the molecule,

the *constitutional formula*, which indicates the *grouping* of the atoms in the molecule,

the *graphical formula*, which indicates the position of every atom and linkage in the molecule.

The four types of formula for normal butane and iso-butane are :

	Empirical formula	Molecular formula	Constitutional formula	Graphical formula
Normal butane	C_2H_5	C_4H_{10}	$CH_3(CH_2)_2CH_3$	see above
Iso-butane	C_2H_5	C_4H_{10}	$HC(CH_3)_3$	see above

and for normal pentane, iso-pentane, and tetramethyl methane, thus :

$$
\begin{array}{c}
\text{H} \\
|\\
\text{H—C—H} \\
|\\
\text{H—C—H} \\
|\\
\text{H—C—H} \\
|\\
\text{H—C—H} \\
|\\
\text{H—C—H} \\
|\\
\text{H}
\end{array}
$$

normal pentane

$$
\begin{array}{c}
\text{H} \\
|\\
\text{H—C—H} \\
|\\
\text{H—C—H} \\
\text{H} \quad | \quad \text{H} \\
\backslash \quad | \quad / \\
\text{H—C—C—C—H} \\
| \quad | \quad | \\
\text{H} \quad \text{H} \quad \text{H}
\end{array}
$$

iso-pentane

$$
\begin{array}{c}
\text{H} \\
|\\
\text{H—C—H} \\
\text{H} \qquad | \qquad \text{H} \\
\backslash \qquad | \qquad / \\
\text{H—C——C——C—H} \\
| \qquad | \qquad | \\
\text{H} \quad | \quad \text{H} \\
\text{H—C—H} \\
|\\
\text{H}
\end{array}
$$

tetramethyl methane

These conventional graphical formulae emphasize the distinctions between isomerides, but they obscure the true spatial relations of the atoms in the molecules. The planar graphical formula for dichloromethane suggests, for example, the possibility of two isomerides having the constitutions

$$
\begin{array}{c}
\text{H} \\
|\\
\text{Cl—C—H} \\
|\\
\text{Cl}
\end{array}
\qquad \text{and} \qquad
\begin{array}{c}
\text{H} \\
|\\
\text{Cl—C—Cl} \\
|\\
\text{H}
\end{array}
$$

These formulae, however, are merely two different representations of one and the same tetrahedral arrangement which is obtained by depicting either of them in three dimensions.

To take another example, the conventional formula for dibromohexane,

$$
\begin{array}{c}
\text{H} \; \text{H} \; \text{H} \; \text{H} \; \text{H} \; \text{H} \\
| \; | \; | \; | \; | \; | \\
\text{Br—C—C—C—C—C—C—Br} \\
| \; | \; | \; | \; | \; | \\
\text{H} \; \text{H} \; \text{H} \; \text{H} \; \text{H} \; \text{H}
\end{array}
$$

implies that the two bromine atoms are as remote from one another as they can be, and by no means suggests that they might be jointly concerned in any chemical reaction. If, however, dibromohexane is dissolved in dry ether and treated with metallic sodium, both atoms of bromine in the molecule are removed to form sodium bromide, and a ring compound is formed by the linkage of the two bonds set free on the carbon atoms at the end of the chain. The course of this reaction is made clear, when the conventional straight chain of carbon atoms in the dibromohexane molecule is drawn to conform more nearly to the actual disposition of the carbon atoms in the molecule, thus :

$$\begin{array}{c}
\text{H H H Br} \\
\text{C---C} \quad \text{Br} \\
\text{H} \quad \text{C---H} \\
\text{H} \quad \text{C---C} \quad \text{H} \\
\text{H H H H}
\end{array} \quad + \quad 2Na \quad = \quad
\begin{array}{c}
\text{H H H H} \\
\text{C---C} \\
\text{H} \quad \quad \text{H} \\
\text{C} \quad \quad \text{C} \\
\text{H} \quad \quad \text{H} \\
\text{C---C} \\
\text{H H H H}
\end{array} \quad + \quad 2NaBr.$$

Homologous series. When the paraffins are arranged in order of increasing molecular weight they form a regular series, thus :

Methane	CH_4
Ethane	C_2H_6
Propane	C_3H_8
Butane	C_4H_{10}
Pentane	C_5H_{12}

in which the molecular formula of each member of the series contains one atom of carbon and two atoms of hydrogen more than the molecular formula of the preceding member. Such a series is an example of a *homologous series*.

A series of organic compounds in which the molecular formula of a given member differs from that of adjacent members by one atom of carbon and two atoms of hydrogen is known as a homologous series. The members of the series are known as *homologues*. The chemical properties of all the members of a homologous series are closely similar ; the physical properties vary with molecular weight, and with molecular constitution.*

A general molecular formula may be assigned to each homologous series. The general formula of the paraffins, for example, is C_nH_{2n+2} and that of the alcohols is $C_nH_{2n+1}OH$. If $n=1$, the formula represents that of methyl alcohol, CH_3OH. If $n=2$, the formula represents that of ethyl alcohol, C_2H_5OH.

The olefines. In the molecule of a paraffin adjacent carbon atoms are invariably linked by a single covalent bond. In the other series of hydrocarbons at least one pair of adjacent carbon atoms in the molecule are linked by more than one covalent bond. Hydrocarbons containing a double covalent linkage are known as *olefines*. The olefines are a homologous series having the general formula C_nH_{2n}. Ethylene, $H_2C=CH_2$, is the simplest member of the olefine series. Ethylene may be theoretically derived from

---

* Table IX, p. 104, gives the boiling points of the simpler members of the paraffin series. It will be seen from this table that the boiling points of the *normal* paraffins increase (but not regularly) with increasing molecular weight, and that the boiling points of *isomers* are lower than those of the corresponding normal compounds.

ethane by the removal of two hydrogen atoms from the ethane molecule, so as to leave one free covalency on each of the carbon atoms, thus :

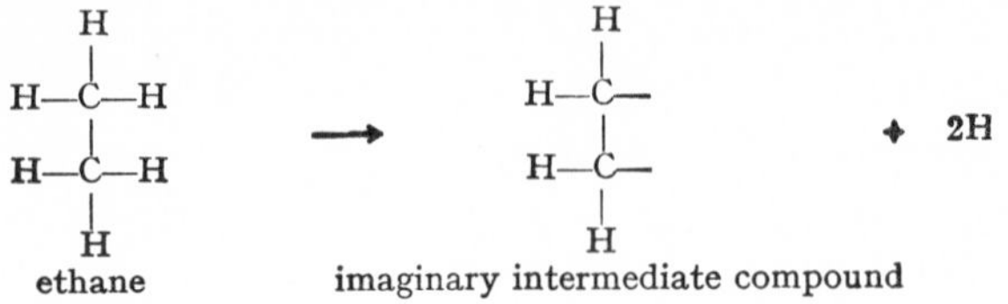

ethane   imaginary intermediate compound

The two free covalent bonds then link together, thus :

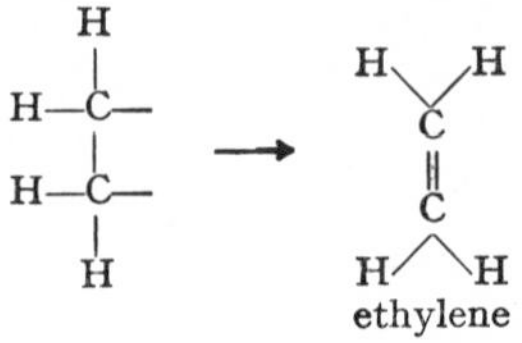

ethylene

Alternatively, it may be imagined that the molecule of ethylene is derived by the elimination of four atoms of hydrogen from two molecules of methane, thus :

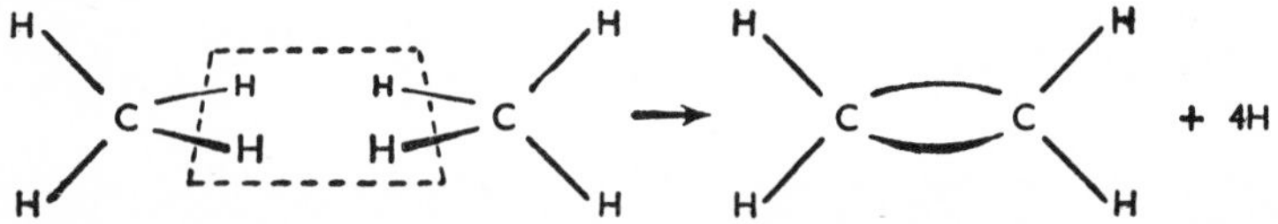

The molecules in the diagram are drawn, according to the convention described in the legend under Fig. 2, p. 30, to show the arrangement of the atoms in three dimensions. It should be noticed that the four hydrogen atoms in the molecule of ethylene lie in one and the same plane.

It is clear from a consideration of the above diagram that the formation of the double bond in the molecule of ethylene must require a modification of the tetrahedral disposition of the covalent bonds of the two carbon atoms. The angle between the two covalent bonds forming the double bond is much less than the tetrahedral angle of $109° 28'$. The double bond, therefore, represents a condition of strain in the molecule, and it would be deduced that the double bond is the point at which the molecule would be most readily attacked by chemical reagents. This deduction is confirmed by experiment. Ethylene undergoes numerous additive reactions in which the strain in the molecule is eliminated by the conversion of the double bond to a single bond. For example, ethylene reacts with chlorine, thus :

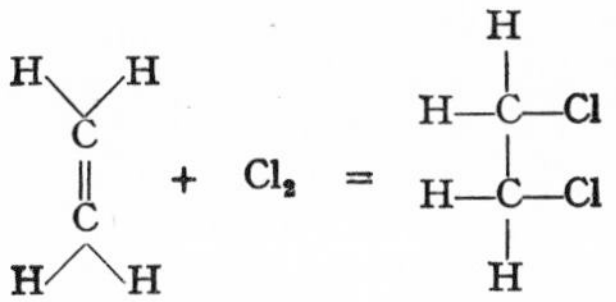

Members of the olefine series display isomerism when there are more than three carbon atoms in the molecule. For example, there are three isomerides of butylene :

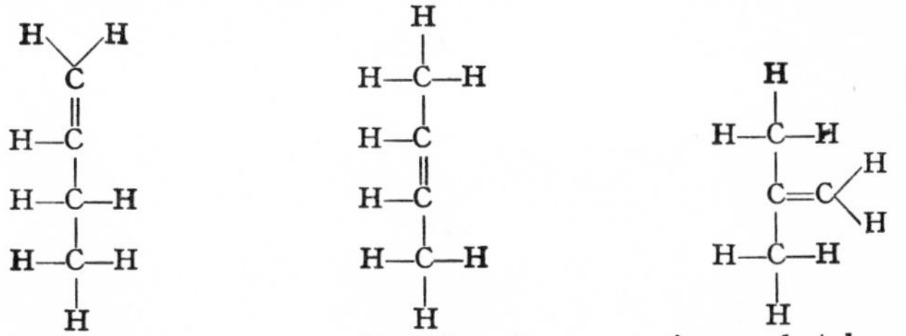

n-butylene   β-butylene   iso-or γ-butylene

The acetylenes. The simplest hydrocarbon containing a triple covalent bond in the molecule is acetylene. Acetylene may be imagined to be derived from ethane by the removal of four hydrogen atoms from the molecule, so as to leave two free covalencies on each of the carbon atoms, thus :

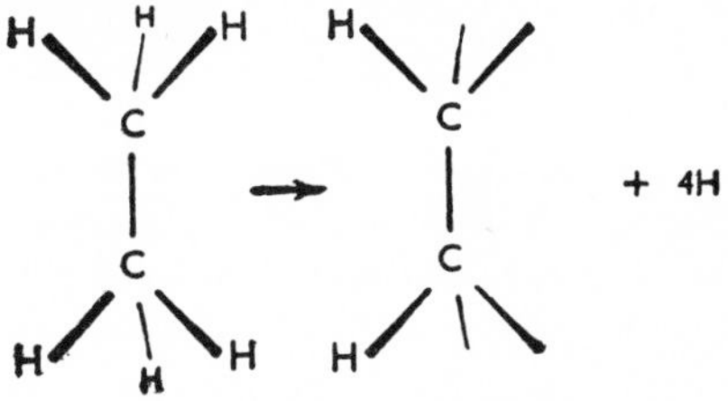

The four free covalencies then link together :

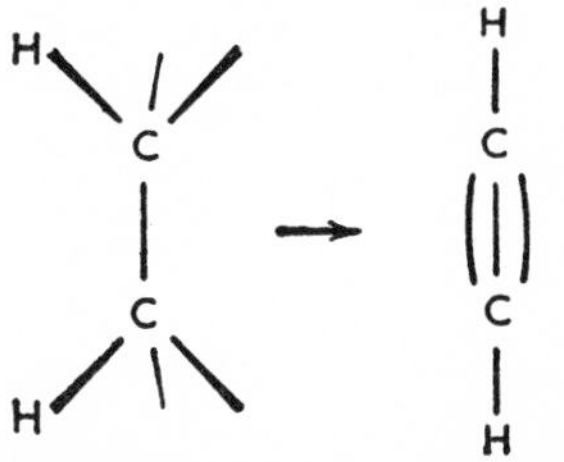

Monohalogen derivatives of the paraffins. The principal classes of compounds, other than the hydrocarbons, in the aliphatic division of organic chemistry are derived by replacing one of the

hydrogen atoms in the molecule of a paraffin by an atom of another monovalent element, or by a monovalent group of atoms.

The monohalogen derivatives of the paraffins are obtained by the replacement of one hydrogen atom in the molecule of a paraffin by an atom of one of the halogens. This reaction may be carried out in practice by exposing a mixture of the hydrocarbon and chlorine to sunlight.* By this treatment,

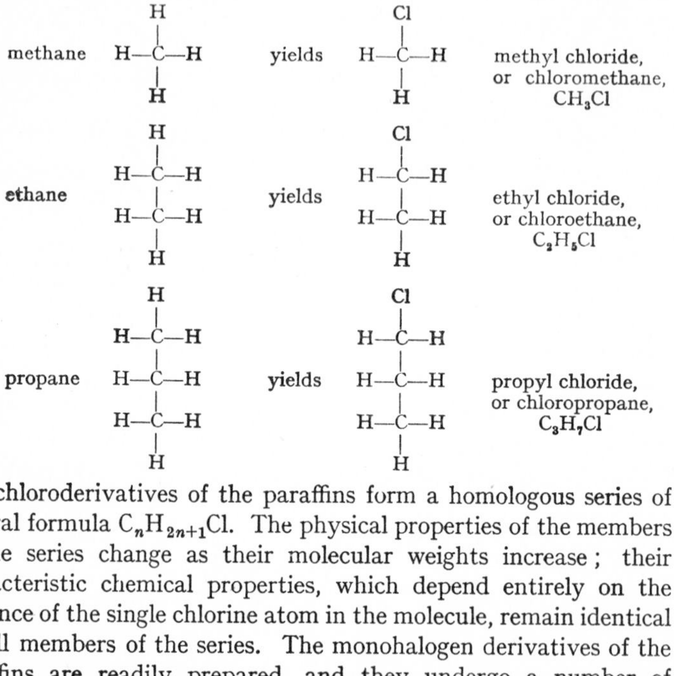

methane
$$H-\underset{\underset{H}{|}}{\overset{\overset{H}{|}}{C}}-H$$
yields
$$H-\underset{\underset{H}{|}}{\overset{\overset{Cl}{|}}{C}}-H$$
methyl chloride, or chloromethane, CH_3Cl

ethane
$$\begin{array}{c} H-\overset{\overset{H}{|}}{\underset{|}{C}}-H \\ H-\overset{|}{\underset{\underset{H}{|}}{C}}-H \end{array}$$
yields
$$\begin{array}{c} H-\overset{\overset{Cl}{|}}{\underset{|}{C}}-H \\ H-\overset{|}{\underset{\underset{H}{|}}{C}}-H \end{array}$$
ethyl chloride, or chloroethane, C_2H_5Cl

propane
$$\begin{array}{c} H-\overset{\overset{H}{|}}{\underset{|}{C}}-H \\ H-\overset{|}{\underset{|}{C}}-H \\ H-\overset{|}{\underset{\underset{H}{|}}{C}}-H \end{array}$$
yields
$$\begin{array}{c} H-\overset{\overset{Cl}{|}}{\underset{|}{C}}-H \\ H-\overset{|}{\underset{|}{C}}-H \\ H-\overset{|}{\underset{\underset{H}{|}}{C}}-H \end{array}$$
propyl chloride, or chloropropane, C_3H_7Cl

The chloroderivatives of the paraffins form a homologous series of general formula $C_nH_{2n+1}Cl$. The physical properties of the members of the series change as their molecular weights increase ; their characteristic chemical properties, which depend entirely on the presence of the single chlorine atom in the molecule, remain identical for all members of the series. The monohalogen derivatives of the paraffins are readily prepared, and they undergo a number of reactions leading to the formation of other compounds. They are, therefore, important substances in synthetical chemistry.

Nomenclature of the monohalogen derivatives of the paraffins. The group $—CH_3$, $—C_2H_5$, or $—C_3H_7$, which remains after the removal of one atom of hydrogen from a paraffin molecule is denoted by substituting the suffix " yl " in place of " ane " in the name of the paraffin, thus :

CH_4 methane $—CH_3$ methyl
C_2H_6 ethane $—C_2H_5$ ethyl
C_3H_8 propane $—C_3H_7$ propyl.

* Bromine derivatives may also be made by the direct action of bromine or a paraffin, but iodine derivatives cannot be made in this way (see p. 144).

The monovalent groups, methyl, ethyl and propyl, conform to the formula $-C_nH_{2n+1}$, and are denoted generally by the term "alkyl". The halogen derivatives of the paraffins may be regarded either as additive compounds of the alkyl groups with the halogens, or, as substitution compounds formed by the replacement of one hydrogen atom in the molecule of a paraffin by a halogen atom. If a given halogen derivative, say C_2H_5Cl, is regarded as an addition compound of the group ethyl and chlorine, it is denoted as ethyl chloride ; if it is regarded as a substitution compound of ethane it is denoted as chloroethane. It is a general rule that the name of a group of atoms followed by the name of a halogen ending in "ide" indicates addition, and that the name of a halogen ending in "o" prefixed to the name of an organic compound indicates substitution. For example, ethylene chloride is $ClCH_2-CH_2Cl$; chloroethylene is $ClCH = CH_2$.

Isomerism of the monohalogen derivatives of the paraffins. Since all the hydrogen atoms in the molecule of methane are arranged symmetrically about the carbon atom, there is only one monochloromethane, CH_3Cl. Similarly there is only one monochloroethane, C_2H_5Cl. There are, however, two isomers of monochloropropane,

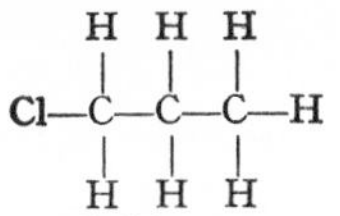

normal chloropropane   and   iso-chloropropane.

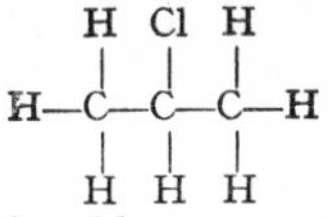

and there are four isomers of monochlorobutane

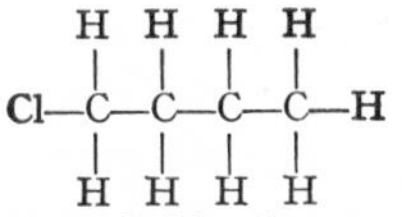

normal chlorobutane 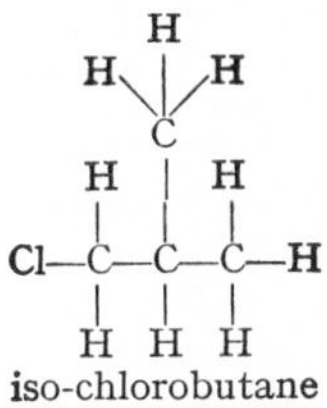   iso-chlorobutane

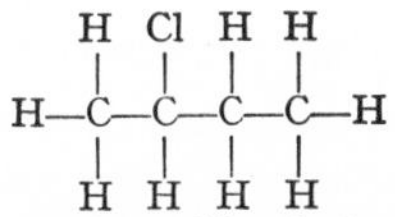

secondary chlorobutane 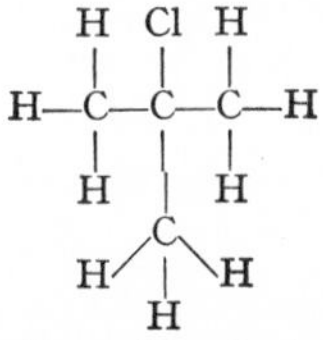   tertiary chlorobutane

Other important classes of organic compounds may be derived in theory by substituting one monovalent atom or group for a hydrogen atom in the molecule of a paraffin. Among these classes are :

alcohols, in which the substituent is the hydroxyl group OH, for example, methyl alcohol CH_3OH, and ethyl alcohol C_2H_5OH ;

nitro compounds, in which the substituent is the nitro group NO_2, for example, nitromethane CH_3NO_2, and nitro ethane $C_2H_5NO_2$;

amines, in which the substituent is the amino group NH_2, for example, methylamine CH_3NH_2, and ethylamine $C_2H_5NH_2$;

alkyl cyanides, in which the substituent is the cyanide group CN, for example, methyl cyanide CH_3CN, and ethyl cyanide C_2H_5CN ;

fatty acids, in which the substituent is the carboxyl group COOH, for example, acetic acid CH_3COOH.

From this point of view acetic acid is regarded as derived from methane by the replacement of one atom of hydrogen in the molecule by the carboxyl group, COOH.

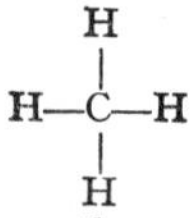

$$\underset{\text{methane}}{H-\overset{\displaystyle H}{\underset{\displaystyle H}{C}}-H} \qquad \underset{\text{acetic acid}}{H-\overset{\displaystyle H}{\underset{\displaystyle H}{C}}-COOH}$$

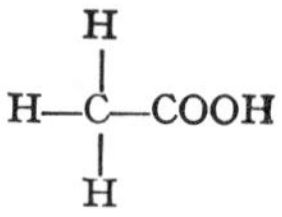

The molecule of acetic acid, however, contains a chain of two carbon atoms, and for this reason it is also to be regarded as a derivative of ethane

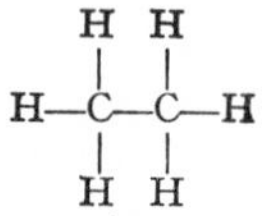

$$\underset{\text{ethane}}{H-\overset{\displaystyle H}{\underset{\displaystyle H}{C}}-\overset{\displaystyle H}{\underset{\displaystyle H}{C}}-H} \qquad \underset{\text{acetic acid}}{H-\overset{\displaystyle H}{\underset{\displaystyle H}{C}}-C\!\!\begin{array}{c}O\\ OH\end{array}}$$

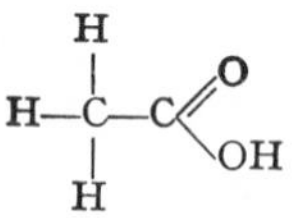

There is no alternative but to regard formic acid as a derivative of methane

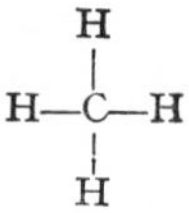

$$\underset{\text{methane}}{H-\overset{\displaystyle H}{\underset{\displaystyle H}{C}}-H} \qquad \underset{\text{formic acid}}{H-C\!\!\begin{array}{c}O\\ OH\end{array}}$$

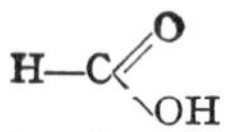

Similar considerations apply to the classification of methyl cyanide. It may be regarded either as derived from methane by the substitution of the cyanide group for one atom of hydrogen, or as derived from ethane by the substitution of a nitrogen atom for three atoms of hydrogen.

Several important classes of aliphatic compounds are derived from the fatty acids, including :

acid chlorides, in which an atom of chlorine has replaced the hydroxyl group in the carboxyl group of the acid, for example, acetyl chloride,

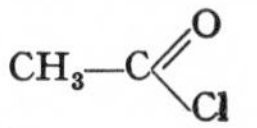

$$CH_3-C{\overset{O}{\underset{Cl}{}}}$$

is derived from acetic acid

$$CH_3-C{\overset{O}{\underset{OH}{}}}$$

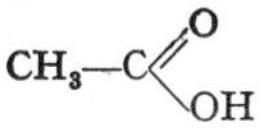

amides, in which the amino group, NH_2, has replaced the hydroxyl group in the carboxyl group of the acid, for example, acetamide,

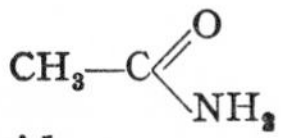

$$CH_3-C{\overset{O}{\underset{NH_2}{}}}$$

is derived from acetic acid

$$CH_3-C{\overset{O}{\underset{OH}{}}}$$

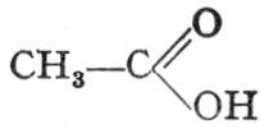

anhydrides, derived by the elimination of the elements of water from two molecules of the acid ; acetic anhydride is derived from two molecules of acetic acid, thus

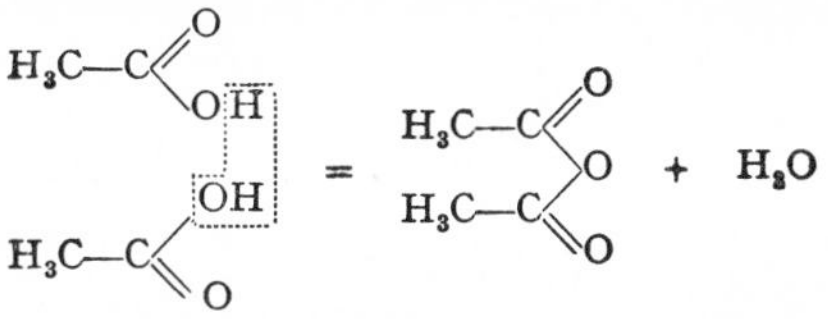

$$H_3C-C{\overset{O}{\underset{OH}{}}} \quad = \quad H_3C-C{\overset{O}{\underset{}{}}}O \quad + \quad H_2O$$
$$H_3C-C{\overset{}{\underset{O}{}}OH} \qquad H_3C-C{\overset{}{\underset{O}{}}}$$

esters, derived by the elimination of the elements of water from one molecule of an alcohol and one molecule of an acid ; **ethyl acetate** is derived from ethyl alcohol and acetic acid, thus :

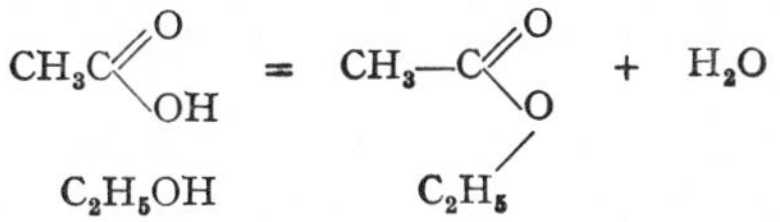

$$CH_3C{\overset{O}{\underset{OH}{}}} \quad = \quad CH_3-C{\overset{O}{\underset{O}{}}} \quad + \quad H_2O$$
$$C_2H_5OH \qquad\qquad C_2H_5$$

Three other classes of simple aliphatic compounds deserve mention in this brief summary. These are the ethers, the aldehydes and the ketones.

The **ethers** may be derived in theory from the alcohols by the replacement of the hydrogen atom in the hydroxyl group by an alkyl group. Dimethyl ether is derived from methyl alcohol by the replacement of the hydrogen atom in the hydroxyl group by a methyl group, thus :

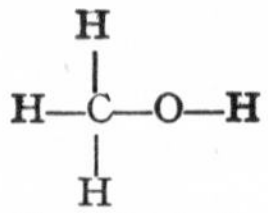

$$\underset{\text{methyl alcohol}}{\overset{\displaystyle H}{\underset{\displaystyle H}{H-C-O-H}}}$$

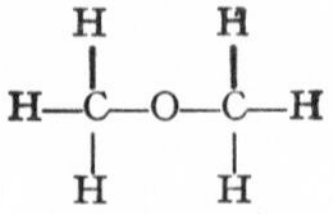

$$\underset{\text{dimethyl ether}}{\overset{\displaystyle H \quad H}{\underset{\displaystyle H \quad H}{H-C-O-C-H}}}$$

Diethyl ether is similarly derived from ethyl alcohol

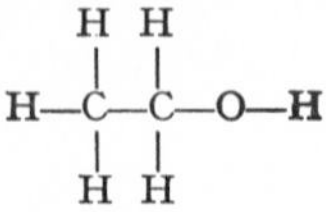

$$\underset{\text{ethyl alcohol}}{\overset{\displaystyle H \quad H}{\underset{\displaystyle H \quad H}{H-C-C-O-H}}}$$

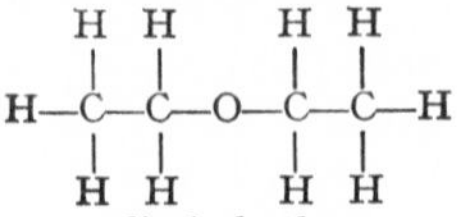

$$\underset{\text{diethyl ether}}{\overset{\displaystyle H \quad H \quad\quad H \quad H}{\underset{\displaystyle H \quad H \quad\quad H \quad H}{H-C-C-O-C-C-H}}}$$

Mixed ethers may be obtained by using as the substituent group an alkyl group other than that present in the alcohol, thus methyl ethyl is

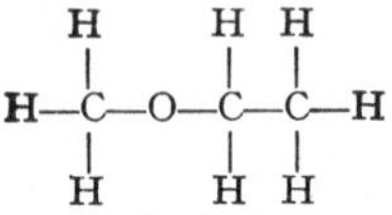

$$\underset{\text{methyl ethyl ether}}{\overset{\displaystyle H \quad\quad H \quad H}{\underset{\displaystyle H \quad\quad H \quad H}{H-C-O-C-C-H}}}$$

The **aldehydes** are compounds containing the group $-C\!\!\underset{O}{\overset{H}{\diagup}}$ in the molecule. Formaldehyde is related to methane, and acetaldehyde to ethane, thus

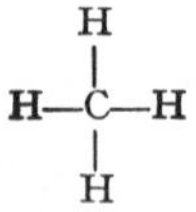

$$\underset{\text{methane}}{\overset{\displaystyle H}{\underset{\displaystyle H}{H-C-H}}}$$

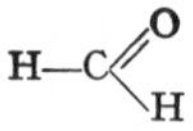

$$\underset{\text{formaldehyde}}{H-C\!\!\underset{\diagdown H}{\overset{\diagup O}{}}}$$

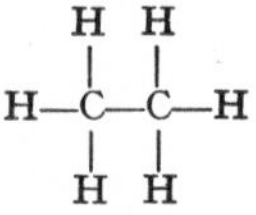

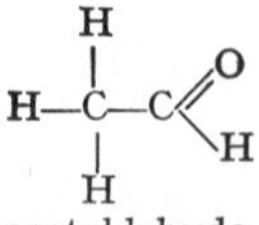

$$\underset{\text{ethane}}{\overset{\displaystyle H \quad H}{\underset{\displaystyle H \quad H}{H-C-C-H}}}$$

$$\underset{\text{acetaldehyde}}{\overset{\displaystyle H}{\underset{\displaystyle H}{H-C}}-C\!\!\underset{\diagdown H}{\overset{\diagup O}{}}}$$

The **ketones** may be derived in theory from the aldehydes by the replacement of the hydrogen atom in the aldehyde group $-C\!\!\underset{O}{\overset{H}{\diagup}}$, by an alkyl group. Acetone, the first member of the ketone series, is derived by replacing the aldehydic hydrogen atom in acetaldehyde by the methyl group

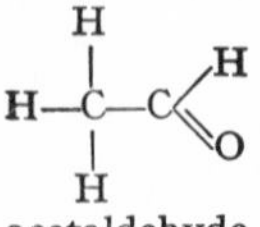

$$\underset{\text{acetaldehyde}}{\overset{\displaystyle H}{\underset{\displaystyle H}{H-C}}-C\!\!\underset{\diagdown O}{\overset{\diagup H}{}}}$$

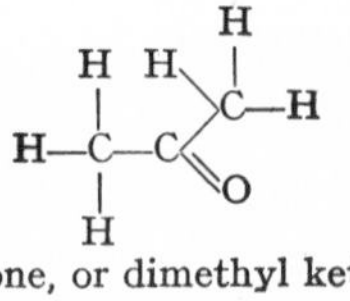

$$\underset{\text{acetone, or dimethyl ketone}}{\overset{\displaystyle H \; H}{\underset{\displaystyle H}{H-C-C}}-C\!\!\underset{\diagdown O}{\overset{\displaystyle H}{}}}$$

Nomenclature. The nomenclature of members of a homologous series is based either on that of the paraffins or on that of the acids. The names of the monohalogen derivatives of the paraffins, the alcohols, the amines, and certain other classes of compounds are based on those of the paraffins ; the names of the amides and aldehydes are based on those of the acids. If the compounds CH_3CN and C_2H_5CN are regarded as derivatives of methane and ethane respectively, they are denoted as methyl cyanide and ethyl cyanide ; if they are regarded as derivatives of acetic and propionic acids, they are denoted as acetonitrile and propionitrile. Table VIII gives the names and molecular formulae of the first five members of certain classes of aliphatic compounds.

Aromatic compounds. Compounds in the aromatic division of organic chemistry contain the ring of six carbon atoms which is present in the molecule of benzene C_6H_6. It has been mentioned on p. 27 that the molecule of benzene is a resonance system of two structures

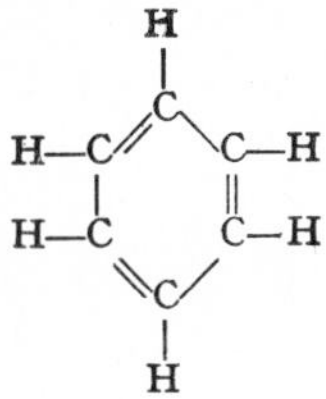

and

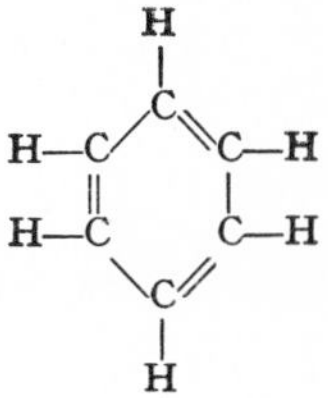

For the purpose of writing structural equations to describe those chemical reactions of benzene which are independent of the presence of double bonds in the molecule, the structural formula is drawn as

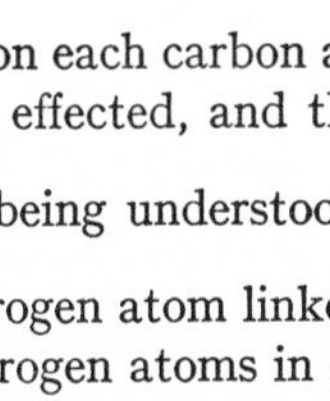

omitting the fourth bond on each carbon atom. For many purposes a further simplification is effected, and the molecule is drawn as a regular hexagon ⬡ , it being understood that each corner of the hexagon represents a hydrogen atom linked to a carbon atom.

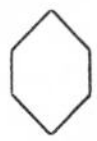

One or more of the hydrogen atoms in the benzene molecule may be replaced by an alkyl group such as methyl, ethyl or propyl, giving

TABLE VIII

THE NAMES AND MOLECULAR FORMULAE OF THE SIMPLER MEMBERS OF CERTAIN CLASSES OF ALIPHATIC COMPOUNDS

Paraffin C_nH_{2n+2}	Halogen derivative $C_nH_{2n+1}Cl$	Alcohol $C_nH_{2n+1}OH$	Primary amine $C_nH_{2n+1}NH_2$	Nitrile, or cyanide $C_nH_{2n-1}N$	Aldehyde $C_nH_{2n}O$	Ketone $C_nH_{2n}O$	Acid $C_nH_{2n}O_2$
Methane CH_4	Methyl chloride, or chloromethane CH_3Cl	Methyl alcohol CH_3OH	Methyl-amine CH_3NH_2	Hydrogen cyanide HCN	Formaldehyde $H.CHO$		Formic acid $H.COOH$
Ethane C_2H_6	Ethyl chloride, or chloroethane C_2H_5Cl	Ethyl alcohol C_2H_5OH	Ethyl-amine $C_2H_5NH_2$	Acetonitrile, or methyl cyanide $CH_3.CN$	Acetaldehyde $CH_3.CHO$		Acetic acid $CH_3.COOH$
Propane C_3H_8	Propyl chloride, or chloropropane * C_3H_7Cl	Propyl alcohol * C_3H_7OH	Propyl-amine * $C_3H_7NH_2$	Propionitrile, or ethyl cyanide $C_2H_5.CN$	Propaldehyde $C_2H_5.CHO$	Acetone $CH_3.CO.CH_3$	Propionic acid $C_2H_5.COOH$
Butane * C_4H_{10}	Butyl chloride, or chlorobutane * C_4H_9Cl	Butyl alcohol * C_4H_9OH	Butyl-amine * $C_4H_9NH_2$	Butyronitrile, or propyl cyanide * $C_3H_7.CN$	Butalde-hyde * $C_3H_7.CHO$	Methyl ethyl ketone $CH_3.CO.C_2H_5$	Butyric acid * $C_3H_7.COOH$
Pentane * C_5H_{12}	Amyl chloride, or chloropentane * $C_5H_{11}Cl$	Amyl-alcohol * $C_5H_{11}OH$	Amyl-amine * $C_5H_{11}NH_2$	Valeronitrile, or butyl cyanide * $C_4H_9.CN$	Valeralde-hyde * $C_4H_9.CHO$	Methyl propyl ketone * $CH_3.CO.C_3H_7$	Valeric acid * $C_4H_9.COOH$

* This compound exists in isomeric forms.

respectively methyl benzene, usually denoted as toluene, ethyl benzene and propyl benzene.

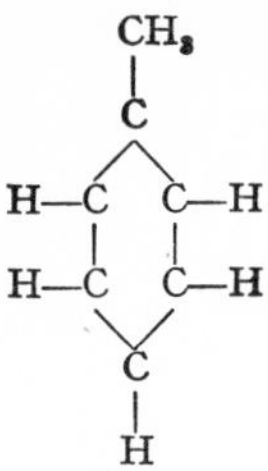

toluene 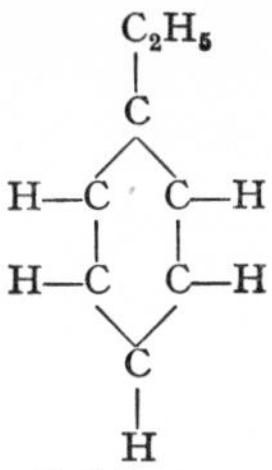 · ethyl benzene 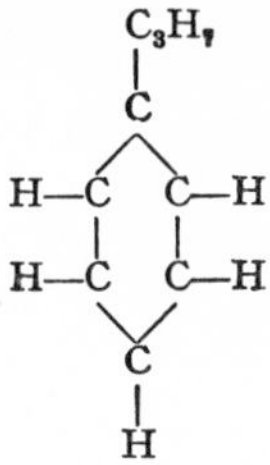 · propyl benzene

A group which is attached to one of the carbon atoms in the benzene ring is known as a **side chain,** and in contradistinction, the ring comprising the six carbon atoms and the residue of hydrogen atoms is known as the *benzene nucleus,* or, shortly, as the **nucleus.** The methyl, ethyl and propyl groups attached to the nucleus in toluene, ethyl benzene and propyl benzene are examples of side chains.

By increasing the number of carbon atoms in the side chain of an aromatic hydrocarbon, a homologous series is derived having the general formula $C_6H_5.C_nH_{2n+1}$. A compound with more than three atoms of carbon in the side chain may display isomerism, the group C_6H_5 playing the same part as the chlorine atom in the monohalogen derivative of a paraffin. For example, propyl benzene $C_6H_5.C_3H_7$ may exist in the forms :

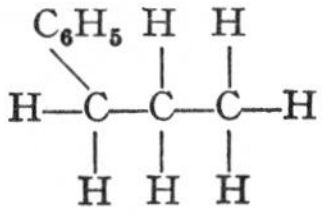

and

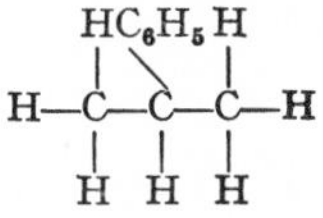

Aromatic hydrocarbons also display a type of isomerism which arises because an alkyl group may be substituted for a hydrogen atom either in the side chain or in the nucleus. Ethyl benzene is isomeric with xylene (dimethyl benzene)

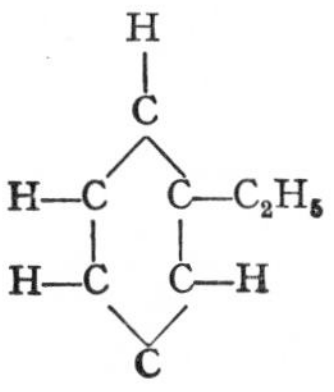

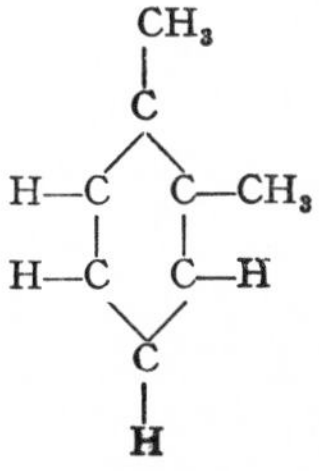

and xylene itself exists in three forms, as there are three different ways in which two methyl groups may replace hydrogen atoms in the nucleus :

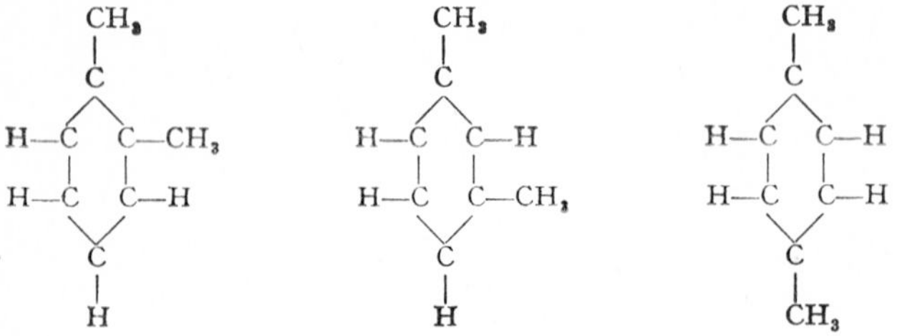

$$
\begin{array}{ccc}
CH_3 & CH_3 & CH_3 \\
| & | & | \\
C & C & C \\
\diagdown\diagup & \diagdown\diagup & \diagdown\diagup \\
H{-}C \quad C{-}CH_3 & H{-}C \quad C{-}H & H{-}C \quad C{-}H \\
| \quad | & | \quad | & | \quad | \\
H{-}C \quad C{-}H & H{-}C \quad C{-}CH_3 & H{-}C \quad C{-}H \\
\diagup\diagdown & \diagup\diagdown & \diagup\diagdown \\
C & C & C \\
| & | & | \\
H & H & CH_3
\end{array}
$$

In general, aromatic compounds are derived from benzene and its homologues by the replacement of an atom of hydrogen in the molecule by some other atom or group. If the replacement takes place in the *side chain*, many of the properties of the compound thus derived will be those of an aliphatic compound. For example, an atom of chlorine may replace one of the hydrogen atoms in the side chain of toluene giving benzyl chloride

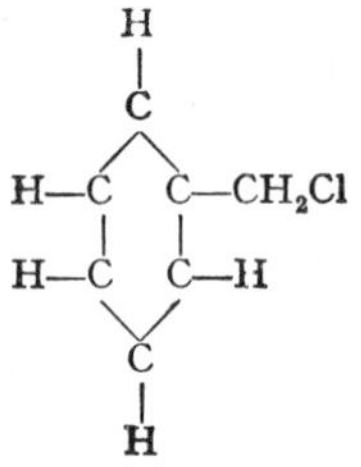

$$
\begin{array}{c}
H \\
| \\
C \\
\diagdown\diagup \\
H{-}C \quad C{-}CH_2Cl \\
| \quad | \\
H{-}C \quad C{-}H \\
\diagup\diagdown \\
C \\
| \\
H
\end{array}
$$

If the structural formula is written thus

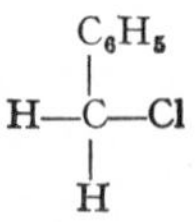

$$
\begin{array}{c}
C_6H_5 \\
| \\
H{-}C{-}Cl \\
| \\
H
\end{array}
$$

the compound is seen to be a derivative of methyl chloride ; the properties of benzyl chloride dependent on the presence of the chlorine atom on the molecule are, in fact, similar to those of methyl chloride.

If the substituent atom replaces a hydrogen atom in the *nucleus*, the resultant molecule possesses properties which are peculiar to aromatic compounds. The names and structural formulae of a few of the more important simple compounds arising from nuclear substitution are given below:

chlorobenzene

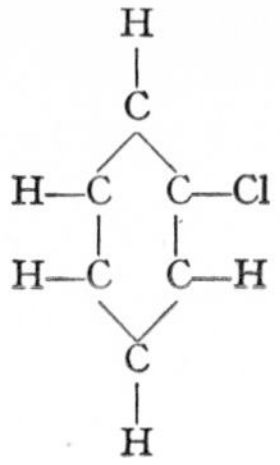

$$H\text{---}C \quad C\text{---}Cl$$

nitrobenzene

$$H\text{---}C \quad C\text{---}NO_2$$

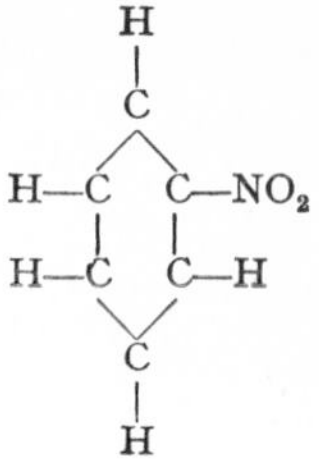

aminobenzene, or aniline

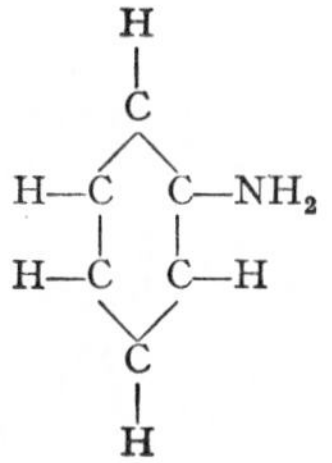

$$H\text{---}C \quad C\text{---}NH_2$$

phenol

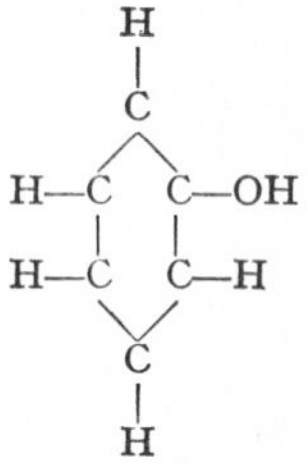

$$H\text{---}C \quad C\text{---}OH$$

benzaldehyde

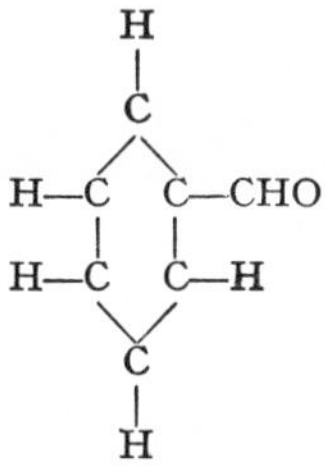

$$H\text{---}C \quad C\text{---}CHO$$

benzoic acid

$$H\text{---}C \quad C\text{---}COOH$$

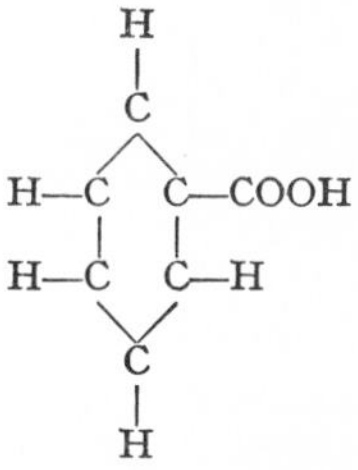

It is apparent from the brief outline given above that the number and variety of organic compounds is dependent to a great extent on the phenomenon of isomerism; different compounds possessing distinct properties may be constituted of the same groups occupying different relative positions in the molecule. In this introductory survey of organic compounds, conventional graphical formulae have been used, in which the carbon chain in open chain compounds is shown as straight, and the four covalent bonds of the carbon atom are projected on to one plane (p. 35). The use of this convention obscures two types of isomerism, geometrical isomerism and optical isomerism, both of which depend on the spatial distribution of the four bonds of the carbon atom.

Geometrical isomerism is exhibited by certain derivatives of ethylene. To explain geometrical isomerism it is first necessary to consider a property of carbon atoms linked by a single covalent bond; this property is known as *free rotation*. The molecule of ethane has the structure

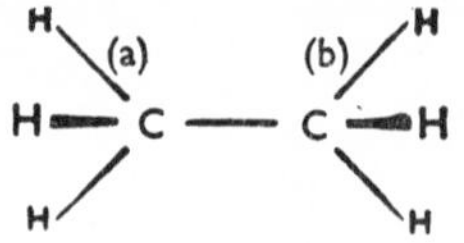

If the methyl group containing the carbon atom " *a* " is imagined to rotate about the axis joining the two carbon atoms, while the methyl group containing the carbon atom " *b* " remains stationary, it is possible to deduce the energy of the molecule at each stage of the rotation. It is found that the maximum variation of energy is very small, and it is concluded that in ethane the rotation of one carbon atom with respect to the other is unrestricted. The two carbon atoms linked by a single covalent bond are therefore said to possess free rotation. The free rotation of the carbon atoms in ethane is fully confirmed by chemical evidence. For example, only one substance is known with the formula $CH_2Cl.CH_2Cl$. The non-existence of the imaginary isomers

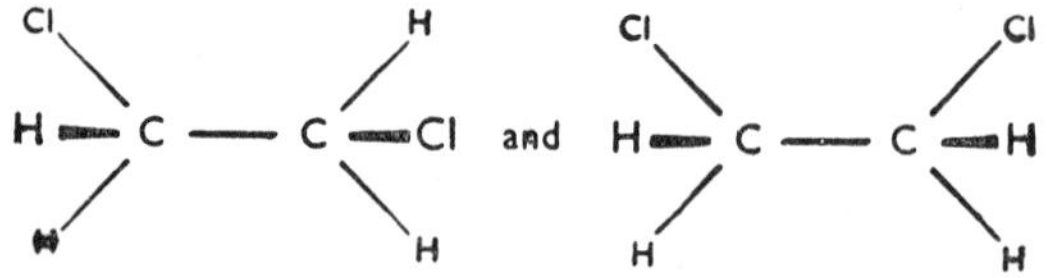

must mean that the orientation of the two methylene chloride groups to one another is not fixed, that is, that the carbon atoms possess free rotation about the C—C axis.

The molecule of ethylene has the structure

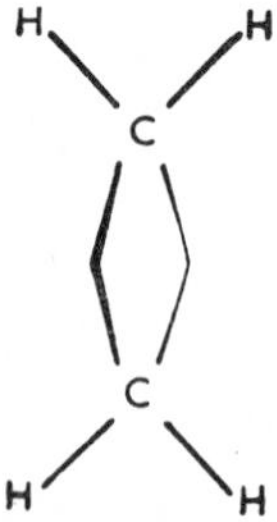

If one methylene group is imagined to rotate on the axis joining the two carbon atoms, it may be deduced that for each rotation of 360° there are two positions of equal minimum energy. These positions correspond to the arrangement in which the four hydrogen atoms in the ethylene molecule lie in one and the same plane. There are two such arrangements for each rotation of 360°, but since all hydrogen atoms are identical, it is impossible to distinguish between them. If, however, one hydrogen atom on each carbon atom in the molecule of ethylene is replaced by some other monovalent atom or group, for example, chlorine, each planar arrangement of the atoms in the molecule is distinguishable by means of the relative positions of the chlorine and hydrogen atoms, as shown by the graphical formulae :

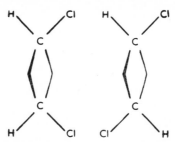

These formulae represent two isomeric compounds. From the formulae it is clear that one carbon atom in the molecule cannot be rotated with respect to the other without rupture of the double bond. The two compounds represented, therefore, are not readily inter-convertible. These compounds are said to exhibit *geometrical isomerism*. Geometrical isomerism displayed by ethylene derivatives arises because carbon atoms linked by a double bond have lost the property of free rotation.

This interpretation of the structure of ethylene derivatives explains the existence of the two acids of the same molecular formula :

maleic acid   fumaric acid

Optical isomerism is exhibited by molecules which are related to one another as object to mirror image. The simplest compounds showing optical isomerism are derivatives of methane in which all the four hydrogen atoms are replaced by different atoms or groups.

Two different arrangements, and only two, of the four atoms or groups are possible ;

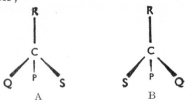

Examination will show that these arrangements are non-superposable. Superficially they appear similar, just as a right hand and a left hand appear similar, but, just as a right hand cannot be made

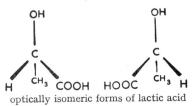

optically isomeric forms of lactic acid

to coincide with a left hand, so the structure A cannot by any degree of twisting or turning be made to coincide with the structure B. The existence of two forms of lactic acid, one obtained from sour milk and the other from muscle, is explained by isomerism of this type.

To sum up, organic chemistry is the study of the nature and behaviour of substances consisting of molecules built up on frameworks of covalently linked carbon atoms. In the hydrocarbons the valencies of the carbon atoms not used for bonding carbon atoms together are linked to hydrogen atoms ; in other classes of compounds one or more of the hydrogen atoms is replaced by some other atom or group. The properties and relationships of some of the most important classes of organic compounds are described in detail in Chapters V to XXVIII.

CHAPTER III

LABORATORY TECHNIQUE (A): MANIPULATION

THE practical operations of organic chemistry are usually carried out either to determine the constitution of an organic compound, or to prepare it. The methods for determining the constitution of a simple organic compound are explained in Chapter IV ; the present chapter is concerned with methods of preparation.

The experimental procedure for the preparation of an organic compound normally takes longer, and needs more careful control, than that required for the preparation of an inorganic compound.

In most inorganic preparations it is possible to bring the reagents together in one phase, and to contrive that the required product alone is formed in some other phase. The required product is thus obtained rapidly, quantitatively, and in conditions in which its final purification is quick and easy. For example, consider the preparation of silver chloride. Solutions of silver nitrate and sodium chloride are mixed, and the precipitated silver chloride is filtered off, washed and dried.

$$AgNO_3 + NaCl = NaNO_3 + AgCl \downarrow .$$

The simplicity and speed of this preparation depends on the spontaneous separation of the silver chloride in the solid phase from the excess of reagents and the by-product sodium nitrate, which remain throughout in the liquid phase. In consequence of the spontaneous separation of the silver chloride from the other substances :

(i) the reaction is irreversible,

(ii) the weight of silver chloride produced is chemically equivalent either to the weight of silver nitrate originally taken if the sodium chloride was added in excess, or, to the weight of sodium chloride taken if the silver nitrate was added in excess,

(iii) the silver chloride is pure as soon as it has been freed from adhering solution.

In most organic preparations the reaction takes place, and the required product remains, in one and the same phase. In these conditions the reaction is reversible. It attains an equilibrium before any of the reagents has been completely used up, and at its conclusion the required product is in solution with excess of the reagents, and with any by-products which may have been formed in side reactions. The preparation, therefore, is comparatively slow, the conversion of reagents to products is incomplete, and an elaborate procedure must be used to isolate the one substance required from all the other substances present at the end of the reaction.

These general considerations may be illustrated by the preparation of ethyl acetate. This preparation is based on the reaction described by the equation :

$$C_2H_5OH + CH_3.COOH \rightleftharpoons CH_3.COOC_2H_5 + H_2O.$$

The reaction is reversible, and if it takes place in a closed vessel, the production of ethyl acetate ceases when equilibrium has been attained. The experiment, therefore, is conducted so that the products leave the reaction vessel as fast as they are formed. A mixture of pure acetic acid and ethyl alcohol is slowly added to a flask containing a mixture of ethyl alcohol and concentrated sulphuric acid maintained at 140°. The concentrated sulphuric acid is present to reduce the concentration of water in the system ; the temperature is raised to 140° to cause ethyl acetate and water to distil out of the reaction flask. Some unchanged ethyl alcohol (B.P. 78°) and acetic acid (B.P. 119°) as well as diethyl ether formed by the action of sulphuric acid on ethyl alcohol, will, however, be present in the vapour. If the vapour distilling from the reaction vessel is condensed, the resulting liquid consists of ethyl acetate and water, and small proportions of ethyl alcohol, acetic acid and ether. Pure ethyl acetate is obtained from this mixture by removing the acetic acid, ethyl alcohol and water by chemical means,* and the ether by distillation. Even under carefully controlled conditions only about 55 per cent. of the ethyl alcohol originally taken is converted to ethyl acetate.

It will be seen from the above example that a description of the preparation of an organic compound is far from complete if it mentions only the reagents which must be assembled and the conditions under which they react. An adequate description must mention also the operations which are to be carried out to isolate the required compound in a pure state. The principal operations used for this purpose are discussed in the following paragraphs.

Simple distillation. If a mixture of one volatile substance with completely non-volatile substances is heated, the volatile substance alone vaporises. If the vapour is led away and condensed, the

* For details see the description of the preparation of ethyl acetate on D. 258.

condensate consists of the volatile substance free from the other substances.

The apparatus for a simple distillation usually consists of a distilling flask, a condenser and a receiving vessel. The distilling flask is a long-necked vessel, with a side tube sealed into the neck, Fig. 8. The condenser may be an air-condenser or a water-condenser. The *air-condenser*, Fig. 9, is a glass tube 30–50 cm. long and about 1 cm. in diameter. One end is widened to take a cork. The air-condenser is used for condensing vapours of liquids which have boiling points above 130°, and which are readily condensed by the cooling effect

Fig. 8.
Distilling flask.

of air convection currents. The *water-condenser*, Fig. 10, consists of a tube, usually 60–80 cm. long, similar to that used for an air-condenser. The greater part of the length of the tube is enclosed in a jacket of

Fig. 9.   Air condenser.

glass or metal through which a stream of cold water may be passed. The water-condenser is used for condensing vapours of liquids with boiling points in the temperature range 30° to 130° ; the glass tube

Fig. 10.   Water condenser.

is likely to crack if vapour at a temperature above 130° is passed through the water-condenser. The receiving vessel, for many distillations, is an open conical flask.

When a distillation is to be carried out the apparatus is assembled as shown in Fig. 11. The liquid to be distilled is placed in the distilling flask, together with a few fragments of unglazed porcelain. The rough surface of the porcelain furnishes numerous " nuclei " on which bubbles of the vapour begin to form when the liquid is heated. Superheating of the liquid and the formation of large bubbles leading to " bumping " is thus prevented, and the liquid boils smoothly.

The mouth of the neck of the distilling flask is closed with a cork carrying a thermometer, adjusted so that the bulb is opposite the side-tube. During the distillation some of the vapour which is

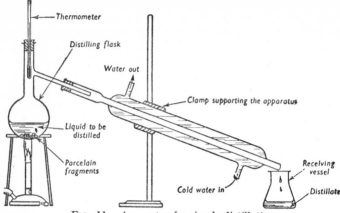

FIG. 11. Apparatus for simple distillation.

distilling condenses on the bulb, and the temperature recorded is therefore, the boiling point of the distillate, and *not* that of the mixture in the flask.

A bored cork is fitted to the wide neck of the condenser, and the side-tube of the distilling flask is inserted into the cork. A distilling flask up to about 200 c.c. capacity is safely held in position by the side-tube, and the single clamp round the condenser jacket is adequate support for the whole apparatus. The receiving vessel is placed to catch the drops leaving the lower end of the condenser. For the distillation of liquids with boiling points between 30° and 80° the distilling flask is heated by a hot water bath. If the boiling point of the liquid is above 80°, the flask is heated on a sand bath, or on a wire gauze.

If the condensate is volatile, an adaptor, Fig. 12, is fitted to the end of the condenser, thus:

FIG. 12. Adaptor fitted to the end of a condenser.

The condensate is then delivered into the body of the receiver which is chilled in ice-water or a freezing mixture. If the condensate is hygroscopic, it must be prevented from absorbing moisture from the air. For this purpose a Buchner flask, Fig. 13, is used as the re-

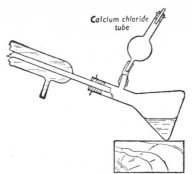

FIG. 13. Buchner flask used as a receiving vessel for hygroscopic condensates.

ceiving vessel, and the side arm is fitted with a calcium chloride tube. A round-bottomed flask fitted with a knee-tube is sometimes used for distillation instead of a distilling flask when there is no need to observe the boiling point of the distillate, Fig. 14.

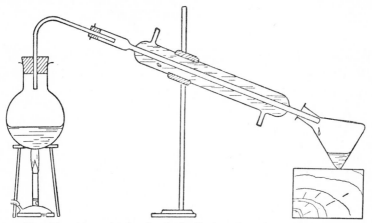

FIG. 14. Apparatus for simple distillation when observation of the boiling point is unnecessary.

Fractional distillation or fractionation. The boiling point of a liquid, whether a pure substance or a mixture, is the temperature at which the liquid is in equilibrium with the vapour at a pressure of

760 mm. If a system of two volatile substances, which are miscible in the liquid state, is maintained at the boiling point, it is normally found that the composition of the liquid is different from that of the vapour with which it is in equilibrium.

For example, Fig. 15 shows the equilibrium diagram for the pair of miscible liquids chloroform (B.P. 61·4°) and benzene (B.P. 80·2°)

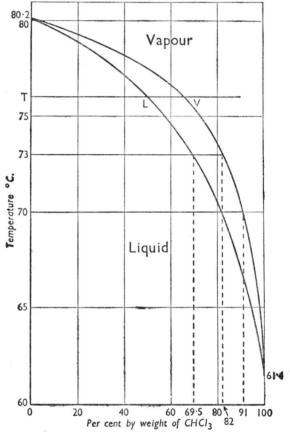

FIG. 15.   Boiling point-composition diagram for the system chloroform (CHCl₃)—benzene (C₆H₆).

at a pressure of 760 mm. The composition of the system in percentages by weight of chloroform is plotted on the abscissae, and the temperature on the ordinates. The diagram consists of two curves. The lower curve gives the temperature at which a liquid of given composition begins to boil, and the upper curve the temperature at which a vapour of given composition begins to condense. An isothermal, T, drawn across the diagram cuts the lower curve at L, and the upper curve at V. At the temperature T the liquid of composition L is boiling, and the vapour of composition V is condensing. Hence the liquid of composition L and the vapour of composition V are in equilibrium at the temperature T. For example, at 73° a liquid containing 69·5 per cent. by weight of chloroform is in equilibrium with a vapour containing 82 per cent. of chloroform. It will be seen that the vapour contains the higher proportion of the more volatile constituent.

If a large volume * of a liquid mixture containing 69·5 per cent. of chloroform is heated it begins to boil at 73°, and the vapour liberated contains 82 per cent. of chloroform. It can be seen from the diagram that if this vapour is condensed, transferred to another distilling flask, and re-heated it will begin to boil at 70°, and the vapour initially generated will contain 91 per cent. of chloroform. By a series of distillations in which the first portion of each distillate is collected and redistilled, a small quantity of pure chloroform could eventually be obtained. Such a process is described as *fractional distillation*. If it were carried out in this discontinuous manner, however, the method would be tedious and the yield small.

By means of a fractionation column fractional distillation is carried out in one vessel in a single operation. Fractional distillation, or as it is more usually called, *fractionation*, is conducted by means of the apparatus shown in Fig. 16. The fractionating column consists of a glass tube about 12 mm. internal diameter, packed with sections of glass tubing. The sections are supported on a thin glass rod sealed across the tube. The glass sections used for the lower part of the column are about 5 mm. long and 6 mm. external diameter. Those used for the remaining layers gradually diminish in size, and in the uppermost layers are about 3 mm. long and 5 mm. diameter. The length of the column actually packed is usually 20–30 cm. For most distillations the tube is left exposed to the air, but for the distillation of high-boiling liquids it is jacketed with cotton-wool.

A round-bottomed flask is fitted to the lower end of the column by means of a cork as shown in Fig. 16. The upper end of the column is closed by a cork carrying a thermometer, of which the bulb is opposite the side tube ; the thermometer will then record the boiling point of the liquid distilling over into the condenser.

* It is necessary to suppose that a large volume of liquid is taken so that its composition is only very slightly altered by the formation of chloroform-rich vapour.

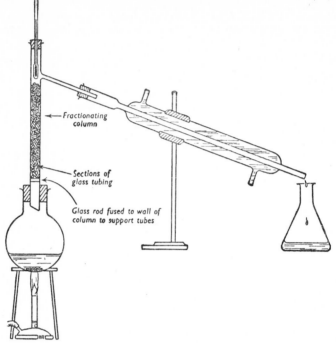

Fig. 16. Apparatus for fractional distillation

The action of the column may be explained by considering the fractionation of a mixture of ethyl bromide (B.P. $38\cdot4°$) and benzene (B.P. $80\cdot2°$). The equilibrium diagram for this system is given in Fig. 17. For convenience in describing the processes taking place in the column, the diagram is drawn with the *highest* temperatures at the *bottom*, and the *lowest* temperatures at the *top*. Alongside the equilibrium diagram is a sketch of the fractionating column so placed that the temperature ranges in the column correspond to those on the equilibrium diagram. When the column is working there is a continuous fall in temperature from the bottom to the top, but to simplify the explanation, it may be supposed that the column is divided into sections in each of which there is a uniform temperature. In the lowest section it is supposed that there is a uniform temperature of 60°, and in the remaining sections uniform temperatures of 55°, 50°, 45° and 40° respectively.

Suppose that the liquid in the flask contains 30 per cent. of ethyl bromide. From the equilibrium diagram it may be seen that this liquid boils at 65° to yield a vapour containing 86 per cent. of ethyl

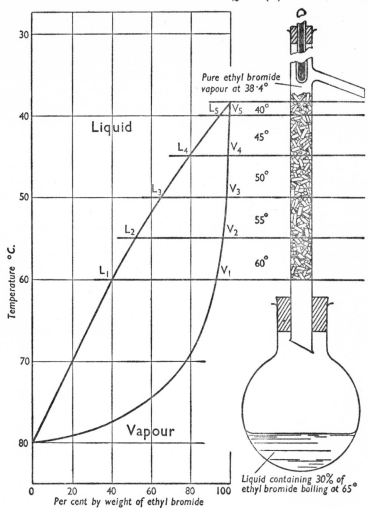

Pure ethyl bromide
vapour at 38·4°

Liquid

L_5 V_5 40°
L_4 V_4 45°
L_3 V_3 50°
L_2 V_2 55°
L_1 V_1 60°

Vapour

Liquid containing 30% of
ethyl bromide boiling at 65°

Per cent by weight of ethyl bromide

FIG. 17.   Boiling point-composition diagram for the system ethyl
bromide-benzene.

bromide. The boiling liquid merely serves to feed the column with
vapour, and it need not be further considered.

The vapour at·65° containing 86 per cent. of ethyl bromide passes
into the section of the fractionating column at 60°.   Some of it
condenses to liquid on the walls of the column and on the glass tubes,
and ultimately the equilibrium appropriate to 60° is reached between
the liquid and the vapour.   From the equilibrium diagram it can be

seen that this liquid L_1 contains 40 per cent. of ethyl bromide, and the vapour V_1 93 per cent. of ethyl bromide. The liquid L_1 trickles back into the flask, and the vapour passes upwards into the section of the column at 55°. Here a new equilibrium is established between the liquid L_2 containing 52 per cent. of ethyl bromide, and the vapour V_2 containing 95 per cent. of ethyl bromide. The liquid L_2 trickles back into the section of the column at 60° where it gives up a proportion of ethyl bromide to the vapour phase, so that it may attain the composition of 40 per cent. ethyl bromide appropriate to the equilibrium at 60°. The vapour V_2 passes into the section of the column at 50°, where a third equilibrium is established yielding a vapour V_3 containing 97 per cent. of ethyl bromide. Similarly the vapour V_4 at 45° contains 98·5 per cent. of ethyl bromide, and the vapour V_5 at 40°, 99·5 per cent. At the top of the column the temperature falls to 38·4°, and pure ethyl bromide vapour passes into the condenser.

It is essential for efficient fractionation that equilibrium shall be completely attained in each section of the column. If, in the example just described, a liquid rich in ethyl bromide from the top of the column runs back into the flask without yielding up the appropriate proportion of the ethyl bromide to the ascending vapour, or if vapour relatively rich in benzene passes up the column without continuously changing in composition, it is clear that the separation of the two constituents of the original mixture must be incomplete. Fractionation must, therefore, be carried out (i) in the absence of draughts, (ii) with the column mounted vertically, (iii) very slowly indeed. The rate at which the condensate collects in the receiving flask should not exceed one drop per four or five seconds.

If the constituents of a system of two volatile miscible liquids under certain conditions of temperature and composition form a *maximum boiling point mixture*, then the fractionation of a mixture of any other composition * first yields a condensate consisting of one of the liquids in a pure condition. The composition of the liquid remaining in the distilling flask changes as the fractionation proceeds, until ultimately the maximum boiling point mixture is obtained. This mixture then fractionates unchanged, yielding a condensate of its own composition.

If the constituents of a system of two volatile miscible liquids under certain conditions of temperature and composition form a

* If the composition of the original mixture happened to be that of the maximum or minimum boiling point mixture, the mixture would fractionate without change of composition, and no separation of the constituents would be effected.

minimum boiling point mixture, then the fractionation of a mixture
of any other composition first yields a condensate consisting of the
minimum boiling point mixture. The composition of the liquid
remaining in the distilling flask changes until it ultimately consists of
one of the pure constituents, which is then collected as the condensate.
Hence fractionation does not effect a complete separation of the
constituents of a liquid mixture if they form either a maximum or a
minimum boiling point mixture.

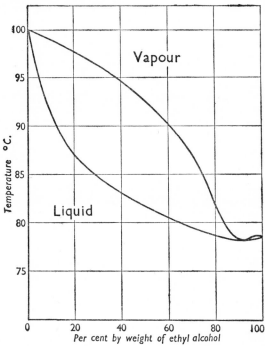

FIG. 18.   Boiling point-composition diagram for the system water-
ethyl alcohol. The minimum boiling point mixture boils at 78·2°; the
composition of the mixture is 95·6 per cent. by weight of ethyl alcohol.

Minimum boiling point mixtures are frequently found among
systems of organic compounds when the molecule of one of the
constituents contains the group —OH. A mixture of ethyl alcohol
and water is one example of such a system. The equilibrium
diagram is given in Fig. 18. It will be seen that a mixture of 95·6
per cent. by weight of alcohol and 4·4 per cent. of water boils at
78·2°, and that the vapour evolved from this mixture has the same
composition as the liquid. If, therefore, a mixture containing 50

per cent. of alcohol and 50 per cent. of water is fractionated, the vapour leaving the head of the column contains 4·4 per cent. of water, and the composition of this vapour remains constant as long as there is any alcohol left in the distilling flask. The condensate of this vapour is *rectified spirit*. The 4·4 per cent. of water in rectified spirit can be removed by the method described on p. 161.

Distillation under reduced pressure. Distillation under reduced pressure is used for the purification of liquids which decompose below their boiling points under atmospheric pressure. As the pressure of a boiling liquid is lowered, the tendency to " bump " is greatly increased. Low pressure distillations are, therefore, carried out in an apparatus designed to minimise " bumping ". A suitable apparatus, in which " bumping " is reduced by drawing a fine stream of air bubbles through the boiling liquid, is shown in Fig. 19. The two-necked flask is known as a Claisen flask. The left-hand neck is sealed by a rubber stopper which carries a stout capillary tube

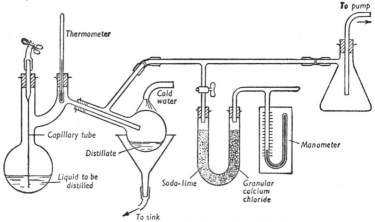

FIG. 19. Apparatus for distillation under reduced pressure.

closed by a short piece of pressure tubing and a screw clip. The drawn-out end of the capillary tube reaches to within 1 mm. of the bottom of the flask. The right-hand neck is closed by a rubber stopper carrying a thermometer. The side-tube passes through a rubber stopper into a distilling flask which serves the double purpose of condenser and receiving vessel. The side-tube of this distilling flask is connected to a manometer and, through a trap, to a filter pump. The U-tube containing soda-lime and calcium chloride is present to prevent contamination of the mercury in the manometer.

To conduct the distillation, the liquid to be distilled is placed in the Claisen flask, the stopper carrying the capillary tube is inserted, and the filter pump is turned on. As the pressure falls, the screw clip is adjusted so that a steady stream of bubbles leaves the fine end of the capillary tube. The Claisen flask is then heated steadily, usually by means of an oil-bath. If the boiling point of the distilling liquid is to be recorded it is necessary to read the thermometer and the manometer, and to observe the barometric pressure.

Distillation in steam. If two immiscible liquids are placed together in the same vessel, each exerts the vapour pressure, appropriate to the temperature, which it would exert if the other were not present. If the containing vessel is heated, the system boils when the sum of the vapour pressures exerted by each liquid is equal to the pressure of the atmosphere. For example, the system water-nitrobenzene boils at 99°, at which temperature the vapour pressure of water is 733 mm., and that of nitrobenzene is 27 mm., making a total pressure of 760 mm. Nitrobenzene boils at 211°, and hence the effect of boiling a mixture of nitrobenzene and water is to volatilise the nitrobenzene at a temperature 112° below its boiling point, and the water at a temperature 1° below its boiling point.

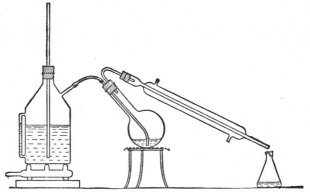

FIG. 20. Apparatus for distillation in steam. (From Mann & Saunders:
Practical Organic Chemistry.)

Distillation in steam is, therefore, valuable as a means of purifying sparingly volatile liquids, which are immiscible with water, from impurities which are non-volatile under the conditions of the experiment.

The apparatus used is shown in Fig. 20. It should be noted that the flask containing the liquid to be steam distilled is heated indirectly by the introduction of a current of steam which hastens the distillation by carrying the vapour from the flask into the condenser. Impure nitrobenzene, for example, is placed in the round-bottomed flask closed by a cork fitted with two tubes, one for introducing steam from the kettle, the other to lead the mixed vapours to the condenser. The distillate which collects in the receiver is a mixture of nitrobenzene and water. The proportions by weight of the two liquids in the distillate depend (i) on their relative vapour pressures at the boiling point of the mixture, (ii) on their relative molecular weights. This is made clear by the following calculation :

$$\frac{\text{Weight of nitrobenzene in distillate}}{\text{weight of water in distillate}} = \frac{\text{wt. of nitrobenzene in vapour}}{\text{wt. of steam in vapour}}$$

$$= \frac{\text{density of nitrobenzene} \times \text{volume of nitrobenzene in vapour}}{\text{density of steam} \times \text{volume of steam in vapour}}$$

$$= \frac{\text{molecular wt. of nitrobenzene} \times \text{vol. of nitrobenzene in vapour}}{\text{molecular weight of steam} \times \text{volume of steam in vapour}}$$

$$= \frac{123 \times \text{volume of nitrobenzene in vapour}}{18 \times \text{volume of steam in vapour}}.$$

But according to the law of partial pressures, the ratio of the volumes (measured at atmospheric pressure) of the vapours of nitrobenzene and steam in the mixed vapours is equal to the ratio of their partial pressures, hence :

$$\frac{\text{weight of nitrobenzene in distillate}}{\text{weight of water in distillate}} = \frac{123 \times 27}{18 \times 733} = \frac{1}{3 \cdot 97}.$$

The distillate obtained as a result of fractional distillation is a mixture of two liquids, the purified organic compound and water. These liquids are mutually insoluble. They are separated by the method described below.

Separation of immiscible liquids. This process, which is usually known shortly as *separation*, is used for isolating the constituents of a mixture of liquids which are insoluble in one another. If such a mixture, say, of chloroform and water, is allowed to stand, two layers are formed, the denser chloroform being at the bottom.

The separation is usually carried out in a separating funnel, Fig. 21. The mixture is poured into the funnel through the neck, and is allowed to remain undisturbed until the boundary between the liquids is sharply defined. The lower layer is then run off into a beaker through the stem of the

FIG. 21.   funnel, the tap being closed just before the
Separating funnel.   boundary reaches it. The tap is opened again, and

a small volume of liquid is discarded so that the boundary falls below the tap. The upper layer is then poured through the neck of the funnel into another vessel.

Extraction from aqueous solution with organic solvents. Many organic compounds are much more soluble in organic solvents such as ether, chloroform, benzene and toluene, than they are in water. For example, at 25° the solubility of aniline in toluene is about 12 times its solubility in water. If an aqueous solution of aniline is shaken with toluene, a large proportion of the aniline is transferred from the water to the toluene. By carrying out this operation in a separating funnel, and separating the toluene layer from the aqueous layer, a solution of aniline in toluene is obtained free from any substances insoluble in toluene, which may have been originally present in the aqueous solution.

The proportion of aniline which is extracted from the water may be calculated from the equation

$$\frac{C_t}{C_w} = K,$$

where C_t is the concentration of aniline in toluene in gram-molecules per litre, and C_w is the concentration of aniline in water in the same units, and K is a constant known as the *distribution coefficient*.* For aniline distributed between water and toluene $K = 12$.

The efficiency of the extraction process may be illustrated by means of a numerical example. Suppose 500 c.c. of water containing 2 gm. of aniline in solution are shaken with 100 c.c. of toluene. Let x be the weight of aniline which passes into solution in the toluene leaving $2 - x$ gm. of aniline in the water. The molecular weight of aniline is 93.

Then $C_w = \dfrac{1000}{500} \times \dfrac{2 - x}{93}$ gram-molecules per litre.

Hence, $C_t = C_w \times K.$

$= \dfrac{1000}{500} \times \dfrac{2 - x}{93} \times 12$ gram-molecules per litre,

and the weight of aniline in 100 c.c. of toluene, x, is given by:

$x = \dfrac{1000}{500} \times \dfrac{2 - x}{93} \times 12 \times \dfrac{100}{1000} \times 93.$

Hence $x = 1\cdot41$ gm.

This example shows that nearly ¾ of the weight of aniline in 500 c.c. of water has been extracted by 100 c.c. of toluene.

* K is sometimes known as the *partition coefficient*. The simple relation stated above holds only if the distributed substance is neither associated nor dissociated in either solution. For the relationships applicable to more complicated systems the reader should consult a text-book of Physical Chemistry.

It should be noted that the efficiency of extraction is increased if the total volume of organic solvent employed is shaken with the aqueous solution in small quantities at a time. For example, suppose that two volumes of toluene each of 50 c.c., are shaken with 500 c.c. of water originally containing 2 gm. of aniline. Let the weight of aniline which passes into the first 50 c.c. be y gm., and the weight which passes into the second 50 c.c. be z gm.

For the first 50 c.c. of toluene,

$$y = \frac{1000}{500} \times \frac{2-y}{93} \times 12 \times \frac{50}{1000} \times 93 \text{ gm. of aniline.}$$

Hence, $y = 1 \cdot 09$ gm., and $0 \cdot 91$ gm. of aniline remain in the water.
For the second 50 c.c. of toluene

$$z = \frac{1000}{500} \times \frac{0 \cdot 91 - z}{93} \times 12 \times \frac{50}{1000} \times 93 \text{ gm. of aniline.}$$

Hence, $z = 0 \cdot 49$ gm.
The total weight of aniline removed from the water by the two successive extractions is $y + z = 1 \cdot 58$ gm.

Diethyl ether is an organic solvent which is commonly used for extracting organic compounds from aqueous solution. Examples of its use are found in the preparation of aniline, p. 388, and of phenol p. 418. Each of these compounds is very much more soluble in ether than in water, and hence a single extraction using a relatively small volume of ether effects almost complete removal of the organic compound from aqueous solution. After the ethereal solution has been separated from the aqueous layer, it is usually dried, and the ether is then removed by distillation, using special precautions. These processes are described below.

Drying of organic liquids. It is frequently essential to free an organic compound from traces of water which may have been absorbed either from the air, or from aqueous solutions of reagents used in its preparation. Distillation will not as a rule effect complete separation of water from an organic compound, and it is necessary to dry it by chemical methods. The commonest drying agent is anhydrous calcium chloride, which is made by heating calcium chloride hexahydrate to its fusion point, 782°. The product is slightly alkaline, owing to the loss of small quantities of hydrogen chloride liberated in the hydrolysis :

$$CaCl_2 + H_2O \rightleftharpoons CaO + 2HCl.$$

The dehydrating power of anhydrous calcium chloride depends on the formation of the hexahydrate,

$$CaCl_2 + 6H_2O = CaCl_2,6H_2O.$$

Calcium chloride, however, also combines with ethyl alcohol to form the compound $CaCl_2,4C_2H_5OH$, and with ammonia to form

$CaCl_2,8NH_3$, and also with many derivatives of alcohol and ammonia. It cannot be used, therefore, for drying organic substances containing the groups $-OH$ or $-NH_2$.

The organic liquid to be dried is placed with several lumps of the granular anhydrous calcium chloride in a stoppered flask, and the mixture is allowed to stand for several hours. It is then filtered using a dry funnel with a small quantity of glass wool pressed into the apex. The filtered liquid is then further purified by distillation.

The following substances other than anhydrous calcium chloride may also be used as drying agents. Drying agents which are fine powders must be filtered from the dried liquid by means of filter paper instead of glass wool.

(i) Powdered anhydrous magnesium sulphate and powdered anhydrous sodium sulphate. These substances are not highly reactive and they can be used for drying most organic liquids. Their action, however, is slower than that of calcium chloride.

(ii) Quicklime, anhydrous potassium carbonate, and anhydrous potassium hydroxide. These substances are alkaline, and cannot be used for drying acids, phenols, or esters or other compounds liable to hydrolysis. Potassium hydroxide is used for drying aniline (p. 389), and quicklime is used in the preparation of absolute alcohol (p. 161).

(iii) Metallic sodium may be used for removing the last traces of water from the few organic compounds, principally ethers, which do not react with it. Its use in the preparation of pure ether is described on p. 179.

Evaporation of ethereal solutions. Diethyl ether is a very volatile compound (B.P. 35°) and it is also highly inflammable and forms explosive mixtures with air. Moreover, if the dense vapour is permitted to escape from an apparatus without special precautions, it forms a layer on the surface of the bench which will ignite if it reaches a flame, and the explosion may travel back to the apparatus and set it on fire. When a large class is conducting experiments involving the use of ether it is advisable to secure that there are no flames in the laboratory.

An ethereal solution is, therefore, never evaporated in an open dish. The ether must be removed by distillation. The apparatus employed is shown in Fig. 22.

A distilling flask of about 60 c.c. capacity is fitted with a dropping funnel. The side-tube is attached to a water condenser through the jacket of which passes a fast stream of really cold water. The receiving vessel is a Buchner flask. A long piece of rubber tubing connected to the side-arm of the flask reaches to the floor of the

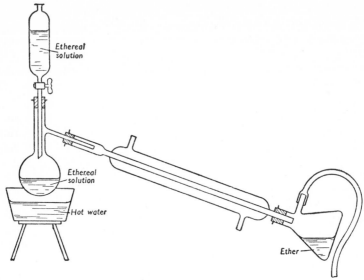

Ethereal solution

Ethereal solution

Hot water

Ether

FIG. 22. Apparatus for the distillation of ether from an ethereal solution.

laboratory so that any ether vapour which leaves the Buchner flask is carried well below bench level. All the corks used in the apparatus must fit securely.

A few fragments of unglazed porcelain are placed in the distilling flask and the dropping funnel is fixed in position. The ethereal solution to be evaporated is poured into the dropping funnel, and about 25 c.c. are run into the flask. The distilling flask is warmed with a water-bath previously heated to about 65° at a safe distance from the apparatus. As the ether distils, more of the ethereal solution from the funnel is run into the distilling flask.

Recrystallisation. Recrystallisation is the principal method for the purification of solid organic compounds. A solvent is selected in which the organic compound is more soluble at high temperatures than it is at room temperature. The impure compound is dissolved in the boiling solvent, and on cooling the solution the pure compound crystallises out. Impurities which are insoluble in the solvent are eliminated by filtration of the hot solution before it is crystallised. Impurities which are soluble in the solvent remain in the mother liquor. It may be assumed with confidence that soluble impurities constituting up to, say, 5 per cent. of the original impure compound do not crystallise along with the compound which is being purified. The following example shows that this assumption is justified.

Suppose that the compound A is contaminated with an impurity X to the extent of 5 per cent., and that 100 c.c. of methylated spirit (i) at 78° dissolve 50 gm. of A and 10 gm. of X, (ii) at 20° dissolve 6 gm. of A and 3 gm. of X.

If 20 gm. of the impure compound are dissolved in 50 c.c. of methylated spirit at 78°, a clear solution is obtained. If this solution is cooled to 20°, 16 gm. of A crystallise, leaving 3 gm. in solution, but the whole of X, with which the solution is not saturated at this temperature, remains in solution. It should be noted that the complete purification of A has been effected, although its solubility is considerably greater than that of the impurity X.

The solvents most frequently employed in recrystallisation are ethyl alcohol, a mixture of alcohol and water, methylated spirit, acetone, acetic acid, a mixture of acetic acid and water, and water.

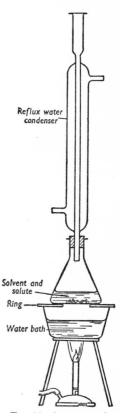

Ether is not a suitable solvent for recrystallisation because its inflammability makes it dangerous, and also because, on account of its volatility, it is liable to deposit solids by evaporation instead of crystallisation. Certain derivatives of ether, such as monoethyl glycol, $C_2H_5OC_2H_4OH$, are increasingly used as solvents for recrystallisation.

The process of recrystallisation is carried out in the three stages : (i) the choice of solvent, (ii) the preparation of the solution and the precipitation of the crystals, (iii) the draining and drying of the crystals.

The choice of the solvent must be made experimentally. About 0·5 gm. of the material to be recrystallised is powdered and placed in a test-tube. Enough solvent is added to cover the substance. If it all dissolves in the cold the solvent is clearly useless for recrystallisation. If it does not dissolve in the cold, the solvent is gently boiled, and more solvent is added if necessary, until the solid is just brought into solution. If more than about one-third of a test-tube of solvent is required, it is unsuitable as it does not dissolve the solid sufficiently readily. The most suitable solvent dissolves the 0·5 gm. of material in 1 or 2 c.c. When a clear solution of convenient concentration has been made, the test-tube is chilled in ice-water and

FIG. 23. Apparatus for preparing a solution of a substance in a volatile solvent.

the inside of the tube is scratched with a glass rod to promote crystallisation. If a good crop of crystals is obtained the solvent used may be chosen for the recrystallisation on a full scale.

For the full scale recrystallisation, a solution must be prepared which is almost saturated at the boiling point of the solvent. When a volatile solvent, such as methylated spirit, is employed, it is essential to prevent its loss by evaporation during the course of the experiment. Loss of an appreciable quantity of the solvent would lead to premature crystallisation, and might also cause the precipitation of impurities. The preparation of the solution is, therefore, carried out in a flask fitted to a reflux water-condenser, Fig. 23.

For example, consider the recrystallisation of iodoform, using methylated spirit as the solvent. The iodoform is placed in the conical flask with a little methylated spirit which is brought to the boil on a water-bath. Any methylated spirit which is vaporised is liquefied in the condenser and returned to the flask. Further quantities of methylated spirit are added down the condenser until the iodoform is just completely dissolved.

The flask is then removed from the water-bath and detached from the condenser, and the solution is rapidly filtered into another clean conical flask. The filter paper should be very

small and fluted, and the funnel should also be very small, and the stem should be cut away almost at the apex, Fig. 24. Unless these precautions are taken the solution may crystallise in the funnel and filtration will be impeded and may be stopped altogether.

Fig. 24. Funnel for the filtration of a hot solution.

The conical flask containing the filtrate is gently shaken in a stream of cold water from the tap so that the solution is rapidly chilled. Numerous small crystals are thus produced ; mother liquor is less likely to be occluded in small crystals than in large ones. The contents of the flask are allowed to stand so that the maximum amount of precipitation may occur.

The final stage of the process of recrystallisation is the separation of the crystals from the mother liquor. Care must be taken to see that the crystals are freed from the mother liquor by *draining* and not by evaporation. If the mother liquor drains away from the crystals it carries soluble impurities with it, but if it is allowed to evaporate in contact with the crystals, it will deposit all other substances in solution.

The crystals are turned out of the conical flask into a Buchner funnel mounted in a Buchner flask connected to a filter pump, Fig. 25. The filter pump is kept running at such a rate that the mother liquor is sucked through the filter paper as quickly as possible. The removal of the mother liquor must be assisted by pressing the crystals on the filter paper very firmly with a clean cork. In a short time the mother liquor drains away and the crystals are dry and powdery. The funnel is then withdrawn from the flask and the pump is turned off. The conical flask in which the precipitation was carried out is rinsed with a few c.c. of methylated spirit, which becomes partially saturated with regard to iodoform by dissolving the crystals on the side of the flask. This solution is then poured into the Buchner funnel and allowed to remain in contact with the iodoform for 5 minutes. At the end of this period the funnel is put back in the Buchner flask, the pump is turned on, and the pressing with the cork is repeated.

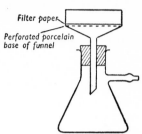

Filter paper

Perforated porcelain base of funnel

FIG. 25.   Apparatus for filtration of crystals from the mother liquor.

Final traces of the mother liquor may be removed by pressing the iodoform crystals between layers of absorbent paper. The crystals are spread on a pad of 5 or 6 layers of paper, and are covered by a similar pad. The top of the pile is then pressed and struck by the hand. The sheets of paper are discarded and replaced as they become soiled with absorbed mother liquor. When the sheets in contact with the crystals remain clean, the crystals are left for a while exposed to the air.

This method of removing mother liquor has the disadvantage that abraded particles of paper may become mixed with the crystals. This may be avoided by allowing the crystals to dry by evaporation in a desiccator. The simplest form of desiccator is shown in Fig. 26. The drying agent is anhydrous calcium chloride which fills the base ; the crystals are placed on a watch-glass which stands on the gauze. A more efficient type of desiccator is shown in Fig. 27. The base contains concentrated sulphuric acid, and an annular tray

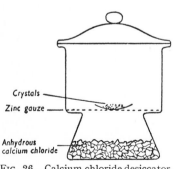

Crystals

Zinc gauze

Anhydrous calcium chloride

FIG. 26.   Calcium chloride desiccator.

holds a mixture of flake caustic soda and shavings of paraffin wax. These absorbents free the atmosphere in the desiccator from water

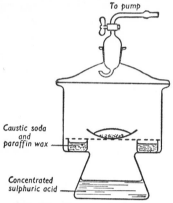

To pump

Caustic soda
and
paraffin wax

Concentrated
sulphuric acid

Fig. 27. Vacuum desiccator.

vapour, from alkaline and acid vapours, and from vapour of the organic solvent. Evaporation is accelerated by exhausting the desiccator. The crystals are placed in a watch-glass which stands on the gauze ; another watch-glass serves as a cover, and prevents air, which enters the desiccator when the vacuum is released, from blowing the crystals into the sulphuric acid.

The removal of the final traces of mother liquor by evaporation in a desiccator is satisfactory only if the mother liquor is almost free from impurities in solution. For a fine preparation two recrystallisations should be made ; the first being completed by drying the crystals between folds of absorbent paper, the second by evaporation in a desiccator.

TESTS FOR PURITY

1. Liquids. The purity of a liquid is examined by determining its boiling point. The determination is made by conducting a distillation in the apparatus shown in Fig. 11, p. 56. Since the liquid will have been purified by distillation the only impurities present must be volatile. From the curves given in Figs. 15 and 17, pp. 58 and 61, it is seen that the boiling point of a mixture of volatile liquids at a given atmospheric pressure depends on the composition of the mixture. If, therefore, the thermometer in the distillation apparatus registers a steadily increasing series of temperatures as the distillation proceeds, it may be assumed that the original liquid was a mixture. If the boiling point is *sharp*, that is, if it remains constant from the beginning to the end of the distillation, the original liquid may be either (i) a pure chemical compound, or, (ii) a constant boiling point mixture (see p. 62). In order to distinguish between a pure compound and a constant boiling point mixture the distillation must be carried out under two different pressures. If the liquid is a single compound the composition of the distillate is unaffected by changes of pressure ; if the liquid is a constant boiling point mixture a change of pressure alters the composition of the distillate.

2. *Solids.* The purity of a solid is determined by the examination of its melting point. If the melting point is *sharp,** that is, if the temperatures of the beginning and the end of melting do not differ by more than 1°, the solid is almost certainly a pure compound. If the melting point is indefinite, the solid is either impure, or decomposes before the melting point is reached.

The experimental determination of the melting point of a solid is carried out using the apparatus shown in Fig. 28. The long-necked hard-glass flask contains medicinal paraffin. This substance is particularly serviceable as a heating medium because

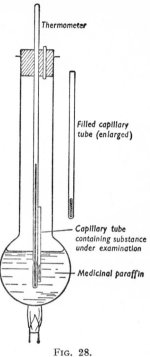

Thermometer

Filled capillary tube (enlarged)

Capillary tube containing substance under examination

Medicinal paraffin

   (i) its specific heat is low, and consequently its temperature can be changed readily by slight heating or cooling ;

  (ii) it is almost non-inflammable, even when hot ;

 (iii) it is non-corrosive, and, owing to its low specific heat, it causes only slight burns if spilt while hot on the hands ;

  (iv) it may be heated to 220° without decomposition.

Fig. 28.
Melting point apparatus.

The mouth of the flask is closed by a cork carrying a thermometer. The cork is pierced by a groove to allow for the expansion and contraction of the air in the flask.

A thin-walled capillary tube is made by drawing down a soft-glass test-tube. The tube is cut into lengths of about 6 cm., and each length is sealed at one end.

The organic compound to be examined is placed on a piece of **dry**

* Sharp melting points are given by mixtures in which
 (i) the constituents are in the exact proportion of a eutectic mixture,
 (ii) the constituents are totally immiscible in one another in both the solid and the liquid states.

The chance of fulfilling condition (i) is so unlikely that it can be disregarded. Organic compounds are almost invariably miscible to some extent in the liquid state, and therefore the chance of fulfilling condition (ii) may also be disregarded.

porous plate and pulverised with a spatula. Sufficient powder is introduced into one of the capillary tubes * to fill about 1 cm. of its length from the sealed end, Fig. 28.

The thermometer is withdrawn from the paraffin and the capillary tube is placed against it so that the filled end is as close as possible to the bulb. No fastening is necessary ; the surface tension of the oil causes the capillary tube to adhere to the thermometer. The thermometer with the capillary attached is then replaced in the oil, which is slowly heated by a small flame. For a reliable determination of the melting point the rise in temperature of the oil over the last 30° before the melting point must be very slow. The temperatures of the beginning and the end of melting are noted.

3. *Identification by mixed melting points.* The identity of a given compound may be proved by the method of mixed melting points. If, for example, it is desired to establish the identity of a compound thought to be acetanilide its melting point is taken. It is then mixed with pure acetanilide and the melting point of the mixture is observed. If the two melting points are identical, and if that of the mixture is sharp, it follows that the original substance is acetanilide. If it had been some other substance the melting point of the mixture would have been indefinite, and different from that of the original substance.

* This is done by forcing some of the powder into the mouth of the tube. The tube is then held vertically and stroked transversely with the milled edge of a coin. This process is repeated until sufficient of the powder is in the tube.

CHAPTER IV

LABORATORY TECHNIQUE (B) : DETERMINATION OF THE MOLECULAR CONSTITUTION OF AN ORGANIC COMPOUND

In order to elucidate the molecular constitution of an organic compound it is necessary to determine :

(i) the nature of the constituent elements ;
(ii) the proportions by weight in which the constituent elements are present ;
(iii) the empirical formula ; *
(iv) the molecular weight ;
(v) the molecular formula, and
(vi) the constitutional formula.

Sections I, II and III of this Chapter describe the general methods for the qualitative and quantitative analysis of an organic compound, and how the empirical formula of the compound is deduced from the results of this analysis. Section IV gives an account of the methods available for determining the molecular weight of an organic compound. Section V outlines briefly how the molecular and constitutional formulae are deduced. Section VI gives an account of a eudiometric method by which the constitution of a gaseous hydrocarbon can be determined directly.

I. IDENTIFICATION OF THE CONSTITUENT ELEMENTS IN AN ORGANIC COMPOUND

(i) **Carbon, hydrogen and oxygen.** The presence of carbon and hydrogen in an organic compound may usually be taken for granted. Carbon and hydrogen are detected experimentally by heating a mixture of 0·5 gm. of the compound and 3–4 gm. of pure dry copper oxide in a hard-glass tube, and passing the gases evolved into lime-water. The formation of a white precipitate of calcium carbonate indicates the presence of carbon dioxide in the gases, and hence the presence of carbon in the original compound. Condensation of moisture (which may be identified as water by its property of turning anhydrous copper sulphate blue) on the cooler parts of the

---

* Definitions of the four types of formulae used to describe an organic compound are given on p. 35.

hard-glass tube indicates that the original compound contained hydrogen.

The organic compound, if a solid, must be finely ground, and the copper oxide must be previously roasted in air and cooled in a desiccator to eliminate moisture and all carbonaceous material. The hard-glass tube should be fitted with a cork and delivery tube,

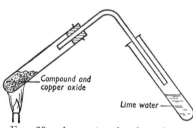

Compound and copper oxide

Lime water

FIG. 29. Apparatus for detecting the presence of carbon in an organic compound.

and the mouth of the delivery tube should reach to just above the lime water in the test-tube, Fig. 29. Alternatively, the cork and delivery tube may be dispensed with, and the thumb may be held lightly over the mouth of the hard-glass tube during heating; when the heating is finished, the gaseous contents of the hard-glass tube are " poured " into a test-tube containing lime water. Whichever method is used, the test-tube containing the lime water should be closed with the thumb and well shaken, so that the lime water is mixed with the gas in the tube. If the original organic compound is suspected to contain sulphur, the gases must be passed through a solution of potassium dichromate in dilute sulphuric acid, before admission to the lime water tube, in order that any sulphur dioxide evolved may be oxidised and destroyed.

There is no systematic procedure for detecting oxygen in an organic compound. Its presence may be inferred indirectly if the existence in the molecule of such groups as hydroxyl, carbonyl or carboxyl is established.

(ii) The Lassaigne sodium test for nitrogen, sulphur and the halogens. The organic compound is heated with metallic sodium. If it contained carbon and nitrogen, sodium cyanide is then formed ; if it contained chlorine, bromine, iodine or sulphur, sodium chloride, sodium bromide, sodium iodide or sodium sulphide are formed respectively.

A short, hard-glass test-tube is dropped through a circular hole in a stout iron or copper sheet, supported horizontally, so that it is suspended by the rim. Two small pellets of sodium are placed in the tube, which is heated until the sodium just melts. About 0·3 gm. of the organic compound, *in small quantities at a time*, is dropped on to the molten sodium. The reaction after each addition is allowed to subside before the next is made. When all the compound has been added the tube is heated in a Bunsen flame, at first cautiously and later vigorously. The heating is continued for a short time after the evolution of fumes has ceased, in order to ensure that all the metallic sodium has been converted to oxide. The tube is pressed upwards with a clean wire gauze, seized in a test-tube holder, and reheated to redness. While still hot the tube, held vertically, is pressed down into 20 c.c. of distilled water contained in a small mortar. The tube immediately fractures, and the excess of sodium oxide reacts vigorously with the water. When the reaction is over, the contents of the mortar are ground up with a pestle to ensure that all the sodium salts pass into solution. The solution is filtered and the filtrate is divided into three portions. These portions are used to test for sodium cyanide, sodium sulphide and the sodium halides, in the following manner.

(a) *Test for sodium cyanide, indicating nitrogen (and carbon) in the original compound.*

To the first portion of the filtrate is added a freshly prepared solution of ferrous sulphate in distilled water, and the mixture is heated for a few minutes. Since the solution normally contains sodium hydroxide derived from the excess of sodium originally taken, some ferrous hydroxide is precipitated. If no precipitate is formed the solution is made alkaline with sodium hydroxide solution. The ferrous sulphate combines with any sodium cyanide in the solution to form sodium ferrocyanide :

$$FeSO_4 + 6NaCN = Na_4Fe(CN)_6 + Na_2SO_4.$$

The contents of the tube are cooled, a few drops of ferric chloride are added, and the solution is acidified with concentrated hydrochloric acid. If the solution contained sodium ferrocyanide it turns a greenish-blue, and a deep-blue precipitate of Prussian blue, ferric ferrocyanide, is thrown down :

$$3Na_4Fe(CN)_6 + 4FeCl_3 = Fe_4[Fe(CN)_6]_3 + 12NaCl.$$

A small quantity of Prussian blue in the solution can be best observed by diluting and filtering the solution, and washing the filter paper with water. Specks of Prussian blue on the filter paper are easily seen.

(b) *Test for sodium sulphide, indicating sulphur in the original compound.*

To the second portion of the filtrate is added a freshly prepared solution of sodium nitroprusside, $Na_2Fe(CN)_5.NO,2H_2O$. If sodium sulphide is present a brilliant purple coloration is obtained.

(c) *Tests for the halogens, indicating their presence in the original compound.*

A. *In the absence of nitrogen and sulphur.* The third portion of the filtrate is acidified with dilute nitric acid, and silver nitrate solution is added. The formation of a white or yellow precipitate indicates the presence of a chloride, bromide, or iodide in the solution.

To differentiate between the three halogens, dilute sulphuric acid is added to a few c.c. of the filtrate from the sodium fusion until the solution is just acid to litmus. 1 c.c. of benzene and 1 c.c. of chlorine water are added, and the mixture is shaken. If chlorine alone is present the mixture remains colourless, if bromine is present the benzene layer is coloured brown, if iodine is present the benzene is coloured violet.

B. *In the presence of nitrogen or sulphur.* If the filtrate from the sodium fusion contains sodium cyanide, a white precipitate of silver cyanide is obtained on the addition of silver nitrate solution, and the test for the halogens described above is obscured. If the filtrate contains sodium sulphide a black precipitate of silver sulphide is obtained, which also interferes with the above test. If nitrogen or sulphur have been shown to be present, therefore, the filtrate from the sodium fusion is made just acid with dilute nitric acid, and is then gently evaporated to half its bulk in an open dish. The sodium sulphide and sodium cyanide are thus converted to sodium nitrate, and the liberated hydrogen sulphide and hydrogen cyanide are expelled from the solution. If silver nitrate is then added to the solution, a white or yellow precipitate of silver halide is obtained free from silver sulphide and silver cyanide.

II. QUANTITATIVE ESTIMATION OF THE ELEMENTS PRESENT IN AN ORGANIC COMPOUND

(i) Estimation of hydrogen and carbon in compounds which do not contain nitrogen, sulphur, or a halogen

In principle, a weighed quantity of the organic compound is

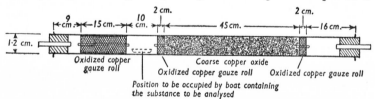

FIG. 30. A hard-glass tube prepared for a combustion analysis. (In order clearly to display the arrangement of the contents of the tube, its diameter is exaggerated in comparison with its length.)

heated with excess of copper oxide, so that the constituent hydrogen and carbon are completely oxidised to water and carbon dioxide. The products of combustion are passed successively through anhydrous calcium chloride and potassium hydroxide solution. The increase in weight of the calcium chloride and the potassium hydroxide solution indicate respectively the weights of water and carbon dioxide which have been produced. From the knowledge that 18 gm. of water contain 2 gm. of hydrogen, and that 44 gm. of carbon dioxide contain 12 gm. of carbon, the weights of hydrogen and carbon in the weight of the compound originally taken can be calculated.

The estimation is carried out experimentally as follows. A hard-glass tube is packed with copper oxide in the manner shown in Fig. 30. It is mounted in a furnace, Fig. 31, consisting of a row of burners, each of which can be regulated independently. The furnace is closed by a number of fire-clay tiles, each of which can be independently swung back to uncover the hard-glass tube. It is thus possible to control the temperature of any portion of the length of the hard-glass tube. By means of the aspirator, a slow current of air may be passed through the hard-glass tube. The air is freed from moisture and carbon

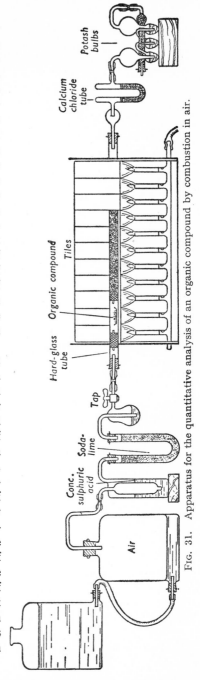

FIG. 31. Apparatus for the quantitative analysis of an organic compound by combustion in air.

dioxide by passage successively through concentrated sulphuric acid
and soda-lime. The rate at which the air is passing is indicated by
the rate of bubble-formation in the small wash-bottle, containing
sulphuric acid, next to the hard-glass tube.

The absorption vessels consist of a U-tube containing granular
anhydrous calcium chloride, Fig. 32, and bulbs containing potassium

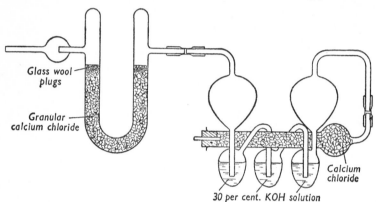

Glass wool plugs

Granular calcium chloride

Calcium chloride

30 per cent. KOH solution

Fig. 32. Absorption vessels used in a combustion analysis.

hydroxide solution. The calcium chloride U-tube carries a small
glass bulb on the arm through which the gas enters, and much of
the water formed by the combustion of the organic compound condenses in this bulb. When the U-tube is not in use the ends of the
connecting arms are closed by short lengths of rubber tubing plugged
by glass rods.

The potash bulbs contain 30 per cent. potassium hydroxide solution. The exit tube from the third bulb is connected to a glass tube
filled with anhydrous calcium chloride ; this prevents loss of water
from the apparatus by the evaporation of water from the potassium
hydroxide solution when gas is passing through it. When the bulbs
are not in use the open ends of the connecting tubes are closed with
rubber tubes plugged with glass rods.

To carry out a combustion, the hard-glass tube is placed in the
furnace, and a slow current of air is passed through it while the
length of coarse copper oxide is heated to low redness ; the portion of
the tube not containing the coarse copper oxide is allowed to remain
cold. A small porcelain boat is weighed empty, and about 0·2 gm.
of the compound to be analysed is placed in it, and the boat is
weighed again. The difference gives the accurate weight of the
compound taken. The calcium chloride tube and the potash bulbs

are accurately weighed after the removal of the rubber stoppers from the connecting tubes. The weighed absorption tubes are then connected to the hard-glass tube in the manner shown in Fig. 31.

The boat containing the compound is inserted in the hard-glass tube. The current of air is turned on so that about 2 bubbles per second pass into the hard-glass tube. The boat now commences to get hot by radiation from the hot copper oxide. The heating is very gradually increased by closing the tiles above the boat, and later by lighting the burners under the boat. The compound under analysis, according to its nature, either volatilizes or undergoes thermal decomposition. In either case volatile products are carried by the stream of air into the layer of hot copper oxide, where they are oxidised ; the copper oxide is reduced to metallic copper. It should be emphasized that the stream of air is not intended to oxidise the compound, but only to drive the vapours into the copper oxide. If the current of air is too rapid, part of the decomposition products of the organic compound may remain in contact with the copper oxide only long enough to be oxidised to carbon monoxide (which is not absorbed by potash at room temperature) or, in extreme cases, may escape oxidation altogether. The gradual combustion of the organic compound normally takes about 2 hours.

The organic compound frequently chars during the combustion, leaving a deposit of non-volatile carbon in the boat. Such a deposit is converted to carbon dioxide by passing a slow stream of oxygen through the apparatus in place of the stream of air. When all the carbon has burnt away the supply of oxygen is cut off, and air is passed through the apparatus until the gas leaving the potash bulbs fails to rekindle a glowing splint.

When the combustion is complete the absorption vessels are disconnected, and allowed to stand for at least one hour in the balance room. They are then reweighed.

(ii) Estimation of hydrogen and carbon in compounds containing nitrogen

If the compound to be analysed contains nitrogen, oxides of nitrogen may be formed during the combustion. These oxides of nitrogen would dissolve in the potassium hydroxide solution, and thus spoil the accuracy of the carbon estimation.

The products of the combustion of an organic compound containing nitrogen are therefore passed over red-hot copper before they are led into the absorption vessels. The hot copper reduces any oxides of nitrogen to nitrogen which is not absorbed by calcium chloride or potash.

For the combustion of an organic compound containing nitrogen part of the column of copper oxide in the hard-glass tube is removed and a roll of bright copper gauze is inserted in its place, Fig. 33.

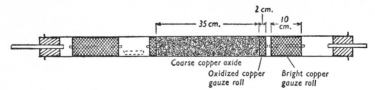

FIG. 33. Modified arrangement in the hard-glass tube for the analysis of an organic compound containing nitrogen. (The diameter of the tube is exaggerated in comparison with its length.)

The roll of bright copper gauze is made by heating a roll of copper gauze in a blow-pipe flame until it is red-hot. It is then dropped into a boiling-tube containing about 5 c.c. of hot methylated spirit. The alcohol vapour reduces the copper oxide on the surface of the copper to metal, and excess of alcohol burns at the mouth of the tube. The flame is extinguished, and the copper is cooled out of contact with air by filling the boiling-tube with cold methylated spirit. The copper roll is removed from the spirit, washed with ether, dried, and kept in a vacuum desiccator until it is to be used.

(iii) Estimation of hydrogen and carbon in compounds containing halogen

If the organic compound to be analysed contains chlorine, bromine, or iodine, free halogen may be liberated during the combustion. The free halogen would be absorbed in the potash, and the accuracy of the carbon estimation would be spoiled. The products of combustion of an organic compound containing halogen are, therefore, passed over a roll of red-hot silver gauze before being led to the absorption vessels. The hot metallic silver reacts with free halogen to yield the stable, non-volatile silver halide. The silver gauze is placed in the hard-glass tube in the position occupied by bright copper gauze as shown in Fig. 33.

If the organic compound to be analysed contains nitrogen as well as halogen, a bright copper roll is placed next to the copper oxide in the hard-glass tube, and a roll of silver gauze is placed next to the copper roll.

(iv) Estimation of hydrogen and carbon in a compound containing sulphur

If the organic compound to be analysed contains sulphur, oxides of sulphur may be formed during the combustion. These oxides of sulphur will be absorbed in the potash bulbs, and the determination of the carbon content of the compound will be inaccurate. In order to prevent oxides of sulphur reaching the potash bulbs, the copper oxide used in the combustion tube for oxidising the organic compound is replaced by a mixture of 3 parts by weight of lead chromate to 1 part by weight of copper oxide. This mixture oxidises sulphur to the non-volatile lead sulphate which remains in the combustion tube. It oxidises the carbon and hydrogen in the organic compound to carbon dioxide and water which are collected in absorption vessels as described in the previous experiments.

Example of the calculation of the percentage by weight of hydrogen and carbon in an organic compound from the results of a combustion analysis.

Weight of boat and the organic compound	1·3859 gm.
Weight of boat alone	1·1742 ,,
Weight of compound taken	0·2117 ,,
Weight of calcium chloride tube at end of combustion	33·9443 ,,
Weight of calcium chloride tube at beginning of combustion	33·8172 ,,
Weight of water formed	0·1271 ,,

Hence, weight of hydrogen yielded by 0·2117 gm. of the compound

$$= \frac{0·1271 \times 2}{18} = 0·0141 \text{ gm.}$$

and percentage by weight of hydrogen in the compound

$$= \frac{0·0141 \times 100}{0·2117} = 6·66.$$

Weight of potash bulbs at end of combustion	52·0540 gm.
Weight of potash bulbs at beginning of combustion	51·7435 ,,
Weight of carbon dioxide formed	0·3105 ,,

Hence weight of carbon yielded by 0·2117 gm. of the compound

$$= \frac{0·3105 \times 12}{44} = 0·08468 \text{ gm.}$$

and percentage by weight of carbon in the compound

$$= \frac{0·08468 \times 100}{0·2117} = 40·0.$$

(v) Estimation of nitrogen in an organic compound

(a) **Dumas' method.** This method is of general application to all nitrogenous organic compounds. A weighed quantity of the organic compound is intimately mixed with copper oxide, and the mixture is heated in a hard-glass tube. The organic compound is oxidised by the hot copper oxide to carbon dioxide, steam and nitrogen, and possibly some oxides of nitrogen. A current of carbon dioxide is passed through the tube in order to sweep the products of oxidation over a hot roll of bright copper gauze, which converts oxides of nitrogen to nitrogen, and then through concentrated potassium hydroxide solution, which absorbs the water vapour and carbon dioxide. The nitrogen from the organic compound alone passes on. It is collected in a graduated tube in which its volume is measured.

The apparatus used is shown in Fig. 34. The furnace is similar to

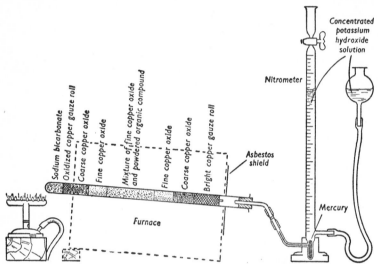

FIG. 34. Dumas' apparatus for the estimation of nitrogen in an organic compound.

that used in the determination of carbon and hydrogen. For the present experiment it is tilted, so that any water which condenses in the cool end of the hard-glass tube is prevented from running back on to the hot glass. The hard-glass tube is similar to that used in the previous experiments, except that it is somewhat longer, and is sealed at one end.

The hard-glass tube is charged with the following materials, beginning at the sealed end :

(a) powdered sodium bicarbonate, for a length of 6 cm.,

(b) a short copper gauze roll,

(c) coarse copper oxide, for a length of 10 cm.,

(d) fine copper oxide, for a length of 10 cm.,

(e) a mixture of finely powdered copper oxide and the powdered organic compound ; the mixture is prepared by grinding about 0·3 gm. of the organic compound with about 10 gm. of the copper oxide in a mortar ; it occupies about 25–30 cm. of the length of the tube, (*f*) fine copper oxide, for a length of 10 cm.,

(*g*) coarse copper oxide, for a length of 10 cm.,

(*h*) a bright copper gauze roll.

In order to fill the tube, it is clamped in the vertical position, and the necessary materials are introduced from the top in the above sequence ; a clean funnel is used for the introduction of the powders.

The charged tube is placed in the furnace and connected to the Schiff's nitrometer as shown in Fig. 34. The nitrometer is filled with 30 per cent. potassium hydroxide solution, which serves as a levelling liquid and as an absorbent for carbon dioxide. At the base of the nitrometer tube there is a small quantity of mercury which prevents the potash solution from entering the combustion tube.

The extreme tip of the combustion tube is now gently heated. Carbon dioxide is evolved from the sodium bicarbonate, and sweeps out the air from the tube. The removal of the air is judged to be complete when all the bubbles of gas entering the nitrometer completely dissolve in the potassium hydroxide solution. As soon as all the air has been expelled from the tube the levelling reservoir of the nitrometer is raised so that the solution fills the graduated tube to the tap at the top. The tap is then closed.

The bright copper roll, the two sections of coarse copper oxide and the two sections of fine copper oxide are now successively brought to a dull-red heat. The end of the mixture of copper oxide and the organic compound nearest the nitrometer is then gradually heated, and the area heated is slowly extended backwards along the column, until all the combustion tube in the furnace is at a dull-red heat. The heating of the tube causes expansion of the carbon dioxide in it, and in the later stages, the evolution of nitrogen, carbon dioxide and steam from the organic compound. The heating must be so carefully controlled that at no stage does the rate of escape of bubbles into the nitrometer exceed one per second. During the combustion the burner under the sodium bicarbonate is adjusted so that the evolution of carbon dioxide is only just maintained.

When the combustion is complete (this normally takes about 20 minutes) the burner under the sodium bicarbonate is moved forward so that the rate of generation of carbon dioxide is increased. The carbon dioxide then sweeps out the nitrogen from the combustion tube into the nitrometer. When the bubbles entering the potash solution in the nitrometer all completely dissolve (thus showing that all the nitrogen in the hard-glass tube has been transferred to the nitrometer) the nitrometer is detached from the combustion tube and allowed to stand in a cool place for at least an hour. The height of the reservoir is then adjusted until the levels of liquid in both limbs of the nitrometer are equal, and the volume of the nitrogen is read. The temperature of the room and the atmospheric pressure are noted. The method gives good results if carefully carried out. Care must be taken to see that the combustion is slow and complete. Any carbon monoxide or methane which escape combustion will collect in the nitrometer and falsify the measurement of the volume of nitrogen liberated from the organic compound.

Example of the calculation of the percentage by weight of nitrogen in acetamide from the results of a nitrogen estimation by Dumas' method.

Weight of weighing tube and acetamide	8·2965 gm.
Weight of weighing tube after taking a portion of the acetamide for the experiment	8·1423 ,,
Weight of acetamide taken for the experiment	0·1542 ,,
Volume of nitrogen collected in the nitrometer, measured under laboratory conditions	30·8 c.c.
Room temperature	15°
Atmospheric pressure	770 mm.
Water vapour pressure over 30 per cent. potassium hydroxide solution at 15°	8·5 mm.

Hence pressure on the nitrogen = 770 − 8·5 = 761·5 mm.

30·8 c.c. of nitrogen corrected to N.T.P. become

$$\frac{30·8 \times 761·5 \times 273}{760 \times 288} = 29·26 \text{ c.c.}$$

At N.T.P. 1 litre of nitrogen weighs 1·251 gm. and therefore, 29·26 c.c. weigh

$$\frac{29·26 \times 1·251}{1000} = 0·0366 \text{ gm.}$$

Hence 0·1542 gm. of acetamide contain 0·0366 gm. of nitrogen, and 100 gm. of acetamide contain 23·73 gm. of nitrogen.

(*b*) **Kjeldahl's method.** This method is not of general application. It gives unreliable results if the organic compound under analysis contains a nitrogen atom directly linked to another nitrogen atom, or to an oxygen atom. It gives good results, however, when used for the analysis of amines, pyridine, alkaloids, amino-acids and proteins. As it is fairly rapid, and the apparatus required is not elaborate, it is extensively used for estimating nitrogen in certain foodstuffs, drugs and fertilisers in which these compounds occur.

Kjeldahl's method is carried out in two stages. In the first the nitrogenous compound is heated with a mixture of concentrated sulphuric acid and potassium sulphate, by which the organic compound is oxidised, and the nitrogen is converted to ammonium sulphate. In the second stage the solution thus obtained is made alkaline with sodium hydroxide, and the ammonia which is liberated on heating is passed into a measured volume of standard acid solution.

A weighed quantity (about 0·5–1 gm.) of the organic compound is placed in a long-necked flask of about 200 c.c. capacity. 20 c.c. of concentrated sulphuric acid are added, and the flask is gently heated in a fume-cupboard for about 30 minutes, Fig. 35. About 10 gm. of potassium sulphate are then added and the flask is heated, so that the contents just boil, until a clear solution is obtained.

This solution is cooled and carefully added to 100 c.c. of water, containing a few drops of methyl orange, in the large flat-bottomed flask, Fig. 36.

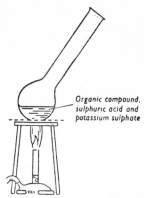

Organic compound, sulphuric acid and potassium sulphate

FIG. 35.   Kjeldahl's method for the estimation of nitrogen in an organic compound. Apparatus for the conversion of the nitrogen to ammonium sulphate.

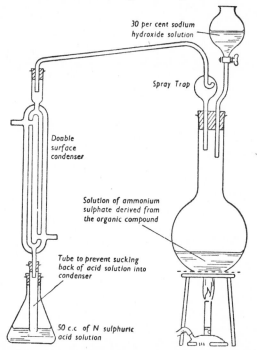

30 per cent sodium hydroxide solution

Spray Trap

Double surface condenser

Solution of ammonium sulphate derived from the organic compound

Tube to prevent sucking back of acid solution into condenser

50 c.c of N sulphuric acid solution

FIG. 36.   Kjeldahl's method for the estimation of nitrogen in an organic compound.

A few gm. of granulated zinc are added to the solution, so that the hydrogen liberated by its action with the sodium hydroxide may assist in driving the ammonia into the standard acid. 30 per cent. sodium hydroxide solution is slowly run into the flask while the contents are boiled. Ammonia is liberated and dissolves in the steam which forms in the condenser and runs down into the conical flask. The conical flask contains 50 c.c. of standard sulphuric acid solution (approximately normal) delivered from a pipette. When the methyl orange in the large flask has remained yellow for 20 minutes without the further addition of sodium hydroxide solution, the boiling is stopped, the apparatus is disconnected, and the acid solution in the conical flask is titrated against standard sodium hydroxide solution, using methyl orange as indicator.

Example of the calculation of the percentage by weight of nitrogen in glycine by Kjeldahl's method.

Weight of weighing tube and glycine	7·0182 gm.
Weight of weighing tube after taking a portion of the glycine for the experiment	6·4821 ,,
Weight of glycine taken for the experiment	0·5361 ,,
Volume of N. sulphuric acid solution * in the conical flask	50·00 c.c.
Volume of N. sodium hydroxide solution * required to neutralise the sulphuric acid remaining after the experiment	42·92 ,,
Therefore, volume of N. sulphuric acid solution equivalent to the ammonia generated in the experiment	7·08 ,,

This is equivalent to $\dfrac{7·08 \times 17}{1000}$ gm. of ammonia,

or, $\dfrac{7·08 \times 14}{1000}$ gm. of nitrogen.

Hence, 0·5311 gm. of glycine contain $\dfrac{7·08 \times 14}{1000}$ gm. of nitrogen, and the percentage of nitrogen in glycine is $\dfrac{7·08 \times 14 \times 100}{1000 \times 0·5361} = 18·49.$

The calculated value is 18·67.

(vi) Estimation of halogens in an organic compound by Carius' method

Chlorine, bromine and iodine in an organic compound are estimated by heating a known weight of the compound with fuming nitric

---

* In order to allow the principles of the calculation to stand out boldly, normal solutions of sulphuric acid and of sodium hydroxide are deemed to have been used in the experiment. In actual practice, standard solutions of approximately normal strength would be employed.

acid and silver nitrate in a sealed tube at a temperature of 260–270° for 4–6 hours. The fuming nitric acid oxidises the organic compound, and the liberated halogen combines with the silver to form silver halide. At the conclusion of the heating the contents of the tube are diluted with water, and the insoluble silver halide is separated by filtration and weighed. Since the composition of the silver halide is known, the percentage by weight of the halogen in the original organic compound may be calculated.

The experimental procedure by which this method is carried out is briefly described in the following paragraphs. For a detailed account of the manipulation a larger work must be consulted.

One end of a soft-glass tube about 50 cm. long and 2 cm. external diameter, and having a wall-thickness of about 3 mm., is sealed in the blow-pipe flame to give a rounded end of uniform thickness, Fig. 37 (a). This tube is generally referred to as the Carius tube. About 1 gm. of finely powdered silver nitrate and 1·5–2 c.c. of fuming nitric acid (density 1·5) are introduced into the Carius tube in such a way that the sides of the tube are neither dusted by the silver nitrate nor wetted by the nitric acid. Sufficient of the organic compound to yield about 0·3 gm. of silver halide is accurately weighed in a small glass tube.* This tube is placed in the mouth of the Carius tube and allowed to slide to the bottom where it takes up the position shown in Fig. 37 (b). The open end of the Carius tube is then drawn off and sealed so that the end is in the form of a capillary 2–3 cm. long, Fig. 37 (c).

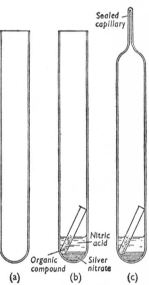

Fig. 37.   The Carius tube. (These diagrams are not drawn to scale ; the tube is about 50 cm. long and 2 cm. diameter.)

The Carius tube is then rolled in thick paper and inserted in a

---

* The filtration, washing, drying and weighing of the silver halide precipitate are most efficiently carried out on about 0·3 gm. of precipitate. If the percentage of halogen in the organic compound is quite unknown, it is impossible to calculate what weight of the compound will yield about 0·3 gm. of silver halide. In this case it is necessary first to carry out the experiment assuming that the organic compound contains about 50 per cent. of halogen. If the weight of silver halide obtained differs greatly from 0·3 gm. the experiment is repeated using the appropriately adjusted weight of the organic compound.

strong iron tube so that the capillary is just projecting from the open end. The iron tube is placed in a furnace which is raised to a temperature of 270° in the course of about 2 hours, and maintained at this temperature for another 4 hours. The furnace is then allowed to cool for at least 12 hours.

As a result of the decomposition of the organic compound by the nitric acid, the Carius tube is filled with gas under more than atmospheric pressure. This gas is released by fusing the tip of the capillary of the Carius tube while it is still in the furnace. The Carius tube is then withdrawn from the furnace and cut open. The contents are washed out with water into a beaker, the small glass tube is removed, and the suspension of silver halide is boiled for 15 minutes to coagulate the fine particles, and to destroy any additive compounds which the silver halide may have formed with silver nitrate. The silver halide is then filtered off through a weighed Gooch crucible, washed and dried in an oven at 130°. The Gooch crucible is then cooled and reweighed.

Example of the calculation of the percentage by weight of bromine in bromobenzene from the results of a Carius estimation.

Weight of bromobenzene taken	0·2562 gm.
Weight of Gooch crucible and silver bromide	10·0492 ,,
Weight of Gooch crucible alone	9·7426 ,,
Weight of silver bromide	0·3066 ,,

187·8 gm. of silver bromide contain 79·9 gm. of bromine.
Hence 0·3066 gm. of silver bromide contain

$$\frac{79\cdot9 \times 0\cdot3066}{187\cdot8} = 0\cdot1304 \text{ gm. of bromine.}$$

Therefore, the percentage by weight of bromine in bromobenzene

$$= \frac{0\cdot1304 \times 100}{0\cdot2562} = 50\cdot93.$$

(vii) Estimation of sulphur in an organic compound by Carius method

Sulphur in an organic compound is estimated by heating a known weight of the compound with fuming nitric acid in a sealed tube at a temperature of 260–270° for 4–6 hours. The organic compound is decomposed, and the sulphur is oxidised to sulphuric acid which is precipitated and weighed as barium sulphate.

The experimental procedure is similar to that used in the estimation of the halogens. 1·5–2·0 c.c. of fuming nitric acid are introduced into a Carius tube, and an accurately weighed quantity of the organic compound (sufficient to give about 0·3 gm. of barium sulphate *) is added. The Carius tube is sealed and heated in the furnace. When the Carius tube has been opened in the manner described in paragraph (vi), the contents are washed into a beaker, and diluted with water. Barium chloride solution is added drop by drop until precipitation of the barium sulphate is complete. The suspension is then boiled to coagulate the precipitate, and filtered through a weighed Gooch crucible. The precipitate is washed, and the crucible is dried at 130°, cooled and weighed.,

Example of the calculation of the percentage by weight of sulphur in crystalline sulphanilic acid from the results of a Carius estimation.

Weight of sulphanilic acid taken   0·2242 gm.
Weight of Gooch crucible and barium sulphate   8·6829 ,,
Weight of Gooch crucible alone   8·4326 ,,
Weight of barium sulphate   0·2503 ,,

233·5 gm. of barium sulphate contain 32·06 gm. of sulphur.
Hence 0·2503 gm. of barium sulphate contain

$$\frac{32·06 \times 0·2503}{233·5} = 0·0344 \text{ gm. of sulphur.}$$

Therefore, the percentage by weight of sulphur in crystalline sulphanilic acid is

$$\frac{0·0344 \times 100}{0·2242} = 15·35.$$

III. CALCULATION OF THE EMPIRICAL FORMULA OF AN ORGANIC COMPOUND WHEN THE PERCENTAGE COMPOSITION IS KNOWN

The empirical formula of an organic compound may be deduced if its percentage composition is known. The method of deduction is best explained by means of an example. Suppose it is desired to establish the empirical formula of succinamide from the results of a qualitative analysis which shows that it contains only carbon, hydrogen, nitrogen and possibly oxygen, and a quantitative analysis which shows that the percentages by weight of carbon, hydrogen and nitrogen in succinamide are :

Carbon	41·30 per cent.
Hydrogen	6·91
Nitrogen	24·17
Total	72·38 per cent.

Carbon, hydrogen and nitrogen constitute only 72·38 per cent. by weight of succinamide ; the difference between 72·38 and 100,

* The footnote on p. 91 applies to the determination of sulphur, *mutatis mutandis.*

namely, 27·62, is assumed to be the percentage by weight of oxygen in succinamide.

The atomic proportions of the four elements in succinamide are found by dividing the percentage by weight of each element by its atomic weight. The atomic proportions are :

$$\begin{aligned}
\text{Carbon} & \quad 41\cdot30/12 = 3\cdot441 \\
\text{Hydrogen} & \quad 6\cdot91/1 \ = 6\cdot91 \\
\text{Nitrogen} & \quad 24\cdot17/14 = 1\cdot726 \\
\text{Oxygen} & \quad 27\cdot62/16 = 1\cdot726.
\end{aligned}$$

The empirical formula expresses the atomic proportions of the elements in the molecule as integral values. To convert the above numbers to integers, each is divided by the smallest. The atomic proportions then become :

$$\begin{aligned}
\text{Carbon} & \quad 3\cdot441/1\cdot726 = 1\cdot994 \\
\text{Hydrogen} & \quad 6\cdot91 \ /1\cdot726 = 4\cdot004 \\
\text{Nitrogen} & \quad 1\cdot726/1\cdot726 = 1 \\
\text{Oxygen} & \quad 1\cdot726/1\cdot726 = 1.
\end{aligned}$$

The atomic proportions of carbon and hydrogen respectively are 2 and 4, within the limits of error of the experiment. The empirical formula of succinamide may therefore be written C_2H_4ON.

IV. DETERMINATION OF THE MOLECULAR WEIGHT OF AN ORGANIC COMPOUND

If the organic compound is a volatile liquid its molecular weight is determined by Victor Meyer's method, or by Hofmann's method. If it is a solid, its molecular weight is determined by observations on the depression of the freezing point, or the elevation of the boiling point, of a suitable solvent in which it is dissolved. Accounts of these methods will be found in text-books of physical chemistry.

The values of the molecular weights of organic acids and bases obtained by the application of these physical methods, however, are frequently only approximate. Many organic acids and bases are difficult to prepare in the pure state, and some are liable to undergo thermal decomposition when heated. Moreover, organic acids are electrolytically dissociated in aqueous solution, and are sometimes associated when dissolved in organic solvents. A special method, described below, is therefore employed for determining the molecular weight of an organic acid.

There is a good method for determining the equivalent of a base. There is, however, no dependable means for deciding what multiple of the equivalent is the accurate molecular weight. It is necessary to assume that the accurate molecular weight of a base is that multiple of the equivalent which is closest to the approximate value of the molecular weight ascertained by physical methods.

(i) Determination of the molecular weight of an organic acid

The method is based on the relation between the equivalent of an acid and its molecular weight. This relation is given by the expression

basicity × equivalent = molecular weight.

The methods available for determining the *basicity* of an acid not requiring a previous knowledge of its molecular weight are :

(i) the determination of the number of distinguishable sodium salts which may be prepared from it, and

(ii) the application of Ostwald's empirical rule that the difference between the equivalent conductivities of the neutral sodium salt in $N/32$ and $N/1024$ solutions is 10 for a monobasic acid, 20 for a dibasic acid, and 30 for a tribasic acid.

The *equivalent* of an organic acid is determined by a quantitative analysis of the silver salt. The silver salt is chosen because it is easily prepared and dried, and its analysis can be made by simple ignition in a crucible, during which all the organic material is burnt away, and a residue of pure silver remains. The equivalent of the acid is ascertained by calculating the number of parts by weight of it which yield the quantity of the silver salt which on ignition produces 107·9 parts by weight of metallic silver. For this calculation it is necessary to know only the weight of silver salt which is ignited, and the weight of metallic silver which is left.

In order to convert the organic acid to the silver salt it is first dissolved in water, and dilute ammonia solution is added until, after stirring, the solution smells of ammonia. The solution is then boiled until red litmus paper held in the steam no longer turns blue. The solution thus neutralised is then cooled, and silver nitrate is added until precipitation is complete. The silver salt is separated by filtration, washed well to remove all the silver nitrate, and dried in a steam oven. When cool it is powdered.

A crucible and lid are weighed, about 0·5 gm. of the salt is placed in the crucible, and the whole is weighed again. The crucible is then heated with a Bunsen flame in a pipe-clay triangle, gently at first and later at a red heat, until it contains only a gray residue of silver. The crucible and its contents are cooled in a desiccator and re-weighed. The ignition is repeated until the weight is constant.

Example of the calculation of the equivalent of succinic acid from the analysis of silver succinate.

Weight of crucible, lid, and silver succinate	5·3371 gm.
Weight of crucible and lid	5·0247 ,,
Weight of silver succinate taken	0·3124 ,,
Weight of crucible, lid and silver	5·2279 ,,
Weight of crucible and lid	5·0247 ,,
Weight of silver	0·2032 ,,

The equivalent of silver succinate is the weight which contains 107·9 gm. of silver.

From the experimental data the equivalent of silver succinate is

$$\frac{0·3124 \times 107·9}{0·2032} = 166·0.$$

The equivalent of succinic acid is given by the relation :

equivalent of succinic acid = equivalent of silver succinate – equivalent of silver + equivalent of hydrogen

$$= 166·0 - 107·9 + 1$$
$$= 59·1.$$

The basicity of succinic acid is 2, and hence the molecular weight

$$= 59·1 \times 2$$
$$= 118·2.$$

(ii) Determination of the molecular weight of an organic base

The method makes use of the relation between the equivalent of a base and its molecular weight which is given by the expression :

acidity × equivalent = molecular weight.

The *acidity* of a base is the number of equivalents of acid which is required to neutralise one molecular weight of the base. It indicates the number of OH ions which are set free when one molecule of a soluble organic base is dissolved in water. There is no method for determining the acidity of a base unless its molecular weight is at least approximately known. The acidity, however, must be a whole number. It may, therefore, be taken as the nearest integer to the quotient obtained by dividing the equivalent into the value of the molecular weight estimated by physical methods mentioned at the beginning of this section.

The *equivalent* of an organic base is determined by the quantitative analysis of the chloroplatinate. The chloroplatinate of a base has the general formula, $B_2H_2PtCl_6$, where B is a monoacid base. The chloroplatinates are crystalline solids, sparingly soluble in water. On ignition in air the chloroplatinate of an organic base decomposes, and, when the organic material has burnt away, a residue of pure platinum remains. The equivalent of the base is ascertained by calculating the number of parts by weight of it which are combined with 97·6 parts by weight of platinum in the chloroplatinate. For this calculation it is necessary to know only the weight of the chloro-platinate of the base, and the weight of metallic platinum which is left after ignition in air.

The organic base, or the aqueous solution of its hydrochloride, is added to a solution of chloroplatinic acid, H_2PtCl_6, prepared by dissolving platinum in aqua regia. The chloroplatinate is formed and at once crystallises. The suspension is cooled in ice-water, and filtered through a Buchner funnel. The crystals are washed with ice-cold water and dried in a vacuum desiccator.

A crucible and lid are weighed, about 0·5 gm. of the chloroplatinate is placed in the crucible, and the whole is weighed again. The cru-cible and its contents are heated over a Bunsen flame, cooled in a desiccator, and weighed. The heating, cooling and weighing are repeated until the weight is constant.

Example of the calculation of the equivalent and molecular weight of aniline from the analysis of aniline chloroplatinate.

Weight of crucible, lid and aniline chloroplatinate	6·5492 gm.
Weight of crucible and lid	6·0371 ,,
Weight of aniline chloroplatinate taken	0·5121 ,,
Weight of crucible, lid and platinum	6·2048 ,,
Weight of crucible and lid	6·0371 ,,
Weight of platinum	0·1677 ,,

The equivalent of aniline chloroplatinate with reference to aniline is that weight which contains 97·6 gm. of platinum, that is one-half of the atomic weight of platinum.

From the experimental data the equivalent of aniline chloroplatinate is

$$\frac{0 \cdot 5121 \times 97 \cdot 6}{0 \cdot 1677} = 298 \cdot 1.$$

The equivalent of aniline is given by the relation

equivalent of aniline = equivalent of aniline chloroplatinate
                        − equivalent of chloroplatinic acid

$$= 298 \cdot 1 - 205$$
$$= 93 \cdot 1.$$

Since aniline is taken to be a monoacid base, this value is also that of the molecular weight.

V. DETERMINATION OF THE MOLECULAR AND CONSTITU-TIONAL FORMULA OF AN ORGANIC COMPOUND WHEN THE EMPIRICAL FORMULA AND THE MOLECULAR WEIGHT ARE KNOWN

The molecular weight of a compound is equal to the sum of the atomic weights of the constituent elements in the numbers repre-sented in the molecular formula. The empirical formula weight is the sum of the weights of the constituent atoms in the numbers represented by the empirical formula. The factor, n, by which the empirical formula must be multiplied to give the atomic proportions in which the constituent elements are present in the molecule is therefore, given by the expression

$$n = \frac{\text{molecular weight}}{\text{empirical formula weight}}.$$

For example the molecular weight of succinamide is 116. The empirical formula is C_2H_4ON (p. 94), and the empirical formula weight is

$$2 \times 12 \quad + \quad 4 \times 1 \quad + \quad 16 + 14 \quad = \quad 58.$$

The molecular formula is $(C_2H_4ON)_n$, and $n = \dfrac{116}{58} = 2.$

Hence the molecular formula is $(C_2H_4ON)_2$, or $C_4H_8O_2N_2$.

When the molecular formula of a compound has been ascertained, the constitutional formula is elucidated by an examination of the chemical relationships of the compound. Succinamide, for example, is formed by treating succinyl chloride (p. 296) with ammonia, and succinyl chloride is formed by the action of phosphorus pentachloride on succinic acid. These reactions show that if succinic acid has the constitution

$$CH_2COOH$$
$$|$$
$$CH_2COOH,$$

then that of succinamide must be

$$CH_2CONH_2$$
$$|$$
$$CH_2CONH_2.$$

The arguments by which the constitutional formulae of typical organic compounds are established are given in the chapters of this book in which those compounds are described.

VI. DETERMINATION OF THE NUMBER OF HYDROXYL GROUPS IN THE MOLECULE OF AN ORGANIC COMPOUND

If an organic compound containing a hydroxyl group in the molecule is treated with a mixture of acetic anhydride and acetic acid, the hydroxyl group is acetylated, p. 252. If the acetyl derivative thus obtained is boiled with excess of a solution of sodium hydroxide, the original hydroxyl compound is regenerated, and some of the sodium hydroxide is neutralised by conversion to sodium acetate, according to an equation of the form,

$$R.OCOCH_3 + NaOH = R.OH + CH_3.COONa,$$

where R.OH is the hydroxyl compound. The equation shows that one gram-molecule of sodium hydroxide is used up in hydrolysing one gram-molecule of an acetyl derivative prepared from a compound which contains one hydroxyl group in the molecule. If the hydroxyl compound contains two hydroxyl groups in the molecule, the equation for the hydrolysis of the acetyl derivative takes the form,

$$R'(OCOCH_3)_2 + 2NaOH = R'(OH)_2 + 2CH_3.COONa.$$

Hence, if n gram-molecules of sodium hydroxide are used up in hydrolysing one gram-molecule of the acetyl derivative, then the acetyl derivative contains n acetyl groups in the molecule, and the hydroxyl compound from which it was formed contains n hydroxyl groups in the molecule.

A method for determining the number of hydroxyl groups in the molecule of an organic compound is based on this principle. It may be exemplified by an experiment to determine the number of hydroxyl groups in the molecule of glycerol.

Glycerol is first heated with a mixture of acetic anhydride and acetic acid to form glyceryl acetate. This is a simple qualitative preparation, and it is not necessary to measure accurately the quantities of the reagents used. The glyceryl acetate, a liquid B.P. 258°, is isolated from the excess of the reagents, dried and purified by distillation. Its molecular weight is then determined by a suitable standard method. About 2 gm. of the glyceryl acetate is accurately weighed in a 200 c.c. conical flask. 50 c.c. of N.NaOH solution is added from a pipette ; a few very small fragments of unglazed porcelain are also added. The flask is fitted to a reflux water condenser, and the reagents are boiled for about half an hour. The flask is then cooled, the inside of the condenser is washed down with a little distilled water, and the hydrolysed solution is titrated against $N.H_2SO_4$ solution, using phenolphthalein as indicator. A parallel experiment is usually carried out without the glyceryl acetate, in order to estimate small accidental losses of reagents.

Example of calculation.

Weight of glyceryl acetate taken	2·204 gm.
Volume of N.NaOH solution added	50·0 c.c.
Volume of $N.H_2SO_4$ solution required	19·7 c.c.
Volume of $N.H_2SO_4$ solution required in control experiment	49·8 c.c.
Hence, volume of N.NaOH solution used in hydrolysis	30·1 c.c.

The molecular weight of glyceryl acetate is 218. The volume of N.NaOH solution used in hydrolysing this weight is

$$\frac{218 \times 30 \cdot 1}{2 \cdot 204} = 2980 \text{ c.c.}$$

Since 1000 c.c. N.NaOH = 40 gm. NaOH = 1 acetyl group = 1 OH group, the number of hydroxyl groups in the molecule of glycerol is 2·98, or, since this number must be integral, **3**.

VII. DETERMINATION OF THE MOLECULAR FORMULA OF A GASEOUS HYDROCARBON BY EUDIOMETRIC ANALYSIS

If a known volume of a gaseous hydrocarbon is mixed with excess of air and the mixture is exploded, the hydrocarbon is oxidised to carbon dioxide and steam. When the steam has condensed to water, the gases present in the apparatus are carbon dioxide, nitrogen, and the residue of oxygen which has not been used up in the oxidation. It is necessary to observe (i) the original volume of the hydrocarbon, (ii) the volume of air added, (iii) the volume of carbon dioxide formed, (iv) the volume of oxygen not required for the combustion of the hydrocarbon. The molecular formula of the hydrocarbon may then be deduced by the following argument.

Let the molecular formula of the hydrocarbon be C_xH_y. Then the chemical equation for its combustion may be written

$$C_xH_y \; + \; \left(x + \frac{y}{4}\right)O_2 \; = \; xCO_2 + \frac{y}{2}H_2O.$$

According to Avogadro's hypothesis, the number of molecules of each gas taking part in the combustion is proportional to its volume, provided that all volumes are reduced to the same temperature and pressure. Hence,

$x =$ the volume of carbon dioxide (at room temperature and pressure) produced by the combustion of 1 c.c. of the hydrocarbon,

$\dfrac{y}{2} =$ the volume of steam (reduced to room temperature and pressure) produced by the combustion of 1 c.c. of the hydrocarbon,

$\left(x + \dfrac{y}{4}\right) =$ the volume of oxygen (at room temperature and pressure) actually used in the combustion of 1 c.c. of the hydrocarbon.

If v c.c. of the hydrocarbon were originally taken, the equation becomes

$$vC_xH_y \; + \; v\left(x + \frac{y}{4}\right)O_2 \; = \; vxCO_2 + \frac{vy}{2}H_2O,$$

and,

$v\left(x + \dfrac{y}{4}\right) =$ the volume of oxygen actually used in the combustion of the hydrocarbon, which is equal to the volume of

oxygen originally taken (calculated on the assumption
that the measured volume of air contained 20·9 per cent.
by volume of oxygen) *less* the volume of oxygen remaining at the end of the experiment, ...(i)

$vx =$ the volume of carbon dioxide formed. ....(ii)

Since the value of v is known, if the appropriate experimental
quantities are introduced into the right-hand side of equations (i)
and (ii), the values of x and y can be calculated.

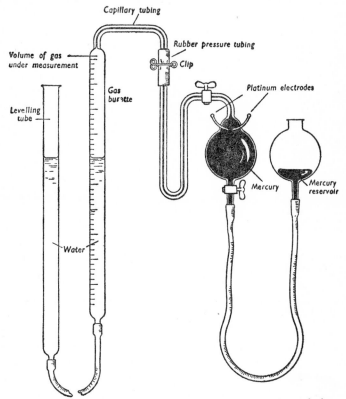

FIG. 38. Hempel's gas burette (*left*) connected to the explosion
pipette (*right*).

An example of this method of analysis is furnished by the determination of the constitution of methane using Hempel's gas apparatus. *Hempel's apparatus* consists of a gas-burette and a number of
gas pipettes. The gas-burette is a long accurately graduated glass
tube capable of holding about 100 c.c. of gas, Fig. 38. It is con-

nected to a levelling tube by means of a long piece of pressure tubing. The levelling liquid is water. By adjusting the position of the levelling tube the gas in the burette is brought to atmospheric pressure. The upper end of the gas-burette is sealed to a capillary tube which is closed by a short length of rubber tubing fitted with a clip. The gas pipettes required for the experiment are (i) the explosion pipette containing mercury, Fig. 38, (ii) an absorption pipette containing potassium hydroxide solution, Fig. 39, (iii) an absorption pipette containing an alkaline solution of potassium pyrogallate. The capillary tube of each gas pipette can be attached to the capillary tube of the gas-burette by means of a short length of pressure tubing, Fig. 38. When the junction has been made, the gas in the burette can be forced into the pipette by raising the levelling tube;

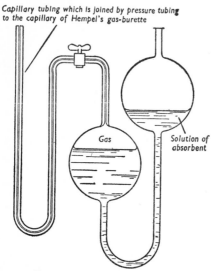

Capillary tubing which is joined by pressure tubing to the capillary of Hempel's gas-burette

Gas

Solution of absorbent

FIG. 39. Absorption pipette.

gas may be transferred from the pipette back again to the burette by lowering the levelling tube.

The gas-burette is connected to a reservoir of methane, and a small volume (about 10 c.c.) of this gas is drawn into the burette, where its volume is accurately measured at room temperature and pressure. The capillary tubes of the gas-burette and the explosion pipette are connected by pressure tubing, and the methane is passed into the pipette. The gas-burette, now full of water, is detached from the explosion pipette and filled with air. An accurately measured volume of air (about 100 c.c.) is passed from the gas-burette into the explosion pipette, where it mixes with the methane. The pressure on the mixture is reduced by lowering the mercury reservoir, the stop-cocks are closed, and the spark is passed across the platinum electrodes. By opening the stop-cocks, raising the mercury reservoir, and lowering the levelling tube, the residual gas is transferred back to the gas-burette, where its volume is measured at room temperature and pressure. The gas is then transferred to the absorption pipette containing potassium hydroxide solution, the clip is closed, and the pipette is well shaken. The residual gas is passed into the gas-burette again, and its volume is measured. The diminution in volume, which has resulted from exposing the gas to potassium hydroxide solution, represents the volume of carbon dioxide formed by combustion of the hydrocarbon. Finally, the gas is transferred to the absorption pipette containing alkaline potassium pyrogallate solution, shaken with the solution, and transferred back again to the gas-burette. The diminution in volume which occurs when the gas is exposed to alkaline potassium pyrogallate solution represents the volume of oxygen which remained after the carbon and hydrogen of the hydrocarbon had been converted to carbon dioxide and water.

The deduction of the constitution of methane from the above observations is illustrated by the following numerical example.

Let the volume of methane taken be   8·0 c.c.

Let the volume of air taken be   100·0 c.c.

$\therefore$ Volume of oxygen taken is $\dfrac{100 \times 20 \cdot 9}{100}$ =   20·9 c.c.

Volume of gas after explosion   92·0 c.c.

Volume of gas after exposure to potassium hydroxide solution   84·2 c.c.

     Hence, volume of carbon dioxide formed is 92·0 – 84·2   =   7·8 c.c.

Volume of gas after exposure to alkaline potassium pyrogallate solution   79·3 c.c.

     Hence, volume of oxygen *unused* in the combustion is   84·2 – 79·3   =   4·9 c.c.*

     and hence the volume of oxygen *used* in the combustion is   20·9 – 4·9   =   16·0 c.c.

Using the experimental values, equations (i) and (ii) may be written :

$$vx = 7 \cdot 8 \quad \dotfill \text{(i)}$$

$$v\left(x + \frac{y}{4}\right) = 16 \cdot 0 \dotfill \text{(ii)}$$

Hence, since $v = 8 \cdot 0$, within the limits of error of the experiment, $x = 1$ and $y = 4$, and the molecular formula of methane is CH_4.

* Consideration of the chemical equation at the bottom of p. 100 shows that the only gases remaining in the pipette after the exposure to potassium hydroxide solution are the nitrogen (79·1 c.c.) from the air originally taken and the unused oxygen. The volume of oxygen unused, according to this consideration, is

$$84 \cdot 2 \quad - \quad 79 \cdot 1 \quad = \quad 5 \cdot 1 \text{ c.c.}$$

Exposure of the residual gas to potassium pyrogallate is, therefore, not strictly necessary, but the data it provides serve as a valuable check, and the procedure illustrates that which is normally employed in gas analysis.

CHAPTER V

THE PARAFFINS

TABLE IX *

Name	Formula	M.P.	B.P.
Methane	CH_4	$-184°$	$-161°$
Ethane	$CH_3.CH_3$	$-172°$	$-88°$
Propane	$CH_3.CH_2.CH_3$	$-190°$	$-45°$
Butane	$CH_3.CH_2.CH_2.CH_3$	$-135°$	$+1°$
iso-Butane	$CH_3.CH_3.CH.CH_3$	$-145°$	$-10·2°$
Pentane	$CH_3.(CH_2)_3.CH_3$	$-131°$	$+36°$
iso-Pentane	$(CH_3)_2.CH.CH_2.CH_3$	$-160°$	$30°/747$ mm.
Hexane	$CH_3.(CH_2)_4.CH_3$	$-95°$	$69°$
iso-Hexane	$(CH_3)_2.CH.(CH_2)_2.CH_3$		$63°$
Octane	$CH_3.(CH_2)_6.CH_3$	$-56°$	$+125°$
Decane	$CH_3.(CH_2)_8.CH_3$	$-32°$	$+174°$

METHANE

Methane, the first member of the paraffin series, is a gas which is chemically non-reactive, and sparingly soluble in water. It occurs naturally in the gas which issues from petroleum fields, p. 470. Methane is the principal constituent of " fire-damp ", the gas which is liberated from gassy coal mines ; these mines are liable to be dangerous on account of the formation of explosive mixtures of methane and air. Methane is one of the gases liberated by the destructive distillation of coal, and it constitutes about 40 per cent. of coal-gas. It is set free during the fermentation of cellulose under water ; the bubbles which rise when a marsh or the bottom of a pond is disturbed contain methane, carbon dioxide and nitrogen. Methane is also present in human intestinal gases.

PRINCIPAL REACTIONS IN WHICH METHANE IS PRODUCED

1. **The reduction of methyl iodide by a zinc-copper couple and ethyl alcohol containing about 5 per cent. of water.** The

* The melting points and boiling points of certain of the paraffins which are not mentioned in Table IX are given on p. 111.

couple liberates nascent hydrogen by reaction with the alcohol, and the hydrogen reduces the methyl iodide,

$$CH_3I + 2H = CH_4 + HI.$$

The experimental procedure for carrying out the reaction is described on p. 106.

2. The action of water on magnesium methyl iodide.

$$Mg\begin{array}{c}CH_3\\I\end{array} + H_2O = Mg\begin{array}{c}OH\\I\end{array} + CH_4.$$

This is an example of one of the Grignard reactions, of which a general account is given on p. 458. Magnesium methyl iodide is made by adding magnesium to methyl iodide dissolved in dry ether ; methane is obtained by dropping water from a dropping funnel on to the ethereal solution. The methane thus prepared is pure.

3. The direct combination of carbon with hydrogen. If pure hydrogen is passed over purified carbon heated to 1100–1200°, a high yield of methane is obtained. Hydrogen passed over a mixture of gas-black and nickel at 475° yields a mixture of gases containing 50 per cent. of methane.

4. The action of water on aluminium carbide.

$$Al_4C_3 + 12H_2O = 3CH_4 + 4Al(OH)_3.$$

The aluminium carbide is placed in a flask fitted with a dropping funnel and a delivery tube. Water is added slowly from the dropping funnel, and the methane is collected over water. Dilute hydrochloric acid may be used instead of water, with the advantage that the aluminium chloride produced remains in solution. The methane obtained from aluminium carbide is contaminated with acetylene and hydrogen.

5. The action of heat on a mixture of sodium acetate and soda-lime.

$$CH_3.COONa + NaOH = CH_4 + Na_2CO_3.$$

1 part of anhydrous sodium acetate is mixed with 4 parts of soda-lime. The mixture is heated in a hard-glass tube fitted with a delivery tube, and the methane is collected over water. The methane produced is contaminated with hydrogen and ethylene. A purer product is obtained if barium oxide is used instead of soda-lime.

6. The fermentation of wet cellulose. If filter paper, made into a pulp with water, is mixed with horse dung and kept at 50°, a mixture of methane and carbon dioxide is evolved. If the carbon dioxide is removed by absorption in potassium hydroxide solution, methane is left in a high state of purity.

Laboratory preparation of methane. Pure methane for use in the laboratory is most conveniently prepared by the reduction of methyl iodide by a zinc-copper couple in the presence of ethyl alcohol containing about 5 per cent. of water (Reaction 1 above).

The zinc-copper couple is prepared either (*a*) by heating copper powder with pieces of zinc foil or zinc filings in an atmosphere of hydrogen or coal-gas, or, (*b*) by immersing granulated zinc in a dilute solution of copper sulphate until it is coated with a film of copper. The couple is placed in a flask, Fig. 40, and a mixture of approximately

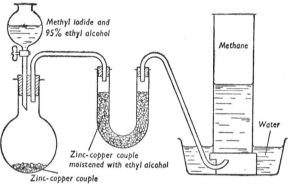

Methyl Iodide and
95% ethyl alcohol

Methane

Water

Zinc-copper couple
moistened with ethyl alcohol

Zinc-copper couple

FIG. 40. Apparatus for the preparation of methane.

equal proportions of methyl iodide and 95 per cent. ethyl alcohol is added from the dropping funnel. Methane is evolved in the cold, and, after passage through a U-tube containing a zinc-copper couple moistened with alcohol to remove any admixed methyl iodide, is collected over water.

Industrial preparation of methane. Methane for use as a fuel in industry is obtained from the gas, known as " natural gas ", which emanates from petroleum deposits, p. 470. The " activated sludge " method of sewage disposal used in Great Britain yields a gas containing 70 per cent. of methane, which is the source of power for the plant.

PROPERTIES, STRUCTURE AND USES OF METHANE

Properties. Methane is a colourless and odourless gas. It is slightly soluble in water ; 100 volumes of water dissolve 5·56 volumes of methane at 0°, and 3·3 volumes at 20°. Methane is somewhat more soluble in alcohol. It is stable at normal temperatures, but if passed through a red-hot tube it is largely decomposed into its elements. At the same time small quantities of ethane, ethylene, acetylene, benzene and naphthalene are formed.

The most remarkable chemical property of methane is its inertness. It is unaffected at ordinary temperatures and pressures by fuming sulphuric acid, nitric acid, aqueous potassium permanganate solution, bromine, bromine water, phosphorus pentoxide, or potassium hydroxide. Under ordinary conditions methane reacts only with oxygen, fluorine, chlorine and, less vigorously, with bromine vapour. Methane burns in air or oxygen with a pale blue flame to form carbon dioxide and water ; it forms explosive mixtures with air or oxygen. It reacts with ozone at ordinary temperatures yielding formaldehyde.

If methane is brought into contact with fluorine an explosion occurs, even in the dark. The chief products of the reaction are hydrogen fluoride and carbon tetrafluoride ; some free carbon may be deposited. If special precautions are taken to moderate the reaction, for example, by allowing methane to mix with fluorine diluted with nitrogen in a metal tube packed with copper gauze, a mixture of the four possible substitution products, CH_3F, CH_2F_2, CHF_3, CF_4, is formed.

Methane reacts with chlorine, but only if the mixture is exposed to light. In direct sunlight methane explodes with chlorine forming hydrogen chloride and free carbon,

$$CH_4 + 2Cl_2 = 4HCl + C.$$

In diffused daylight methane undergoes substitution reactions with chlorine by which hydrogen chloride is formed, and some or all of the hydrogen atoms in the molecule of methane are replaced by atoms of chlorine, for example,

$$CH_4 + Cl_2 = CH_3Cl + HCl.$$

It is found that, in whatever proportions chlorine is mixed with methane, the reaction in diffused daylight leads to a mixture of all four of the possible substitution products, CH_3Cl, CH_2Cl_2, $CHCl_3$, CCl_4. The reactions of bromine vapour with methane are similar to those of chlorine but less vigorous. Iodine does not react.

Structure of methane. The molecular formula of methane is shown to be CH_4 by eudiometric analysis, p. 100. The tetracovalent carbon atom is linked to four unicovalent hydrogen atoms.

The absence of any isomeric forms of monochloromethane CH_3Cl, shows that compounds of identical structure are produced when any one of the hydrogen atoms in the molecule of methane is replaced by an atom of chlorine, and, therefore, that the four hydrogen atoms occupy similar positions in the molecule. The absence of any isomeric forms of dichloromethane, CH_2Cl_2, shows that the molecule of methane is non-planar. If all the atoms of the molecule were in a single plane, two isomeric forms of dichloromethane would be expected, with the constitutions :

$$
\begin{array}{cc}
\begin{array}{c}
H \\
| \\
Cl-C-H \\
| \\
Cl
\end{array}
&
\begin{array}{c}
H \\
| \\
Cl-C-Cl \\
| \\
H
\end{array}
\end{array}
$$

If, however, dichloromethane is assigned a three-dimensional structure, so that the carbon atom is at the centre of a regular tetrahedron and the atoms with which it is combined are at the four corners, only one form of dichloromethane is possible, with the constitution

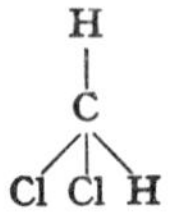

$$
\begin{array}{c}
H \\
| \\
C \\
\diagup | \diagdown \\
Cl \ Cl \ H
\end{array}
$$

A corresponding tetrahedral arrangement is therefore ascribed to the molecule of methane. Further evidence for the spatial configuration of atoms or groups combined with a carbon atom is furnished by the phenomenon of optical isomerism, p. 303.

Uses of methane. In the form of natural gas methane is used as a fuel. Pure methane has no chemical use on an industrial scale.

ETHANE

Ethane, the second member of the paraffin series, is a gas. Its properties closely resemble those of methane.

PRINCIPAL REACTIONS IN WHICH ETHANE IS PRODUCED

1. The reduction of ethyl iodide by a zinc-copper couple and ethyl alcohol mixed with about 5 per cent. of water. Nascent hydrogen formed by the action of alcohol on the zinc-copper couple reduces the ethyl iodide according to the equation,

$$C_2H_5I \ + \ H_2 \ = \ C_2H_6 \ + \ HI.$$

This reaction is carried out in the same way as the similar reaction for the preparation of methane.

2. The action of water on magnesium ethyl iodide.

$$Mg\begin{matrix} \diagup C_2H_5 \\ \diagdown I \end{matrix} \ + \ H_2O \ = \ C_2H_6 \ + \ Mg\begin{matrix} \diagup OH \\ \diagdown I \end{matrix} \ .$$

This reaction is an example of a Grignard reaction, p. 458. Magnesium is added to ethyl iodide dissolved in dry ether, and water is slowly added to the solution from a dropping funnel.

3. The action of sodium on methyl iodide. Wurtz's reaction.

$$CH_3I + 2Na + ICH_3 = CH_3.CH_3 + 2NaI.$$

Thin slices of metallic sodium are suspended in ether contained in a small flask fitted with a reflux water condenser. Methyl iodide is slowly added from a tap-funnel of which the stem passes through the

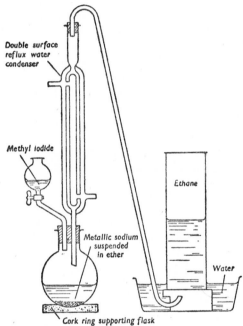

FIG. 41. Apparatus for the preparation of ethane by Wurtz's reaction.

cork of the flask, Fig. 41. The ethane is collected, after the air has been displaced from the apparatus, from a delivery tube fitted to the top of the condenser.

4. The action of heat on a mixture of sodium propionate and soda-lime.

$$C_2H_5.COONa + NaOH = C_2H_6 + Na_2CO_3.$$

The reagents are mixed together and heated in a hard-glass tube.

5. The action of heat on a mixture of sodium succinate and soda-lime.

$$\begin{matrix} CH_2.COONa \\ | \\ CH_2.COONa \end{matrix} \quad + \quad 2NaOH \quad = \quad C_2H_6 \quad + \quad 2Na_2CO_3.$$

6. The reduction of ethylene or acetylene by hydrogen in the presence of nickel at 140°.

$$CH_2{=}CH_2 \quad + \quad H_2 \quad = \quad C_2H_6.$$
$$CH{\equiv}CH \quad + \quad 2H_2 \quad = \quad C_2H_6.$$

7. The electrolysis of a solution of sodium or potassium acetate. Kolbe's method. The solution contains the ions :

$$CH_3.COO^-, Na^+, OH^-, H^+.$$

During electrolysis the $CH_3.COO^-$ ions are discharged at the anode, and at once undergo decomposition into ethane and carbon dioxide, thus

$$2CH_3.COO^- = C_2H_6 + 2CO_2.$$

The ethane is liberated as a gas. The H^+ ions are discharged at the cathode from which the hydrogen escapes as a gas. Na^+ ions and OH^- ions are not discharged ; they remain in solution as sodium hydroxide which may form sodium carbonate with some of the carbon dioxide set free at the anode. The ethane is passed through potassium hydroxide solution to remove the remainder of the carbon dioxide and collected over water.

Laboratory preparation of ethane. Ethane is prepared in the laboratory by the reduction of ethyl iodide using a zinc-copper couple and ethyl alcohol. The experimental details are similar to those described under the laboratory preparation of methane, p. 106.

PROPERTIES AND CONSTITUTION OF ETHANE

Properties. Ethane is a colourless and odourless gas. It is almost insoluble in water, and only slightly soluble in alcohol. Like methane, ethane is chemically inert ; it reacts only with oxygen and the halogens. It burns in air with a feebly luminous flame, and it forms explosive mixtures with air or oxygen. It is attacked by fluorine, chlorine and bromine in a similar manner and under the same conditions as methane. It is interesting to note that although chlorine in its reaction with methane always yields a mixture of the four possible substitution products, the reaction with ethane takes place progressively. Ethyl chloride is first formed,

$$C_2H_6 + Cl_2 = CH_3.CH_2Cl + HCl,$$

then ethylidene dichloride,

$$CH_3.CH_2Cl \ + \ Cl_2 \ = \ CH_3.CHCl_2 \ + \ HCl,$$

then methyl chloroform

$$CH_3.CHCl_2 \ + \ Cl_2 \ = \ CH_3.CCl_3 \ + \ HCl,$$

and finally hexachloroethane, C_2Cl_6.

Constitution of ethane. The molecular formula of ethane is shown to be C_2H_6 by eudiometric analysis. If the tetracovalency of carbon and the mono-covalency of hydrogen are to be preserved, the molecular constitution of ethane must be

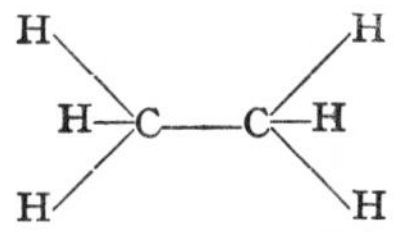

This constitution is confirmed by the Wurtz synthesis of ethane, in which sodium is allowed to react with methyl iodide, Reaction **3**, p. 109. It should be noted, as a result of the spatial distribution of the four covalencies of the carbon atom, that all the six hydrogen atoms in the ethane molecule occupy identical positions.

GENERAL PROPERTIES OF MEMBERS OF THE PARAFFIN SERIES

Members of the paraffin series may be prepared by methods analogous to those described for the preparation of ethane. The higher members are conveniently obtained by the reduction of the appropriate ketones by Clemmensen's reaction, which is illustrated by the reduction of acetone to propane, p. 222.

The members of the paraffin series from CH_4 to C_4H_{10} are gases at ordinary temperatures ; the members from C_5H_{12} to $C_{16}H_{34}$ are liquids, and the higher members are waxy solids. Paraffin wax is a mixture of solid paraffins. The difference between the boiling points of successive normal members decreases as the series is ascended. For example,

	B.P.		B.P.	Difference
CH_4	$-161°$	C_2H_6	$-88°$	$73°$
C_6H_{14}	$69°$	C_7H_{16}	$98°$	$29°$
$C_{11}H_{24}$	$197°$	$C_{12}H_{26}$	$216°$	$19°$

If a hydrocarbon exists in two or more isomeric forms, the boiling point of the isomer which possesses an unbranched carbon chain is always higher than the boiling point of any other isomer ; for a paraffin of given molecular weight, the more branched the carbon chain, the lower the boiling point.

Methane is slightly soluble in water, but all the other members are insoluble. The gaseous members of the series are slightly soluble in alcohol, the liquid members are fairly soluble, and the solid members are progressively less soluble.

The paraffins decompose if heated to 500–700°. Methane and ethane are decomposed to hydrogen and carbon. Higher members of the series undergo changes which are of great importance in the manufacture of motor spirit, p. 471.

Like methane and ethane, the other members of the paraffin series are resistant to the action of acids and alkalis and reducing agents, and they are not easily oxidised. The nitro group, $-NO_2$, can be introduced into the paraffin molecule, however, by heating the paraffin with dilute nitric acid (D. 1·07–1·15) at 110–120° under pressure, or by passing a mixture of the vapours of the paraffin and nitric acid through a hot tube at 400° under a pressure of about 10 atmospheres. Nitroparaffins are used as solvents for degreasing machinery.

The most characteristic reactions of the paraffins are substitution reactions with chlorine or bromine, by which atoms of hydrogen in the paraffin molecule are replaced by atoms of these halogens. These substitution reactions are facilitated by sunlight, and by the presence of iodine, antimony pentachloride, ferric chloride or iron. The first halogen atom to enter the molecule does so most easily, and as the number of halogen atoms in the molecule increases, substitution becomes more difficult. The ultimate product of chlorination is CCl_4 for methane, C_2Cl_6 for ethane, and C_3Cl_8 for propane. On vigorous chlorination, however, propane cracks, yielding C_2Cl_6 and CCl_4. The higher paraffins also tend to crack on chlorination, yielding hexachlorobenzene and carbon tetrachloride ; bromination yields the corresponding bromine compounds. Members of the paraffin series do not undergo additive reactions * and they are described, therefore, as saturated compounds.

Paraffins of the type $(CH_3)_3CH$, which contain in the molecule one carbon atom directly linked to a single hydrogen atom only, are more reactive than straight chain paraffins. They readily undergo substitution reactions with the halogens, and they may be oxidised to fatty acids and carbon dioxide by chromic acid or by potassium permanganate.

---

* An additive reaction is one in which two substances combine together to form a single compound without the liberation of any other substance. The reaction between ethylene and chlorine, mentioned on p. 38, is a characteristic example of an additive reaction.

NOMENCLATURE OF THE PARAFFINS

The systematic names of members of the paraffin series have the termination " ane ". The names of certain members of the series are given in Table IX, p. 104. If a paraffin possesses several isomeric forms it is necessary to assign to each isomeride a name which indicates its molecular structure. The systematic name for a given paraffin is chosen in accordance with the following rules.

(i) A normal paraffin has a molecular structure in which the carbon atoms are arranged in an unbranched chain.

(ii) The simple names " butane ", " pentane ", and so on, are reserved for normal paraffins.

(iii) A paraffin possessing a complex structure is assumed to be derived from the normal paraffin corresponding to the *longest* chain of carbon atoms in the molecule. For example, the paraffin having the structure

$$H_3C—\overset{\displaystyle H}{\underset{\displaystyle H}{C}}—\overset{\displaystyle H}{\underset{\displaystyle CH_3}{C}}—\overset{\displaystyle H}{\underset{\displaystyle CH_3}{C}}—CH_3$$

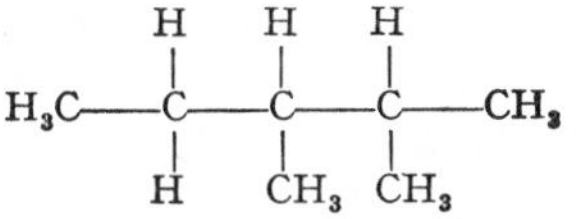

is regarded, for the purposes of nomenclature, as a dimethyl derivative of pentane, and the paraffin having the structure

$$H_3C—\overset{\displaystyle H}{\underset{\displaystyle H}{C}}—\overset{\displaystyle H}{\underset{\displaystyle H}{C}}—\overset{\displaystyle H}{\underset{\displaystyle CH_3}{C}}—C_2H_5$$

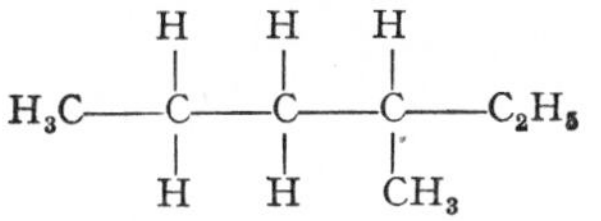

as a monomethyl derivative of hexane.

(iv) The carbon atoms in the longest chain in the molecule are numbered, and a branch attached to the chain is indicated by specifying (*a*) the number of the carbon atom at which the branching starts, and (*b*) the name of the alkyl group constituting the branch. For example, the two paraffins mentioned above would be named thus :

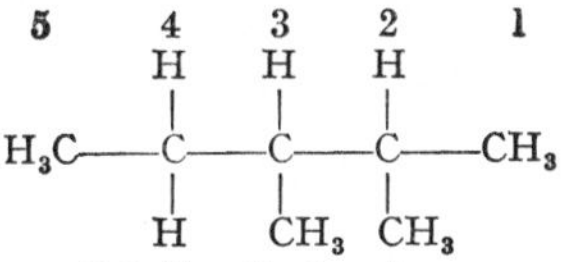

$$\underset{2:3\text{-dimethylpentane}}{\overset{\displaystyle 5\quad 4\quad 3\quad 2\quad 1}{H_3C—C—C—C—CH_3}}\qquad\underset{3\text{-methylhexane}}{\overset{\displaystyle 6\quad 5\quad 4\quad 3\quad 2\quad 1}{HC_3—C—C—C—C—CH_3}}$$

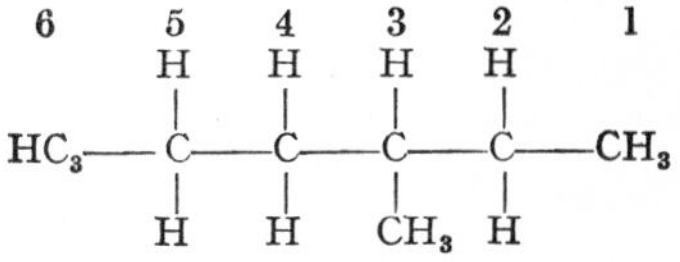

The direction of the numbering along the carbon chain is chosen so that the numbers used to indicate the branching are as small as possible.

A less cumbrous nomenclature is commonly employed to indicate the isomers of the paraffins which possess only one or two isomeric forms. The prefix " iso " is used to show that the molecule possesses a symmetrical $\rangle$— shaped structure. For example,

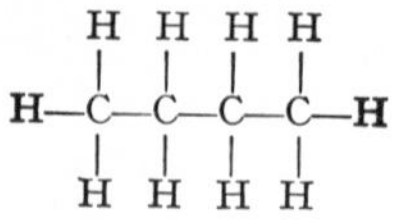

normal butane 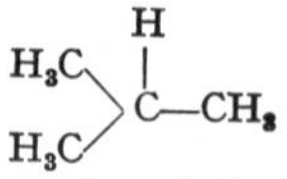   iso-butane (2-methyl propane)

The less complex paraffins are also conveniently described as alkyl derivatives of methane. In this system, for example, iso-butane would be named trimethylmethane.

CHAPTER VI

THE OLEFINES

TABLE X

Name		Formula	M.P.	B.P.
Ethylene		C_2H_4	$-169°$	$-104°$
Propylene		C_3H_6	$-185°$	$-48°$
Butylene :	1-butene	C_4H_8	$-130°$	$-5°$
	2-butene			$+1°$
	2-methyl-1-propene			$-6°$

ETHYLENE

The first member of the olefine series is ethylene, a colourless gas, sparingly soluble in water. It is chemically active, and undergoes many additive reactions which are described on p. 119. On account of its chemical reactivity ethylene is not found free in nature. It is, however, an important constituent of the gas liberated during the refining of petroleum, and it also occurs in small quantities in coal gas.

PRINCIPAL REACTIONS IN WHICH ETHYLENE IS PRODUCED

1. The dehydration of ethyl alcohol.

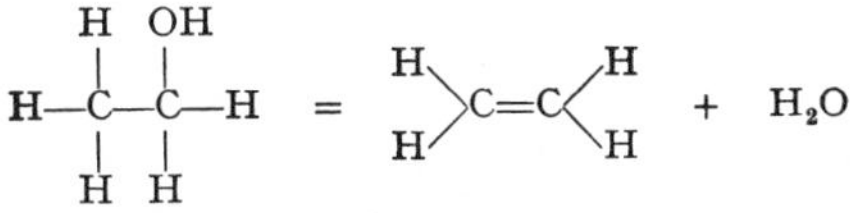

$$\begin{array}{c} H \ \ OH \\ | \ \ | \\ H-C-C-H \\ | \ \ | \\ H \ \ H \end{array} = \begin{array}{c} H \\ \diagdown \\ H \diagup \end{array} C=C \begin{array}{c} H \\ \diagdown \\ H \end{array} + H_2O$$

There are several methods by which this reaction can be brought about. In the laboratory it is convenient to heat a mixture of ethyl alcohol and excess concentrated sulphuric acid to 170°. The reaction takes place in two stages. In the first, ethyl hydrogen sulphate is formed,

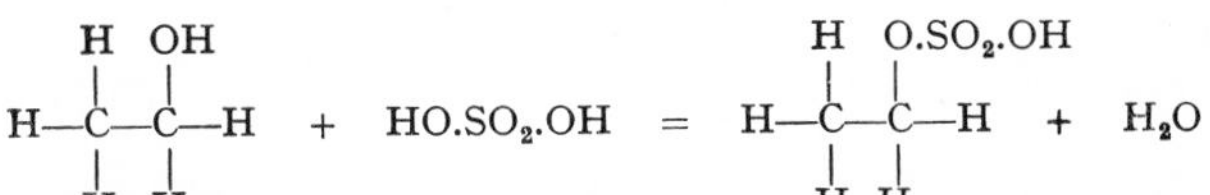

$$\begin{array}{c} H \ \ OH \\ | \ \ | \\ H-C-C-H \\ | \ \ | \\ H \ \ H \end{array} + HO.SO_2.OH = \begin{array}{c} H \ \ O.SO_2.OH \\ | \ \ | \\ H-C-C-H \\ | \ \ | \\ H \ \ H \end{array} + H_2O$$

In the second, the ethyl hydrogen sulphate decomposes, liberating ethylene and regenerating sulphuric acid,

$$\begin{array}{cc} H & O.SO_2.OH \\ | & | \\ H-C-C-H \\ | & | \\ H & H \end{array} \quad = \quad \begin{array}{c} H \\ \end{array}\hspace{-0.3em}C=C\hspace{-0.3em}\begin{array}{c} H \\ \end{array} \quad + \quad HO.SO_2.OH$$

The experimental details are described on p. 117. This method of obtaining ethylene has the disadvantages (a) that sulphuric acid is an oxidising agent, and its use, therefore, leads to a certain amount of charring, and to the liberation of some carbon dioxide and sulphur dioxide, and (b) that some of the ethyl alcohol is converted to ether by reaction with the ethyl hydrogen sulphate according to the equation,

$$\begin{array}{c} H \\ | \\ H-C-H \\ | \\ H-C-O.SO_2.OH \\ | \\ H \end{array} \quad + \quad \begin{array}{c} H \\ | \\ H-C-H \\ | \\ HO-C-H \\ | \\ H \end{array} \quad = \quad \begin{array}{cc} H & H \\ | & | \\ H-C-H & H-C-H \\ | & | \\ H-C-O-C-H \\ | & | \\ H & H \end{array} \quad + \quad HO.SO_2.OH$$

The production of sulphur dioxide may be avoided by using phosphoric acid instead of sulphuric acid ; the alcohol is dropped on to syrupy phosphoric acid heated to 220°. The yield is good, and the ethylene is pure except for the presence of ether vapour.

2. The electrolysis of potassium succinate solution. Kolbe's reaction. The solution of potassium succinate contains the ions

$$\begin{array}{c} CH_2.COO^{--} \\ | \\ CH_2.COO \end{array} \quad K^+ \quad H^+ \quad OH^-.$$

On electrolysis the succinate ions are discharged at the anode, and at once undergo decomposition, liberating ethylene and carbon dioxide,

$$\begin{array}{c} CH_2.COO \\ | \\ CH_2.COO \end{array} \quad = \quad \begin{array}{c} CH_2 \\ \| \\ CH_2 \end{array} \quad + \quad 2CO_2$$

At the cathode the H^+ ions are discharged, and hydrogen escapes as a gas. K^+ and OH^- ions remain in solution undischarged, and give a solution of potassium hydroxide, which may form potassium carbonate with some of the carbon dioxide set free at the anode. Before collection, the ethylene should be passed through potassium hydroxide solution to free it from carbon dioxide.

3. The thermal decomposition of paraffins. For example, one of the several ways in which propane decomposes at a red heat is in accordance with the equation :

$$CH_3.CH_2.CH_3 \quad = \quad CH_4 \quad + \quad CH_2:CH_2.$$

Laboratory preparation of ethylene. Ethylene is most conveniently prepared in the laboratory by the dehydration of ethyl alcohol with concentrated sulphuric acid.

40 c.c. of concentrated sulphuric acid are slowly added, with thorough mixing and cooling, to 20 c.c. of rectified spirit contained in a 200 c.c. flat-bottomed flask. 2–3 gms. of clean, dry sand are added to the contents of the flask to ensure the smooth evolution of the ethylene subsequently set free. The flat-bottomed flask is connected by a cork and glass delivery tube to a wash-bottle containing 10 per cent. aqueous sodium hydroxide solution to absorb the carbon dioxide and sulphur dioxide which are formed by the oxidation of the alcohol by the sulphuric acid. A second delivery tube leads from the wash-bottle to a beehive stand in a pneumatic trough filled with water, Fig. 42.

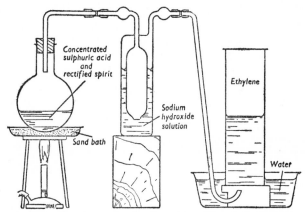

Concentrated
sulphuric acid
and
rectified spirit

Ethylene

Sodium
hydroxide
solution

Sand bath

Water

FIG. 42. Apparatus for the preparation of ethylene.

The flat-bottomed flask is heated over a sand-bath. The liquid in the flask becomes darker as the temperature rises, and ultimately ethylene is evolved with gentle effervescence. The gases from the delivery tube leading into the pneumatic trough should be allowed to escape into the air for several minutes, to allow all the air in the apparatus to be replaced by ethylene. To make certain that the ethylene evolved is practically free from air, a test-tube of the gas is collected by filling a tube with water and inverting it over the end of the delivery tube. When the test-tube is full of gas it is withdrawn from the trough, the end being closed with the finger, and the gas is exposed to the flame of a Bunsen burner at some distance from the apparatus. If the test-tube contains pure ethylene, the gas burns with a clear pale blue flame ; if the test-tube contains a mixture of ethylene and air, the gas explodes with a sharp report. When this test shows that pure ethylene is being evolved several gas-jars of the gas may be collected. At the conclusion of the experiment the delivery tubes should be disconnected *before* the flame is removed ; unless this precaution is observed the sodium hydroxide solution may " suck back " into the sulphuric acid.

Industrial preparation of ethylene. In this country ethylene is obtained on the industrial scale by the catalytic dehydration of ethyl alcohol, p. 494. In America it is obtained as a by-product in the cracking of petroleum, p. 472.

PROPERTIES, CONSTITUTION AND USES OF ETHYLENE

Properties. Ethylene is a colourless gas with a sweetish odour. It may be safely compressed, and it is stored and transported under pressure in steel cylinders. It is sparingly soluble in water (6 per cent. at $0°$), but it dissolves fairly readily in alcohol or ether. Ethylene burns in air or oxygen ; if it is burnt at a jet, in air the flame is luminous and smoky, and in oxygen bright and smokeless. Ethylene forms explosive mixtures with air or oxygen ; the products of the explosion depend on the proportions in which the reacting gases are mixed. Possible reactions are represented by the equations :

$$C_2H_4 \; + \; O_2 \; = \; 2CO \; + \; 2H_2,$$
$$\text{and} \; C_2H_4 \; + \; 3O_2 \; = \; 2CO_2 \; + \; 2H_2O.$$

Ethylene also burns in chlorine forming hydrogen chloride and liberating carbon,

$$C_2H_4 \; + \; 2Cl_2 \; = \; 4HCl \; + \; 2C.$$

In all the above reactions the molecule of ethylene is disrupted, momentarily setting free atoms of carbon which may combine with oxygen, and atoms of hydrogen which may combine with oxygen or chlorine.

The characteristic reactions of ethylene, however, are those in which the molecule enters into simple additive reactions with other substances. An **additive reaction** may be defined as *a reaction in which two substances combine together to form a single new compound without the liberation of any other substance.* For instance, if a mixture of ethylene and hydrogen is passed over platinum black at ordinary temperatures, or over reduced nickel at $140°$, ethane is formed,

$$C_2H_4 \; + \; H_2 \; = \; C_2H_6.$$

This reaction can be simply explained by assuming that one of the covalencies of the double bond in the ethylene molecule becomes disengaged, and one hydrogen atom from the hydrogen molecule satisfies each of the free covalencies,

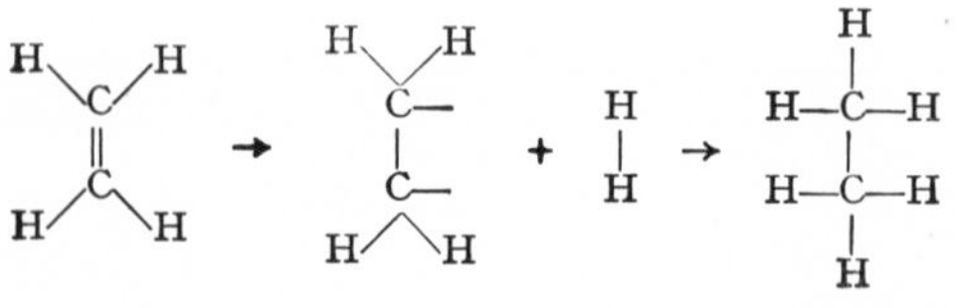

Organic compounds which contain in the molecule at least one carbon atom linked to another atom by a double or triple bond frequently take part in additive reactions. Compounds which possess this property are said to be *unsaturated*. Compounds, such as the paraffins, in which every carbon atom in the molecule is linked by single covalent bonds to four other atoms, do not undergo additive reactions and are said to be *saturated*.

Ethylene undergoes numerous additive reactions. A list of the more important is given below.

1. Addition of hydrogen, giving ethane. This reaction, which has already been mentioned, takes place when a mixture of ethylene and hydrogen is exposed to platinum black in the cold, or to reduced nickel at 140°.

2. Addition of the halogens, giving halogen derivatives of ethane. When mixed with chlorine at room temperature ethylene yields ethylene dichloride,

$$
\begin{array}{c}
\text{H} \qquad \text{H} \\
\ \ \ \diagdown \!\! \diagup \\
\ \ \ \ \text{C} \\
\ \ \ \ \| \qquad\qquad + \quad
\begin{array}{c}\text{Cl}\\|\\\text{Cl}\end{array} \quad = \quad
\begin{array}{c}
\text{H}\\|\\
\text{H---C---Cl}\\|\\
\text{H---C---Cl}\\|\\
\text{H}
\end{array}
\\
\ \ \ \ \text{C} \\
\ \ \diagup \ \diagdown \\
\text{H} \qquad \text{H}
\end{array}
$$

With bromine vapour ethylene reacts similarly to give ethylene dibromide. It has been shown that the reaction with bromine vapour will not take place in a vessel coated with paraffin wax; a polar* material, such as glass, must be present to catalyse it. Ethylene dibromide is usually obtained by passing ethylene through liquid bromine covered with a layer of water. Ethylene combines with iodine dissolved in alcohol to yield ethylene di-iodide.

3. Addition of halogen oxyacids giving halogenohydrins. Ethylene combines rapidly with bromine water in the cold, yielding ethylene bromohydrin. A bromine atom attacks one carbon atom at the double bond, and a hydroxyl group attacks the other, thus :

$$
\begin{array}{c}
\text{H} \qquad \text{H} \\
\ \ \ \diagdown \!\! \diagup \\
\ \ \ \ \text{C} \\
\ \ \ \ \| \qquad\qquad + \quad
\begin{array}{c}\text{O---H}\\\\\text{Br}\\|\\\text{Br}\end{array} \quad = \quad
\begin{array}{c}
\text{H}\\|\\
\text{H---C---OH}\\|\\
\text{H---C---Br}\\|\\
\text{H}
\end{array} \quad + \text{HBr}
\\
\ \ \ \ \text{C} \\
\ \ \diagup \ \diagdown \\
\text{H} \qquad \text{H}
\end{array}
$$

* For a discussion of the mechanism of this reaction, see p. 23.

An aqueous solution of hypochlorous acid converts ethylene to ethylene chlorohydrin,

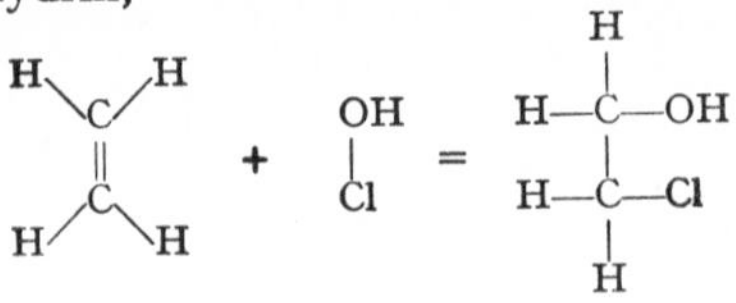

$$
\underset{H}{\overset{H}{\diagdown}}C\overset{H}{\diagup}\quad + \quad \overset{OH}{\underset{Cl}{|}} \quad = \quad
\begin{array}{c}
H \\
| \\
H-C-OH \\
| \\
H-C-Cl \\
| \\
H
\end{array}
$$

The chlorohydrin is more conveniently prepared, however, by passing a mixture of ethylene and carbon dioxide into a suspension of bleaching powder in water, when hypochlorous acid available for combining with the ethylene is liberated in the reaction,

$$Ca(ClO)_2, Ca(OH)_2, CaCl_2 \; + \; 2CO_2$$
$$= \; 2CaCO_3 \; + \; CaCl_2 \; + \; 2HClO.$$

4. Addition of the halogen hydracids, giving halogen derivatives of ethane. Hydrogen bromide and hydrogen iodide in concentrated aqueous solution at 100° combine with ethylene to yield respectively ethyl bromide and ethyl iodide,

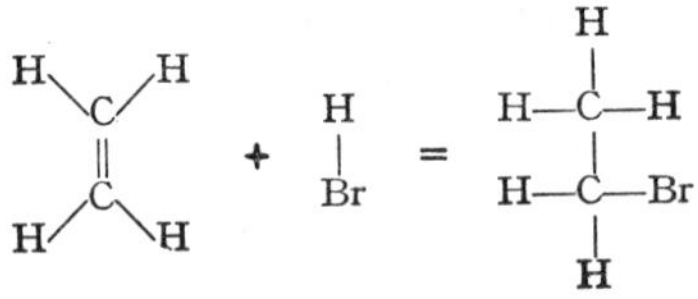

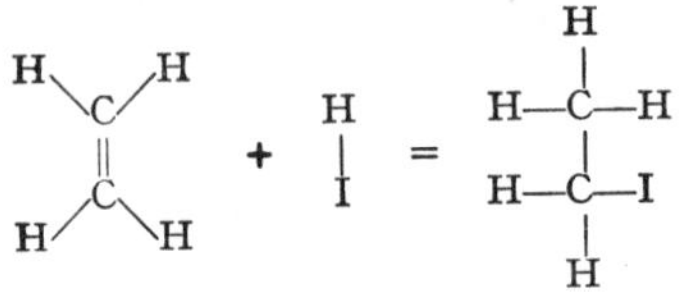

$$
\underset{H}{\overset{H}{\diagdown}}C\overset{H}{\diagup}\quad + \quad \overset{H}{\underset{Br}{|}} \quad = \quad
\begin{array}{c}
H \\
| \\
H-C-H \\
| \\
H-C-Br \\
| \\
H
\end{array}
$$

$$
\underset{H}{\overset{H}{\diagdown}}C\overset{H}{\diagup}\quad + \quad \overset{H}{\underset{I}{|}} \quad = \quad
\begin{array}{c}
H \\
| \\
H-C-H \\
| \\
H-C-I \\
| \\
H
\end{array}
$$

5. Addition of sulphuric acid, giving ethyl hydrogen sulphate. Anhydrosulphuric acid (sulphuric acid containing dissolved sulphur trioxide) rapidly absorbs ethylene, forming ethyl hydrogen sulphate,

$$
\underset{H}{\overset{H}{\diagdown}}C\overset{H}{\diagup}\quad + \quad \overset{H}{\underset{O-SO_2.OH}{|}} \quad = \quad
\begin{array}{c}
H \\
| \\
H-C-H \\
| \\
H-C-O-SO_2.OH \\
| \\
H
\end{array}
$$

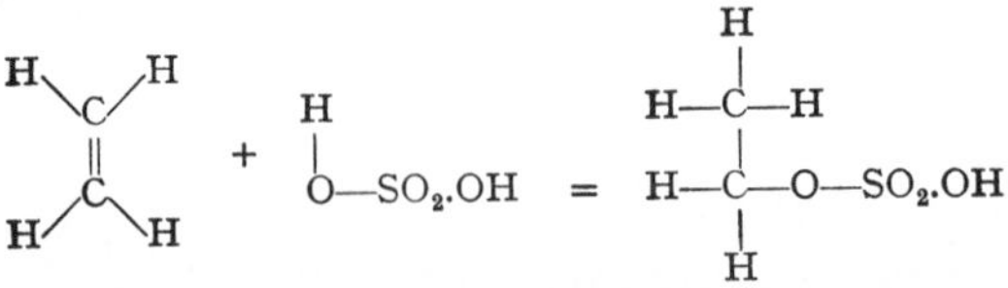

Ordinary concentrated sulphuric acid reacts similarly, but more slowly ; ethylene is scarcely absorbed by sulphuric acid of less than 95 per cent. concentration. This reaction is of great practical importance. Anhydrosulphuric acid is used as the absorbing agent for ethylene in the analysis of gaseous mixtures, and in the separation of ethylene from other gases produced in the cracking of petroleum. If the sulphuric acid containing ethyl hydrogen sulphate is heated, the above reaction is reversed and ethylene is set free ; if it is diluted with water and warmed, ethyl alcohol is liberated and may be obtained by distillation,

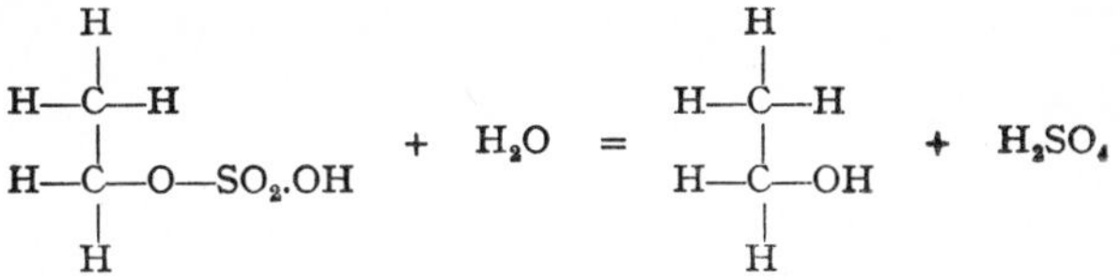

$$\begin{matrix} H \\ | \\ H-C-H \\ | \\ H-C-O-SO_2.OH \\ | \\ H \end{matrix} \;+\; H_2O \;=\; \begin{matrix} H \\ | \\ H-C-H \\ | \\ H-C-OH \\ | \\ H \end{matrix} \;+\; H_2SO_4$$

6. Oxidation. When ethylene is shaken with a 1 per cent. aqueous solution of potassium permanganate containing sodium carbonate, it is oxidised to glycol,

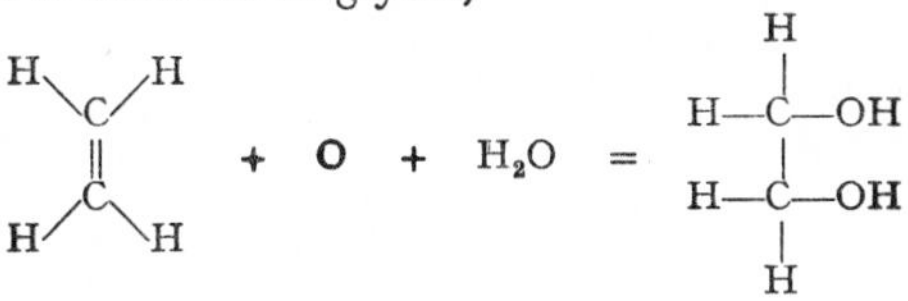

$$\begin{matrix} H \quad H \\ \diagdown C \diagup \\ || \\ \diagup C \diagdown \\ H \quad H \end{matrix} \;+\; O \;+\; H_2O \;=\; \begin{matrix} H \\ | \\ H-C-OH \\ | \\ H-C-OH \\ | \\ H \end{matrix}$$

The potassium permanganate is reduced, first to a green solution of potassium manganate, and then to a brown precipitate of manganese dioxide, leaving a colourless solution. A dilute solution of potassium permanganate in the presence of acid also oxidises ethylene to glycol. A concentrated solution of potassium permanganate oxidises ethylene to carbon dioxide and water.

7. Addition of ozone, giving ethylene ozonide.

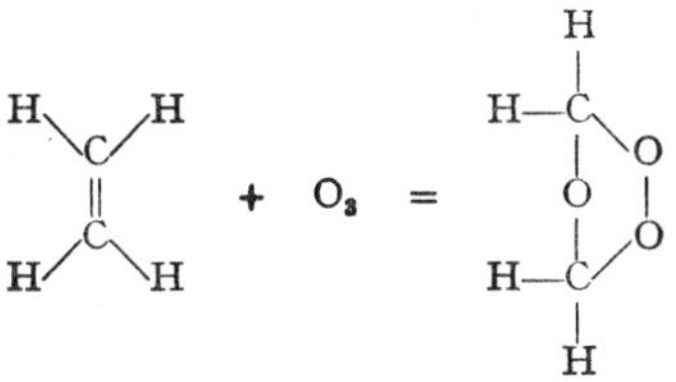

$$\begin{matrix} H \quad H \\ \diagdown C \diagup \\ || \\ \diagup C \diagdown \\ H \quad H \end{matrix} \;+\; O_3 \;=\; \begin{matrix} H \\ | \\ H-C \diagdown \\ \quad | \quad O \\ O \; | \\ \quad | \diagup O \\ H-C \diagup \\ | \\ H \end{matrix}$$

Ethylene ozonide is unstable, and breaks down if gently warmed with water or dilute acids, to formic acid and formaldehyde,

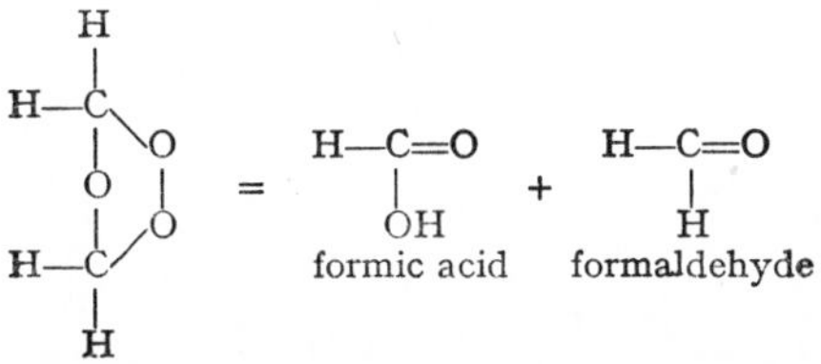

$$\begin{matrix} H \\ | \\ H-C \diagdown \\ \quad | \quad O \\ O \; | \\ \quad | \diagup O \\ H-C \diagup \\ | \\ H \end{matrix} \;=\; \begin{matrix} H-C=O \\ | \\ OH \\ \text{formic acid} \end{matrix} \;+\; \begin{matrix} H-C=O \\ | \\ H \\ \text{formaldehyde} \end{matrix}$$

8. Addition of sulphur monochloride. Sulphur monochloride, S_2Cl_2, reacts with ethylene to give mustard gas,

$$
\underset{H}{\overset{H}{>}}C\!=\!\underset{H}{\overset{H}{<}}C \;+\; \underset{Cl\;Cl}{\overset{S\!-\!S}{\mid\;\mid}} \;+\; \underset{H}{\overset{H}{>}}C\!=\!\underset{H}{\overset{H}{<}}C \;=\;
\begin{array}{c}
HH \\
\mid\mid \\
H\!-\!C\!-\!-\!-\!S\!-\!-\!-\!C\!-\!H \\
\mid\mid \\
H\!-\!C\!-\!Cl\quad Cl\!-\!C\!-\!H \\
\mid\mid \\
HH
\end{array}
\;+\; S
$$

Sulphur dichloride, SCl_2, reacts similarly except that there is no separation of sulphur.

Structure of ethylene. The molecular formula of ethylene is shown to be C_2H_4 by eudiometric analysis. The tetracovalency of the carbon atoms in a molecule of this formula can be satisfied, however, only if they are linked by a double bond, thus,

$$
\underset{H}{\overset{H}{>}}C\!=\!C\underset{H}{\overset{H}{<}}
$$

Each covalent link of the double bond corresponds to a pair of electrons held in common by each of the two carbon atoms. Strong evidence for the existence of the double bond in the molecule of ethylene is furnished by its numerous additive reactions. Arguments based on the phenomenon of geometrical isomerism, which is described on p. 314, prove that the two carbon atoms and the four hydrogen atoms of the ethylene molecule all lie in one and the same plane.

Uses of ethylene. Ethylene was once used as an anaesthetic; its use for this purpose has been discarded in Great Britain because of its inflammability and unpleasant after-effects. It is used for ripening green fruit. It is the starting point for the manufacture of mustard gas, ethylene glycol, ethylene chlorohydrin leading to the local anaesthetic novocain, ethylene dichloride, ethylene diamine, and ethylene oxide leading to glycol monoethyl ether. In America, where there are plentiful supplies of ethylene in the refinery gases of the petroleum industry, it is used for making ethyl alcohol.

Tests for ethylene. If ethylene is brought into contact with a 1 per cent. solution of potassium permanganate made alkaline with sodium carbonate, the purple permanganate solution is first changed to a green solution of potassium manganate, which is then reduced to a brown precipitate of manganese dioxide. This test does not distinguish ethylene from acetylene which reacts similarly with potassium permanganate solution.

If ethylene is shaken with bromine water the brown solution rapidly becomes colourless as the bromine is absorbed by the ethylene to form ethylene bromohydrin. Bromine is also absorbed from bromine water by acetylene, but comparatively slowly. Ethylene is without action on an ammoniacal solution of cuprous chloride, and is thus readily distinguished from acetylene, p. 134.

THE HIGHER OLEFINES

Preparation. The higher olefines may be generally prepared by the dehydration of the appropriate alcohols, or by the elimination of the elements of hydrogen bromide from alkyl bromides by the action of alcoholic potassium hydroxide solution, see page 148.

CHEMICAL REACTIONS OF THE HIGHER OLEFINES

1. Additive reactions. The olefines combine additively with hydrogen in the presence of nickel, with chlorine and bromine, with hydrogen iodide, hydrogen bromide and less readily with hydrogen chloride, with hypochlorous acid and hypobromous acid, and with sulphuric acid. Sulphuric acid absorbs butylene and propylene more readily than ethylene ; the constituents of a mixture of these gases may be separated by exposing it successively to solutions of sulphuric acid of increasing concentration.

The additive reactions of the olefines take place by the saturation of the double linkage, for example propylene reacts with bromine thus,

$$
\begin{array}{c}
\text{H} \quad \text{H} \\
| \quad | \quad \text{H} \\
\text{H—C—C=C} \\
| \qquad \text{H} \\
\text{H}
\end{array}
\;+\;
\begin{array}{c}
\text{Br} \\
| \\
\text{Br}
\end{array}
\;=\;
\begin{array}{c}
\text{H} \quad \text{H} \quad \text{H} \\
| \quad | \quad | \\
\text{H—C—C—C—H} \\
| \quad | \quad | \\
\text{H} \quad \text{Br} \quad \text{Br}
\end{array}
$$

It might be expected that an olefine molecule which is not symmetrical about the double bond would react with a molecule consisting of two different atoms or groups to yield two products with different constitutions. For example, propylene might react with hydrobromic acid to yield a mixture of normal propyl bromide and iso-propyl bromide,

$$
\begin{array}{c}
\text{H} \quad \text{H} \quad \text{Br} \\
| \quad | \quad | \\
\text{H—C—C—C—H} \\
| \quad | \quad | \\
\text{H} \quad \text{H} \quad \text{H}
\end{array}
\qquad\qquad
\begin{array}{c}
\text{H} \quad \text{Br} \quad \text{H} \\
| \quad | \quad | \\
\text{H—C—C—C—H} \\
| \quad | \quad | \\
\text{H} \quad \text{H} \quad \text{H}
\end{array}
$$

normal propyl bromide   iso-propyl bromide

It is found, however, that an olefine combines with a hydrogen halide, or hypochlorous acid, or sulphuric acid, in such a way that the carbon atom linked to the smallest number of hydrogen atoms becomes attached to the halogen atom of the hydrogen halide, the OH group of the hypochlorous acid, or the $O.SO_2.OH$ group of the sulphuric acid. In accordance with this generalisation, which is known as

Markownikoff's rule*, iso-propyl bromide is produced when propylene reacts with hydrogen bromide.

2. Reaction with ozone. Olefines combine with ozone to form ozonides. The reaction is carried out by passing ozonised oxygen through the cooled solution of the olefine in an inert solvent such as chloroform. It takes place in two stages ; in the first stage an unstable form of ozonide is produced, I, which changes into a more stable form, II.

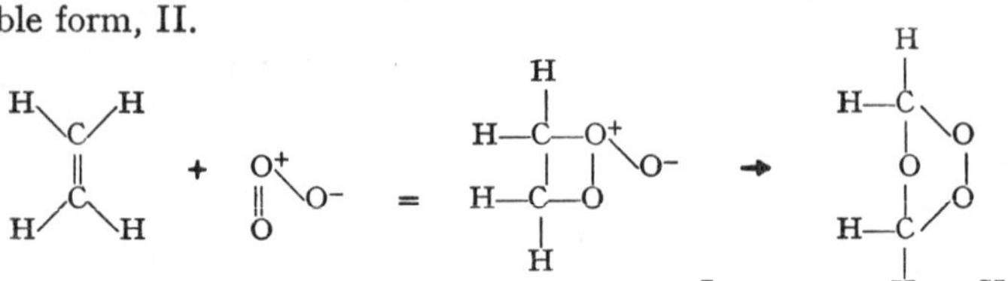

I   II

Most ozonides are highly explosive. A molecule of an ozonide is decomposed by water in such a way that it is broken apart at the position of the double bond in the original olefine. Propylene ozonide yields a mixture of formaldehyde and acetic acid,

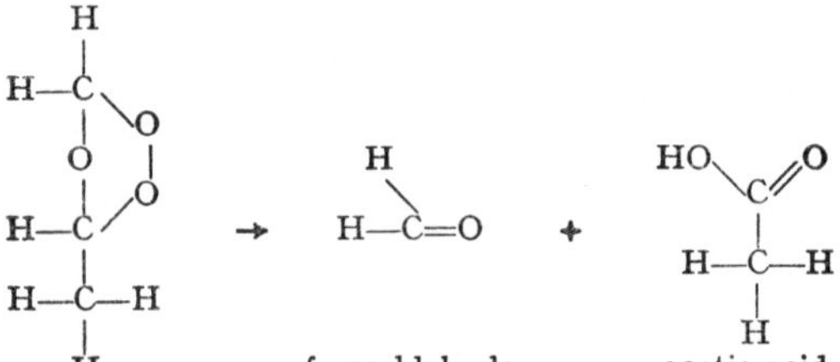

formaldehyde   acetic acid

The breaking down of an olefine into two simple substances in this manner is known as *ozonolysis*. Ozonolysis may be carried out in one stage by passing ozonised oxygen through the olefine in aqueous or acetic acid solution ; there is no need to isolate the unstable ozonide. The position of the double bond in the original olefine is easily determined by identifying the products of ozonolysis, and the lengths of the carbon chains on each side of the double bond are thus revealed.

3. Oxidation. The higher olefines are attacked by cold solutions of potassium permanganate or of chromic acid, but not by cold nitric acid. A dilute solution of potassium permanganate causes the double bond to be saturated by the addition of two hydroxyl groups,

---

* The course of an additive reaction is determined by the polarity (p. 23), of the doubly-linked carbon atoms in the unsaturated molecule, which in turn is decided by the presence and position of certain atoms or groups which influence this polarity. Markownikoff's rule applies only to the olefenic hydrocarbons ; numerous exceptions will be found if attempts are made to apply it to more complex unsaturated compounds.

$$H-\overset{\overset{\displaystyle H}{|}}{\underset{\underset{\displaystyle H}{|}}{C}}-C=C\overset{\diagup H}{\diagdown H} \;+\; O \;+\; H_2O \;=\; H-\overset{\overset{\displaystyle H}{|}}{\underset{\underset{\displaystyle H}{|}}{C}}-\overset{\overset{\displaystyle H}{|}}{\underset{\underset{\displaystyle OH}{|}}{C}}-\overset{\overset{\displaystyle H}{|}}{\underset{\underset{\displaystyle OH}{|}}{C}}-H$$

but more concentrated solutions rupture the molecule at the double bond and produce a mixture of acids or ketones. Normal butylene, for example, yields a mixture of propionic acid and formic acid,

$$CH_3.CH_2.CH : CH_2 \;+\; 4O \;=\; CH_3.CH_2COOH \;+\; H.COOH.$$

If mixed with air and passed over a silver catalyst at 400°, ethylene gives ethylene oxide, p. 324.

4. Polymerisation. The olefines readily polymerise in the presence of either sulphuric acid or zinc chloride, or when heated under pressure to about 500°. Use is made of the third method for making motor spirit from cracked petroleum (p. 472). A typical reaction is the union of two molecules of iso-butylene to produce a polymer which is an intermediate in the manufacture of octane,

$$2\;\; \overset{H_3C}{\underset{H_3C}{\diagup}}\!\!\diagdown C=CH_2 \;=\; H_3C-\overset{\overset{\displaystyle H_3C}{|}}{\underset{\underset{\displaystyle CH_3}{|}}{C}}-\overset{\overset{\displaystyle H}{|}}{\underset{\underset{\displaystyle H}{|}}{C}}-C\overset{\diagup CH_3}{\diagdown CH_2}$$

| Iso-butylene | 2:2:4-trimethyl-4-pentene |

CONJUGATED SYSTEMS

There are classes of hydrocarbons containing more than one double bond in the molecule. If the double bonds are separated from one another by more than one single link, as in 1:4-pentadiene,

$$\overset{H}{\underset{H}{\diagup}}\!\!\diagdown C=\overset{\overset{\displaystyle H}{|}}{C}-\overset{\overset{\displaystyle H}{|}}{\underset{\underset{\displaystyle H}{|}}{C}}-\overset{\overset{\displaystyle H}{|}}{C}=C\overset{\diagup H}{\diagdown H}$$

the properties of the molecule are in agreement with the assumptions that the double bonds are independent, and that each possesses complete ethylenic properties. If, however, the molecule of a hydrocarbon contains a chain of atoms linked by alternate double and single bonds, the properties of the double bonds are modified. A chain of atoms linked by alternate double and single bonds is known as a *conjugated system*. The simplest compound with a conjugated structure is butadiene,

$$\overset{H}{\underset{H}{\diagup}}\!\!\diagdown C=\overset{\overset{\displaystyle H}{|}}{C}-\overset{\overset{\displaystyle H}{|}}{C}=C\overset{\diagup H}{\diagdown H}$$

The most noteworthy chemical property of a conjugated system is its tendency to undergo additive reactions leading to the formation of terminal * additive compounds. If butadiene, for example, is dissolved in an inert solvent and allowed to react with just sufficient bromine to form a dibromo derivative, the product contains 80 per cent. of the terminal additive compound

$$\begin{array}{ccccc} & Br & H & H & Br \\ & | & | & | & | \\ H-C&-C&=C&-C&-H \quad\quad I \\ & | & & & | \\ & H & & & H \end{array}$$

and 20 per cent. of the vicinal * additive compound

$$\begin{array}{cccc} & Br & Br & H \\ & | & | & | \quad\quad H \\ H-C&-C&-C&=C{<}_{H} \quad\quad II \\ & | & | & \\ & H & H & \end{array}$$

It should be noted that the vicinal compound, II, is the result of a simple saturation of one of the double bonds ; the other double bond remains in its original position unaffected. In the terminal additive compound, I, however, both double bonds have been attacked, and the addition of bromine atoms to the end carbon atoms has resulted in the replacement of the central single bond by a double bond.

Three important abnormalities in constitutional properties are found in conjugated systems :

(i) the bond length of the double bond is longer than the normal double bond length which is $1\cdot33$ Å ;

(ii) the bond length of the single bond is shorter than the normal single bond length which is $1\cdot5$ Å ;

(iii) the heat of combustion of a conjugated compound, and its heat of hydrogenation per hydrogen molecule added, are lower than the corresponding constants of its non-conjugated isomer ; the conjugated system, therefore, is more stable than the isomeric non-conjugated system.

NOMENCLATURE OF THE OLEFINES

The systematic name applied to a member of the olefine series is derived by replacing by " ene " the termination " ane " in the name of the member of the paraffin series with the same number of carbon atoms in the molecule. The older names ethylene, propylene and

* The expression *terminal additive compound* is used to describe a compound formed by the addition of atoms or groups to the carbon atoms forming the opposite ends of a carbon chain. The expression *vicinal additive compound* is used to describe a compound formed by the addition of atoms or groups to two adjacent carbon atoms previously linked together by a double covalent bond.

butylene are commonly employed, however, for the simpler members of the series. The system is exemplified by the following table.

TABLE XI

Paraffin	Formula	Systematic name of corresponding olefine	Formula	Older name
Ethane	C_2H_6	ethene	C_2H_4	ethylene*
Propane	C_3H_8	propene	C_3H_6	propylene
Butane	C_4H_{10}	butene	C_4H_8	butylene

The position of the double bond in the molecule is indicated by numbering the carbon atoms in the chain, and specifying the number of one of the carbon atoms which are linked by the double bond, thus

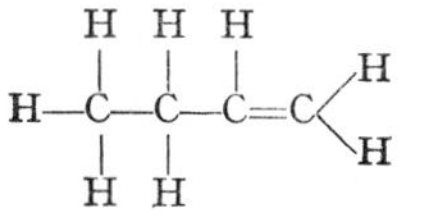

1-butene 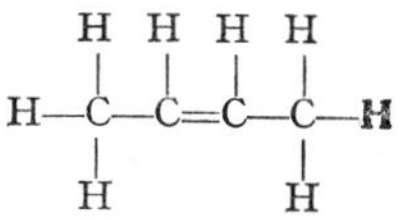   2-butene

Some authors use a variant of this system, in which a capital delta is used to denote the double bond, of which the position is indicated by a numerical suffix. In this scheme 1-butene would be written as Δ^1-butene.

If the molecule contains a branched chain, the branching is indicated by the method used in naming the paraffins, thus

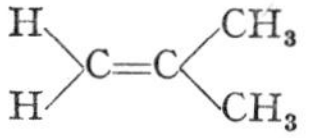

2-methyl-2-propene, or, 2-methyl-Δ^2-propene

* *Methylene* is the name given to the group $=CH_2$, theoretically derived by the removal of two atoms of hydrogen from the molecule of methane. The group is frequently met with in the structure of organic molecules (all normal paraffin chains longer than that of ethane contain one or more methylene groups), but it has no free existence.

CHAPTER VII

ACETYLENE

Acetylene, C_2H_2, is a colourless gas, slightly soluble in water and alcohol, and chemically reactive. It is formed during the incomplete combustion of such substances as methane, ethyl alcohol and coal-gas.

PRINCIPAL REACTIONS IN WHICH ACETYLENE IS PRODUCED

1. The action of a boiling alcoholic solution of potassium hydroxide on ethylene dibromide. Ethylene dibromide, a liquid B.P. 131°, is allowed to drop slowly into a boiling alcoholic solution of potassium hydroxide. The potassium hydroxide reacts with the ethylene dibromide to form potassium bromide, water and acetylene,

$$CH_2Br.CH_2Br + 2KOH = 2KBr + 2H_2O + C_2H_2.$$

This reaction can be regarded as the elimination of two molecules of hydrogen bromide from one molecule of ethylene dibromide,

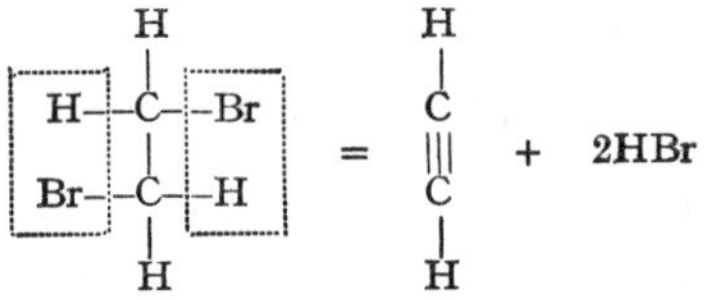

Experimental details of a method of preparing acetylene based on this reaction are given on p. 130.

Ethylidene dibromide, $CH_3.CHBr_2$, also yields acetylene when treated with potassium hydroxide under the above conditions.

2. The action of a boiling alcoholic solution of potassium hydroxide on monochloroethylene (vinyl chloride). Acetylene is liberated when monochloroethylene, a gas B.P. $-18°$, is passed into a boiling alcoholic solution of potassium hydroxide. The products of the reaction are acetylene, potassium chloride and water. The reaction may be represented as the elimination of one molecule of hydrogen chloride from a molecule of monochloroethylene,

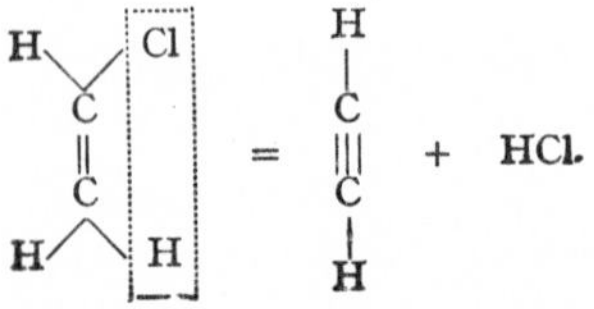

3. The action of potassium cyanide on cuprous acetylide or on silver acetylide. Pure acetylene is evolved when cuprous acetylide is dissolved in a warm aqueous solution of potassium cyanide,

$$Cu_2C_2 + 8KCN + 2H_2O$$
$$= C_2H_2 + 2K_3[Cu(CN)_4] + 2KOH.$$

The other products of the reaction are potassium cupro-cyanide and potassium hydroxide. A parallel reaction occurs when silver acetylide is dissolved in potassium cyanide solution,

$$Ag_2C_2 + 8KCN + 2H_2O$$
$$= C_2H_2 + 2K_3[Ag(CN)_4] + 2KOH.$$

4. The action of cold water on calcium carbide. Acetylene and calcium hydroxide are formed when cold water is brought into contact with calcium carbide,

$$CaC_2 + 2H_2O = C_2H_2 + Ca(OH)_2.$$

Acetylene thus prepared is contaminated with hydrogen sulphide, formed by the action of water on calcium sulphide present as an impurity in the calcium carbide. If the impure acetylene is passed through a 10 per cent. solution of cupric sulphate, the hydrogen sulphide is removed by conversion into insoluble cupric sulphide.

5. The electrolysis of a solution of potassium fumarate,

$$\begin{array}{l} CH.COOK \\ \| \\ CH.COOK \end{array}$$

The solution contains the ions

$$K^+, OH^-, H^+, \begin{array}{l} CH.COO^{--} \\ \| \\ CH.COO \end{array}$$

During electrolysis the

$$\begin{array}{l} CH.COO^{--} \\ \| \\ CH.COO \end{array}$$

ions are discharged at the anode and undergo decomposition to acetylene and carbon dioxide, thus

$$\begin{array}{l} CH.COO \\ \| \\ CH.COO \end{array} = \begin{array}{l} CH \\ \||| \\ CH \end{array} + 2CO_2.$$

The acetylene is liberated as a gas. The H^+ ions are discharged at the cathode, and the hydrogen escapes as a gas. K^+ and OH^- ions are not discharged ; they remain in solution as potassium hydroxide

E

which may dissolve some of the carbon dioxide set free at the anode. The acetylene is passed through a solution of potassium hydroxide to remove the remainder of the carbon dioxide, and collected over water.

6. The striking of an electric arc between carbon poles in an atmosphere of hydrogen. In these conditions an equilibrium is set up between hydrogen, carbon, methane and acetylene.

Laboratory preparation of acetylene. Acetylene for use in the laboratory is usually obtained from a cylinder in which it is stored in solution in acetone absorbed on a porous material such as kieselguhr * under a pressure of about 10 atmospheres. The acetylene so obtained is pure after it has been freed from acetone vapour by passage through water.

Acetylene is very conveniently prepared by allowing water to drop slowly on to small lumps of calcium carbide. This method is used in the acetylene generators attached to cycle lamps and hand lamps. Acetylene so prepared, however, is impure.

A pure gas is obtained by the action of alcoholic potassium hydroxide solution on ethylene dibromide. A 300 c.c. bolt-head flask is fitted with a double surface reflux water condenser, and a dropping funnel as shown in Fig. 41, p. 109. A delivery-tube leads from the top of the condenser to pneumatic trough. 100 c.c. of methylated spirit and 25 gms. of powdered potassium hydroxide are placed in the bolt-head flask, and the mixture is heated on a water-bath, under the reflux condenser, until the potassium hydroxide is almost completely dissolved. 15 c.c. of ethylene dibromide are added from the dropping funnel, drop by drop, to the boiling solution in the flask. Acetylene is evolved as a gas and potassium bromide is precipitated. As soon as the escaping acetylene is shown to be free from admixed air by the test described under the laboratory preparation of ethylene (p. 117), it is collected in gas-jars.

Industrial preparation of acetylene. Acetylene is prepared industrially by the action of water on calcium carbide, or by exposing to an electric arc any mixture of hydrocarbon gases obtained in industry, such as refinery gases, coke oven gas or natural gas.

PROPERTIES, CONSTITUTION AND USES OF ACETYLENE

Properties. Acetylene is a gas which liquefies at 1° under a pressure of 48 atmospheres, and condenses to a white solid which sublimes at $-83.6°$. Unless special precautions are taken the compression of acetylene is dangerous, as acetylene is liable to decompose into its elements explosively if compressed to more than 2 atmo-

* Kieselguhr is the name given to naturally occurring deposits of silica in a highly porous condition. These deposits have been formed from the siliceous coverings of marine and fresh-water algae known as diatoms.

spheres. In Germany during the war, however, acetylene diluted with
nitrogen and contained in vessels packed with tubes or rings, so that
there were no large empty spaces, was used as a chemical reagent
at pressures up to 20 atmospheres and temperatures up to 200°.
The instability of acetylene is related to its heat of formation,
– 54·2 Cal., which shows that it is a highly endothermic compound.
Acetylene can be detonated with silver fulminate under atmospheric
pressure.

Acetylene is colourless when pure. It has an ethereal odour, but
as prepared from calcium carbide, it is usually contaminated with
derivatives of sulphur and phosphorus which give it a characteristic
and disagreeable odour. Acetylene is soluble in its own volume of
water, and in six times its own volume of alcohol ; it is more soluble
in acetone. Its absorption coefficient at room temperature and at
atmospheric pressure in water is 1·0, in alcohol is 0·167, and in
acetone is 24. Its absorption coefficient in acetone under 12 atmospheres pressure is 300.

Acetylene is an unsaturated compound. The reagents which
combine additively with ethylene also combine with acetylene,
usually with greater vigour. Acetylene also combines additively
with antimony pentachloride, and with mercuric chloride or mercuric
nitrate in concentrated aqueous solutions. These reactions have no
counterpart in the chemistry of ethylene. Acetylene reacts with
heated sodium or potassium to yield C_2HNa and C_2Na_2, or the corresponding potassium compounds; ethylene does not undergo any
substitution reactions. The principal chemical reactions of acetylene
are described in greater detail below.

1. Combustion. Acetylene issuing from a jet burns in air with
a very smoky flame, but if a special burner is used, designed to secure
the correct mixture of acetylene and air, the flame is free from smoke
and is highly luminous. A mixture of acetylene and oxygen burns
with an intensely hot flame,

$$C_2H_2 \ + \ 2\tfrac{1}{2}O_2 \ = \ 2CO_2 \ + \ H_2O \ + \ 310,435 \text{ calories.}$$

The temperature of the oxy-acetylene flame is so high that it is used
for welding steel. If a separate jet of oxygen is directed on to a steel
plate at the point where it is heated by the oxy-acetylene flame, the
iron is oxidised, and the oxide produced fuses, and is blown away by
the flame. The plate is thus pierced and appears to have been cut.
Acetylene forms a wide range of explosive mixtures with air or
oxygen. The mixtures explode with such extreme violence that it is
unsafe to explode them in an open gas-jar.

←2. Oxidation. Acetylene is oxidised to oxalic acid by a dilute alkaline solution of potassium permanganate,

$$
\begin{array}{c}
\text{H} \\
| \\
\text{C} \\
||| \\
\text{C} \\
| \\
\text{H}
\end{array}
\quad + \quad 4\text{O} \quad = \quad
\begin{array}{l}
\text{O}{=}\text{C}{-}\text{OH} \\
\qquad | \\
\text{O}{=}\text{C}{-}\text{OH.}
\end{array}
$$

A solution of chromic acid oxidises acetylene to acetic acid.

3. Addition of hydrogen, giving ethylene and ethane. Acetylene combines with hydrogen at ordinary temperatures in the presence of platinum black, or at 70–140° in the presence of reduced nickel, to give first ethylene, and then ethane,

$$
\begin{array}{c}
\text{H} \\ | \\ \text{C} \\ ||| \\ \text{C} \\ | \\ \text{H}
\end{array}
+
\begin{array}{c}
\text{H} \\ | \\ \text{H}
\end{array}
=
\begin{array}{c}
\text{H}\diagdown\ \diagup\text{H} \\ \text{C} \\ || \\ \text{C} \\ \text{H}\diagup\ \diagdown\text{H}
\end{array}
,
\begin{array}{c}
\text{H}\diagdown\ \diagup\text{H} \\ \text{C} \\ || \\ \text{C} \\ \text{H}\diagup\ \diagdown\text{H}
\end{array}
+
\begin{array}{c}
\text{H} \\ | \\ \text{H}
\end{array}
=
\begin{array}{c}
\text{H} \\ | \\ \text{H}{-}\text{C}{-}\text{H} \\ | \\ \text{H}{-}\text{C}{-}\text{H} \\ | \\ \text{H}
\end{array}
$$

4. Addition of halogens, giving halogen derivatives of ethylene and ethane. Acetylene reacts explosively with gaseous chlorine, and with chlorine water, to yield hydrogen chloride and carbon,

$$\text{C}_2\text{H}_2 \ + \ \text{Cl}_2 \ = \ 2\text{HCl} \ + \ 2\text{C}.$$

Acetylene can be made to combine smoothly with chlorine by absorbing it in sufficient antimony pentachloride to form the additive compound $\text{SbCl}_5.\text{C}_2\text{H}_2$. On distillation this compound decomposes into antimony trichloride, and a mixture of the two isomeric forms of dichloroethylene

$$
\text{SbCl}_5.\text{C}_2\text{H}_2 \ = \ \text{SbCl}_3 \ + \quad
\begin{array}{c}
\text{H}\diagdown\ \diagup\text{Cl} \\ \text{C} \\ || \\ \text{C} \\ \text{H}\diagup\ \diagdown\text{Cl}
\end{array}
\quad \text{and} \quad
\begin{array}{c}
\text{H}\diagdown\ \diagup\text{Cl} \\ \text{C} \\ || \\ \text{C} \\ \text{Cl}\diagup\ \diagdown\text{H}
\end{array} .
$$

If the same process is carried out using excess of antimony pentachloride, tetrachloroethane, or "Westron" (p. 491) $\text{C}_2\text{H}_2\text{Cl}_4$, is formed.

Acetylene and bromine water combine only very slowly ; this is in marked contrast with the explosive reaction between acetylene and chlorine water, and with the rapid reaction between bromine water and ethylene.

5. Addition of halogen hydracids, giving halogen derivatives of ethylene and ethane. Acetylene combines with hydrogen chloride to yield first chloroethylene, and then ethylidene dichloride.

$$
\begin{array}{c}
H \\
| \\
C \\
||| \\
C \\
| \\
H
\end{array}
+
\begin{array}{c}
H \\
| \\
Cl
\end{array}
=
\begin{array}{c}
H\diagdown\;\diagup H \\
C \\
|| \\
C \\
H\diagup\;\diagdown Cl
\end{array}
,
\qquad
\begin{array}{c}
H\diagdown\;\diagup H \\
C \\
|| \\
C \\
H\diagup\;\diagdown Cl
\end{array}
+
\begin{array}{c}
H \\
| \\
Cl
\end{array}
=
\begin{array}{c}
H \\
| \\
H-C-H \\
| \\
H-C-Cl \\
| \\
Cl
\end{array}
$$

Hydrogen bromide reacts similarly.

6. Reaction with sulphuric acid, giving acetaldehyde. Concentrated sulphuric acid absorbs acetylene according to the equation,

$$
\begin{array}{c}
H \\
| \\
C \\
||| \\
C \\
| \\
H
\end{array}
+
2
\begin{array}{c}
H \\
| \\
O.SO_2.OH
\end{array}
=
\begin{array}{c}
H \\
| \\
H-C-H \\
| \\
H-C-O.SO_2.OH \\
| \\
O.SO_2.OH
\end{array}
$$

If the resulting solution is diluted and distilled, acetaldehyde is produced,

$$
\begin{array}{c}
CH_3 \\
| \\
H-C-O.SO_2.OH \\
| \\
O.SO_2.OH
\end{array}
+
H_2O
=
\begin{array}{c}
CH_3 \\
| \\
C \\
H\diagup\;\diagdown O
\end{array}
+
2H_2SO_4.
$$

The reactions occurring during the absorption of acetylene in sulphuric acid and the subsequent dilution and distillation of the products, may be summarised as the addition of the elements of a molecule of water to a molecule of acetylene,

$$
\begin{array}{c}
H \\
| \\
C \\
||| \\
C \\
| \\
H
\end{array}
+
H_2O
=
\begin{array}{c}
H \\
| \\
H-C-H \\
| \\
C \\
H\diagup\;\diagdown O
\end{array}
$$

Such an addition may also be brought about, either directly by heating acetylene and water to 325°, or indirectly by treating with a dilute mineral acid the precipitate formed by shaking acetylene with a concentrated solution of mercuric chloride or nitrate. Acetaldehyde is made commercially by passing acetylene into warm dilute sulphuric acid to which small quantities of mercuric sulphate and ferric sulphate have been added, p. 490.

7. Reaction with ozone. Acetylene combines with ozone to form an ozonide.

8. Polymerisation, giving benzene. When heated to about 400° at atmospheric pressure acetylene polymerises to benzene and various other aromatic hydrocarbons such as toluene, diphenyl, and naphthalene.

9. Substitution reactions, giving metallic acetylides. The hydrogen atoms in acetylene are capable of being replaced by atoms of metals. Sodium and potassium derivatives of the types C_2HNa and C_2Na_2, are formed when acetylene is passed over heated potassium or sodium, and copper acetylide, C_2Cu_2, and silver acetylide Ag_2C_2, separate as precipitates when acetylene is passed into ammoniacal solutions of cuprous chloride or silver nitrate respectively. Cuprous acetylide is a brownish-red solid substance, and silver acetylide is colourless ; both are amorphous. If dry they detonate when struck, or when heated to a little above 100°. They dissolve in hydrochloric acid, or in warm potassium cyanide solution to give acetylene,

$$C_2Ag_2 \;+\; 2HCl \;=\; H.C{\equiv}C.H \;+\; 2AgCl,$$
$$C_2Ag_2 \;+\; 8KCN \;+\; 2H_2O$$
$$=\; H.C{\equiv}C.H \;+\; 2K_3[Ag(CN)_4] \;+\; 2KOH.$$

The product formed by the action of hydrochloric acid is liable to be contaminated with vinyl chloride ; a pure specimen of acetylene may be obtained by the use of potassium cyanide. Mercurous and mercuric acetylides are also known.

Constitution of acetylene. The molecular formula of acetylene is shown to be C_2H_2 by eudiometric analysis. The tetracovalency of the carbon atoms in the molecule can be satisfied only if they are linked by a triple bond, thus,

$$H-C{\equiv}C-H.$$

Each covalent link of the triple bond corresponds to a pair of electrons held in common by the two carbon atoms. The chemical reactions of acetylene are clearly in accordance with this highly unsaturated structure.

Uses of acetylene

Acetylene is used as an illuminant, in the oxy-acetylene flame for welding and " cutting " steel, and as the starting point for the manufacture of acetaldehyde, and of chlorine derivatives of ethane.

Test for acetylene. A very small quantity of acetylene in a gas can be detected by passing the gas through an ammoniacal solution of cuprous chloride. If acetylene is present, a red precipitate of cuprous acetylide is formed. The ammoniacal solution of cuprous chloride is prepared by adding dilute ammonia solution to copper sulphate solution until the bluish-white precipitate formed just dissolves to give a deep-blue solution. Hydroxylamine hydrochloride solution is then added drop by drop to reduce the cupric ions to cuprous ions. The reduction is complete when the solution is colourless.

CHAPTER VIII

HALOGEN DERIVATIVES OF THE ALIPHATIC HYDROCARBONS

TABLE XII

Name	Formula	M.P.	B.P.
Methyl chloride	CH_3Cl		$-23\cdot7°$
Methyl bromide	CH_3Br		$4\cdot5°$
Methyl iodide	CH_3I		$43°$
Ethyl chloride	$CH_3.CH_2Cl$		$12\cdot5°$
Ethyl bromide	$CH_3.CH_2Br$		$38°$
Ethyl iodide	$CH_3.CH_2I$		$72\cdot3°$
Ethylene dichloride	$CH_2Cl.CH_2Cl$		$83°$
Ethylidene dichloride	$CH_3.CHCl_2$		$58°$
Ethylene dibromide	$CH_2Br.CH_2Br$	$9\cdot5°$	$131°$
Ethylidene dibromide	$CH_3.CHBr_2$		$110°$
Chloroform	$CHCl_3$		$61°$
Iodoform	CHI_3	$120°$	Sublimes
Carbon tetrachloride	CCl_4		$76°$
Vinyl chloride	$CH_2 : CHCl$		$-18°$
Allyl chloride	$CH_2 : CH.CH_2Cl$		$45°$

The halogen derivatives of the aliphatic hydrocarbons are colourless gases or liquids, insoluble in water. They undergo numerous and varied chemical reactions, and, in consequence, they are used extensively in the preparation and synthesis of organic compounds.

THE MONOHALOGEN DERIVATIVES OF THE PARAFFINS

The simplest members of the class of compounds known as the monohalogen derivatives of the paraffins are methyl chloride, methyl bromide and methyl iodide, and ethyl chloride, ethyl bromide and ethyl iodide. Molecules of these compounds are derived by the replacement of one atom of hydrogen in a molecule of methane, or of ethane, by one atom of the halogen. The six compounds are closely similar in constitution, and in their methods of preparation and properties. In the present chapter ethyl bromide is chosen as the most representative member of the monohalogen derivatives of the paraffins. It is, therefore, considered in detail on pp. 140–143, and the points of difference between the other members of the series and ethyl bromide are mentioned on p. 148.

ETHYL BROMIDE

Ethyl bromide is a volatile liquid, denser than water, in which it is insoluble. If pure it is colourless, but if it contains traces of bromine liberated by slight decomposition, it is coloured brown. It has a sweetish odour.

PRINCIPAL REACTIONS IN WHICH ETHYL BROMIDE IS PRODUCED

1. The action of bromine vapour on ethane. If a mixture of ethane and bromine vapour is exposed to daylight, a reaction occurs in which bromine atoms replace one or more of the hydrogen atoms in the ethane molecule, and ethyl bromide is formed according to the equation,

$$C_2H_6 \ + \ Br_2 \ = \ C_2H_5Br \ + \ HBr.$$

Unless the conditions are carefully controlled, however, other bromine derivatives of ethane, such as $C_2H_4Br_2$ and $C_2H_3Br_3$, are formed at the same time.

2. The direct action of hydrobromic acid on ethyl alcohol. If ethyl alcohol is heated in a distilling flask with constant boiling point hydrobromic acid solution, ethyl bromide and water are formed,

$$C_2H_5OH \ + \ HBr \ = \ C_2H_5Br \ + \ H_2O.$$

The hydrobromic acid must be present in excess ; four chemical equivalents of hydrogen bromide should be taken for each equivalent of ethyl alcohol. The ethyl bromide is condensed and purified as described on p. 139. The yield is over 80 per cent.

3. The action of ethyl alcohol on potassium bromide and concentrated sulphuric acid. This reaction, in principle, is similar to Reaction 2 above. The sulphuric acid reacts with the potassium bromide to form hydrogen bromide,

$$H_2SO_4 \ + \ KBr \ = \ KHSO_4 \ + \ HBr,$$

D.C.

and with ethyl alcohol to form ethyl hydrogen sulphate,

$$C_2H_5OH + H_2SO_4 = C_2H_5.HSO_4 + H_2O.$$

The hydrogen bromide and ethyl hydrogen sulphate then react together to give ethyl bromide with the regeneration of sulphuric acid,

$$HBr + C_2H_5.HSO_4 = C_2H_5Br + H_2SO_4.$$

If the intermediate formation of ethyl hydrogen sulphate is disregarded, the reaction between the hydrogen bromide and ethyl alcohol may be represented shortly by the equation describing Reaction 2.

The function of the sulphuric acid in the series of reactions is threefold : it acts chemically in forming ethyl hydrogen sulphate and in liberating hydrogen bromide, it acts catalytically in promoting the reaction between ethyl hydrogen sulphate and hydrogen bromide, and it acts as an absorbent for the water which is formed. Its reactivity steadily falls off as it becomes diluted by the water produced in the reaction.

The ethyl bromide thus prepared is contaminated with water, hydrobromic acid, sulphur dioxide (the sulphur dioxide is formed by the reduction of the sulphuric acid by the organic reagents), and diethyl ether formed in a side-reaction between ethyl alcohol and ethyl hydrogen sulphate. Full experimental details of this method for preparing ethyl bromide are given on p. 139.

4. The action of bromine and red phosphorus on ethyl alcohol. A mixture of ethyl alcohol and red phosphorus is placed in a flask fitted with a dropping funnel and attached to a water condenser. The apparatus is similar to that shown in Fig. 47, p. 200. Liquid bromine is added to the mixture drop by drop from the dropping funnel while the flask is cooled with cold water to moderate the reaction. The ethyl bromide is subsequently distilled from a water-bath, and collected in a receiver chilled by ice-water.

The bromine and the phosphorus first react to yield phosphorus tribromide, which attacks the ethyl alcohol, forming ethyl bromide and phosphorous acid,

$$2P + 3Br_2 = 2PBr_3,$$
$$3C_2H_5OH + PBr_3 = 3C_2H_5Br + H_3PO_3.$$

Side-reactions may occur leading to the formation of hydrogen bromide and phosphorus ethers, thus,

$$3C_2H_5OH + PBr_3 = P(OC_2H_5)_3 + 3HBr.$$

5. The action of hydrobromic acid on ethylene. A concentrated aqueous solution of hydrobromic acid at 100° combines with ethylene to yield ethyl bromide,

$$
\begin{array}{c}
\text{H} \\
\backslash \\
\text{H}
\end{array}
\text{C}=\text{C}
\begin{array}{c}
\text{H} \\
/ \\
\text{H}
\end{array}
+ \text{HBr} =
\begin{array}{ccc}
\text{H} & \text{H} \\
| & | \\
\text{H}-\text{C}-\text{C}-\text{H} \\
| & | \\
\text{H} & \text{Br.}
\end{array}
$$

Laboratory preparation of ethyl bromide. Ethyl bromide is conveniently prepared in the laboratory by the reaction between ethyl alcohol, potassium bromide and sulphuric acid. The chemistry of the reaction has been discussed under Reaction 3, p. 137. 37 c.c. of ethyl alcohol are placed in a 500 c.c. bolt-head flask, Fig. 43, and 40 c.c. of concentrated sulphuric acid are slowly added with continual shaking.

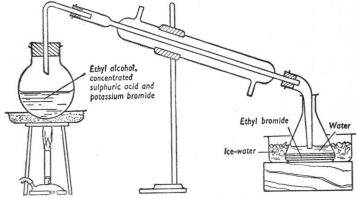

Ethyl alcohol, concentrated sulphuric acid and potassium bromide

Ethyl bromide   Water

Ice-water

Fig. 43. Apparatus for the preparation of ethyl bromide.

50 gm. of powdered potassium bromide are added, the flask is attached to a water condenser and gently heated on the sand-bath. Ethyl bromide distils over, and by means of the adaptor fitted to the end of the condenser, the condensed liquid is collected under the surface of the water in the receiving flask. Loss of the volatile distillate by evaporation is thus prevented. When no more oily drops of ethyl bromide come over, the liquid in the receiving flask is transferred to a separating funnel. The lower heavy layer of ethyl bromide is run off, and the upper layer is discarded. The ethyl bromide is then gently shaken with 10 per cent. sodium carbonate solution in a separating funnel to remove hydrobromic acid and sulphur dioxide. When the evolution of carbon dioxide has ceased, the lower layer of ethyl bromide is run off, and shaken in a separating funnel with an equal volume of water to remove traces of sodium carbonate. The lower layer of ethyl bromide is run off into a flask containing a few pieces of anhydrous calcium chloride which extracts dissolved water from the ethyl bromide. After about 20 minutes the ethyl bromide is decanted from the moist lumps of calcium chloride through a small fluted filter paper into a distilling flask. The distilling flask is attached to a condenser leading to a small conical receiving flask, chilled by a mixture of ice and water. The distilling flask is heated on

a water-bath, and the fraction of the distillate boiling between 35 and 40° is collected. Ethyl bromide thus prepared contains some diethyl ether.

PROPERTIES AND CONSTITUTION OF ETHYL BROMIDE

Properties. Ethyl bromide enters into a number of important chemical reactions which are summarised in the following list.

1. Reduction, giving ethane. Reducing agents such as sodium amalgam and water, zinc and dilute hydrochloric acid, or a zinc-copper couple in contact with ethyl alcohol mixed with a little water, convert ethyl bromide to ethane,

$$H-\underset{\underset{H}{|}}{\overset{\overset{H}{|}}{C}}-\underset{\underset{H}{|}}{\overset{\overset{H}{|}}{C}}-Br \ + \ H_2 \ = \ H-\underset{\underset{H}{|}}{\overset{\overset{H}{|}}{C}}-\underset{\underset{H}{|}}{\overset{\overset{H}{|}}{C}}-H \ + \ HBr.$$

The conditions for the reduction of ethyl bromide by a zinc-copper couple and alcohol are similar to those described for the preparation of methane on p. 106.

2. Hydrolysis, giving ethyl alcohol. Boiling water, aqueous alkalis, or moist silver oxide, hydrolyse ethyl bromide to ethyl alcohol,

$$H-\underset{\underset{H}{|}}{\overset{\overset{H}{|}}{C}}-\underset{\underset{H}{|}}{\overset{\overset{H}{|}}{C}}-Br \ + \ KOH \ = \ H-\underset{\underset{H}{|}}{\overset{\overset{H}{|}}{C}}-\underset{\underset{H}{|}}{\overset{\overset{H}{|}}{C}}-OH \ + \ KBr.$$

The reagents should be placed in a flask fitted to a reflux water condenser, and boiled for 10 minutes.

3. Reaction with dry silver oxide, giving diethyl ether. *Moist* silver oxide hydrolyses ethyl bromide to ethyl alcohol (Reaction 2), but *dry* silver oxide, when warmed with ethyl bromide converts it to diethyl ether,

$$H-\underset{\underset{H}{|}}{\overset{\overset{H}{|}}{C}}-\underset{\underset{H}{|}}{\overset{\overset{H}{|}}{C}}-Br \ + \ Ag_2O \ + \ Br-\underset{\underset{H}{|}}{\overset{\overset{H}{|}}{C}}-\underset{\underset{H}{|}}{\overset{\overset{H}{|}}{C}}-H$$

$$= \ H-\underset{\underset{H}{|}}{\overset{\overset{H}{|}}{C}}-\underset{\underset{H}{|}}{\overset{\overset{H}{|}}{C}}-O-\underset{\underset{H}{|}}{\overset{\overset{H}{|}}{C}}-\underset{\underset{H}{|}}{\overset{\overset{H}{|}}{C}}-H \ + \ 2AgBr.$$

4. Reaction with sodium ethoxide, giving diethyl ether. (Wiliamson's synthesis of ether.) Ethyl bromide reacts with warm sodium ethoxide to yield diethyl ether,

$$H-\underset{\underset{H}{|}}{\overset{\overset{H}{|}}{C}}-\underset{\underset{H}{|}}{\overset{\overset{H}{|}}{C}}-Br \;+\; NaO-\underset{\underset{H}{|}}{\overset{\overset{H}{|}}{C}}-\underset{\underset{H}{|}}{\overset{\overset{H}{|}}{C}}-H$$

$$= H-\underset{\underset{H}{|}}{\overset{\overset{H}{|}}{C}}-\underset{\underset{H}{|}}{\overset{\overset{H}{|}}{C}}-O-\underset{\underset{H}{|}}{\overset{\overset{H}{|}}{C}}-\underset{\underset{H}{|}}{\overset{\overset{H}{|}}{C}}-H \;+\; NaBr.$$

This reaction is of importance in establishing the constitution of diethyl ether.

5. Reaction with alcoholic potash. A warm solution of potassium hydroxide in alcohol reacts with ethyl bromide to form diethyl ether according to an equation similar to that in Reaction 4 above.*

6. Reaction with metallic sodium, giving butane. Wurtz's reaction. If metallic sodium is suspended in a solution of ethyl bromide in dry ether contained in a flask fitted to a reflux water condenser, and the solution is warmed, sodium bromide is eliminated and butane is formed.

$$H-\underset{\underset{H}{|}}{\overset{\overset{H}{|}}{C}}-\underset{\underset{H}{|}}{\overset{\overset{H}{|}}{C}}-Br \;+\; 2Na \;+\; Br-\underset{\underset{H}{|}}{\overset{\overset{H}{|}}{C}}-\underset{\underset{H}{|}}{\overset{\overset{H}{|}}{C}}-H$$

$$= H-\underset{\underset{H}{|}}{\overset{\overset{H}{|}}{C}}-\underset{\underset{H}{|}}{\overset{\overset{H}{|}}{C}}-\underset{\underset{H}{|}}{\overset{\overset{H}{|}}{C}}-\underset{\underset{H}{|}}{\overset{\overset{H}{|}}{C}}-H \;+\; 2NaBr.$$

7. Reaction with methyl bromide and metallic sodium, giving propane. Wurtz's reaction. If a mixture of ethyl bromide and methyl bromide in solution in ether is warmed with metallic sodium, propane is formed,

$$H-\underset{\underset{H}{|}}{\overset{\overset{H}{|}}{C}}-\underset{\underset{H}{|}}{\overset{\overset{H}{|}}{C}}-Br \;+\; 2Na \;+\; Br-\underset{\underset{H}{|}}{\overset{\overset{H}{|}}{C}}-H$$

$$= H-\underset{\underset{H}{|}}{\overset{\overset{H}{|}}{C}}-\underset{\underset{H}{|}}{\overset{\overset{H}{|}}{C}}-\underset{\underset{H}{|}}{\overset{\overset{H}{|}}{C}}-H \;+\; 2NaBr.$$

Some butane and ethane are formed at the same time.

* It is frequently stated that ethyl bromide yields ethylene when treated with hot alcoholic potash. In a letter to *Nature*, 1947, *160*, 406 (where further references are given) Austin, Hughes and Ingold state that little or no ethylene is evolved in this reaction; the yield is less than 1 per cent.

8. Reaction with bromobenzene in the presence of metallic sodium, giving ethyl benzene. Fittig's reaction. If metallic sodium is suspended in a solution of ethyl bromide and bromobenzene in ether, and the solution is warmed, ethyl benzene is formed,

$$C_2H_5Br + 2Na + C_6H_5Br = C_6H_5.C_2H_5 + 2NaBr.$$

9. Reaction with benzene in the presence of aluminium chloride, giving ethyl benzene. Friedel-Crafts reaction. A vigorous reaction occurs when ethyl bromide is added to a mixture of benzene and pure dry aluminium chloride. The products of the reaction are ethyl benzene and hydrogen bromide,

$$C_6H_6 + C_2H_5Br = C_6H_5.C_2H_5 + HBr.$$

The aluminium chloride is a catalyst.

10. Reaction with silver acetate, giving ethyl acetate. If ethyl bromide is warmed with a solution of silver acetate in alcohol or ether, a precipitate of silver bromide is formed and ethyl acetate remains in solution,

$$C_2H_5Br + CH_3.COOAg = CH_3.COOC_2H_5 + AgBr.$$

The conversion of the silver acetate to ethyl acetate is almost quantitative.

11. Double decomposition with sodium or potassium cyanide, giving ethyl cyanide (propionitrile). Potassium cyanide, dissolved in a mixture of water and ethyl alcohol, reacts with ethyl bromide to yield ethyl cyanide and potassium bromide. Since potassium cyanide is an ionic compound, the effective reagent must be the cyanide ion, $C{\equiv}N^-$.

$$H-\underset{\underset{H}{|}}{\overset{\overset{H}{|}}{C}}-\underset{\underset{H}{|}}{\overset{\overset{H}{|}}{C}}-Br + C{\equiv}N^- = H-\underset{\underset{H}{|}}{\overset{\overset{H}{|}}{C}}-\underset{\underset{H}{|}}{\overset{\overset{H}{|}}{C}}-C{\equiv}N + Br.^-$$

12. Double decomposition with silver cyanide, giving ethyl iso-cyanide. Silver cyanide, when heated with ethyl bromide converts it to ethyl iso-cyanide; silver bromide is formed at the same time. Silver cyanide is not an ionic compound; its crystals are composed of indefinitely long chains of atoms in the arrangement C—N—Ag—C—N—Ag, of which the elements react thus,

$$H-\underset{\underset{H}{|}}{\overset{\overset{H}{|}}{C}}-\underset{\underset{H}{|}}{\overset{\overset{H}{|}}{C}}-Br + AgNC = H-\underset{\underset{H}{|}}{\overset{\overset{H}{|}}{C}}-\underset{\underset{H}{|}}{\overset{\overset{H}{|}}{C}}-\overset{+}{N}{\equiv}\bar{C} + AgBr.$$

**13. Double decomposition with silver nitrite, giving nitro-
ethane mixed with ethyl nitrite.**   Silver nitrite (which is probably
not an ionic compound) when warmed with ethyl bromide yields
silver bromide and a mixture of nitroethane and ethyl nitrite

H—C—C—Br + AgNO₂ = AgBr + { ... }

(with structures: ethyl nitrite H—C—C—O—N=O ; nitro-ethane)

Potassium nitrite reacts similarly.

**14. Reaction with ammonia in alcoholic solution, giving a
mixture of ethylamine hydrobromide, diethylamine hydrobromide, triethylamine hydrobromide and tetraethyl
ammonium bromide.**   This reaction is considered in detail in
Chapter XI, p. 186.

In order to complete the account of the chemical properties of
ethyl bromide it is necessary to mention two types of reaction which
are of great importance in synthetical chemistry, the reaction of
ethyl bromide in ethereal solution with clean dry magnesium to yield
a Grignard reagent, magnesium ethyl bromide,

$$C_2H_5Br + Mg = C_2H_5—Mg—Br,$$

and the reaction with the sodium or potassium derivatives of such
compounds as phthalimide, ethyl acetoacetate and ethyl malonate,
to give ethyl derivatives of these compounds.   These reactions,
which are of wide application and of great theoretical interest, are
discussed in detail in later chapters.

Constitution of ethyl bromide.   The relation of ethyl bromide
to ethane is established by Reaction 1, p. 140.   If the constitution of
ethyl alcohol (p. 165) is assumed, the structure of ethyl bromide is
confirmed by Reaction 2.

Tests for ethyl bromide.   Ethyl bromide gives a pale yellow precipitate of silver bromide when vigorously shaken with aqueous silver
nitrate solution in the cold ; the precipitate is insoluble in excess of
dilute nitric acid.   Other monohalogen derivatives of the paraffins, and
halogen derivatives of aromatic hydrocarbons which have halogen in a
side-chain, also give precipitates when shaken with silver nitrate solution.

When ethyl bromide is hydrolysed by a boiling solution of sodium
hydroxide in alcohol, sodium bromide, insoluble in alcohol, is precipitated.   It may be filtered off, dissolved in water, and its identity confirmed by the appropriate tests.   Other alkyl bromides behave similarly.

GENERAL REVIEW OF THE MONOHALOGEN DERIVATIVES OF THE PARAFFINS

The chemistry of ethyl bromide, which has been considered in the previous sections of this chapter, illustrates the general chemistry of the monohalogen derivatives of the paraffins. The chemical properties of the propyl halides and the butyl halides resemble those of ethyl bromide so closely that it is unnecessary to enumerate the reactions of these compounds in detail. The remaining sections of this chapter, therefore, give a general account of the preparations and properties of the more important alkyl halides.

THE PRINCIPAL METHODS OF PREPARATION OF THE MONOHALOGEN DERIVATIVES OF THE PARAFFINS

1. The halogenation of a paraffin. The chlorine and bromine derivatives of the lower members of the paraffin series are formed by the direct action of chlorine or of bromine vapour on the paraffin. These reactions are promoted by sunlight, and by a catalyst such as iodine. Direct halogenation of a paraffin is not a convenient method for preparing a monohalogen derivative, however, as it is difficult to control the reaction so that only the monohalogen derivative is formed. Moreover, the higher members of the paraffin series tend to crack on halogenation, yielding halogen derivatives of lower members, cf. p. 112. The iodine derivatives cannot be obtained by the action of iodine alone on a paraffin. The reaction of iodine on ethane, for example,

$$I_2 + C_2H_6 \rightleftharpoons C_2H_5I + HI,$$

is reversible, and it proceeds only if iodic acid or mercuric oxide is present to oxidise, and so destroy, the hydriodic acid as fast as it is formed.

2. The action of a halogen acid on an alcohol. The action of a halogen acid on an alcohol, as exemplified by the reaction of hydriodic acid with ethyl alcohol to yield ethyl iodide,

$$HI + C_2H_5OH \rightleftharpoons C_2H_5I + H_2O,$$

is reversible. The position of equilibrium varies with the nature of the acid and the alcohol employed. In practice, it is found that alcohols standing above propyl in the homologous series give good yields of alkyl bromides and iodides when treated with a concentrated aqueous solution of hydrobromic acid or hydriodic acid at 100°, provided that a generous excess of the acid is used. The yield of methyl chloride or ethyl chloride obtained by the action of a concentrated aqueous solution of hydrochloric acid on the corresponding alcohol is poor, but these chlorides are readily prepared by passing gaseous hydrogen chloride into a mixture of absolute alcohol and anhydrous zinc chloride (Grove's method). The anhydrous zinc chloride combines with the water formed in the course of the reaction, and so enables it to proceed to completion. The use of Grove's method for preparing an alkyl chloride is illustrated by the preparation of ethyl chloride described below.

Grove's method for preparing ethyl chloride. Absolute ethyl alcohol, to which one-half of its weight of anhydrous zinc chloride has been added, is placed in a flask fitted with a side-tube, a safety tube, and a reflux condenser closed with a calcium chloride tube, Fig. **44**. Hydrogen chloride is passed into the flask by means of the side-tube until the alcohol is saturated. The calcium chloride tube is then removed from the top of the condenser and replaced by a delivery tube leading to wash-bottle I containing water, which is connected in turn by delivery tubes to wash-bottles II and III, containing dilute potassium hydroxide

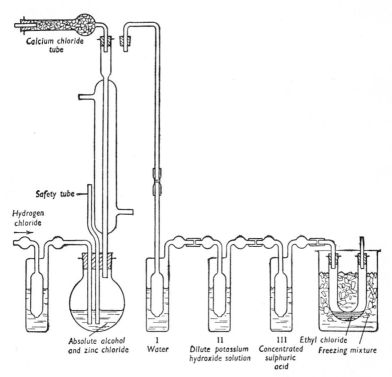

FIG. 44.   Apparatus for the preparation of ethyl chloride by Grove's method.

solution and concentrated sulphuric acid respectively. Wash-bottle III is connected to a U-tube immersed in a freezing mixture.

The contents of the flask are then warmed on a water-bath and ethyl chloride is evolved. Most of the alcohol vapour which boils off from the solution is condensed in the reflux condenser and returns to the flask : any which escapes condensation dissolves in the water in the first wash-bottle. Hydrogen chloride carried over with the ethyl chloride either dissolves in the water or reacts with the potassium hydroxide solution in wash-bottle II. The ethyl chloride is dried by the concentrated sulphuric acid in wash-bottle III, and liquefied in the chilled U-tube. The safety tube fitted to the reaction flask prevents water from being sucked out of the wash-bottle I owing to the rapid solution of hydrogen chloride in the alcohol.

The alkyl chlorides and bromides can be made by heating the appropriate alcohol with a mixture of concentrated sulphuric acid and potassium chloride or bromide, as described in detail on p. 139. Alkyl iodides cannot be made by this method, because the hydrogen iodide liberated in the first stage of the reaction (cf. p. 137) would be immediately oxidised to free iodine by the concentrated sulphuric acid.

3. The action of a phosphorus halide on an alcohol. Phosphorus trihalides and phosphorus pentahalides react with an alcohol according to equations of the type :

$$PCl_5 + C_2H_5OH = C_2H_5Cl + POCl_3 + HCl,$$
$$POCl_3 + 3C_2H_5OH = 3C_2H_5Cl + H_3PO_4,$$
$$PCl_3 + 3C_2H_5OH = 3C_2H_5Cl + H_3PO_3.$$

Side-reactions of the type,

$$PCl_3 + 3C_2H_5OH = P(OC_2H_5)_3 + 3HCl,$$

always occur, however, and diminish the value of these reactions as a means of preparing alkyl halides. For the preparation of alkyl bromides (p. 138) and iodides, the phosphorus halide is made *in situ* by mixing phosphorus with bromine or iodine. The method is not suitable for the preparation of alkyl chlorides, because large proportions of the reagents are used up in side-reactions, and the yield of alkyl chloride is low. As an example of the application of this method, the preparation of ethyl iodide is described below.

The preparation of ethyl iodide by the action of ethyl alcohol on a mixture of iodine and red phosphorus. 2·5 gm. of red phosphorus and 25 c.c. of alcohol are placed in a round-bottomed flask attached to an efficient reflux water condenser, Fig. 23, p. 71. 25 gm. of powdered iodine are added to the contents of the flask in small quantities of 3 or 4 gm. at a time ; the flask is momentarily detached from the condenser to enable each addition to be made. The reaction is moderately vigorous, and the contents of the flask become hot. When all the iodine has been added, the product is allowed to stand for 10 minutes and is then heated for 1 hour on a boiling water-bath. The flask is then disconnected from the reflux condenser. The flask and condenser are connected by means of a knee-tube so that the contents of the flask may be distilled. The flask is heated on a boiling water-bath, and the distillate consisting of ethyl iodide and unchanged ethyl alcohol is collected in a small conical flask, Fig. 14, p. 57. The distillate is placed in a separating funnel and shaken with 10 per cent. sodium carbonate solution to remove hydrogen iodide and alcohol. The lower layer of ethyl iodide is run off, and again shaken with an equal volume of water to remove traces of sodium carbonate. The lower layer of ethyl iodide is separated and transferred to a conical flask. A few pieces of fused calcium chloride are added and the mixture is shaken intermittently for 15–20 minutes ; water and alcohol are absorbed by the calcium chloride. The dry ethyl iodide is then filtered through a small fluted filter paper into a distilling flask and redistilled.

The yield is 24 gm. ; this is equivalent to 35 per cent. of the theoretical yield calculated on the weight of the alcohol taken, and 78 per cent. of the theoretical yield calculated on weight of the iodine taken. The loss is due to side-reactions between the alcohol and phosphorus triiodide, such as

$$3C_2H_5OH + PI_3 = P(OC_2H_5)_3 + 3HI.$$

4. The action of an olefine on a halogen acid. Alkyl bromides and iodides may be obtained by passing the appropriate olefine into a concentrated aqueous solution of hydrobromic acid or hydriodic acid at 100° (cf. p. 123). For example, ethylene reacts with hydrobromic acid to yield ethyl bromide, p. 139. The methyl halides cannot be obtained by an analogous reaction, as the methylene group, $H_2C{=}$, has no free existence. The rule for predicting which isomeride of the alkyl halide is produced when a halogen acid reacts with propylene or with a higher member of the olefine series, is given on p. 123. The olefines do not react with hydrochloric acid.

5. Special reactions. Methyl chloride is made commercially by heating trimethylamine hydrochloride with hydrochloric acid,

$$N(CH_3)_3.HCl + 3HCl = 3CH_3Cl + NH_4Cl.$$

Trimethylamine hydrochloride is obtained from the waste products of the beet sugar industry, and from herring brine.

Methyl iodide may be made by adding dimethyl sulphate, a colourless poisonous liquid, B.P. 188°, drop by drop to a dilute aqueous solution of potassium iodide,

$$(CH_3)_2SO_4 + 2KI = K_2SO_4 + 2CH_3I.$$

PROPERTIES AND USES OF THE ALKYL MONOHALIDES

Properties. The physical properties of certain members of the monohalogen derivatives of the paraffins are set out in Table XII, p. 136. The lower members of the series are colourless gases or volatile liquids, not soluble in water. The densities of the halogeno-paraffins in the liquid state are much greater than that of water. The propyl halides and higher members of the series react with a hot alcoholic solution of potassium hydroxide to yield olefines. For example, iso-propyl bromide yields propylene, thus,

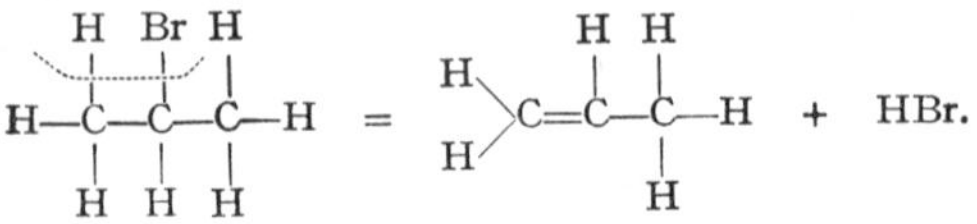

$$
\underset{\substack{|\quad|\quad| \\ H\ H\ H}}{H-\overset{\overset{\displaystyle H\ Br\ H}{|\quad|\quad|}}{C-C-C}-H} = \underset{H}{\overset{H}{}}\!\!\!\!>\!\!C=\overset{\overset{\displaystyle H\ H}{|\quad|}}{C-\underset{\underset{\displaystyle H}{|}}{C}}-H \ + \ HBr.
$$

The yield, however, varies with the nature of the alkyl group, the halogen, and the experimental conditions. As already mentioned, p. 141, ethyl bromide yields diethyl ether when treated with alcoholic potash. The methyl halides clearly cannot take part in reactions of the type shown in the equation, as there is only one carbon atom in the molecule. With these exceptions all members of the series undergo the typical reactions described for ethyl bromide on p. 140.

Alkyl halides containing more than 5 carbon atoms in the molecule tend to react with *aqueous*, as well as with alcoholic solutions of alkalis, to yield olefines according to reactions of the type shown above. The conversion of a higher member of the alkyl halides to the corresponding alcohol, therefore, is carried out indirectly through the intermediate formation of the corresponding alkyl acetate. For example, hexyl alcohol is obtained from hexyl iodide by first forming hexyl acetate by reaction with silver acetate,

$$C_6H_{13}I \ + \ CH_3.COOAg \ = \ CH_3.COOC_6H_{13} \ + \ AgI.$$

The hexyl acetate is then hydrolysed with aqueous potassium hydroxide solution to potassium acetate and hexyl alcohol,

$$CH_3.COOC_6H_{13} \ + \ KOH \ = \ CH_3.COOK \ + \ C_6H_{13}OH.$$

Uses of the alkyl halides. Methyl chloride is used as a local anaesthetic. It is liquefied easily on compression, B.P. $-23\cdot7°$, and if sprayed on to the skin and allowed to evaporate, it produces intense cold which renders the affected part insensitive to pain. Methyl chloride is also used as a solvent for extracting perfumes from flowers. Methyl bromide is used as a fire-extinguisher. Methyl chloride and methyl iodide are used as methylating agents, by which the methyl group may be introduced into the molecule of another organic compound. Ethyl chloride is used as an anaesthetic, particularly for short operations on children.

Tests for alkyl monohalides. The alkyl monohalides react with an aqueous solution of silver nitrate in the cold to give a precipitate of silver halide. The ethyl monohalides yield the corresponding potassium salts when warmed with an alcoholic solution of potassium hydroxide. These tests are described for ethyl bromide on p. 143.

A test which differentiates ethyl iodide and methyl iodide from other halogeno-derivatives of the paraffins depends on the formation of a crystalline compound of pyridine and ethyl iodide (or methyl iodide). If a few drops of pyridine are placed in a test-tube and a little ethyl iodide is added and the mixture is warmed, colourless crystals of pyridine ethiodide are formed, $C_6H_5N.C_2H_5I$. Methyl iodide yields the corresponding methiodide in the cold.

DIHALOGENO-PARAFFINS

The dihalogeno-paraffins, which are derived by the replacement of two atoms of hydrogen in the molecule of a paraffin by atoms of a halogen, may be exemplified by ethylene dibromide, $CH_2Br.CH_2Br$, and its isomer ethylidene dibromide, $CH_3.CHBr_2$.

ETHYLENE DIBROMIDE, $CH_2Br.CH_2Br$

Ethylene dibromide is a colourless oil, much denser than water ; its density is 2·189. It is fairly volatile, B.P. 131°, M.P. 9·5°.

Principal reactions in which ethylene dibromide is produced.

1. The combination of ethylene with bromine.

$$\begin{array}{ccc} H-C-H & & H-\overset{\displaystyle H}{\underset{\displaystyle |}{\overset{\displaystyle |}{C}}}-Br \\ \| & + \ Br_2 \ = & | \\ H-C-H & & H-\underset{\displaystyle H}{\underset{\displaystyle |}{\overset{\displaystyle |}{C}}}-Br \end{array}$$

This reaction is used in the laboratory preparation of ethylene dibromide described below. It establishes the symmetrical *constitution of ethylene dibromide*.

2. The action of phosphorus tribromide on ethylene glycol.

$$3 \begin{array}{c} CH_2OH \\ | \\ CH_2OH \end{array} + 2PBr_3 = 3 \begin{array}{c} CH_2Br \\ | \\ CH_2Br \end{array} + 2H_3PO_3.$$

This reaction is analogous to the reaction of phosphorus tribromide on ethyl alcohol to yield ethyl bromide.

3. The action of hydrobromic acid on ethylene glycol. When hydrogen bromide is passed into glycol heated to about 100°, ethylene bromohydrin is formed. When this compound is heated with hydrogen bromide at a higher temperature, ethylene dibromide is formed,

$$\begin{matrix} CH_2OH \\ | \\ CH_2OH \end{matrix} + HBr = \begin{matrix} CH_2Br \\ | \\ CH_2OH \end{matrix} + H_2O,$$

$$\begin{matrix} CH_2Br \\ | \\ CH_2OH \end{matrix} + HBr = \begin{matrix} CH_2Br \\ | \\ CH_2Br \end{matrix} + H_2O.$$

Laboratory preparation of ethylene dibromide. Ethylene dibromide is prepared in the laboratory by the direct addition of bromine to ethylene. Pure ethylene is passed through two wash-bottles, each containing liquid bromine covered with a layer of water to diminish the loss of bromine by evaporation. When the bromine is decolorised the contents of the wash-bottles are transferred to a separating funnel. The heavy oily layer of ethylene dibromide is run off and washed with dilute sodium carbonate solution. The lower layer of ethylene dibromide is again removed, dried over fused calcium chloride, and distilled.

Chemical properties of ethylene dibromide. The chemical properties of ethylene dibromide are determined by the presence of two bromine atoms in the molecule. Ethylene dibromide exhibits the typical reactions of ethyl bromide, p. 140, with the difference that in each reaction one molecule of ethylene dibromide reacts with *two* equivalents of the other reagent, one for each bromine atom. For example, one molecule of ethylene dibromide is hydrolysed by *two* equivalents of potassium hydroxide in aqueous solution to yield one molecule of ethylene glycol,

$$\begin{matrix} CH_2Br \\ | \\ CH_2Br \end{matrix} + 2KOH = \begin{matrix} CH_2OH \\ | \\ CH_2OH \end{matrix} + 2KBr.$$

Again, *two* molecules of hydrobromic acid are eliminated from one molecule of ethylene dibromide by the action of potassium hydroxide in alcoholic solution. In the first stage of this reaction, bromo-ethylene (vinyl bromide) is formed, and in the second, acetylene,

$$CH_2Br.CH_2Br = CH_2{=}CHBr + HBr,$$
$$H_2C{=}CHBr = HC{\equiv}CH + HBr.$$

The experimental conditions for carrying out this reaction are described on p. 130.

Ethylene dibromide is added to motor spirit containing the anti-knock lead tetra-ethyl. The lead is then expelled from the cylinders of the engine as the volatile lead tetrabromide, and its deposition on the pistons is avoided.

Constitution of ethylene dibromide. The molecular formula of ethylene dibromide is $C_2H_4Br_2$. On reduction with alcohol and the zinc-copper couple it yields ethane, and hence it must be a derivative of ethane. Reaction 1, p. 149, proves that one bromine atom is attached to each of the two carbon atoms in the molecule of ethylene dibromide.

ETHYLIDENE DIBROMIDE, $CH_3.CHBr_2$

Ethylidene dibromide is a dense liquid, Sp. Gr. 2·08, B.P. 110°. Ethylidene dibromide is isomeric with ethylene dibromide, since both compounds have the same molecular formula, $C_2H_4Br_2$.

Principal reactions in which ethylidene dibromide is produced.

1. The action of phosphorus pentabromide on acetaldehyde.

$$H-\underset{\underset{H}{|}}{\overset{\overset{H}{|}}{C}}-C\diagdown_{O}^{H} + PBr_5 = H-\underset{\underset{H}{|}}{\overset{\overset{H}{|}}{C}}-\underset{\underset{Br}{|}}{\overset{\overset{H}{|}}{C}}-Br + POBr_3.$$

2. The action of hydrogen bromide on acetylene.

$$HC{\equiv}CH + HBr = H_2C{=}CHBr,$$
$$H_2C{=}CHBr + HBr = H_3C.CHBr_2.$$

It should be noted that the bromine atom of the hydrogen bromide molecule attaches itself to the carbon atom in the vinyl bromide molecule which is linked to the smaller number of hydrogen atoms ; this is in accordance with the rule on p. 123.

Chemical properties of ethylidene dibromide. The chemical reactivity of ethylidene dibromide depends on the presence of the two bromine atoms in the molecule. Its reactions, therefore, correspond to the typical reactions of ethyl bromide, and are similar in general to those of ethylene dibromide. In a few instances the reactions of ethylidene dibromide reflect its constitutional difference from ethylene dibromide. For example, the hydrolysis of ethylidene dibromide by aqueous potassium hydroxide solution produces acetaldehyde, according to the equation,*

$$H_3C.CHBr_2 + 2KOH = H_3C.CHO + 2KBr + H_2O,$$

* The immediate product of the hydrolysis of ethylidene dibromide is ethylidene dihydroxide.

$$H-\underset{\underset{H}{|}}{\overset{\overset{H}{|}}{C}}-\underset{\underset{Br}{|}}{\overset{\overset{H}{|}}{C}}-Br + 2KOH = H-\underset{\underset{H}{|}}{\overset{\overset{H}{|}}{C}}-\underset{\underset{OH}{|}}{\overset{\overset{H}{|}}{C}}-OH + 2KBr.$$

The molecule of ethylidene dihydroxide contains two hydroxyl groups linked to one carbon atom. This arrangement is unstable and the molecule breaks down into water and acetaldehyde,

$$H-\underset{\underset{H}{|}}{\overset{\overset{H}{|}}{C}}-\underset{\underset{OH}{|}}{\overset{\overset{H}{|}}{C}}-OH = H-\underset{\underset{H}{|}}{\overset{\overset{H}{|}}{C}}-C\diagdown_{O}^{H} + H_2O.$$

whereas the hydrolysis of ethylene dibromide yields ethylene glycol, p. 150.

Constitution of ethylidene dibromide. Ethylene dibromide and ethylidene dibromide are isomeric, and the only possible isomeride of ethylene dibromide is a compound in which both the bromine atoms in the molecule are attached to the same carbon atom. The formula $CH_3.CHBr_2$, therefore, must represent the constitution of ethylidene dibromide.

TRIHALOGENO-PARAFFINS

The trihalogeno-paraffins are derived by the replacement of three hydrogen atoms in the molecule of a paraffin by atoms of a halogen. The most important members of this class of compounds are chloroform, $CHCl_3$, and iodoform, CHI_3.

CHLOROFORM

Chloroform is a heavy colourless liquid, Sp. Gr. 1·5 at 15°, B.P. 61°. It is insoluble in water. It is not inflammable at room temperature, but if heated it burns in air with a green-edged flame.

PRINCIPAL REACTIONS IN WHICH CHLOROFORM IS PRODUCED

1. The chlorination of methane. Chloroform is one of the four substitution products, CH_3Cl, CH_2Cl_2, $CHCl_3$, CCl_4, formed by exposing a mixture of methane and chlorine to diffused daylight.

2. The action of an aqueous suspension of bleaching powder on acetone. A vigorous reaction occurs when acetone is added to bleaching powder suspended in water. The course of the reaction may be explained by assuming that the calcium hypochlorite, $Ca(ClO)_2$, in bleaching powder,

$$Ca(ClO)_2,CaCl_2,Ca(OH)_2,H_2O,$$

undergoes hydrolysis, and liberates hypochlorous acid and calcium hydroxide,

$$Ca(ClO)_2 + 2H_2O = 2HOCl + Ca(OH)_2.$$

The hypochlorous acid then chlorinates the acetone,

$$CH_3.CO.CH_3 + 3Cl-O-H = CH_3.CO.CCl_3 + 3H_2O,$$

and the calcium hydroxide converts the trichloroacetone to calcium acetate and chloroform,

$$2CH_3.CO.CCl_3 + Ca(OH)_2 = Ca(CH_3.COO)_2 + 2CHCl_3.$$

There must be many side-reactions as the experimental yield is only 30 per cent. of the calculated.

3. The action of an aqueous suspension of bleaching powder on ethyl alcohol. It may be assumed that the bleaching powder is first hydrolysed to hypochlorous acid and calcium hydroxide. The hypochlorous acid oxidises the ethyl alcohol to acetaldehyde, a reaction which may be summed up in the simple equation,

$$CH_3.CH_2OH + HOCl = CH_3.CHO + H_2O + HCl,$$

and then chlorinates the acetaldehyde to trichloroacetaldehyde,

$$CH_3.CHO + 3ClOH = CCl_3.CHO + 3H_2O.$$

The calcium hydroxide then hydrolyses the trichloroacetaldehyde (chloral) to chloroform and calcium formate,

$$2CCl_3.CHO + Ca(OH)_2 = Ca(H.COO)_2 + 2CHCl_3.$$

4. The action of sodium hydroxide solution on chloral, chloral hydrate or trichloroacetic acid. When chloral or chloral hydrate is warmed with aqueous sodium hydroxide solution, pure chloroform and sodium formate are liberated,

$$CCl_3.CHO + NaOH = CHCl_3 + Na.HCOO,$$
$$CCl_3.CH(OH)_2 + NaOH = CHCl_3 + Na.HCOO + H_2O.$$

When trichloroacetic acid is warmed with sodium hydroxide solution, chloroform and potassium carbonate are formed,

$$CCl_3.COOH + 2NaOH = CHCl_3 + Na_2CO_3 + H_2O.$$

Laboratory preparation of chloroform. In the laboratory, chloroform is made by the action of bleaching powder on acetone or ethyl alcohol. The preparation, using acetone, is carried out thus. 100 gm. of bleaching powder are triturated with 250 c.c. of water in a mortar, and the cream so formed is transferred to a litre flask fitted with a reflux water-condenser. 44 c.c. of acetone are poured down the condenser into the flask. The reaction starts immediately, and the contents of the flask boil vigorously. If the boiling is too violent, the flask is cooled. When the reaction has subsided, the flask is heated on a water-bath for 5–10 minutes. The apparatus is then dismantled and reassembled for a simple distillation, Fig. 14, p. 57. The flask is heated on a water-bath, and the chloroform is distilled. The distillate is shaken with dilute sodium hydroxide solution, dried over anhydrous calcium chloride, and distilled.

CHEMICAL REACTIONS AND USES OF CHLOROFORM

1. Atmospheric oxidation. Chloroform undergoes atmospheric oxidation, which is facilitated by exposure to light, to give carbonyl chloride and hydrogen chloride,

$$CHCl_3 + O = COCl_2 + HCl.$$

2. Hydrolysis. A warm alcoholic solution of potassium hydroxide decomposes chloroform yielding potassium formate and potassium chloride. The first stage of the reaction probably leads to the production of trihydroxymethane,

$$H-C\begin{smallmatrix}Cl\\<Cl\\Cl\end{smallmatrix} + 3KOH = H-C\begin{smallmatrix}OH\\<OH\\OH\end{smallmatrix} + 3KCl.$$

A molecule containing more than one hydroxyl group on any single carbon atom is unstable ; such a molecule decomposes with the elimination of a molecule of water to form a new molecule containing the group —C=O. Trihydroxymethane decomposes to yield water and formic acid,

$$H-C\begin{smallmatrix}OH\\<OH\\OH\end{smallmatrix} = H-C\begin{smallmatrix}O\\<\\OH\end{smallmatrix} + H_2O.$$

The formic acid is neutralised by the potassium hydroxide to give potassium formate,

$$H-C\begin{smallmatrix}O\\<\\OH\end{smallmatrix} + KOH = H-C\begin{smallmatrix}O\\<\\OK\end{smallmatrix} + H_2O.$$

3. The phenylcarbylamine reaction, or Hofmann's reaction. If chloroform is warmed with a mixture of aniline and alcoholic potassium hydroxide solution, phenyl iso-cyanide (phenylcarbylamine) is set free. This is a substance with a characteristic offensive odour, and the reaction may be used as a test for chloroform,

$$HCCl_3 + C_6H_5NH_2 + 3KOH = C_6H_5NC + 3KCl + 3H_2O.$$

4. The action with phenol and sodium hydroxide to give salicylaldehyde. The Reimer-Tiemann reaction. A mixture of chloroform and a concentrated solution of phenol and sodium hydroxide is placed in a flask fitted with a reflux water-condenser, and heated on a water-bath at 70° for two hours. At the end of this time, the flask contains salicylaldehyde and sodium chloride, besides small quantities of the unchanged reagents. The separation of salicylaldehyde from the mixture is described on p. 438. The reaction may be described by the equation,

$$CHCl_3 + C_6H_5OH + 3NaOH$$
$$= C_6H_4.OH.CHO + 2H_2O + 3NaCl.$$

5. Action with metallic sodium. A violent explosion occurs if chloroform is brought into contact with molten sodium. Lassaigne's test must not be applied to chloroform. Carbon tetrachloride behaves similarly.

Uses of chloroform. Chloroform is an anaesthetic : it was first recommended for this purpose by Sir James Simpson in 1847. It is falling into disfavour as it is highly toxic. For use as an anaesthetic chloroform must be pure ; especially it must be free from the poisonous carbonyl chloride formed by atmospheric oxidation. It should be kept in the dark in a full, well-stoppered bottle. 1 or 2 per cent. of alcohol may be added to convert any carbonyl chloride to ethyl carbonate,

$$O:C\begin{matrix} Cl \\ Cl \end{matrix} \quad + \quad 2HOC_2H_5 \quad = \quad O:C\begin{matrix} OC_2H_5 \\ OC_2H_5 \end{matrix} \quad + \quad 2HCl.$$

Pure chloroform gives no precipitate when shaken with aqueous silver nitrate solution, and it does not darken when shaken with concentrated sulphuric acid, or with concentrated potassium hydroxide solution. Chloroform is a useful solvent for organic compounds and for iodine.

IODOFORM

Iodoform is a yellow crystalline solid, M.P. 120°. It has a characteristic odour. It is insoluble in water, but is readily soluble in alcohol. It sublimes readily, and is volatile in steam. If heated in a dry tube it decomposes, liberating copious violet fumes of iodine.

Preparation. Iodoform is obtained from acetone, or from ethyl alcohol, by reactions which are similar in principle to those which lead to the formation of chloroform from these compounds. Acetone, or ethyl alcohol, is treated with potassium iodide and sodium hypochlorite in aqueous solution. The sodium hypochlorite reacts with the potassium iodide to form potassium hypoiodite, thus,

$$NaClO \quad + \quad KI \quad = \quad KIO \quad + \quad NaCl.$$

The potassium hypoiodite iodinates the acetone to tri-iodoacetone,

$$CH_3.CO.CH_3 \quad + \quad 3KOI \quad = \quad CH_3.CO.CI_3 \quad + \quad 3KOH,$$

and the acetaldehyde formed by oxidation of the ethyl alcohol to tri-iodoacetaldehyde, thus,

$$CH_3.CH_2OH \quad + \quad NaClO \quad = \quad CH_3.CHO \quad + \quad NaCl \quad + \quad H_2O,$$
$$CH_3.CHO \quad + \quad 3KOI \quad = \quad CI_3.CHO \quad + \quad 3KOH.$$

The tri-iodo derivatives are then hydrolysed by the potassium hydroxide to potassium acetate, or potassium formate, and iodoform which separates from the solution as yellow crystals,

$$CH_3.CO.CI_3 \quad + \quad KOH \quad = \quad CHI_3 \quad + \quad CH_3.COOK,$$
$$CI_3.CHO \quad + \quad KOH \quad = \quad CHI_3 \quad + \quad H.COOK.$$

The same reactions may be brought about by the electrolysis between platinum electrodes of an aqueous solution of acetone, or of ethyl alcohol, and potassium iodide and sodium carbonate. The solution contains the ions K^+, Na^+, I^-, CO_3^{--}, and H^+ and OH^- from the water. The ions which are discharged during electrolysis are H^+ at the cathode, and I^- and OH^- at the anode ; all the other ions remain in solution. The I^- and OH^- ions liberated at the anode react together to yield the hypoiodite ion IO^-. The solution thus contains the ions of sodium hypoiodite which react with the acetone, or the ethyl alcohol, according to the equations given above.

The iodoform reaction. The above reactions of acetone and ethyl alcohol are particular cases of a general reaction, known as the *iodoform reaction,* in which a precipitate of iodoform is produced on the addition of potassium iodide and sodium hypochlorite to certain organic compounds. Organic compounds which undergo the iodoform reaction contain either the group $CH_3.CO.C$ or the group $CH_3.CH.OH$. Among the compounds containing the group $CH_3.CO.C$ are acetone, $CH_3.CO.CH_3$, acetophenone, $CH_3.CO.C_6H_5$, and other methyl ketones, and pyruvic acid $CH_3.CO.COOH$. Among the compounds containing the group $CH_3.CH.OH$ are ethyl alcohol $CH_3.CH_2.OH$, iso-propyl alcohol, $CH_3.CHOH.CH_3$, lactic acid, $CH_3.CHOH.COOH$ and the unstable hydrated form of acetaldehyde, $CH_3.CH(OH)_2$, which probably exists in aqueous solutions of acetaldehyde. Many organic compounds may be recognised by their ability to undergo the iodoform reaction. Ethyl alcohol (which undergoes the iodoform reaction) may be thus distinguished from methyl alcohol (which does not).

Laboratory preparation of iodoform. Iodoform is usually prepared by the action of sodium hypochlorite on an aqueous solution containing potassium iodide, sodium hydroxide and acetone. 2 c.c. of acetone, 80 c.c. of 10 per cent. aqueous potassium iodide solution, and 30 c.c. of 10 per cent. aqueous sodium hydroxide solution are placed in a conical flask, and 70 c.c. of a freshly prepared solution containing 1 gm. molecular weight (74·5 gm.) of sodium hypochlorite per litre are added. The contents of the flask are mixed well, and allowed to stand for 10 minutes. Yellow crystals of iodoform separate, and are isolated from the solution by filtration at the pump. After washing with water and draining, the iodoform is recrystallised from methylated spirit (for details of recrystallisation see p. 72).

Chemical properties of iodoform. The iodine atoms in the molecule of iodoform are bound more firmly than the iodine atom in the molecule of ethyl iodide, for iodoform yields no precipitate of silver iodide when shaken with aqueous silver nitrate solution.

Nevertheless iodoform is hydrolysed by warm aqueous sodium hydroxide solution, or more easily by alcoholic sodium hydroxide solution, to sodium iodide and sodium formate,

$$CHI_3 + 4NaOH = H.COONa + 3NaI + 2H_2O.$$

Iodoform undergoes the phenylcarbylamine reaction when warmed with a mixture of aniline and alcoholic potassium hydroxide solution, in a manner analogous to the corresponding reaction of chloroform, p. 154,

$$HCI_3 + C_6H_5NH_2 + 3KOH = C_6H_5NC + 3KI + 3H_2O.$$

CHAPTER IX

THE ALIPHATIC MONOHYDRIC ALCOHOLS

THE aliphatic alcohols are theoretically derived by the replacement of one or more hydrogen atoms in the molecule of an aliphatic hydrocarbon by the hydroxyl group —OH. If only one hydrogen atom in the molecule is replaced by the hydroxyl group a monohydric alcohol is obtained, such as ethyl alcohol,

$$
\begin{array}{cc}
\text{H} & \text{H} \\
| & | \\
\text{H—C—C—H} \\
| & | \\
\text{H} & \text{H} \\
\text{ethane}
\end{array}
\qquad
\begin{array}{cc}
\text{H} & \text{H} \\
| & | \\
\text{H—C—C—OH} \\
| & | \\
\text{H} & \text{H} \\
\text{ethyl alcohol}
\end{array}
$$

If two hydrogen atoms are replaced, a dihydric alcohol is obtained, such as ethylene glycol,

$$
\begin{array}{cc}
\text{H} & \text{H} \\
| & | \\
\text{H—C—C—H} \\
| & | \\
\text{H} & \text{H} \\
\text{ethane}
\end{array}
\qquad
\begin{array}{cc}
\text{H} & \text{H} \\
| & | \\
\text{H——C——C——H} \\
| & | \\
\text{OH} & \text{OH} \\
\text{ethylene glycol}
\end{array}
$$

Unsaturated * alcohols are derived by the substitution of hydroxyl groups for hydrogen atoms in the molecules of ethylenic or acetylenic hydrocarbons. For example, allyl alcohol, p. 328, is derived from propylene,

$$
\begin{array}{c}
\text{H} \quad \text{H} \quad \text{H} \\
\diagdown \quad | \quad | \\
\text{C=C—C—H} \\
\diagup \qquad | \\
\text{H} \qquad \text{H} \\
\text{propylene}
\end{array}
\qquad
\begin{array}{c}
\text{H} \quad \text{H} \quad \text{H} \\
\diagdown \quad | \quad | \\
\text{C=C—C—OH} \\
\diagup \qquad | \\
\text{H} \qquad \text{H} \\
\text{allyl alcohol}
\end{array}
$$

The term " alcohol " as used in organic chemistry without any qualification is generally understood to refer to the class of monohydric alcohols derived from the paraffins. " Alcohol " is used colloquially as the name for ethyl alcohol.

ETHYL ALCOHOL

Ethyl alcohol is a colourless liquid with an agreeable odour and a burning taste. It is hygroscopic, and it mixes with water in all proportions with the evolution of heat and contraction in volume ;

* The meaning of " unsaturated " is explained on p. 119.

the maximum contraction of 3·7 per cent. takes place when 1 molar proportion of alcohol (52 volumes) is mixed with 3 molar proportions of water (48 volumes). Ethyl alcohol is soluble in all proportions in almost all organic solvents.

TABLE XIII

Name	Formula	M.P.	B.P.
Methyl alcohol	CH_3OH	$-97\cdot8°$	$64\cdot5°$
Ethyl alcohol	C_2H_5OH	$-117\cdot3°$	$78\cdot5°$
Propyl alcohol	$CH_3.CH_2.CH_2OH$	$-127°$	$97\cdot8°$
Iso-propyl alcohol	$CH_3.CH(OH).CH_3$	$-89°$	$82\cdot3°$
n-Butyl alcohol	$CH_3.(CH_2)_3.OH$	$-89\cdot8°$	$117\cdot7°$
Iso-butyl alcohol	$(CH_3)_2.CH.CH_2OH$	$-108°$	$107\cdot3°$
Secondary butyl alcohol	$CH_3.CH_2.CH(OH).CH_3$	$-89°$	$99\cdot5°$
Tertiary butyl alcohol	$(CH_3)_3.COH$	$25\cdot5°$	$82\cdot8°$

PRINCIPAL REACTIONS IN WHICH ETHYL ALCOHOL IS PRODUCED

1. The fermentation of sugars. Ethyl alcohol is one of the products of the fermentation of sugars by the enzyme zymase. The industrial preparation of ethyl alcohol by fermentation processes is mentioned on p. 161 and is discussed more fully on p. 493.

2. The hydrolysis of ethyl halides. The hydrolytic agent may be either a dilute aqueous alkali solution, or moist freshly precipitated silver oxide. Ethyl bromide is converted to ethyl alcohol on gentle boiling with aqueous sodium hydroxide solution under a reflux water condenser,

$$C_2H_5Br \ + \ NaOH \ = \ C_2H_5OH \ + \ NaBr.$$

The hydrolysis of ethyl hydrogen sulphate has been mentioned on p. 121.

3. The hydrolysis of the ethyl esters of organic acids. If ethyl acetate, for example, is gently boiled with aqueous sodium hydroxide solution in a flask fitted to a reflux water condenser, sodium acetate and ethyl alcohol are formed,

$$CH_3.COOC_2H_5 \ + \ NaOH \ = \ CH_3.COONa \ + \ C_2H_5OH.$$

4. The reduction of acetaldehyde.

(i) *Using sodium amalgam and water.* An aqueous solution of acetaldehyde is shaken with sodium amalgam and water. The acetaldehyde is reduced to ethyl alcohol, which is obtained by decanting the aqueous layer from the mercury, and distilling it,

$$2NaHg \ + \ 2H_2O \ = \ 2Hg \ + \ 2NaOH \ + \ H_2,$$
$$CH_3.CHO \ + \ H_2 \ = \ CH_3.CH_2OH.$$

(ii) *Using gaseous hydrogen and reduced nickel.* A mixture of hydrogen and acetaldehyde vapour is passed through a hard glass tube containing freshly reduced nickel heated to 150–200°. Ethyl alcohol is formed by the addition of hydrogen to the acetaldehyde,

$$CH_3.CHO \ + \ H_2 \ = \ CH_3.CH_2OH.$$

5. The action of formaldehyde on magnesium methyl bromide. Grignard's reaction. Magnesium is added to methyl bromide dissolved in ether, and magnesium methyl bromide is formed,

$$Mg \ + \ CH_3Br \ = \ CH_3MgBr.$$

Formaldehyde is passed into this solution, and an intermediate compound is formed by the reaction,

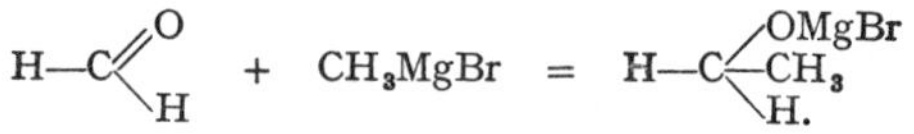

$$H-C{\Large\langle}^O_H \ + \ CH_3MgBr \ = \ H-C{\Large\langle}^{OMgBr}_{CH_3}_{.H.}$$

On treatment with dilute sulphuric acid this compound yields ethyl alcohol,

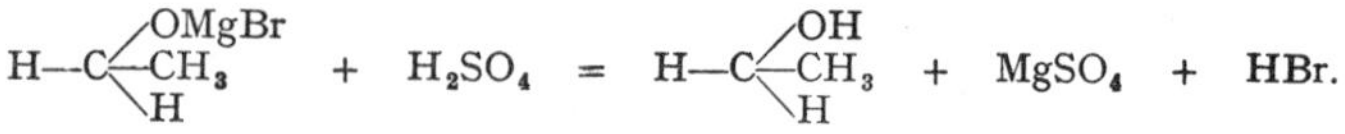

$$H-C{\Large\langle}^{OMgBr}_{CH_3}_{H} \ + \ H_2SO_4 \ = \ H-C{\Large\langle}^{OH}_{CH_3}_{H} \ + \ MgSO_4 \ + \ HBr.$$

6. The action of nitrous acid on ethylamine.

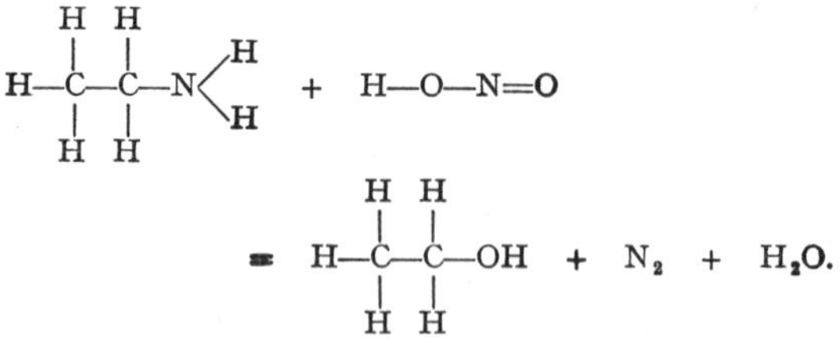

$$H-\underset{\underset{H}{|}}{\overset{\overset{H}{|}}{C}}-\underset{\underset{H}{|}}{\overset{\overset{H}{|}}{C}}-N{\Large\langle}^H_H \ + \ H-O-N=O$$

$$= \ H-\underset{\underset{H}{|}}{\overset{\overset{H}{|}}{C}}-\underset{\underset{H}{|}}{\overset{\overset{H}{|}}{C}}-OH \ + \ N_2 \ + \ H_2O.$$

In practice it is convenient to carry out this reaction starting with ethylamine hydrochloride and sodium nitrite and hydrochloric acid. An aqueous solution of ethylamine hydrochloride is acidified with hydrochloric acid, and an aqueous solution of sodium nitrite is added from a thistle funnel of which the stem reaches to the bottom of the ethylamine hydrochloride solution. Nitrogen is rapidly evolved, and ethyl alcohol may be obtained by distillation of the residual solution.

Preparation of ethyl alcohol. Ethyl alcohol is manufactured from substances rich in starch, such as potatoes or grain, and from substances containing sugar, such as molasses or beetroot. The raw materials are fermented by processes described on pp. 493 and 496 to yield a dilute solution of alcohol in water. The solution is concentrated by fractionation, purified by treatment with charcoal, and then again fractionated to yield rectified spirit. Ethyl alcohol is never prepared in the laboratory ; it is, in fact, one of the principal starting-points for the preparation and manufacture of other aliphatic organic compounds.

Preparation of anhydrous ethyl alcohol. It has been shown on p. 63 that the fractionation of a dilute solution of ethyl alcohol in water yields a distillate containing 95·6 per cent. by weight of alcohol. This distillate is known as *rectified spirit*. Two methods are available for preparing anhydrous ethyl alcohol from rectified spirit.

(i) **Dehydration with freshly prepared quicklime.** 5–10 litres of rectified spirit are placed with 600 gm. of quicklime in a flask fitted with a reflux condenser. The flask is heated on a water-bath for 6 hours in order to promote the combination of the water with the quicklime to form calcium hydroxide. Another 100 gm. of quicklime are then added and 90 per cent. of the volume of alcohol originally taken is distilled over. To prevent the absorption of water vapour from the air, rubber stoppers must be used, and the exits of the apparatus must be closed with calcium chloride tubes, Fig. 13, p. 57. The distillate is known as " absolute alcohol ". It still contains about 0·2 per cent. of water. To remove this water the absolute alcohol is allowed to stand either over calcium turnings or over magnesium amalgam, which decompose the water according to the chemical reactions,

$$Ca + 2H_2O = Ca(OH)_2 + H_2,$$
$$MgHg + 2H_2O = Mg(OH)_2 + H_2 + Hg.$$

The alcohol is then redistilled, taking care to exclude water vapour from the apparatus.

(ii) **Fractionation in the presence of benzene.** A mixture of alcohol, water and benzene is a system which gives rise to a minimum boiling point mixture, p. 63. When a mixture of benzene and alcohol containing a little water is fractionated, the minimum boiling point mixture passes over until all the water is removed, and the residue in the flask consists only of alcohol and benzene. A minimum boiling point mixture of alcohol and benzene then distils until all the benzene is removed, and the subsequent fractions consist of pure alcohol.

CHEMICAL REACTIONS, CONSTITUTION AND USES OF ETHYL ALCOHOL

The chemical reactivity of ethyl alcohol depends upon the presence of the hydroxyl group in the molecule. The reactions of ethyl alcohol may be classified in three types. In reactions of the first type the —OH group alone takes part, and the linkages of the atoms in the remaining group, —C_2H_5, are undisturbed. In reactions of the second type the group —CH_2OH takes part, and in those of the third the linkages throughout the molecule are affected.

I. Reactions of ethyl alcohol in which the group —OH alone takes part.

1. Reaction with sodium or potassium, giving sodium or potassium ethoxide. Metallic sodium or potassium react with ethyl alcohol, liberating hydrogen and forming sodium or potassium ethoxide,

$$2Na \ + \ 2C_2H_5OH \ = \ H_2 \ + \ 2C_2H_5ONa.$$

The reaction is much less vigorous than the actions of these metals with water. Sodium and potassium ethoxides are crystalline substances readily soluble in alcohol. They absorb carbon dioxide from the air. They are hygroscopic and are immediately decomposed by water,

$$C_2H_5ONa \ + \ H_2O \ = \ C_2H_5OH \ + \ NaOH.$$

Sodium ethoxide is an important reagent in organic chemistry. It is used in preparing the sodium derivatives of ethyl acetoacetate and of ethyl malonate.

Sodium in the presence of ethyl alcohol is used as a reducing agent. For example, sodium reacts with an alcoholic solution of ethyl cyanide to yield propylamine,

$$4Na \ + \ 4C_2H_5OH \ + \ C_2H_5CN$$
$$= \ C_2H_5CH_2NH_2 \ + \ 4C_2H_5ONa.$$

2. Reaction with acids, giving ethyl esters. Ethyl alcohol reacts with mineral acids, or with organic acids, to give esters. For example, ethyl alcohol and hydrobromic acid give ethyl bromide,

$$C_2H_5OH \ + \ HBr \ \rightleftharpoons \ C_2H_5Br \ + \ H_2O.$$

Reactions of this class are reversible, and consequently, to secure a good yield of the ester, a dehydrating agent should normally be present to remove the water formed. Hydrogen chloride, zinc chloride or concentrated sulphuric acid may be used for this purpose. Sulphuric acid is usually employed in the preparation of the ethyl esters of organic acids. Ethyl acetate, for example, is made by heating a mixture of ethyl alcohol, acetic acid and concentrated sulphuric acid. The reaction may be summarised by the reversible equation,

$$C_2H_5OH \ + \ CH_3.COOH \ \rightleftharpoons \ CH_3.COOC_2H_5 \ + \ H_2O.$$

3. Reaction with concentrated sulphuric acid, giving ethyl hydrogen sulphate, diethyl ether or ethylene. If concentrated sulphuric acid is added to ethyl alcohol, a solution is obtained in which ethyl hydrogen sulphate is present,

$$H_2SO_4 + C_2H_5OH = C_2H_5.HSO_4 + H_2O.$$

If this solution mixed with excess of sulphuric acid is heated to 170°, ethylene is obtained in accordance with the reaction described on p. 115. If the solution is mixed with excess of alcohol and heated to 140°, diethyl ether is formed,

$$C_2H_5.HSO_4 + C_2H_5OH = C_2H_5OC_2H_5 + H_2SO_4.$$

This important reaction is described on p. 177.

4. Reactions with the phosphorus halides, giving ethyl halides. Phosphorus pentachloride, phosphorus trichloride, phosphorus bromide, or a mixture of iodine and red phosphorus, react energetically with ethyl alcohol to produce ethyl chloride, ethyl bromide or ethyl iodide respectively. These reactions, which are the basis of important methods for preparing the monohalogeno-ethanes, have been mentioned and exemplified on pp. 138 and 146.

5. Reaction with acetyl chloride, or with acetic anhydride, to give ethyl acetate. If equal volumes of acetyl chloride and ethyl alcohol are warmed together, ethyl acetate is formed,

$$CH_3.COCl + C_2H_5OH = CH_3.COOC_2H_5 + HCl.$$

Ethyl acetate is also produced if a mixture of acetic anyhdride and ethyl alcohol is similarly treated,

$$(CH_3.CO)_2O + 2C_2H_5OH = 2CH_3.COOC_2H_5 + H_2O.^*$$

6. Reaction with acetaldehyde, giving acetal. In the presence of an acid, ethyl alcohol combines with acetaldehyde to yield acetal, a liquid, B.P. 103° ; the reaction is reversible,

$$CH_3.C{\overset{\displaystyle H}{\underset{\displaystyle O}{\Big<}}} + 2HOC_2H_5 = CH_3.C{\overset{\displaystyle H}{\underset{\displaystyle OC_2H_5}{\Big<\!\!{-}OC_2H_5}}} + H_2O.$$

II. Reactions in which the group —CH$_2$OH takes part.

7. Dehydrogenation, giving acetaldehyde. If alcohol vapour is passed over metallic copper heated to 250–300°, a mixture of acetaldehyde vapour, hydrogen and unchanged alcohol is obtained,

$$C_2H_5OH = CH_3.CHO + H_2.$$

If the mixture is cooled to 30° most of the alcohol is liquefied, and the remaining vapour may then be condensed to yield a concentrated solution of acetaldehyde in alcohol.

* The structural equation for this reaction is given on p. 253.

8. Oxidation, giving acetaldehyde or acetic acid. An aqueous solution of sodium or potassium dichromate in the presence of dilute sulphuric acid oxidises ethyl alcohol, first to acetaldehyde,

$$CH_3.CH_2OH \ + \ O \ = \ CH_3.CHO \ + \ H_2O,$$

and then to acetic acid,

$$CH_3.CHO \ + \ O \ = \ CH_3.COOH.$$

Acetaldehyde can be obtained as an intermediate product only if it is rapidly removed from attack by the oxidising agent. If a mixture of ethyl alcohol and sodium dichromate solution is allowed to fall from a dropping-funnel, drop by drop, into hot dilute sulphuric acid contained in a flask fitted with a water condenser, Fig. 47, p. 200, the sodium dichromate solution is never in excess, and the acetaldehyde which is formed distils away. If an aqueous solution of alcohol is allowed to drop slowly into a mixture of sodium dichromate solution and dilute sulphuric acid boiling under a reflux condenser, Fig. 48, p. 232, the alcohol is converted to acetic acid.

Ethyl alcohol is oxidised to acetic acid when exposed to the air in the presence of platinum black. It is also oxidised by atmospheric oxygen in the presence of *Bacterium aceti*; vinegar is made by this process. Ethyl alcohol is sometimes employed as a mild reducing agent. It may be used, for example, to reduce benzene diazonium chloride to benzene,

$$CH_3.CH_2OH \ + \ C_6H_5.N_2Cl \ = \ C_6H_6 \ + \ N_2 \ + \ HCl \ + \ CH_3.CHO.$$

III. Reactions in which the molecule of ethyl alcohol acts as a whole.

9. Combustion. Ethyl alcohol burns in air with a pale non-luminous flame, forming water and carbon dioxide,

$$C_2H_5OH \ + \ 3O_2 \ = \ 2CO_2 \ + \ 3H_2O.$$

Alcohol vapour forms explosive mixtures with air or oxygen. A mixture of alcohol and liquid oxygen is used as a propellant for rockets.

10. Dehydration, giving ethylene. Ethyl alcohol reacts with concentrated sulphuric acid to yield ethylene under the conditions mentioned on p. 115.

11. Reaction with sodium hypochlorite and potassium iodide, giving iodoform. The iodoform reaction. Ethyl alcohol is one of the compounds which undergo the iodoform reaction, discussed on p. 156. This reaction may be carried out on a test-tube scale by adding freshly prepared sodium hypochlorite solution to a mixture of a few c.c. of 10 per cent. potassium iodide solution and a little ethyl alcohol. Yellow crystals of iodoform separate ; the yield is increased if the solution is warmed and allowed to stand for 1 or 2 minutes.

12. Action of chlorine, giving chloral alcoholate. If chlorine is passed for several days into absolute alcohol containing ferric chloride to act as a catalyst, chloral alcoholate is formed. This is the first stage in the manufacture of chloral described on p. 216.

Constitution of ethyl alcohol. The molecular formula of ethyl alcohol is shown by the results of its combustion and the determination of its vapour density to be C_2H_6O. There are two ways of arranging the atoms in the molecule to give structural formulae in which the valencies of carbon, oxygen and hydrogen are four, two and one respectively, thus

H H   H   H
| | | |
H—C—C—O—H   H—C—O—C—H
| | | |
H H   H   H
Formula I   Formula II

Chemical evidence shows that Formula I is the molecular formula of ethyl alcohol. Sodium attacks ethyl alcohol, displacing one hydrogen atom from the molecule, and thus showing that one hydrogen atom in the molecule is distinguishable from the other five. Phosphorus pentachloride reacts with ethyl alcohol to replace one atom of hydrogen and the oxygen atom in the molecule by one atom of chlorine. These reactions may be represented by the equations :

$$2C_2H_5OH \;+\; 2Na \;=\; 2C_2H_5ONa \;+\; H_2$$
$$C_2H_5OH \;+\; PCl_5 \;=\; C_2H_5Cl \;+\; POCl_3 \;+\; HCl.$$

Since the six hydrogen atoms in the ethane molecule occupy identical positions (p. 111) there can be only one substance possessing the constitutional formula, C_2H_5OH.

Uses of ethyl alcohol. Ethyl alcohol is used in industry as a solvent, and as the starting-point for the manufacture of other organic compounds, p. 494. In the laboratory it is used as a solvent for the purification of substances by recrystallisation ; methylated spirit in many cases is as suitable for this purpose as pure ethyl alcohol and it is much cheaper. Rectified spirit may be used as the solvent in ebullioscopic methods for determining molecular weights. Absolute alcohol is unsuitable for this purpose, as it is so hygroscopic that the ebullioscopic constant of a given sample is liable to change in the course of the determination. On account of the very low freezing-point of ethyl alcohol it is used in thermometers exposed to conditions in which mercury would solidify.

Tests for ethyl alcohol. There is no reliable specific test for ethyl alcohol. It may be recognised by the fruity odour of ethyl acetate which arises when a little alcohol is warmed with a small quantity of sodium acetate and a few drops of concentrated sulphuric acid. The odour is most easily detected if the liquid mixture is cooled and then poured into water in a boiling-tube. The esters formed by the reaction of acetic acid with other alcohols, however, have somewhat similar odours, which may easily be mistaken for that of ethyl acetate.

If ethyl alcohol is added to a warmed mixture of 1 c.c. of concentrated sulphuric acid with 5 c.c. of concentrated aqueous potassium dichromate solution, acetaldehyde is formed and its odour may be detected.

The iodoform reaction mentioned in Reaction 11, serves to differentiate ethyl alcohol from methyl alcohol, but it does not distinguish between ethyl alcohol and many other compounds, cf. p. 156.

METHYL ALCOHOL

Methyl alcohol is a colourless liquid. It has an agreeable odour and a burning taste ; it is poisonous and gives rise to insanity and blindness. It is miscible in all proportions with water, in which it dissolves with evolution of heat and contraction in volume.

PRINCIPAL REACTIONS IN WHICH METHYL ALCOHOL IS PRODUCED

The range of reactions in which methyl alcohol is produced is much smaller than the corresponding range for ethyl alcohol. No common process of fermentation leads to the formation of methyl alcohol. It cannot be made from any member of the olefine class by treatment with sulphuric acid, as ethylene, the lowest member of the olefine series, contains two atoms of carbon in the molecule. It cannot be made by the reduction of formaldehyde. The hydrolysis of methyl chloride or bromide by sodium hydroxide or potassium hydroxide solution would lead to the production of methyl alcohol, but this method is troublesome in practice, as methyl chloride and methyl bromide are gases. Methyl iodide, B.P. 42°, however, may be hydrolysed to sodium iodide and methyl alcohol by warming it with sodium hydroxide solution in a flask fitted to a reflux condenser,

$$CH_3I + NaOH = NaI + CH_3OH.$$

In the laboratory, therefore, methyl alcohol is produced only by the hydrolysis of methyl iodide, or of the methyl esters of organic acids, or by the action of nitrous acid on methylamine.

1. The hydrolysis of methyl esters of organic acids. Methyl acetate, for example, is placed with aqueous sodium hydroxide solution in a flask fitted with a reflux condenser, and the contents of the flask are gently heated. Sodium acetate and methyl alcohol are produced :

$$H_3C—C\overset{O}{\underset{O—CH_3}{\big\langle}} \quad + \quad NaOH \quad = \quad H_3C—C\overset{O}{\underset{ONa}{\big\langle}} \quad + \quad HOCH_3.$$

The methyl alcohol may be separated from the solution by distillation. Certain methyl esters of organic acids are crystalline solids, for instance, dimethyl oxalate, M.P. 57°. These esters may be purified by recrystallisation, and they are therefore suitable as a source of small quantities of pure methyl alcohol.

2. The action of nitrous acid on methylamine.

$$H—\overset{\overset{\displaystyle H}{|}}{\underset{\underset{\displaystyle H}{|}}{C}}—N\overset{H}{\underset{H}{\big\langle}} \quad + \quad HO—N{=}O \quad = \quad H—\overset{\overset{\displaystyle H}{|}}{\underset{\underset{\displaystyle H}{|}}{C}}—OH \quad + \quad N_2 \quad + \quad H_2O.$$

An aqueous solution of methylamine hydrochloride is acidified with hydrochloric acid, and a solution of sodium nitrite is slowly added from a thistle funnel of which the stem passes to the bottom of the methylamine hydrochloride solution. Nitrogen is evolved, and methyl alcohol may be distilled from the residual solution.

Industrial preparation of methyl alcohol. Methyl alcohol is manufactured from water-gas, p. 488. Water-gas is a mixture of carbon monoxide and hydrogen made by passing steam over white-hot coke,

$$C \quad + \quad H_2O \quad = \quad CO \quad + \quad H_2.$$

The water-gas, after enrichment with hydrogen, is compressed to about 300 atmospheres pressure, and passed over a catalyst consisting of basic zinc chromate, $4ZnO.CrO_3$, at a temperature of about 300°. Under these conditions the carbon monoxide unites with the hydrogen to form methyl alcohol,

$$CO \quad + \quad 2H_2 \quad = \quad CH_3OH.$$

The methyl alcohol so obtained is almost pure ; it may be completely purified by standing over quicklime, followed by careful fractionation.

Anhydrous methyl alcohol. The procedure for making anhydrous, or " absolute " methyl alcohol is similar to that used for making absolute ethyl alcohol. 5–10 litres of methyl alcohol purified by fractional distillation are boiled with quicklime for 6 hours in a flask fitted with a reflux water condenser closed with a calcium chloride tube. The product is then distilled, the distillation being stopped when about 10 per cent. of the original contents remain in the distilling flask. Rubber stoppers must be used throughout the process, and all exits from the apparatus must be closed with calcium chloride tubes.

CHEMICAL REACTIONS AND CONSTITUTION
OF METHYL ALCOHOL

The chemical properties of methyl alcohol are, in the main, similar to those of ethyl alcohol. Methyl alcohol undergoes Reactions 1, 2, 4, 5 and 6 of those described for ethyl alcohol on p. 162, under the same conditions as those applying to the reactions of ethyl alcohol, to yield methyl derivatives where ethyl alcohol yields ethyl derivatives ; the equations representing the reactions of both alcohols are similar in form.

Methyl alcohol, however, cannot undergo reactions which require the presence of more than one carbon atom in the molecule. Therefore the reactions of ethyl alcohol with concentrated sulphuric acid to yield ethylene, with chlorine to yield chloral, and with chlorine and an alkali to yield chloroform, and with iodine and an alkali to yield iodoform, have no parallels in the case of methyl alcohol. The controlled oxidation of methyl alcohol yields formaldehyde and formic acid, just as the oxidation of ethyl alcohol yields acetaldehyde and acetic acid, but the conditions under which formaldehyde and formic acid are produced differ from those required for the production of acetaldehyde and acetic acid. On combustion in air both methyl alcohol and ethyl alcohol yield carbon dioxide and water.

On p. 163, Reaction 3, it is pointed out that ethyl alcohol reacts with concentrated sulphuric acid to yield ethyl hydrogen sulphate, which gives diethyl ether if heated to 140° with excess of ethyl alcohol, or ethylene if heated in the presence of sulphuric acid to 170°. Methyl alcohol behaves similarly in so far as methyl hydrogen sulphate is formed when methyl alcohol is treated with concentrated sulphuric acid,

$$CH_3OH + H_2SO_4 = CH_3.HSO_4 + H_2O,$$

and dimethyl ether is produced when methyl hydrogen sulphate is heated to 140° with excess of methyl alcohol,

$$CH_3.OH + CH_3.HSO_4 = CH_3OCH_3 + H_2SO_4,$$

but in no circumstances does methyl alcohol by reaction with sulphuric acid yield a member of the olefine series. When the solution obtained by the action of concentrated sulphuric acid on methyl alcohol is heated, an equilibrium is established between methyl hydrogen sulphate, dimethyl sulphate and sulphuric acid,

$$2CH_3.HSO_4 \rightleftharpoons (CH_3)_2SO_4 + H_2SO_4.$$

Dimethyl sulphate, a liquid B.P. 188°, is the most volatile of these three substances, and it distils from the solution. The removal of the dimethyl sulphate disturbs the equilibrium, more dimethyl sulphate is formed and volatilises, and ultimately the decomposition of the methyl hydrogen sulphate is complete.

Dimethyl sulphate is most efficiently prepared by allowing methyl alcohol to react with sulphur trioxide at 0°,

$$CH_3OH + SO_3 = CH_3.HSO_4,$$

and distilling under reduced pressure the methyl hydrogen sulphate so formed. Dimethyl sulphate is highly poisonous.

The conditions under which methyl alcohol is *oxidised* to formaldehyde or formic acid are as follows. Formaldehyde is obtained from methyl alcohol by passing a mixture of methyl alcohol vapour and air over metallic platinum, or silver, or copper, at 300–400°,

$$CH_3OH + O = H_2CO + H_2O.$$

The solution of formaldehyde in the mixture of water and unchanged methyl alcohol obtained by condensing the products of the reaction is known as *formalin,* and is used as a disinfectant.

Formic acid is obtained from methyl alcohol by passing a mixture of methyl alcohol vapour and air over platinum black at room temperature. In this experiment the concentration of alcohol vapour in the mixture is limited by the vapour pressure of methyl alcohol at room temperature, and this may account for the oxidation of the alcohol beyond the aldehyde stage,

$$CH_3OH + 2O = H.COOH + H_2O.$$

At higher temperatures, or in the presence of massive platinum, methyl alcohol vapour is oxidised chiefly to formaldehyde. Formic acid is also obtained from methyl alcohol by warming it for a few minutes with a mixture of aqueous sodium dichromate solution and dilute sulphuric acid in a flask fitted to a reflux condenser.

A mixture of manganese dioxide and sulphuric acid converts methyl alcohol to methylal ; formaldehyde is first formed, and in the presence of the acid it combines with unchanged methyl alcohol thus,

$$\begin{matrix} H \\ \\ H \end{matrix}\!\!\Big\rangle C{=}O \; + \; 2HOCH_3 \; = \; \begin{matrix} H \\ \\ H \end{matrix}\!\!\Big\rangle C\!\!\Big\langle\begin{matrix} OCH_3 \\ \\ OCH_3 \end{matrix} \; + \; H_2O.$$

Methyl alcohol, unlike ethyl alcohol, does not reduce benzene diazonium chloride to benzene ; instead it reacts with it to produce phenyl methyl ether, or anisole,

$$C_6H_5N_2Cl + HOCH_3 = C_6H_5OCH_3 + N_2 + HCl.$$

F2   D.C.

Constitution of methyl alcohol. The molecular formula of methyl alcohol is shown by the results of its combustion and the determination of its vapour density to be CH_4O. If carbon, oxygen and hydrogen are exerting their normal covalencies of four, two and one in the molecule, the structural formula must be written :

$$H-\underset{\underset{H}{|}}{\overset{\overset{H}{|}}{C}}-OH.$$

This structure is confirmed by the chemical reactions of methyl alcohol. When methyl alcohol is treated with metallic sodium only one of the four hydrogen atoms in the molecule is displaced, thus indicating that the position of one of the four hydrogen atoms is different from the positions of the other three. On this evidence the equation for this reaction may be written :

$$2CH_3OH + 2Na = 2CH_3ONa + H_2.$$

When methyl alcohol reacts with phosphorus pentachloride, one hydrogen atom and one oxygen atom in the molecule are replaced by one atom of chlorine. This reaction is described by the equation,

$$CH_3OH + PCl_5 = CH_3Cl + POCl_3 + HCl.$$

The molecule of methyl alcohol, therefore, consists of a methyl group, H_3C—, linked to a hydroxyl group, —OH. Its structure may be derived from that of methane by the replacement of one hydrogen atom in the methane molecule by the group —OH.

Uses of methyl alcohol. Methyl alcohol is used as a source of formalin and other organic compounds, p. 489. It is also used as an anti-freeze in car radiators, as a solvent, and for denaturing ethyl alcohol.

Tests for methyl alcohol. A distinctive test for methyl alcohol is furnished by the formation of methyl salicylate when a mixture of methyl alcohol, salicylic acid, and concentrated sulphuric acid is warmed. If the mixture is cooled and poured into a little water in a boiling-tube the odour of methyl salicylate may be detected. Methyl salicylate is the ester which gives the characteristic odour to oil of wintergreen. Ethyl salicylate is the only other ester which possesses an odour at all similar to that of methyl salicylate.

Pure methyl alcohol does not respond to the iodoform test, which may therefore be used to distinguish methyl alcohol from ethyl alcohol.

If methyl alcohol is warmed with a solution of sodium dichromate in dilute sulphuric acid, contained in a flask fitted with a reflux condenser, formic acid is produced in solution. If the solution is distilled formic acid is collected in the first few c.c. of the distillate, and may be recognised by the tests given on p. 244.

THE PROPYL AND BUTYL ALCOHOLS

Propyl alcohol, C_3H_7OH, exists in two isomeric forms:

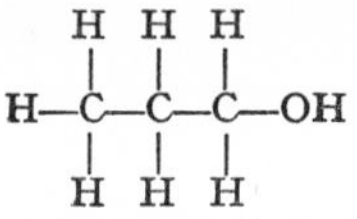

normal propyl alcohol 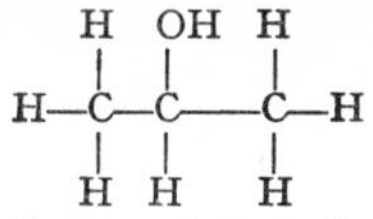   iso-propyl alcohol.

n-Propyl alcohol is made by heating *n*-propyl iodide with a suspension of silver oxide in water, which reacts as silver hydroxide, AgOH,

$$CH_3.CH_2.CH_2I + AgOH = CH_3.CH_2.CH_2OH + AgI.$$

n-Propyl alcohol is a liquid which is miscible with water in all proportions. On oxidation with a solution of sodium dichromate in dilute sulphuric acid it is converted first to propaldehyde and then to propionic acid.

Iso-propyl alcohol can be made in the laboratory by the reduction of acetone with sodium amalgam and water,

$$CH_3.CO.CH_3 + 2H = CH_3.CH.OH.CH_3.$$

On oxidation it yields acetone.

Butyl alcohol, C_4H_9OH, exists in four isomeric forms:

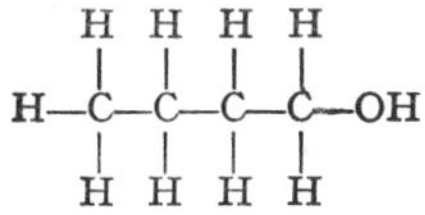

normal butyl alcohol 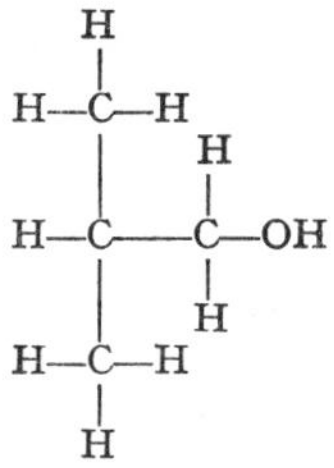   iso-butyl-alcohol

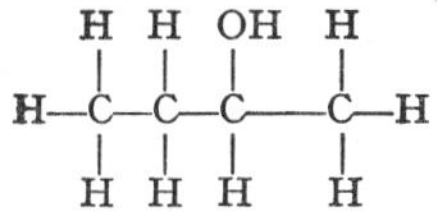

secondary butyl alcohol 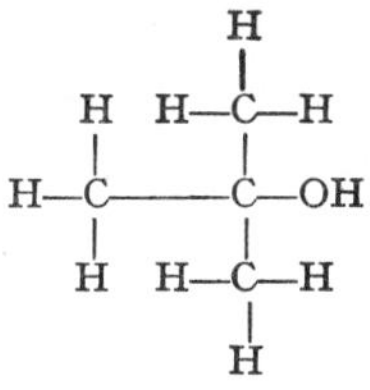   tertiary butyl alcohol

n-Butyl alcohol is of importance in industry, as the alcohol and its esters are valuable solvents. It is made from acetylene, p. 491, from water-gas, p. 489, or by the fermentation of sugars by Fernbach's culture, p. 221.

ISOMERISM IN THE MONOHYDRIC ALCOHOL SERIES

All members of the monohydric alcohol series other than methyl alcohol and ethyl alcohol exhibit isomerism. The isomerism of the alcohols depends either on variations in the branching of the hydro-carbon chain, as in normal butyl alcohol and iso-butyl alcohol, or on the position of the hydroxyl group in the molecule. Isomerism which is due to changes in the position of the hydroxyl group gives rise to primary, secondary, and tertiary alcohols.

Primary alcohols. Molecules of primary alcohols contain the group $-\overset{\overset{\text{H}}{|}}{\underset{\underset{\text{H}}{|}}{\text{C}}}-\text{OH}$, in which the hydroxyl group is bound to a carbon atom which is linked to two hydrogen atoms. Of the alcohols which have already been mentioned, the primary alcohol group is present in methyl alcohol, ethyl alcohol, normal propyl alcohol, normal butyl alcohol, and iso-butyl alcohol. Primary alcohols are formed by (i) the reduction of the appropriate aldehyde by sodium amalgam and water, (ii) the action of formaldehyde on a Grignard reagent, or (iii) the hydrolysis of the corresponding alkyl iodide by moist silver oxide or dilute aqueous alkalis.

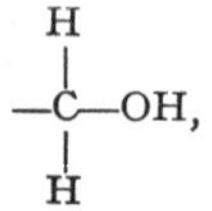

On oxidation with aqueous sodium dichromate solution in the presence of sulphuric acid a primary alcohol yields first an aldehyde,

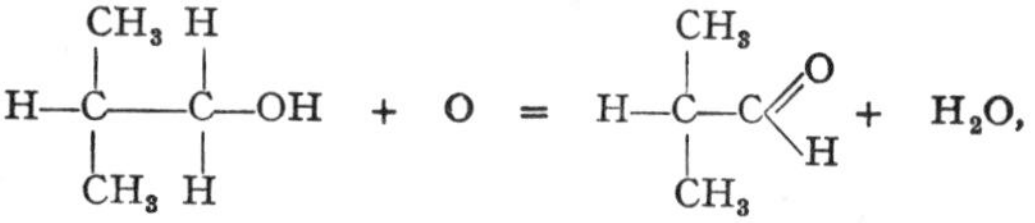

and then a fatty acid containing the same number of carbon atoms in the molecule as the original alcohol,

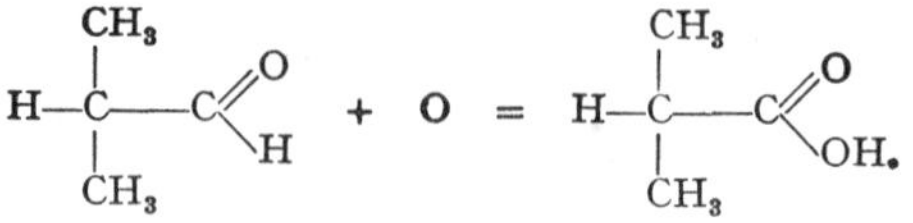

If the vapour of a primary alcohol is passed over heated nickel, the corresponding aldehyde is produced and hydrogen is set free. The reaction is reversible,

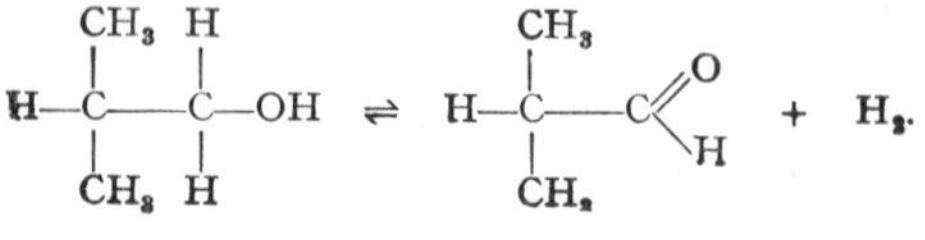

Secondary alcohols. Molecules of secondary alcohols contain the group $\diagdown C \diagup\!\!\!\!{}^H_{OH}$, in which the hydroxyl group is bound to a carbon atom linked to one hydrogen atom. The secondary alcohol group is present in iso-propyl alcohol and secondary butyl alcohol.

Secondary alcohols are formed by (i) the reduction of the appropriate ketone by sodium amalgam and water, (ii) the absorption of an olefine of the type,

$$\begin{matrix} R \diagdown \diagup X \\ C{=}C \\ H \diagup \diagdown H \end{matrix}$$

(where R is an alkyl group, and X may be either a hydrogen atom or an alkyl group) in sulphuric acid, followed by the hydrolysis of the alkyl hydrogen sulphate thus formed, (iii) the action of an aldehyde (other than formaldehyde) or ethyl formate on a Grignard reagent, or (iv) the hydrolysis of the corresponding alkyl iodide.*

On oxidation with aqueous sodium dichromate solution and dilute sulphuric acid a secondary alcohol yields a ketone,

$$\begin{matrix} H_3C \diagdown \diagup H \\ C \\ H_3C \diagup \diagdown OH \end{matrix} + O = \begin{matrix} H_3C \diagdown \\ C{=}O \\ H_3C \diagup \end{matrix} + H_2O.$$

secondary propyl alcohol   acetone

No further reaction occurs leading to the formation of a fatty acid, as ketones are oxidised only with difficulty.

If the vapour of a secondary alcohol is passed over heated nickel, the corresponding ketone is produced and hydrogen is set free,

$$\begin{matrix} H_3C \diagdown \diagup H \\ C \\ H_3C \diagup \diagdown OH \end{matrix} \rightleftharpoons \begin{matrix} H_3C \diagdown \\ C{=}O \\ H_3C \diagup \end{matrix} + H_2.$$

Tertiary alcohols. Molecules of tertiary alcohols contain the group $-\overset{|}{\underset{|}{C}}-OH$, in which the hydroxyl group is attached to a carbon atom which is not linked to a hydrogen atom. The tertiary group is present in tertiary butyl alcohol. Tertiary alcohols are formed by (i) the absorption in sulphuric acid of an olefine of the type

$$\begin{matrix} R_1 \diagdown \diagup X_1 \\ C{=}C \\ R_2 \diagup \diagdown X_2 \end{matrix}$$

(where R_1 and R_2 are alkyl groups, and X_1 and X_2 represent either hydrogen atoms or alkyl groups) followed by hydrolysis of the alkyl hydrogen sulphate so formed, (ii) the action of a ketone or an ester (other than an ester of formic acid) on a Grignard reagent, or

(iii) the hydrolysis of the corresponding alkyl iodide. Tertiary alcohols cannot be formed by the reduction of aldehydes or ketones.

On oxidation, a tertiary alcohol gives a mixture of fatty acids, or of fatty acids and ketones. The number of carbon atoms in a molecule of any of the oxidation products is always less than the number present in a molecule of the original tertiary alcohol. If the vapour of a tertiary alcohol is passed over heated nickel it loses water and yields an olefine,

$$\underset{\text{tertiary butyl alcohol}}{CH_3-\underset{\overset{|}{CH_3}}{\overset{\overset{\displaystyle CH_3}{|}}{C}}-OH} \quad \rightleftharpoons \quad \underset{\text{iso-butylene}}{CH_3-\underset{\overset{|}{CH_3}}{\overset{\overset{\displaystyle CH_2}{\|}}{C}}} + H_2O.$$

The same change occurs when a tertiary alcohol is warmed with a dehydrating agent such as zinc chloride or phosphorus pentoxide ; in some cases heat alone is sufficient to decompose a tertiary alcohol into an olefine and water.

Nomenclature of alcohols. The method of naming the simpler alcohols is apparent from Table XIII, p. 159. More complex alcohols are conveniently described by the *carbinol* system of nomenclature. In this system the molecule of a given alcohol is regarded as a molecule of methyl alcohol in which one or more hydrogen atoms have been replaced by alkyl groups. The molecule of methyl alcohol is designated as " carbinol ", and the name of the given alcohol is obtained by prefixing the names of the substituent alkyl groups to the word " carbinol ". Thus ethyl alcohol, $CH_3.CH_2OH$, is methyl carbinol, secondary butyl alcohol $CH_3.CH_2.CH(OH).CH_3$ is ethyl methyl carbinol, and tertiary butyl alcohol is trimethyl carbinol.

Distinction between primary, secondary and tertiary alcohols. Primary, secondary and tertiary alcohols may be distinguished by the following methods.

1. The vapour of the alcohol is passed over heated nickel. A primary alcohol yields hydrogen and an aldehyde, a secondary alcohol yields hydrogen and a ketone, and a tertiary alcohol yields an olefine and water.

2. The vapour density of the alcohol is determined in three experiments using Victor Meyer's apparatus. In the first experiment the jacket contains boiling xylene, B.P. 140° ; in the second, boiling naphthalene, B.P. 218° ; and in the third, boiling anthracene, B.P. 340°. A primary alcohol is not decomposed at any of these temperatures, and consequently the same value for the vapour density is obtained in all three experiments. A secondary alcohol decomposes above 250°, and

therefore its vapour density is constant for the first two experiments only. The vapour density of a tertiary alcohol, since members of this class of alcohols are easily decomposed, is different in each of the three experiments.

3. The alcohol is oxidised with aqueous sodium dichromate solution and sulphuric acid. A primary alcohol yields an aldehyde or a fatty acid containing the same number of carbon atoms per molecule as the original alcohol, a secondary alcohol yields a ketone, and a tertiary alcohol a mixture of acids or ketones.

4. Victor Meyer's method. This method depends on the reaction between nitroparaffins and nitrous acid. A primary nitroparaffin reacts with nitrous acid to yield a nitrolic acid,

$$
\underset{\substack{| \\ H}}{\overset{\substack{NO_2 \\ |}}{H_3C-C-H}} \ + \ O{=}N{-}OH \ = \ H_3C-C\underset{NOH}{\overset{NO_2}{\diagup}} \ + \ H_2O.
$$

The nitrolic acid is colourless, but the acid ion

$$
\left[H_3C-C\underset{NO}{\overset{NO_2}{\diagup}} \right]^-
$$

is red. A secondary nitroparaffin reacts with nitrous acid to yield a pseudonitrol,

$$
\underset{H_3C}{\overset{H_3C}{\diagdown}}C\underset{NO_2}{\overset{H}{\diagup}} \ + \ HON{=}O \ = \ \underset{H_3C}{\overset{H_3C}{\diagdown}}C\underset{NO_2}{\overset{N=O}{\diagup}} \ + \ H_2O.
$$

A pseudonitrol is not an acid ; it is a neutral compound, soluble in chloroform to give a blue solution. Tertiary nitroparaffins, such as trimethyl nitromethane

$$
\underset{\substack{| \\ CH_3}}{\overset{\substack{CH_3 \\ |}}{CH_3-C-NO_2}}
$$

do not react with nitrous acid.

To carry out the method practically, the alcohol to be tested is converted to the corresponding alkyl iodide by treatment with iodine and red phosphorus, p. 146. It may be noted that tertiary alcohols do not yield alkyl iodides. The alkyl iodide is then converted to the corresponding nitroparaffin by treatment with silver nitrite in alcoholic solution. The nitroparaffin is dissolved in dilute aqueous sodium hydroxide solution, an aqueous solution of sodium nitrite is added, and the solution is acidified by the gradual addition of dilute sulphuric acid. If a primary nitroparaffin is present, as soon as the sulphuric acid has neutralised the excess sodium hydroxide and liberated nitrous acid from the sodium nitrite, ions of the nitrolic acid are formed, which colour the solution a reddish-brown. On further addition of sulphuric acid the ionisation, and hence the coloration, of the nitrolic acid is suppressed, and the colour of the solution fades.

If a secondary nitroparaffin is present, addition of the sulphuric acid produces a blue colour in the solution, which passes into the chloroform layer if the solution is shaken with chloroform.

CHAPTER X

THE ALIPHATIC ETHERS

AN ether is theoretically derived by the substitution of an alkyl group for the hydrogen atom in the hydroxyl group in the molecule of a monohydric alcohol. Diethyl ether is derived by replacing the hydroxyl hydrogen atom in the ethyl alcohol molecule by an ethyl group.

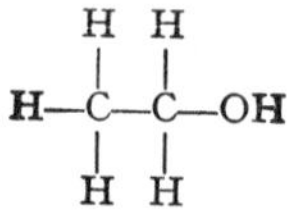

$$\begin{array}{ccccccc} & H & H & & H & H & & H & H \\ & | & | & & | & | & & | & | \\ H- & C- & C- & OH & H- & C- & C- & O- & C- & C- & H \\ & | & | & & | & | & & | & | \\ & H & H & & H & H & & H & H \end{array}$$

ethyl alcohol 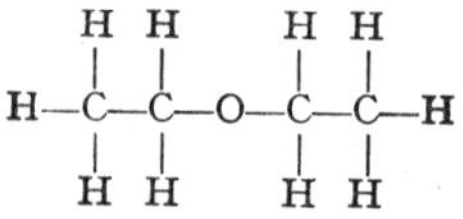   diethyl ether

A simple ether contains two identical alkyl groups in the molecule ; a mixed ether contains two different alkyl groups in the molecule. Methyl ethyl ether, $CH_3OC_2H_5$, is an example of a mixed ether.

The lowest member of the homologous series is dimethyl ether, a gas, B.P. $-23.5°$. Diethyl ether, a very volatile liquid, may be taken as the typical member of the series.

DIETHYL ETHER

Diethyl ether is a colourless mobile liquid with a marked characteristic "ethereal" odour. It is extremely volatile at ordinary temperatures, B.P. $34.9°$, M.P. $-113°$; the vapour is more than $2\frac{1}{2}$ times denser than air. Mixtures of ether vapour and air are explosive. If care is not taken to prevent the escape of ether into the air when it is being prepared or used as a solvent, the heavy ether vapour mixed with air may accumulate in sinks, or in dense layers on the floor or benches of the laboratory. Chance contact with a flame will cause the whole of the mixture to explode, with the danger that the ether being produced or used in the experiment may be ignited.

Ether is soluble in water (at $20°$, 6.60 gm. dissolve in 100 gm. of water), and water is soluble in ether (1.24 gm. of water dissolve in 100 gm. of ether). Ether is miscible in all proportions with ethyl alcohol, and is a solvent for many other organic substances and for iodine, bromine, ferric chloride, and some other inorganic compounds. It plays an important part in the Grignard reactions by acting as a solvent for the magnesium alkyl compounds formed in the course of the reactions.

PRINCIPAL REACTIONS IN WHICH DIETHYL ETHER IS PRODUCED

1. The action of excess of ethyl alcohol on concentrated sulphuric acid. Williamson's continuous etherification process. If concentrated sulphuric acid is added to ethyl alcohol, a solution is obtained containing ethyl hydrogen sulphate,

$$C_2H_5OH + H_2SO_4 = C_2H_5HSO_4 + H_2O$$

If the solution is heated to 140° while the alcohol is in excess, the ethyl hydrogen sulphate reacts with a further quantity of alcohol to yield diethyl ether,

$$C_2H_5HSO_4 + C_2H_5OH = C_2H_5—O—C_2H_5 + H_2SO_4.$$

This reaction is facilitated by the presence of aluminium sulphate. The products of the reaction are ether and water ; the sulphuric acid which is used up in the first phase of the reaction is regenerated in the second phase. In the conditions of the experiment, the water and ether distil over together (see " Distillation in steam ", p. 65), and consequently a given quantity of sulphuric acid should convert an indefinite quantity of alcohol to ether and water. In practice, however, the sulphuric acid is gradually reduced to sulphur dioxide by the organic substances present, and as the concentration of the sulphuric acid diminishes the reaction slowly comes to an end.

The process may be made to continue indefinitely if, instead of sulphuric acid, benzene sulphonic acid, $C_6H_5SO_2.OH$, or syrupy phosphoric acid is used, as these acids do not suffer reduction by organic substances. A reaction in which one of the reagents is regenerated as fast as it is used up, and so remains at constant concentration, is said to be *continuous*. The action of sulphuric acid on ethyl alcohol is usually referred to as the *continuous* process for the production of ether, although, in fact, it does not continue indefinitely.

In a modification of the above method for producing ether, ethyl alcohol vapour is passed over precipitated alumina in a copper tube heated to 260°. The ethyl alcohol is decomposed catalytically into ether and water ; at higher temperatures ethylene is produced instead of ether.

2. The action of sodium ethoxide on ethyl iodide. Williamson's synthesis of ether. A solution of sodium ethoxide in ethyl alcohol reacts with ethyl iodide to yield sodium iodide and diethyl ether,

$$C_2H_5ONa + IC_2H_5 = C_2H_5OC_2H_5 + NaI.$$

3. The action of dry silver oxide on ethyl iodide. A mixture of ethyl iodide and dry silver oxide is shaken together,

$$2C_2H_5I + Ag_2O = C_2H_5OC_2H_5 + 2AgI.$$

Laboratory preparation of diethyl ether. Diethyl ether is made in the laboratory by the action of excess of ethyl alcohol on concentrated sulphuric acid (Reaction I above). The apparatus shown in Fig. 45 is assembled. The stopper, fitted with the thistle funnel and thermometer,

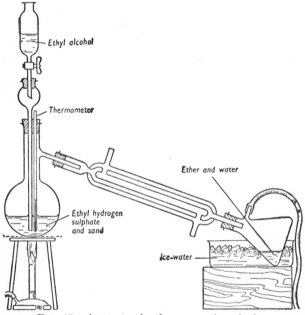

FIG. 45. Apparatus for the preparation of ether.

is withdrawn from the distilling flask, and the flask is detached from the condenser. About 5 gm. of clean dry sand and 45 c.c. of rectified spirit are placed in the flask. It is cooled in ice-water, and 40 c.c. of concentrated sulphuric acid are gradually added to the alcohol with constant shaking to secure thorough mixing. The apparatus is then reassembled, care being taken to see that the bulb of the thermometer is completely immersed in the solution in the flask, and that the end of the stem of the thistle funnel reaches to the bottom of the solution. The flask is heated over a wire gauze by a small Bunsen flame until the thermometer registers 140–145°, when ether begins to distil over. The sand in the flask ensures steady boiling. 50 c.c. of rectified spirit is then allowed to enter the solution, drop by drop, from the dropping funnel at approximately the same rate as that at which the ether distils. The ether is extremely volatile, and therefore a good double-surface water condenser is used to ensure that the condensation is thorough ; for the same reason the receiver is chilled in ice-water. Ether vapour is highly inflammable, and, to prevent its escape into the laboratory at bench level, a Buchner flask is used as a receiver ; a length of rubber tubing is connected to the side-tube, and any ether vapour which volatilises from the receiver is thus led to floor level.

When all the alcohol from the dropping funnel has been added, and the distillation of the ether has ceased (this occurs at about 75 minutes after the beginning of the addition of the alcohol) the gas is turned out, and the distillate is poured into a separating funnel and shaken with 10 per cent. aqueous sodium hydroxide solution, which removes sulphur dioxide (generated by the reduction of the sulphuric acid by the organic substances) and some of the unchanged alcohol which has been carried over with the ether. The layers are allowed to separate ; the lower aqueous layer is rejected, and the upper layer of ether is again extracted with sodium hydroxide solution. The ether is then run into a flask and treated with a good quantity of anhydrous calcium chloride ; this removes the remaining alcohol and water.

The ether is then filtered into a 100 c.c. distilling flask fitted with a thermometer and connected to a double surface condenser. A Buchner flask with a long piece of rubber tubing connected to the side-tube is used for a receiver as before. The distilling flask is cautiously heated by immersion in water at 60° (the water is heated previously away from the apparatus). The ether distils over and the fraction boiling between 34° and 39° is collected.

Pure ether. Ether which is quite free from traces of water and ethyl alcohol is often required in the laboratory, particularly for use in Grignard's reaction. Ether free from these impurities may be prepared by first allowing ordinary ether, in say a Winchester quart bottle, to stand in contact with a good quantity of granular calcium chloride for 24 hours. It is then filtered into another Winchester quart bottle, and treated for about 24 hours with about 25 gm. of freshly extruded sodium wire. The Winchester quart bottle must be closed with a rubber stopper fitted with a calcium chloride tube, so that hydrogen generated by the action of water or alcohol on the sodium may escape, and water vapour from the air may be excluded. The ether is then decanted into a large distilling flask, a few pieces of freshly-cut sodium are added, and the ether is distilled ; all the precautions previously mentioned in connexion with the distillation must be taken. Ether thus obtained is free from water, and almost free from other impurities.

On storage ether undergoes slight atmospheric oxidation to diethyl peroxide $(C_2H_5)_2O_2$. When ether is distilled, any diethyl peroxide present remains in the distillation flask where it may explode during the final stages of the distillation. Diethyl peroxide may be removed from ether by treating it with an acid solution of ferrous sulphate.

PROPERTIES, CONSTITUTION AND USES OF DIETHYL ETHER

Chemical properties. Ether is chemically inert compared with such reactive substances as ethyl bromide or ethyl alcohol ; its chemical inactivity makes it especially valuable as a solvent in which reactions between other substances may be conducted Ether does not react with metallic sodium or potassium, or with alkalis or weak acids, or with phosphorus pentachloride in the cold It reacts with warm concentrated sulphuric acid to form ethyl hydrogen sulphate,

$$C_2H_5OC_2H_5 \quad + \quad 2H_2SO_4 \quad = \quad 2C_2H_5HSO_4 \quad + \quad H_2O,$$

and with concentrated hydriodic acid to give ethyl iodide and water,

$$C_2H_5OC_2H_5 \quad + \quad 2HI \quad = \quad 2C_2H_5I \quad + \quad H_2O.$$

Ether burns in air, with which it forms explosive mixtures,

$$C_2H_5OC_2H_5 \quad + \quad 6O_2 \quad = \quad 4CO_2 \quad + \quad 5H_2O.$$

A mixture of ether vapour and air takes fire if brought into contact with platinum black. Ether explodes if poured into a gas-jar of chlorine in ordinary conditions, but in the dark and in the cold ether may be chlorinated to yield, as a final product, $C_4Cl_{10}O$.

Ether dissolves in aqueous solutions of hydrogen chloride more readily than in water. It is probable that solutions of ether in hydrochloric acid contain the ion $[(C_2H_5)_2OH]^+$ which is the diethyl derivative of the oxonium ion $[H_3O]^+$ which is present in water and in aqueous solutions of acids.

Constitution of diethyl ether. The molecular formula of diethyl ether is shown by analysis and by the determination of its vapour density to be $C_4H_{10}O$. This formula corresponds to a number of isomeric structural formulae, of which the types are :

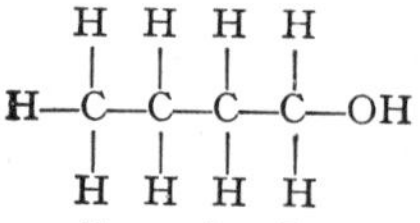

Formula I 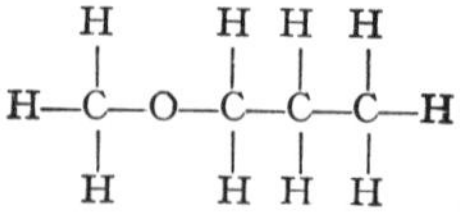   Formula II

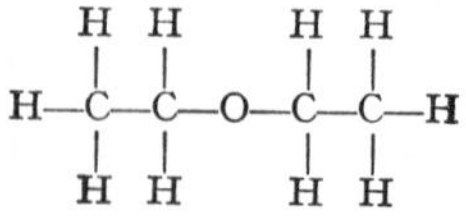

Formula III

The chemical properties of diethyl ether show that it does not contain a hydroxyl group ; it is attacked neither by sodium nor by cold phosphorus pentachloride. Formula I, and other isomeric formulae containing a hydroxyl group, are therefore eliminated. The hydrolysis of diethyl ether, by boiling concentrated hydriodic acid, produces only ethyl iodide and water, and thus confirms Formula III and eliminates Formula II.

Formula III is firmly established by Williamson's synthesis of diethyl ether by the action of sodium ethoxide on ethyl iodide. This reaction must proceed according to the equation,

$$C_2H_5ONa \ + \ IC_2H_5 \ = \ C_2H_5OC_2H_5 \ + \ NaI.$$

Uses of ether. Diethyl ether is used in surgery as an anaesthetic. It is also used as a solvent for resins, fats, oils, and esters.

CHAPTER XI

THE ALIPHATIC AMINES

THE aliphatic amines are theoretically derived from ammonia by the replacement of one or more hydrogen atoms in the molecule by alkyl groups. If one hydrogen atom in the ammonia molecule is replaced by an alkyl group, a *primary amine* is obtained. Monomethylamine, monoethylamine, and monoisobutylamine are examples of primary amines :

$$
\begin{array}{ccc}
\text{H} & \text{CH}_3 & \text{C}_2\text{H}_5 \\
| & | & | \\
\text{N} & \text{N} & \text{N} \\
\text{H}\diagup\diagdown\text{H} & \text{H}\diagup\diagdown\text{H} & \text{H}\diagup\diagdown\text{H} \\
\text{ammonia} & \text{monomethylamine} & \text{monoethylamine}
\end{array}
$$

$$
\begin{array}{c}
\quad\quad\text{H}\ \ \text{H} \\
\text{CH}_3\!\diagdown\ |\ \ |\quad\diagup\text{H} \\
\quad\quad\text{C}\!-\!\text{C}\!-\!\text{N} \\
\text{CH}_3\!\diagup\ |\quad\quad\diagdown\text{H} \\
\quad\quad\quad\text{H}
\end{array}
$$
monoisobutylamine

The primary aliphatic amines may also be theoretically derived by the replacement of one hydrogen atom in a paraffin molecule by the group NH_2, just as the alcohols are derived by the replacement of one hydrogen atom in a paraffin molecule by the group OH.

$$
\begin{array}{ccc}
\text{H}\ \ \text{H} & \text{H}\ \ \text{H} & \text{H}\ \ \text{H} \\
|\ \ \ | & |\ \ \ | & |\ \ \ | \\
\text{H}\!-\!\text{C}\!-\!\text{C}\!-\!\text{H} & \text{H}\!-\!\text{C}\!-\!\text{C}\!-\!\text{NH}_2 & \text{H}\!-\!\text{C}\!-\!\text{C}\!-\!\text{OH} \\
|\ \ \ | & |\ \ \ | & |\ \ \ | \\
\text{H}\ \ \text{H} & \text{H}\ \ \text{H} & \text{H}\ \ \text{H} \\
\text{ethane} & \text{ethylamine} & \text{ethyl alcohol}
\end{array}
$$

If two hydrogen atoms in the ammonia molecule are replaced, a *secondary amine* is obtained. Dimethylamine, diethylamine, and ethylmethylamine are examples of secondary amines :

$$
\begin{array}{ccc}
\text{H} & \text{H} & \text{H} \\
| & | & | \\
\text{N} & \text{N} & \text{N} \\
\text{H}\diagup\diagdown\text{H} & \diagup\diagdown & \diagup\diagdown \\
 & \text{CH}_3\ \ \text{CH}_3 & \text{C}_2\text{H}_5\ \ \text{C}_2\text{H}_5 \\
\text{ammonia} & \text{dimethylamine} & \text{diethylamine}
\end{array}
$$

$$
\begin{array}{c}
\text{H} \\
| \\
\text{N} \\
\diagup\diagdown \\
\text{C}_2\text{H}_5\ \ \text{CH}_3 \\
\textbf{methylethylamine}
\end{array}
$$

If all the hydrogen atoms in the ammonia molecule are replaced by alkyl groups, a *tertiary amine* is obtained. Examples are

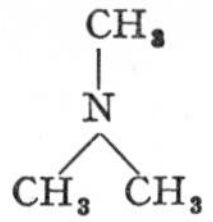

$$CH_3 - N \diagdown_{CH_3}^{CH_3}$$

trimethylamine

$$C_2H_5 - N \diagdown_{CH_3}^{C_3H_7}$$

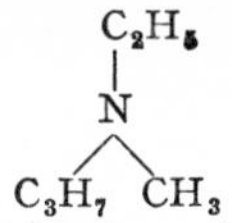

methylethylpropylamine.

The above formulae show that the molecule of a primary amine contains the group —NH_2 linked to an alkyl group ; the molecule of a secondary amine contains the group >NH linked to two alkyl groups ; in the molecule of a tertiary amine the nitrogen atom is linked to three alkyl groups. The use of the terms primary, secondary and tertiary in the classification of amines should be compared with the application of these terms to alcohols, p. 172. In both cases the primary compounds are distinguished by the presence in the molecule of two reactive hydrogen atoms,

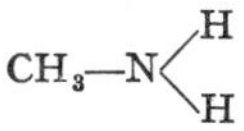

$$CH_3 - N \diagdown_H^H$$

primary amine

$$CH_3 - \overset{\overset{\displaystyle OH}{|}}{C} \diagdown_H^H$$

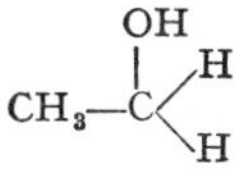

primary alcohol

the secondary compounds have only one reactive hydrogen atom in the molecule,

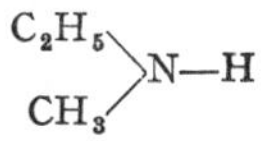

$$\overset{\displaystyle C_2H_5}{\underset{\displaystyle CH_3}{\diagdown}} N - H$$

secondary amine

$$\overset{\displaystyle C_2H_5}{\underset{\displaystyle CH_3}{\diagdown}} C \diagup^{OH}_{H}$$

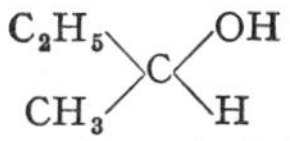

secondary alcohol

and the tertiary compounds have no reactive hydrogen atoms in the molecule

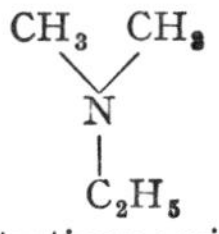

$$\overset{\displaystyle CH_3 \quad CH_3}{N} \atop \underset{\displaystyle C_2H_5}{|}$$

tertiary amine

$$\overset{\displaystyle CH_3 \quad OH}{C} \diagdown_{C_2H_5 \quad CH_3}$$

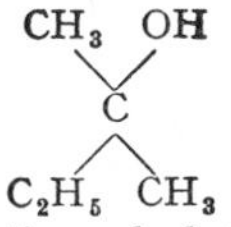

tertiary alcohol

PRIMARY AMINES

The two simplest primary aliphatic amines are monomethylamine CH_3NH_2, a gas, and monoethylamine $C_2H_5NH_2$, a very volatile liquid. Both compounds are soluble in water and in alcohol. Mono-methylamine and monoethylamine are customarily referred to as " methylamine " and " ethylamine " respectively.

ETHYLAMINE

Ethylamine is a colourless, very volatile liquid, B.P. 19°. It has a pungent odour, scarcely distinguishable from that of ammonia. It is miscible with water in all proportions. The solution is alkaline to litmus, and precipitates hydroxides from solutions of certain metallic salts. Ethylamine is more inflammable than ammonia. If a fairly concentrated aqueous solution of ethylamine is boiled in a test-tube, ethylamine may be ignited at the mouth of the tube.

PRINCIPAL REACTIONS IN WHICH ETHYLAMINE IS PRODUCED

It should be noted that many reactions leading to the formation of ethylamine take place in acid solution. The immediate product of such reactions is not free ethylamine, but a salt of ethylamine from which the free base must be liberated by the action of sodium hydroxide.

1. The reduction of compounds in which a nitrogen atom is directly linked to a carbon atom.

(a) The reduction of acetonitrile (methyl cyanide). When acetonitrile is reduced with zinc and sulphuric acid, ethyl ammonium sulphate is formed,

$$CH_3.C\equiv N \quad + \quad 4H \quad = \quad CH_3.CH_2.NH_2$$
$$2CH_3.CH_2.NH_2 \quad + \quad H_2SO_4 \quad = \quad (CH_3.CH_2.NH_3)_2SO_4.$$

When it is reduced with sodium and alcohol, free ethylamine is formed in solution, and may be expelled by boiling.

(b) The reduction of nitroethane. Nitroethane may be reduced to ethylamine hydrochloride by the action of zinc and hydrochloric acid, or stannous chloride and hydrochloric acid,

$$C_2H_5NO_2 \quad + \quad 6H \quad + \quad HCl \quad = \quad [C_2H_5.NH_3]Cl \quad + \quad 2H_2O.$$

(c) The reduction of acetaldoxime, or of acetaldehyde phenyl hydrazone. Acetaldoxime or acetaldehyde phenyl hydrazone may be reduced with zinc dust and acetic acid, or with sodium amalgam and acetic acid, or with sodium and alcohol,

$$CH_3.CH\!\!=\!\!NOH \quad + \quad 4H \quad = \quad CH_3CH_2NH_2 \quad + \quad H_2O,$$
$$CH_3.CH:NNHC_6H_5 \quad + \quad 4H \quad = \quad CH_3CH_2NH_2 \quad + \quad H_2N.C_6H_5.$$

2. The hydrolysis of compounds in which a nitrogen atom is directly linked to carbon atoms.

(a) The hydrolysis of ethyl isocyanide. If ethyl isocyanide (a liquid, B.P. 79°) is heated with dilute hydrochloric acid in a flask fitted to a reflux condenser, it is hydrolysed to ethylamine hydrochloride and formic acid,

$$C_2H_5.\overset{+}{N}\equiv\overset{-}{C} + HCl + 2H_2O = [C_2H_5NH_3]Cl + H.COOH.$$

(b) **The hydrolysis of ethyl isocyanate (ethyl carbimide).** If ethyl isocyanate is heated with sodium hydroxide solution, ethylamine is liberated and sodium carbonate is formed,

$$C_2H_5.N{=}C{=}O + 2NaOH = C_2H_5NH_2 + Na_2CO_3.$$

(c) **The hydrolysis of ethyl phthalimide. Gabriel's method.** If ethyl phthalimide is hydrolysed with hydrochloric acid at about 200°, phthalic acid and ethylamine hydrochloride are formed,

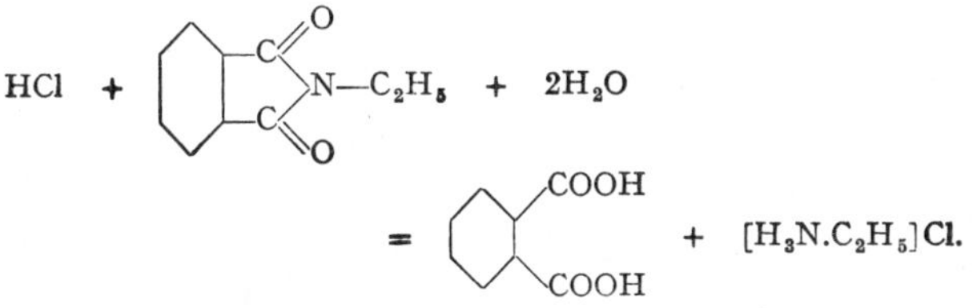

Ethyl phthalimide is also less easily hydrolysed by sodium hydroxide, to yield sodium phthalate and ethylamine,

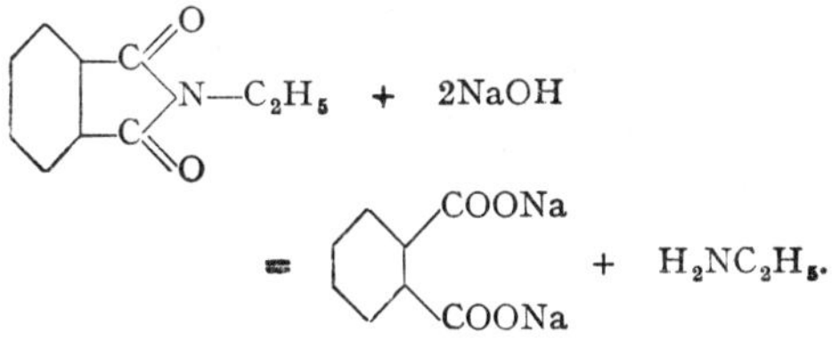

3. The treatment of propionamide with bromine and potassium hydroxide. Hofmann's reaction. Propionamide is first treated with bromine and dilute potassium hydroxide solution, when mono-bromopropionamide is formed,

$$C_2H_5.C{\begin{smallmatrix}\nearrow O\\ \searrow NH_2\end{smallmatrix}} + Br_2 + KOH = C_2H_5.C{\begin{smallmatrix}\nearrow O\\ \searrow N{\begin{smallmatrix}\nearrow H\\ \searrow Br\end{smallmatrix}}\end{smallmatrix}} + KBr + H_2O.$$

The mono-bromopropionamide is then hydrolysed with 30 per cent. potassium hydroxide solution. By an intramolecular change, following the elimination of the elements of hydrobromic acid, ethyl isocyanate is formed,

$$C_2H_5.C{\begin{smallmatrix}\nearrow O\\ \searrow N{\begin{smallmatrix}\nearrow H\\ \searrow Br\end{smallmatrix}}\end{smallmatrix}} + KOH = C_2H_5.N{=}C{=}O + KBr + H_2O,$$

which is then hydrolysed to ethylamine and potassium carbonate,

$$C_2H_5.N{=}C{=}O \ + \ 2KOH \ = \ C_2H_5NH_2 \ + \ K_2CO_3.$$

The experimental details for carrying out this reaction are similar to those given on p. 190 for the preparation of methylamine.

4. The action of heat on a mixture of alanine (α-amino-propionic acid) and barium oxide. Ethylamine is evolved when a mixture of alanine and barium oxide is heated,

$$CH_3CH.NH_2.COOH \ + \ BaO \ = \ CH_3.CH_2.NH_2 \ + \ BaCO_3.$$

This reaction is analogous to the action of heat on a mixture of sodium acetate and soda lime, p. 105.

5. The action of an alcoholic solution of ammonia on ethyl bromide. By means of this reaction the hydrogen atoms in the ammonia molecule are directly replaced by ethyl groups. Ethyl bromide is either (i) heated with a saturated alcoholic solution of ammonia in a sealed tube at 100°, or (ii) added in small quantities at a time, over a period of two or three weeks, to the alcoholic ammonia solution at room temperature. In either case the ammonia reacts with the ethyl bromide to produce ethylamine hydrobromide,

$$C_2H_5Br \ + \ NH_3 \ = \ C_2H_5NH_2 \ + \ HBr,$$
$$C_2H_5NH_2 \ + \ HBr \ = \ [C_2H_5NH_3]^+Br^-.$$

The reaction does not stop at this stage, however, and substitution of the hydrogen atoms attached to the nitrogen atom in the ethyl-amine hydrobromide occurs, giving as the ultimate product a mixture of ethylamine hydrobromide, diethylamine hydrobromide, $[(C_2H_5)_2NH_2]^+Br^-$, triethylamine hydrobromide, $[(C_2H_5)_3NH]^+Br^-$, and tetraethyl ammonium bromide* $[(C_2H_5)_4N]^+Br^-$. Ammonium bromide is also present.

Ethylamine hydrobromide can be obtained from this mixture by making use of two facts, (a) ammonium bromide is sparingly soluble in 90 per cent. alcohol, (b) of the four substituted ammonium bromides, only ethylamine hydrobromide is insoluble in cold chloroform.

Accordingly, the alcoholic solution obtained by the action of ammonia on ethyl bromide is filtered to remove the precipitated ammonium bromide, concentrated to separate the remaining ammonium bromide, and again filtered. The filtrate is evaporated at 130°, until the solid residue is free from alcohol. The residue is

* This is a *quaternary alkyl ammonium compound*. These compounds are derived by substituting an alkyl group for each of the H atoms in the ammonium group NH_4^+.

then extracted with cold chloroform which removes the diethyl-amine, triethylamine, and tetraethylamine hydrobromides, leaving monoethylamine hydrobromide, from which ethylamine is liberated by heating with sodium hydroxide. Other methods for separating the constituents of a mixture of primary, secondary and tertiary amines are mentioned on p. 197.

Laboratory preparation. Ethylamine may be conveniently prepared from propionamide by Hofmann's method, see Reaction 3, p. 185. The experimental procedure is parallel to that described for the preparation of methylamine on p. 190.

CHEMICAL PROPERTIES OF ETHYLAMINE

1. Action as a base. Gaseous ethylamine unites with gaseous hydrogen chloride to form white fumes of ethyl ammonium chloride, usually known as ethylamine hydrochloride,

$$C_2H_5NH_2 \ + \ HCl \ = \ [C_2H_5NH_3]^+Cl^-.$$

Ethylamine in aqueous solution is in equilibrium with ethyl ammonium hydroxide,

$$C_2H_5NH_2 \ + \ H_2O \ \rightleftharpoons \ \left[{C_2H_5 \atop H} \!\!> \!\! N \!\! <\!\! {H \atop H} \right]^+ OH^-,$$

which undergoes electrolytic dissociation, thus,

$$\left[{C_2H_5 \atop H} \!\!> \!\! N \!\! <\!\! {H \atop H} \right]^+ OH^- \ \rightleftharpoons \ \left[{C_2H_5 \atop H} \!\!> \!\! N \!\! <\!\! {H \atop H} \right]^+ \ + \ OH^-.$$

The solution is consequently alkaline, and neutralises acids forming ethyl ammonium salts, for example with dilute sulphuric acid ethyl ammonium sulphate is formed,

$$2[C_2H_5NH_3]^+OH^- \ + \ H_2SO_4 \ = \ [C_2H_5NH_3]_2^+SO_4^{--} \ + \ 2H_2O.$$

The ethyl ammonium salts are soluble in water, and they may be crystallised from aqueous solution.

Ethylamine hydrochloride forms double chlorides with platinic chloride and auric chloride, having the constitutions,

$$(C_2H_5NH_3)_2PtCl_6 \qquad\qquad (C_2H_5NH_3)_2AuCl_6.$$

These double salts are sparingly soluble in water, and on ignition they leave a residue of the pure metal.

Ethylamine hydrochloride is easily decomposed on warming with sodium or potassium hydroxide solution, with the liberation of ethylamine,

$$[C_2H_5NH_3]^+Cl^- \ + \ NaOH \ = \ C_2H_5NH_2 \ + \ H_2O \ + \ NaCl$$

2. Action with ethyl bromide. When ethylamine in alcoholic solution is heated with ethyl bromide, a mixture of diethylamine hydrobromide, triethylamine hydrobromide, and quaternary ethyl ammonium bromide is obtained, from which diethylamine and triethylamine may be isolated by the methods described on p. 197.

3. Action with nitrous acid to give ethyl alcohol. Ethylamine reacts with nitrous acid yielding ethyl alcohol, nitrogen and water,

$$C_2H_5NH_2 + ONOH = C_2H_5OH + N_2 + H_2O.$$

This reaction is best carried out by adding an aqueous solution of sodium nitrite to an acid solution of ethylamine hydrochloride, see p. 160.

4. Action with chloroform and an alcoholic solution of potassium hydroxide. Hofmann's carbylamine reaction. Ethylamine reacts rapidly when warmed with a mixture of chloroform and an alcoholic solution of potassium hydroxide, yielding ethyl isocyanide (carbylamine),

$$C_2H_5NH_2 + CHCl_3 + 3KOH = C_2H_5\overset{+}{N}\!\!\equiv\!\!\overset{-}{C} + 3KCl + 3H_2O.$$

A corresponding reaction is given by all primary amines. The isocyanides have a characteristic offensive odour, and its presence as a result of this reaction may be used as a test, either for chloroform (p. 154) or for a primary amine.

5. Reaction with acetic anhydride or acetyl chloride to give ethyl acetamide. Acetic anhydride reacts with ethylamine to yield a compound in which one hydrogen atom of the amino group is replaced by the acetyl group, $CH_3.CO$,

$$(CH_3.CO)_2O + 2C_2H_5NH_2 = 2C_2H_5NH.COCH_3 + H_2O.$$

The same product is obtained by the action of acetyl chloride on ethylamine. In this case pyridine is added to the reagents to absorb the hydrogen chloride as it is formed,

$$CH_3.COCl + C_2H_5NH_2 = C_2H_5NH.COCH_3 + HCl.$$

These reactions are common to all primary amines, and are of great practical importance (see p. 450).

6. Reactions with ethyl acetate and diethyl oxalate to give ethyl amides. Ethylamine reacts with ethyl acetate to yield ethyl acetamide,

$$CH_3.CO.OC_2H_5 + HNH.C_2H_5 = CH_3.CO.NH.C_2H_5 + HOC_2H_5,$$

and with diethyl oxalate to yield the amide, diethyl oxamide which is soluble in hot water,

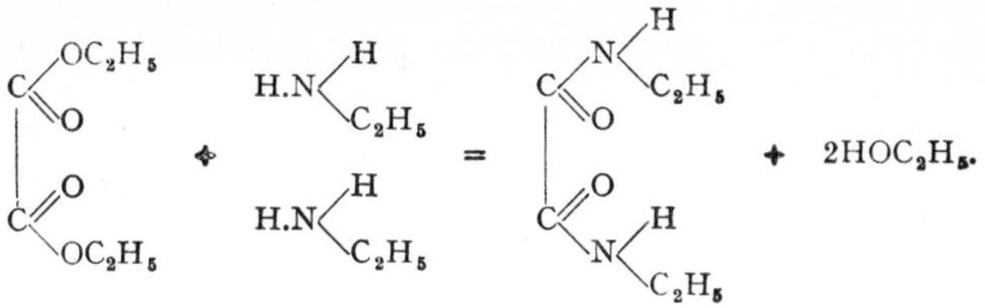

$$C\begin{cases} OC_2H_5 \\ O \end{cases} \quad H.N\begin{cases} H \\ C_2H_5 \end{cases}$$
$$\quad + \quad = \quad + \quad 2HOC_2H_5.$$

7. Reaction with benzoyl chloride or benzene sulphonyl chloride. Ethylamine reacts with benzoyl chloride in alkaline aqueous solution to yield benzoyl ethylamine,

$$C_2H_5NH_2 \quad + \quad C_6H_5.COCl \quad = \quad C_2H_5NH.CO.C_6H_5 \quad + \quad HCl.$$

An aqueous solution of ethylamine hydrochloride and sodium hydroxide is shaken with benzoyl chloride in a corked flask for about 30 minutes. During this period benzoyl ethylamine is precipitated, as it is insoluble in alkaline solution. It is filtered off and re-crystallised from methylated spirit.

If ethylamine hydrochloride, sodium hydroxide and benzene sulphonyl chloride are shaken together, benzene sulphonyl ethyl-amine is formed,

$$C_2H_5NH_2 \quad + \quad C_6H_5.SO_2Cl \quad = \quad C_2H_5NH.SO_2.C_6H_5 \quad + \quad HCl.$$

The hydrogen atom attached to the nitrogen atom in benzene sulphonyl ethylamine is ionisable, and the compound is therefore an *acid* and is soluble in sodium hydroxide solution. It is precipitated from the alkaline solution by the addition of hydrochloric acid, and it may then be filtered off and recrystallised from methylated spirit.

METHYLAMINE

Methylamine is a colourless gas, B.P. – 6°. It has an ammoniacal odour, and is soluble in water and in alcohol.

Principal reactions in which methylamine is produced.

All the methods enumerated for the production of ethylamine are available for the production of methylamine, provided that in each case where an ethyl derivative is employed as a reagent the appropriate methyl derivative is chosen instead. If method 1(a), p. 184, is to be employed for the preparation of methylamine, hydrogen cyanide must be used instead of methyl cyanide. As methylamine is a gas, its hydrochloride, a deliquescent crystalline solid, M.P. 226°, is first prepared and purified. Methylamine is liberated when the hydrochloride is warmed with sodium hydroxide solution.

Laboratory preparation of methylamine hydrochloride. Methylamine hydrochloride is conveniently prepared from acetamide by Hofmann's reaction, p. 185. 12 gm. of acetamide are placed in a conical flask and 10·8 c.c. of bromine are added. The flask is cooled, and 10 per cent. aqueous potassium hydroxide solution is run in, while the flask is shaken, until the colour of the mixture becomes pale-yellow. At this stage the reaction,

$$CH_3-C\underset{NH_2}{\overset{O}{<}} \quad + \quad Br_2 \quad + \quad KOH$$

$$= \quad CH_3-C\underset{N}{\overset{O}{<}}\underset{Br}{\overset{H}{<}} \quad + \quad KBr \quad + \quad H_2O,$$

is completed.

The apparatus shown in Fig. 46 is then assembled. 36 gm. of potassium hydroxide in 60 c.c. of water is placed in the bolt-head flask (with

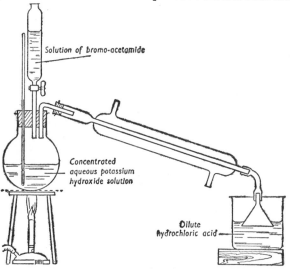

Solution of bromo-acetamide

Concentrated aqueous potassium hydroxide solution

Dilute hydrochloric acid

FIG. 46. Apparatus for the preparation of methylamine hydrochloride.

some unglazed porcelain) which is gently warmed until the thermometer in the potassium hydroxide solution registers 60–70°. The bromo-acetamide solution is placed in the dropping funnel, and is run into the flask at such a rate that the temperature does not rise above 70° ; when the addition is complete, the flask is kept at 60–70° for another ten minutes. At this stage methyl isocyanate is formed and hydrolysed, thus :

$$CH_3-C\underset{N}{\overset{O}{<}}\overset{H}{\underset{Br}{<}} \quad + \quad KOH \quad = \quad CH_3-N{=}C{=}O \quad + \quad KBr \quad + \quad H_2O,$$

$$CH_3-N{=}C{=}O \quad + \quad 2KOH \quad = \quad CH_3.NH_2 \quad + \quad K_2CO_3.$$

The solution is then boiled. The methylamine vapour passes with the steam into the condenser and is absorbed in the dilute hydrochloric acid in the collecting beaker. After 30 minutes the expulsion of the methylamine is complete, and the solution of methylamine hydrochloride in dilute hydrochloric acid is concentrated to 30 c.c. by distilling off excess water and hydrochloric acid. The concentrated solution is evaporated to dryness in an open dish on a boiling water-bath.

The crude methylamine hydrochloride is broken up and heated with 60–70 c.c. of absolute alcohol in a flask fitted with a water reflux condenser. The methylamine hydrochloride passes into solution, but ammonium chloride, which is insoluble, remains as a residue. After 5–10 minutes the liquid is poured through a fluted filter paper into a conical flask. The extraction of the undissolved solid with 20 c.c. of absolute alcohol is repeated, and the filtered solution is added to that in the conical flask. On cooling, colourless crystals of methylamine hydrochloride are deposited.

Industrial preparation. Methylamine is prepared on a large scale by warming a mixture of ammonium chloride and formalin,

$$2HCHO \ + \ NH_4Cl \ = \ [CH_3NH_3]Cl \ + \ H.COOH.$$

The methylamine is liberated from formic and hydrochloric acids by heating with alkali.

Chemical properties of methylamine. The chemical properties of methylamine are so closely parallel to those of ethylamine that there is no need to enumerate them separately. It should be noted, however, that the yield of methyl alcohol obtained by the action of nitrous acid on methylamine hydrochloride is small ; an important by-product of this reaction is methyl nitrite which, being a gas, passes out of the apparatus,

$$CH_3NH_3Cl + HONO = CH_3ONO + NH_4Cl.$$

Methylamine and ethylamine may be differentiated by means of the physical constants of their platini-chlorides, or benzene sulphonyl derivatives.

SECONDARY AMINES

DIETHYLAMINE

Diethylamine is a colourless liquid, B.P. 56°. It is freely soluble in water ; the solution is alkaline to litmus. It has an ammoniacal but fish-like odour.

PRINCIPAL REACTIONS IN WHICH DIETHYLAMINE IS PRODUCED

1. The hydrolysis of p-nitroso diethyl aniline. Diethylamine is evolved when p-nitroso diethyl aniline is steam-distilled in the presence of aqueous sodium hydroxide solution,

$$ON-\langle\ \rangle-N\big\langle {{}^{C_2H_5}\atop{}^{C_2H_5}} \quad + \quad NaOH$$

p-nitroso diethyl aniline

$$= \quad ON-\langle\ \rangle-ONa \quad + \quad H-N\big\langle {{}^{C_2H_5}\atop{}^{C_2H_5}}$$

sodium derivative of   diethylamine
p-nitroso phenol

The distillate is made strongly alkaline with excess of sodium hydroxide, when the diethylamine separates as an oil. It is separated, dried with fused potassium hydroxide, and redistilled.

2. The reaction of ethyl iodide on ethylamine in alcoholic solution. The theoretical quantity of ethyl iodide is heated with an alcoholic solution of ethylamine. The intended reaction is,

$$C_2H_5NH_2 \quad + \quad C_2H_5I \quad = \quad [(C_2H_5)_2NH_2]I,$$

but the tertiary and quaternary ethyl ammonium iodides are always formed at the same time. The diethylamine is separated from the other products by one of the methods described on p. 197.

CHEMICAL PROPERTIES OF DIETHYLAMINE

1. Action as a base. Diethylamine combines with acids directly, thus :

$$(C_2H_5)_2NH \quad + \quad HCl \quad = \quad [(C_2H_5)_2NH_2]Cl.$$

Its aqueous solution contains diethyl ammonium hydroxide,

$$(C_2H_5)_2NH \quad + \quad H_2O \quad = \quad [(C_2H_5)_2NH_2]OH,$$

which neutralises acids, thus :

$$2[(C_2H_5)_2NH_2]OH \quad + \quad H_2SO_4 \quad = \quad [(C_2H_5)_2NH_2]_2SO_4 \quad + \quad 2H_2O.$$

2. Action with nitrous acid. Nitrous acid undergoes an important and characteristic reaction with diethylamine which is quite different from its reaction with ethylamine. If an aqueous solution of sodium nitrite is added to an aqueous solution of diethylamine containing excess of dilute hydrochloric acid, diethyl nitrosoamine, a yellow oil, B.P. 177°, separates and collects on the surface of the aqueous layer, in which it is insoluble,

$$ {{}^{C_2H_5}\atop{}^{C_2H_5}}\big\rangle N-H \quad + \quad HONO \quad = \quad {{}^{C_2H_5}\atop{}^{C_2H_5}}\big\rangle N-NO \quad + \quad H_2O.$$

The nitrosoamine may be decomposed by boiling with concentrated hydrochloric acid. By this reaction diethylamine hydrochloride is regenerated.

$$ {{}^{C_2H_5}\atop{}^{C_2H_5}}\big\rangle N-NO \quad + \quad H_2O \quad + \quad HCl \quad = \quad \left[{{}^{C_2H_5}\atop{}^{C_2H_5}}\big\rangle N\big\langle {{}^{H}\atop{}^{H}} \right]^+ Cl^- \quad + \quad HONO.$$

In the conditions of the experiment, the liberated nitrous acid is immediately decomposed to oxides of nitrogen.

3. Reactions with acid chlorides, acid anhydrides, and esters. The hydrogen atom in the group $>$NH present in the molecule of diethylamine is replaced by an acyl group when diethylamine is treated with an acid chloride, an acid anhydride, or an ester. The product of such a reaction is the diethyl derivative of the amide of the acid. Diethylamine reacts with acetyl chloride, with acetic anhydride, or with ethyl acetate, to give diethyl acetamide, according to the respective equations :

$$(C_2H_5)_2NH + CH_3.CO.Cl = (C_2H_5)_2N.CO.CH_3 + HCl,$$
$$2(C_2H_5)_2NH + (CH_3.CO)_2O = 2(C_2H_5)_2N.CO.CH_3 + H_2O,$$
$$(C_2H_5)_2NH + CH_3.CO.OC_2H_5 = (C_2H_5)_2N.CO.CH_3 + C_2H_5OH.$$

These reactions should be compared with Reactions 5 and 6 of ethylamine, p. 188.

With diethyl oxalate, diethylamine yields the ethyl ester of N-diethyl oxamic acid ; only one carbethoxy group in the diethyl oxalate molecule is attacked, according to the equation,

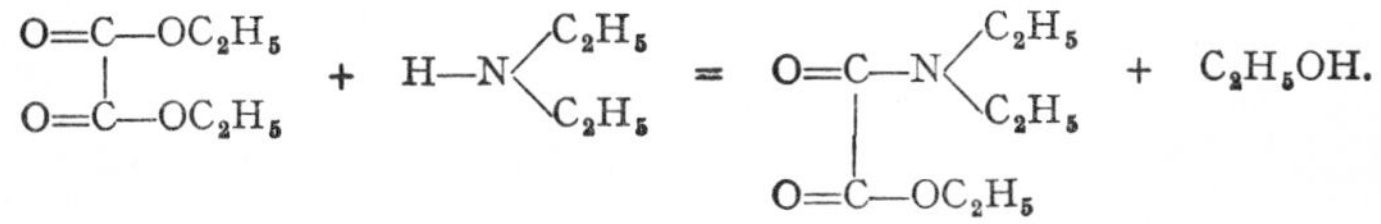

The ethyl ester of N-diethyl oxamic acid is insoluble in hot water, whereas diethyl oxamide, produced by the action of diethyl oxalate on ethylamine, p. 188, is soluble. This difference is the basis of a method for separating primary and secondary amines.

Benzene sulphonyl chloride reacts with diethylamine to yield the compound $(C_2H_5)_2N.SO_2.C_6H_5$. There is no hydrogen atom directly attached to the nitrogen atom in this compound. It is, therefore, *not an acid*, and it is insoluble in sodium hydroxide solution. (Cf. benzene sulphonyl ethylamine, Reaction 7, p. 189.)

Diethylamine does not react with a mixture of chloroform and alcoholic potassium hydroxide solution.

TERTIARY AMINES

TRIETHYLAMINE

Triethylamine, $(C_2H_5)_3N$, is a liquid, B.P. 89°, with a strong fish-like odour. It is less soluble in water than mono- or di-ethylamine. Its solution is alkaline to litmus. Triethylamine is made by the action of ammonia on ethyl chloride in alcoholic solution. It is separated from the mixture of amino compounds so produced by one of the methods described on p. 197. Triethylamine combines with acids, directly or in solution, to give triethyl ammonium salts, for example,

$$(C_2H_5)_3N + HCl = [(C_2H_5)_3NH]Cl.$$

It combines vigorously with alkyl halides in ethereal or alcoholic solution to give quaternary ammonium compounds,

$$(C_2H_5)_3N + C_2H_5I = [(C_2H_5)_4N]I.$$

Since the molecule of triethylamine contains no hydrogen atom directly linked to the nitrogen atom, its reactivity is much less than that of mono- or di-ethylamine. It does not react with nitrous acid, with chloroform and sodium hydroxide solution, with acid chlorides, acid anhydrides, or esters.

QUATERNARY ALKYL AMMONIUM COMPOUNDS

TETRAETHYL AMMONIUM IODIDE

Tetraethyl ammonium iodide, $(C_2H_5)_4NI$, is made by adding ethyl iodide to triethylamine in ethereal solution. The reaction is vigorous, and the reaction vessel may have to be cooled.

Tetraethyl ammonium iodide is a crystalline compound, soluble in water. In aqueous solution it is dissociated thus,

$$[(C_2H_5)_4N]I = [(C_2H_5)_4N]^+ + I^-,$$

and when heated it decomposes thus,

$$[(C_2H_5)_4N]I = (C_2H_5)_3N + C_2H_5I.$$

TETRAETHYL AMMONIUM HYDROXIDE

If the aqueous solution of tetraethyl ammonium iodide is mixed with silver hydroxide and warmed, silver iodide is precipitated and tetraethyl ammonium hydroxide remains in solution,

$$[N(C_2H_5)_4]I + AgOH = [N(C_2H_5)_4]OH + AgI.$$

Tetraethyl ammonium hydroxide is obtained free from other salts by filtering off the insoluble silver iodide and silver hydroxide, and evaporating the filtrate. It is a crystalline deliquescent substance.

Tetraethyl ammonium hydroxide is a strong base; it absorbs carbon dioxide from the air, and liberates ammonia from ammonium salts. At 18° the dissociation constants, multiplied in each case by 10^5, of ammonium hydroxide and its ethyl derivatives are:

NH_4OH	$N(C_2H_5)H_3OH$	$N(C_2H_5)_2H_2OH$
2·94	67·3	106

$N(C_2H_5)_3HOH$	$N(C_2H_5)_4OH$
78·7	100,000

From these figures it will be seen that the compounds which contain a hydrogen atom directly linked to the nitrogen atom are weak bases. The dissociation constant of $N(C_2H_5)_4OH$, however, in which the nitrogen atom is linked only to ethyl groups, is of the same order as that of potassium hydroxide. This marked contrast in basic properties arises because the linkage of the OH group to the tetraethyl ammonium group in tetraethyl ammonium hydroxide is wholly ionic,

$$\left[\begin{array}{c} C_2H_5 \\ | \\ C_2H_5-N-C_2H_5 \\ | \\ C_2H_5 \end{array} \right]^+ OH^-,$$

whereas in those compounds which contain a hydrogen atom directly linked to the nitrogen atom, a bond between this hydrogen atom and the OH group may be established. An aqueous solution of triethyl ammonium hydroxide, therefore, contains the ionic and covalent forms in equilibrium,

$$\left[\begin{array}{c} C_2H_5 \\ | \\ C_2H_5-N-H \\ | \\ C_2H_5 \end{array} \right]^+ OH^- \rightleftharpoons \begin{array}{c} C_2H_5 \\ | \\ C_2H_5-N-H-OH. \\ | \\ C_2H_5 \end{array} *$$

When tetraethyl ammonium hydroxide is heated it decomposes into triethylamine, ethylene and water,

$$[N(C_2H_5)_4]OH = N(C_2H_5)_3 + C_2H_4 + H_2O.$$

The ethylene and water may be regarded as the decomposition products of ethyl alcohol. It should be noted in contrast that tetramethyl ammonium hydroxide when heated yields trimethylamine and methyl alcohol,

$$[N(CH_3)_4]OH = N(CH_3)_3 + CH_3OH,$$

as methyl alcohol is not capable of dissociating into an olefine and water (cf. p. 168).

IDENTIFICATION AND SEPARATION OF THE ALIPHATIC AMINES

There is no general test for all classes of amines ; particular tests must be applied to each class. These tests provide experimental means for distinguishing between primary, secondary and tertiary amines.

---

* According to Pauli's exclusion principle (p. 8) the hydrogen atom must not be regarded as di-covalent. The numerous examples of the linkage of two of the elements fluorine, nitrogen and oxygen to one hydrogen atom, however, indicate that the hydrogen atom, in addition to a single covalency, may exert some other unique form of single linkage. For the sake of simplicity, in the above equation this unique additional linkage is represented as a second covalency.

IDENTIFICATION

PRIMARY ALIPHATIC AMINES

1. *The isocyanide (or carbylamine) reaction.* A few drops of chloroform and 2–3 c.c. of an alcoholic solution of sodium hydroxide are added to a small quantity of the substance under examination. The mixture is well-shaken and gently warmed. The presence of a primary amine is marked by the offensive odour of an isocyanide. For the equation for this reaction see p. 188.

2. *The nitrous acid test.* Aliphatic compounds containing the group —NH₂ yield gaseous nitrogen when they are treated with nitrous acid in aqueous solution. Primary amines alone yield an alcohol as well as nitrogen (see Reaction 3, p. 188), and, therefore, the identification of the alcohol which is formed is an essential part of the nitrous acid test for a primary amine. For example, ethylamine hydrochloride is identified by the nitrous acid test in the following manner. A solution of ethylamine hydrochloride is mixed with hydrochloric acid, and an aqueous solution of sodium nitrite is introduced into the acid solution by means of a thistle funnel of which the stem passes to the bottom of the solution. Nitrogen is freely evolved and the solution which remains contains ethyl alcohol. It is distilled, and the presence of ethyl alcohol in the distillate is proved by the iodoform and ethyl acetate tests, p. 166.

SECONDARY ALIPHATIC AMINES

1. Secondary aliphatic amines do *not* respond to the carbylamine test.*

2. *The nitrous acid test.* Nitrous acid converts a secondary amine to a nitrosoamine. A concentrated aqueous solution of sodium nitrite is gradually added to a solution of the secondary amine, say diethylamine, in excess of hydrochloric acid. The diethyl nitrosoamine separates as an oil. The formation of a nitrosoamine may be confirmed by performing *Liebermann's nitroso reaction* on the oil. The oil must, however, first be thoroughly freed from nitrous acid which itself gives a positive response to Liebermann's test. The mixture of aqueous solution and oil obtained by adding nitrous acid to the secondary amine is transferred to a separating funnel and ether is added. The ethereal layer, in which the nitrosoamine dissolves, is separated and washed with water and dilute sodium hydroxide solution. The ether is then carefully evaporated. 1 drop of the oilv residue is placed in a test-tube, 0·5 gm. of phenol is added and the mixture is warmed for a few seconds. The tube is then cooled and 1 c.c. of concentrated sulphuric acid is added. A greenish-blue coloration is produced which turns red on dilution with water, and greenish-blue again on the addition of sodium hydroxide solution.

TERTIARY AMINES

Tertiary amines do *not* respond either to the carbylamine test * or to the nitrous acid test, and they cannot be identified by any simple chemical reaction.

* It should be remembered that actual samples of secondary and tertiary amines will almost certainly contain small quantities of the primary amine.

SEPARATION OF THE MIXTURE OF AMINES PRODUCED IN HOFMANN'S SEALED TUBE REACTION

If Hofmann's reaction has been carried out by heating, say, an alcoholic solution of ammonia with ethyl chloride, the final product contains a mixture of $[(C_2H_5)NH_3]Cl$, $[(C_2H_5)_2NH_2]Cl$, $[(C_2H_5)_3NH]Cl$, $[(C_2H_5)_4N]Cl$. The excess of ammonia and alcohol is removed by evaporation. The solid residue is distilled in the presence of excess of solid sodium hydroxide, which liberates the primary, secondary and tertiary amines, and converts the quaternary ethyl ammonium chloride to the quaternary base, which decomposes to the tertiary amine, ethylene and water. The distillate, therefore, consists of the primary, secondary and tertiary ethylamines, together with water liberated in the reactions. The distillate is freed from water by the addition of solid potassium hydroxide. The water passes into a separate liquid layer of saturated potassium hydroxide solution, which may be removed from the amine layer by means of a separating funnel.

Three methods are available for the separation of the three amines from the liquid mixture : (a) treatment with ethyl oxalate, (b) treatment with benzene sulphonyl chloride (Hinsberg's method), (c) treatment with nitrous acid.

(a) *Reaction with diethyl oxalate.* The dried amines are treated with diethyl oxalate, which with the primary amine gives diethyl oxamide,

$$O{=}C{-}N(C_2H_5)H$$
$$O{=}C{-}N(C_2H_5)H$$

and with the secondary amine gives the ethyl ester of diethyl oxamic acid,

$$O{=}C{-}N{\Big\langle}{{C_2H_5}\atop{C_2H_5}}$$
$$O{=}C{-}OC_2H_5.$$

The tertiary amine does not react.

The mixture is distilled. Of the three substances present, only the tertiary amine is volatile, and it is therefore obtained alone in the distillate. The residue in the distillation flask is extracted with hot water in which diethyl oxamide is soluble, whereas the ethyl ester of diethyl oxamic acid is not. This ester is separated by filtration, and distilled with potassium hydroxide solution. Potassium oxalate is formed and diethylamine is liberated.

The solution of diethyl oxamide is also distilled with potassium hydroxide solution. Potassium oxalate is formed and ethylamine is liberated.

(b) *Reaction with benzene sulphonyl chloride (Hinsberg's method) or with toluene sulphonyl chloride.* p-toluene sulphonyl chloride

$$CH_3{\cdot}{\big\langle}\bigcirc{\big\rangle}{-}SO_2.Cl$$

is generally used in the laboratory in place of benzene sulphonyl chloride on account of its lower cost.

This method of separation of primary, secondary, and tertiary amines depends on the facts :

(i) that tertiary amines do not react with acid chlorides ;

(ii) that secondary amines react with benzene sulphonyl chloride to give a product which is insoluble in sodium hydroxide solution, p. 193 ;

(iii) that primary amines react with benzene sulphonyl chloride to give a product which is soluble in sodium hydroxide, p. 189.

The mixture of mono-, di-, and tri-ethylamine, dissolved in excess of 5 per cent. aqueous sodium hydroxide solution, is placed in a conical flask. Powdered *p*-toluene sulphonyl chloride is added, and the flask is corked and shaken vigorously for 20–30 minutes. The triethylamine does not react with the *p*-toluene sulphonyl chloride and remains dissolved in the aqueous solution. The diethylamine reacts to give $(C_2H_5)_2NSO_2.C_6H_4.CH_3$ which is neutral and insoluble. The monoethylamine gives $C_2H_5.H.N.SO_2C_6H_4.CH_3$, a substituted amide, which has an acid reaction (p. 189) and therefore dissolves in the alkaline solution.

The neutral insoluble sulphonyl diethylamine is filtered off. The filtrate is acidified with dilute hydrochloric acid to precipitate the sulphonyl monoethylamine, which is separated by filtration. The filtrate contains triethylamine hydrochloride. It is made alkaline with sodium hydroxide solution and steam-distilled, and the liberated triethylamine is collected. The sulphonyl derivatives of mono- and di-ethylamine are hydrolysed with 70 per cent. sulphuric acid, and thus converted into the corresponding ethyl ammonium sulphates, from which the free amines may be obtained by distillation with sodium hydroxide.

(*c*) *Reaction with nitrous acid.* The mixture of mono-, di-, and tri-ethylamine is dissolved in excess of dilute hydrochloric acid and an aqueous solution of sodium nitrite is added. The monoethylamine is converted to ethyl alcohol, and so lost. Diethylamine is converted to diethyl nitrosoamine, and triethylamine is unaffected. The nitrosoamine is extracted from the aqueous solution with ether, and after removal of the ether by evaporation, is boiled with concentrated hydrochloric acid and thus hydrolysed to diethylamine hydrochloride. Diethylamine and triethylamine are obtained from their respective hydrochlorides by distillation with sodium hydroxide.

CHAPTER XII

THE ALIPHATIC ALDEHYDES

THE aldehydes are derived by the elimination of two atoms of hydrogen from the molecule of a primary alcohol, thus,

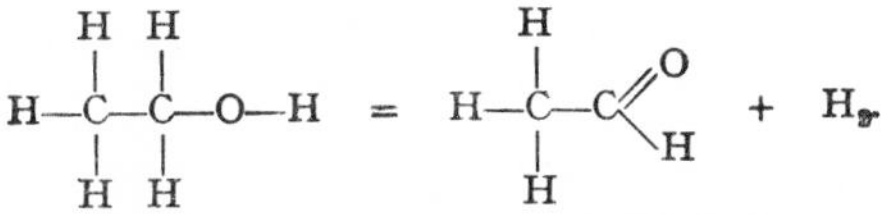

ethyl alcohol   acetaldehyde

The molecules of aldehydes contain the characteristic group $-C\!\!\bigm<\!\!{}^{O}_{H}$.

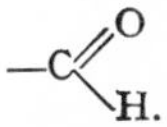

ACETALDEHYDE

Acetaldehyde is a colourless, very volatile liquid, B.P. 21°. It has a characteristic odour, and it is miscible in all proportions with water and alcohol.

PRINCIPAL REACTIONS IN WHICH ACETALDEHYDE IS PRODUCED

1. The dehydrogenation of ethyl alcohol. Acetaldehyde and hydrogen are produced when ethyl alcohol vapour is passed over metallic copper at a temperature of 250–300°, see Reaction 7, p. 163.

2. The oxidation of ethyl alcohol. Acetaldehyde is formed when ethyl alcohol vapour mixed with air is passed over a catalyst of metallic silver maintained at a suitable temperature. It may also be prepared by slowly adding a mixture of ethyl alcohol and aqueous sodium dichromate solution to hot dilute sulphuric acid, see Reaction 8, p. 164. Details for carrying out this experiment are described under " Laboratory preparation " below.

3. The distillation of a mixture of calcium formate and calcium acetate. Acetaldehyde is evolved when an intimate mixture of calcium formate and calcium acetate is heated in a hard-glass tube,

$$(H.COO)_2Ca \quad + \quad (CH_3.COO)_2Ca \quad = \quad 2CH_3.CHO \quad + \quad 2CaCO_3$$

4. The hydrolysis of ethylidene dichloride. If ethylidene dichloride is treated with superheated water, or boiled with an aqueous suspension of lead monoxide, it is hydrolysed to acetaldehyde. The reaction is parallel to the hydrolysis of ethylidene dibromide, described on p. 151.

5. The hydration of acetylene. If acetylene is passed into warm dilute sulphuric acid containing about 1 per cent. of mercuric sulphate as a catalyst, together with a little ferric sulphate, it combines with the elements of water to yield acetaldehyde, see Reaction 6, p. 133.

Laboratory preparation. Acetaldehyde is the starting-point for the preparation of many organic compounds, and its preparation in the laboratory is therefore only an academic exercise. The production of acetaldehyde from ethyl alcohol may be illustrated in the following experiment, using a mixture of aqueous sodium dichromate solution and sulphuric acid as the oxidising agent. The apparatus in Fig. 47 is

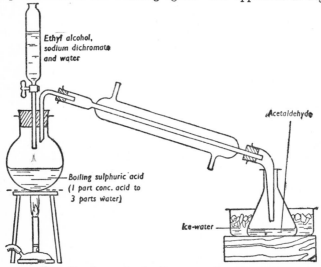

Ethyl alcohol, sodium dichromate and water

Acetaldehyde

Boiling sulphuric acid (1 part conc. acid to 3 parts water)

Ice-water

FIG. 47. Apparatus for the preparation of acetaldehyde.

assembled. A mixture of 50 c.c. of water and 17 c.c. of concentrated sulphuric acid is placed in the bolt-head flask and brought gently to the boil. 50 gm. of crushed sodium dichromate are dissolved in a mixture of 50 c.c. of water and 40 c.c. of ethyl alcohol; the solution is placed in the dropping funnel. The flame under the bolt-head flask is turned out, and the solution in the dropping funnel is allowed to fall, drop by drop, into the flask. A vigorous reaction occurs, and the solution turns green owing to the reduction of sodium dichromate to chromium sulphate. A mixture of acetaldehyde, water, and a little acetic acid distils over, and is collected in the small conical flask, chilled in ice-water.

The yield from this experiment is low, because the acetaldehyde is liable to be oxidised to acetic acid, or converted to acetal by reaction with unchanged ethyl alcohol.

Industrial preparation of acetaldehyde. Acetaldehyde is prepared industrially, (i) by the catalytic hydration of acetylene, Reaction 5, (ii) by the dehydrogenation of ethyl alcohol, Reaction 1, and (iii) by the oxidation of ethyl alcohol with air in the presence of silver, Reaction 2.

CHEMICAL PROPERTIES, CONSTITUTION AND USES
OF ACETALDEHYDE

Chemical properties. The chemical reactions of acetaldehyde may be grouped into (*a*) those in which it undergoes oxidation, reduction and chlorination, (*b*) condensations, and (*c*) polymerisations.

(a) Oxidation, reduction, chlorination.

1. Oxidation of acetaldehyde. Acetaldehyde burns in air or oxygen, yielding carbon dioxide and water. Acetaldehyde is slowly oxidised by air at ordinary temperatures to yield peracetic acid,

$$CH_3-C{\overset{H}{\underset{O}{\diagup\diagdown}}} + O_2 = CH_3-\underset{\underset{O}{\|}}{C}-O-OH,$$

which reacts with unchanged acetaldehyde to give acetic acid,

$$CH_3-\underset{\underset{O}{\|}}{C}-O-OH + CH_3-C{\overset{H}{\underset{O}{\diagup\diagdown}}} = 2CH_3-C{\overset{OH}{\underset{O}{\diagup\diagdown}}}$$

Manganese salts catalyse the second stage of this reaction. Their use is essential in the manufacture of acetic acid from acetaldehyde to prevent the accumulation of the explosive peracetic acid. Acetaldehyde vapour is oxidised to acetic acid when mixed with air and passed over vanadium pentoxide, and acetaldehyde in aqueous solution is oxidised to acetic acid by sodium dichromate or potassium permanganate in the presence of dilute sulphuric acid.

2. Action as a reducing agent. Acetaldehyde readily reduces an ammoniacal solution of silver oxide to metallic silver, and Fehling's solution to cuprous oxide, at the same time being itself oxidised to acetic acid. If these reactions are to be carried out successfully, careful attention must be paid to the experimental procedure. This is described, and the reactions occurring are explained on p. 208.

3. Reduction. Acetaldehyde in aqueous solution may be reduced to ethyl alcohol, either by sodium amalgam, or by zinc and hydro-

chloride acid.   In the presence of nickel, hydrogen reduces acetaldehyde vapour to ethyl alcohol,

$$CH_3-C\overset{H}{\underset{O}{<}} \quad + \quad H_2 \quad = \quad CH_3.CH_2OH.$$

4. Action with phosphorus pentachloride.   Phosphorus
pentachloride reacts readily with acetaldehyde to yield ethylidene
dichloride,

$$CH_3-C\overset{H}{\underset{O}{<}} \quad + \quad PCl_5 \quad = \quad CH_3-C\overset{H}{\underset{Cl}{<}}Cl \quad + \quad POCl_3.$$

5. Chlorination.   Chlorine reacts with acetaldehyde, replacing
the three hydrogen atoms in the methyl group to yield chloral,
$CCl_3.CHO$, p. 216.

6. The iodoform reaction.   Acetaldehyde undergoes the iodoform reaction although its molecule does not contain either of the
groups $CH_3.CH.OH$ or $CH_3.CO.C$ which are characteristic of the
compounds which show this reaction, see p. 156.   To explain this
unexpected property it is suggested that acetaldehyde in aqueous
solution exists to some extent in the hydrated form $CH_3-C\overset{H}{\underset{OH}{<}}OH$;
this hydrated molecule satisfies the structural conditions which are
necessary for the iodoform reaction.

(b) Condensations.

Acetaldehyde enters into reaction with certain other substances
to yield either simple addition compounds, or new compounds
with the elimination of water.   These reactions are of the type
often referred to as *condensations*.   The term *condensation* used
in this sense has no clear unambiguous meaning.   Some authors
attempt to define a condensation as a chemical change in which two
or more molecules of the same or different substances combine, with
the elimination of one or more molecules of water, ethyl alcohol,
ammonia, or some such simple substance, and the formation of a new
compound with a molecular weight greater than that of any of the
reagents.   The reaction between acetaldehyde and hydroxylamine
to yield an oxime (Reaction 10 below) is a simple example of a condensation falling within this definition.   The reaction of two molecules of acetaldehyde to give aldol without the elimination of any
other substance, is also commonly referred to as the *aldol condensation,* and it clearly falls outside the above definition.   The reaction
of two molecules of benzaldehyde to form benzoin, again without

the elimination of any other substance, is also commonly spoken of as the *benzoin condensation*. A condensation may be either a reversible or a non-reversible reaction ; the condensation of acetaldehyde and alcohol to give acetal is reversible ; the aldol condensation is non-reversible. The following definition covers all types of reactions to which the term condensation is habitually applied. *A condensation is a chemical change (which may be reversible or non-reversible) in which two or more molecules of the same or different substances combine, with or without the elimination of one or more molecules of such simple substances as water, ethyl alcohol, or ammonia, to produce a new compound with a molecular weight greater than that of any of the reagents.*

The condensations of acetaldehyde depend on the presence in the molecule of the unsaturated carbonyl group, $\rangle$C=O. The condensations of acetaldehyde with hydrogen cyanide, sodium bisulphite, and ammonia (Reactions 7, 8, 9 below), are additive reactions. The molecules of these compounds contain at least one hydrogen atom, and may be written H—R. When they condense with acetaldehyde the hydrogen atom combines with the oxygen of the carbonyl group to form a hydroxyl group, and the valency bond of the carbon atom, thus set free, then links with the residue, R,

$$CH_3-C\!\!\begin{array}{c}H\\\diagdown\\O\end{array} + \begin{array}{c}H\\|\\R\end{array} = CH_3-\overset{H}{\underset{|}{C}}-O-H + \begin{array}{c}|\\R\end{array} = CH_3-\overset{H}{\underset{\underset{R}{|}}{\overset{|}{C}}}-O-H.$$

The condensations of acetaldehyde with hydroxylamine and phenylhydrazine (Reactions 10 and 11 below) are not additive reactions. In these condensations a molecule of water is set free by the union of the oxygen atom in the carbonyl group of the acetaldehyde with the two hydrogen atoms of the —NH$_2$ group in the molecule of hydroxylamine or phenylhydrazine.

7. Condensation with hydrogen cyanide, giving a cyanhydrin. Hydrogen cyanide reacts with acetaldehyde to yield acetaldehyde cyanhydrin, a colourless liquid, B.P. 103° at 26 mm.,

$$CH_3.C\!\!\begin{array}{c}H\\\diagdown\\O\end{array} + HCN = CH_3.C\!\!\begin{array}{c}\diagup H\\-OH\\\diagdown CN.\end{array}$$

The mechanism of this reaction is discussed on p. 23.

8. Condensation with sodium bisulphite, giving a bisulphite compound. An aqueous solution of sodium bisulphite reacts with acetaldehyde to yield an addition compound, sodium hydroxy ethyl sulphite, usually spoken of as the acetaldehyde bisulphite compound,

$$CH_3.C{\overset{H}{\underset{O}{}}} + HO.SO.ONa = CH_3.C{\overset{H}{\underset{O.SO.ONa.}{-OH}}}$$

The bisulphite compounds of many aldehydes are sparingly soluble in water, and separate as white precipitates when solutions of the aldehyde and sodium bisulphite are mixed. The bisulphite compound of acetaldehyde, however, is so soluble that it cannot readily be crystallised from solution. On being warmed with dilute acids or alkalis, the acetaldehyde bisulphite compound is decomposed, and acetaldehyde is regenerated.

9. Condensation with ammonia, giving an aldehyde-ammonia. A white crystalline compound, known as acetaldehyde ammonia, is obtained by passing dry gaseous ammonia into a solution of acetaldehyde in ether,

$$CH_3.C{\overset{H}{\underset{O}{}}} + NH_3 = CH_3.C{\overset{H}{\underset{NH_2.}{-OH}}}$$

If this compound is distilled with dilute sulphuric acid acetaldehyde is regenerated.

10. Condensation with hydroxylamine, giving an oxime. Hydroxylamine reacts with acetaldehyde to yield acetaldoxime and water,

$$CH_3.C{\overset{H}{\underset{O}{}}} + H_2NOH = CH_3.C{\overset{H}{\underset{NOH}{}}} + H_2O.$$

Acetaldoxime is an odourless volatile liquid which mixes with water in all proportions. Acetaldoxime is decomposed by warm moderately concentrated hydrochloric acid to give acetaldehyde and hydroxylamine hydrochloride,

$$CH_3.C{\overset{H}{\underset{NOH}{}}} + HCl + H_2O = CH_3.C{\overset{H}{\underset{O}{}}} + NH_2OH.HCl.$$

Acetaldoxime dissolves in dilute aqueous alkalis yielding the metallic derivatives

$$CH_3.C{\overset{H}{\underset{NONa}{}}} \quad and \quad CH_3.C{\overset{H}{\underset{NOK.}{}}}$$

Acetaldoxime is liberated from combination with the metal by the action of carbon dioxide. It should be noted that acetaldehyde is not regenerated by the action of alkalis on acetaldoxime.

11. Condensation with phenylhydrazine, giving a phenyl-hydrazone. Phenylhydrazine, in dilute acetic acid solution, reacts with acetaldehyde to yield acetaldehyde phenylhydrazone, which remains in solution,

$$CH_3.C\overset{H}{\underset{O}{\diagdown}} + H_2N.NHC_6H_5 = CH_3.C\overset{H}{\underset{N.NHC_6H_5}{\diagdown}} + H_2O.$$

Hot hydrochloric acid reacts with acetaldehyde phenylhydrazone regenerating acetaldehyde and forming phenylhydrazine hydrochloride.

12. Acetal condensation. In the presence of an acid, acetaldehyde combines with ethyl alcohol to yield acetal, p. 163.

13. Reaction with a Grignard reagent, giving a secondary alcohol. Acetaldehyde unites with a Grignard reagent to give an intermediate addition product which on hydrolysis yields a secondary alcohol. For example, acetaldehyde reacts with phenyl magnesium bromide to yield phenyl methyl carbinol according to the equations,

$$CH_3-C\overset{H}{\underset{O}{\diagdown}} + C_6H_5MgBr = CH_3-\overset{H}{\underset{C_6H_5}{\overset{|}{\underset{|}{C}}}}-OMgBr,$$

$$CH_3-\overset{H}{\underset{C_6H_5}{\overset{|}{\underset{|}{C}}}}-OMgBr + HCl = CH_3-\overset{H}{\underset{C_6H_5}{\overset{|}{\underset{|}{C}}}}-OH + MgBrCl.$$

(c) Polymerisations. In certain conditions, molecules of acetaldehyde combine with one another to form new substances having molecular weights which are integral multiples of that of acetaldehyde ; these chemical changes may be reversible or non-reversible. The physical and chemical properties of the new substances are in every case different from those of acetaldehyde. A chemical reaction of this type is known as polymerisation. *Polymerisation may be defined as : The union of two or more molecules of a chemical compound to produce a new compound having a molecular weight which is an integral multiple of that of the original compound.* The new compound is known as a *polymeride* of the original substance. The physical and chemical properties of a polymeride are different from those of the original substance. Polymerisation is a special case of condensation, in which the reacting molecules are of the same kind. The following reactions of acetaldehyde are examples of polymerisation.

14. Polymerisation to paraldehyde. If a few drops of concentrated sulphuric acid are added to pure acetaldehyde at room temperature, it polymerises with almost explosive violence to paraldehyde $(C_2H_4O)_3$, a liquid, B.P. 124°. Its constitution is probably that of trimethyl trioxymethylene, which is produced according to the equation,

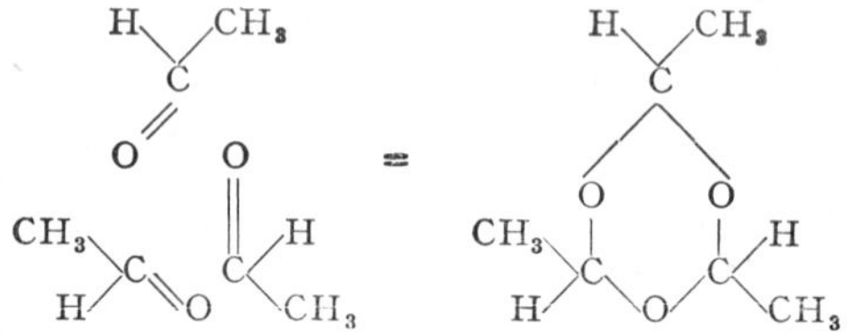

Acetaldehyde is regenerated when paraldehyde is distilled with dilute sulphuric acid.*

15. Polymerisation to metaldehyde. If hydrogen chloride or sulphur dioxide is passed through acetaldehyde cooled in a freezing mixture a white precipitate of metaldehyde is obtained. This precipitate is insoluble in water, and it possesses no aldehydic properties. Its molecular formula is probably $(C_2H_4O)_4$. If metaldehyde is heated in a sealed tube, or distilled with dilute sulphuric acid, acetaldehyde is regenerated.

16. Polymerisation to acetaldehyde resin. If an aqueous solution of acetaldehyde is boiled with dilute sodium or potassium hydroxide solution, a yellow insoluble solid is deposited. This substance has a characteristic odour of bad apples. Its molecular weight is about 50,000. Its constitution is uncertain, but the molecules probably consist of long chains formed by the linking together of acetaldehyde molecules by the repetition of the process in which two molecules of acetaldehyde give a molecule of aldol, Reaction 18, p. 207.

17. Polymerisation to ethyl acetate. If acetaldehyde is brought into contact with aluminium ethylate it condenses to ethyl acetate,

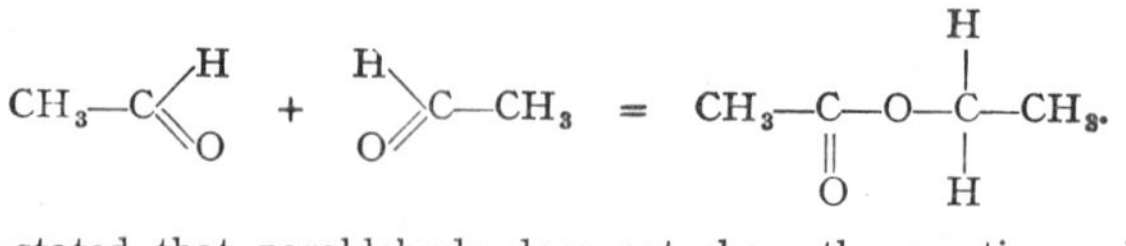

* It is stated that paraldehyde does not show the reactions which are common to aldehydes, but an ordinary sample of paraldehyde gives a yellow resin with sodium hydroxide solution, and a silver mirror after a few minutes warming with ammoniacal silver nitrate solution. Moreover it responds to certain colour tests for aldehydes ; it gives a pink coloration to Schiff's reagent, and a red coloration with alkaline sodium nitroprusside solution. Paraldehyde, however, does not give the iodoform reaction.

This reaction is of particular interest because it is parallel to Cannizzaro's reaction brought about by the action of potassium hydroxide on formaldehyde or benzaldehyde (p. 213).

18. The aldol condensation. The aldol condensation is brought about by allowing acetaldehyde at ordinary temperatures to remain in contact with a catalyst such as zinc chloride, dilute hydrochloric acid, strontia or sodium carbonate solution, when two molecules of acetaldehyde unite to produce a molecule of aldol,

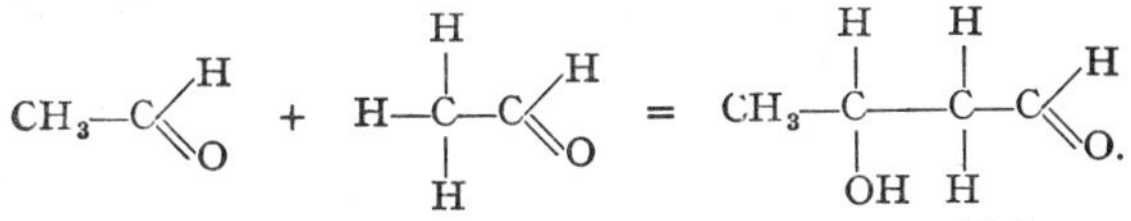

Aldol is a colourless liquid, B.P. 83° at 20 mm., miscible with water. It shows the properties of an aldehyde in forming an aldehyde-ammonia, and in reducing an ammoniacal solution of silver oxide to metallic silver. If distilled at atmospheric pressure or with dehydrating agents the aldol molecule loses a molecule of water to yield crotonaldehyde,

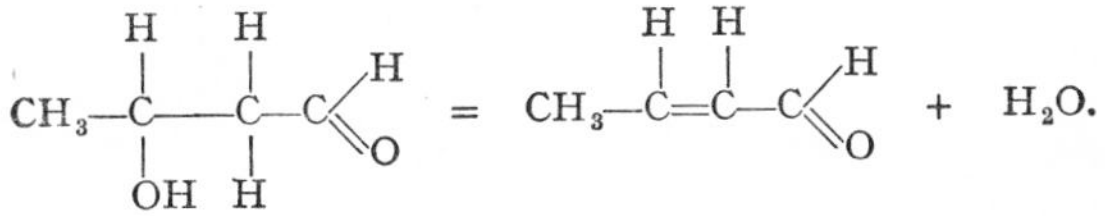

Aldol cannot be reconverted to aldehyde by simple means.

Constitution of acetaldehyde. The molecular formula of acetaldehyde is C_2H_4O. The reduction of acetaldehyde to ethyl alcohol (Reaction 3, p. 201) shows that the two carbon atoms in the molecule are directly linked to one another. If the normal valencies of the constituent elements are to be retained, the only possible structures for the molecule are :

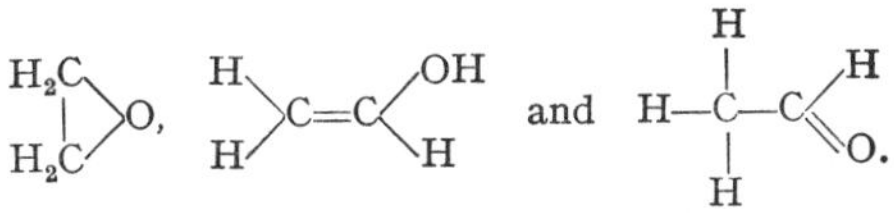

Evidence in favour of the second formula is furnished by :

(i) the action of phosphorus pentachloride on acetaldehyde to yield ethylidene dichloride, Reaction 4, p. 202 ;

(ii) the action of chlorine on acetaldehyde, by which three hydrogen atoms only in the molecule are replaced by chlorine to yield chloral, $CCl_3.CHO$;

(iii) the absence of any simple additive reaction of acetaldehyde with bromine, hydrobromic acid, hypochlorous acid or sulphuric acid : all these substances react additively with ethylene (p. 119) and with other compounds containing a carbon-carbon double bond.

Acetaldehyde is thus proved to be derived from ethane by the replacement of two hydrogen atoms in one of the methyl groups by an atom of oxygen.

Uses. Acetaldehyde is chiefly important as an intermediate product in the manufacture of other organic substances, including acetic acid and *n*-butyl alcohol. Metaldehyde, under the name " meta " is used as a solid fuel for small lamps.

Tests. The following reactions of acetaldehyde are suitable for use as tests.

1. Reduction of ammoniacal silver oxide solution in the cold. Reaction 2, p. 201. The reduction is carried out as follows : 5 c.c. of aqueous silver nitrate solution are placed in a test-tube, and 2 or 3 drops of 10 per cent. sodium hydroxide solution are added. A brown precipitate of silver oxide, Ag_2O, is formed. Diluted ammonia solution is then added drop by drop, until nearly all the precipitate is converted to the soluble silver amine hydroxide, $[Ag.4NH_3]OH$. A small quantity of acetaldehyde is then introduced. The silver amine hydroxide is reduced to metallic silver, which is deposited as a mirror on the walls of the test-tube.

This test is by no means specific for acetaldehyde. Formaldehyde, chloral, chloral hydrate, the salts of formic, lactic and tartaric acids, uric acid, benzoquinone, many amines (including aniline) and certain classes of sugars including glucose and fructose, also respond to it. Paraldehyde and benzaldehyde (which are not soluble in water) produce a silver mirror after several minutes warming and shaking.

2. Reduction of Fehling's solution. Reaction 2, p. 201. Fehling's solution consists essentially of cupric tartrate

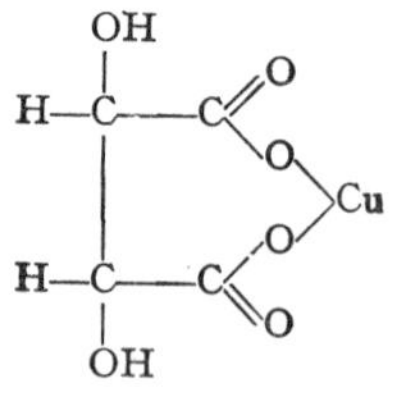

dissolved in aqueous sodium hydroxide solution. It reacts with many organic reducing agents to yield a red precipitate of cuprous oxide, Cu_2O.

The reduction of Fehling's solution by acetaldehyde is best carried out thus. To a few c.c. of a dilute solution of acetaldehyde, 1 c.c. of 10 per cent. sodium carbonate solution is added to ensure that any acetic acid resulting from the atmospheric oxidation of the acetaldehyde is neutralised. 1 or 2 drops of Fehling's solution are then introduced and the solution is warmed. The blue colour of the Fehling's solution disappears and a yellow or red precipitate (the colour depends on the size of the precipitated particles) of cuprous oxide comes down. If more than 1 or

2 drops of Fehling's solution are added, the blue colour masks the colour of the precipitate, and the sodium hydroxide in the solution may resinify the acetaldehyde. Fehling's solution is also reduced by other aliphatic aldehydes, chloral hydrate, the salts of formic acid and lactic acid, many esters of aliphatic acids, chloroform, iodoform, glucose, fructose, uric acid and some phenols.

3. Formation of resin with sodium hydroxide solution. Reaction 16, p. 206. When an aqueous solution of acetaldehyde is warmed with sodium hydroxide solution, it polymerises to a yellow insoluble resin with a characteristic odour of bad apples. This reaction is also shown by other aliphatic aldehydes (with the exception of formaldehyde) and by paraldehyde.

4. Nitroprusside reaction. If to an aqueous solution of acetaldehyde a small quantity of freshly prepared sodium nitroprusside solution $(Na_2[FeNO.(CN)_5].2H_2O)$ is added, followed by excess of dilute sodium hydroxide solution, a red coloration is obtained. This test is also given by acetone and acetophenone, and by other aldehydes and ketones which contain the group

$$\begin{array}{c c} \mathrm{H} & \\ | & \\ -\mathrm{C}-\mathrm{C}- & \\ | & \| \\ \mathrm{H} & \mathrm{O} \end{array}$$

5. Schiff's reaction. Schiff's reagent is an aqueous solution of rosaniline which has been reduced to a colourless compound with sulphur dioxide. If Schiff's reagent is added to an aqueous solution of acetaldehyde in the cold, a magenta colour is produced. Heat or alkaline substances turn Schiff's reagent pink, even in the absence of aldehydes. Schiff's colour reaction is given by formaldehyde and other aliphatic aldehydes, including chloral, but only very slowly by benzaldehyde. It is slowly given by acetone, but not at all by acetophenone, benzophenone, salicylaldehyde, or by chloral hydrate.

6. The iodoform reaction. Reaction 6, p. 202. Acetaldehyde is one of the many substances which undergo the iodoform reaction. The reaction is carried out by adding a few c.c. of 10 per cent. potassium iodide solution and a few c.c. of freshly prepared sodium hypochlorite solution to aqueous acetaldehyde solution. Yellow crystals of iodoform soon separate.

The formation of the sparingly soluble sodium bisulphite compound, the phenyl hydrazone, or the aldehyde oxime, which may be used as tests for certain aldehydes in aqueous solution, cannot be used for acetaldehyde as the acetaldehyde sodium bisulphite compound and acetaldehyde phenyl hydrazone, although crystalline, are highly soluble, and acetaldoxime is a liquid miscible with water.

FORMALDEHYDE

Formaldehyde is a colourless gas, B.P. $-21°$, M.P. $-90°$. It has a characteristic pungent irritating odour. At room temperature it rapidly polymerises to crystalline trioxymethylene with the evolution of heat. Formaldehyde is soluble in water, and most of the experiments described below are performed on the aqueous solution.

PRINCIPAL REACTIONS IN WHICH
FORMALDEHYDE IS PRODUCED

1. The oxidation of methyl alcohol. Formaldehyde is manufactured by passing a mixture of methyl alcohol vapour and air over a heated catalyst, which may be platinum, copper or silver, see p. 169.

$$\begin{array}{c} H \\ | \\ H-C-OH \\ | \\ H \end{array} + O = \begin{array}{c} H \\ \diagdown \\ \diagup \\ H \end{array} C=O + H_2O.$$

The product of this reaction is a mixture of formaldehyde, steam and unchanged methyl alcohol, which is cooled to produce the solution known as *formalin*.

It is difficult to carry out this preparation on a laboratory scale without explosions, and therefore it should not be attempted as a laboratory exercise. The principle of the method may be demonstrated, however, by placing a little methyl alcohol in a beaker, and suspending over it a coil of platinum wire, previously heated to bright redness. The heat evolved by the oxidation of the alcohol on the surface of the platinum maintains the coil at a red heat, and the pungent odour of formaldehyde may be detected.

Pure gaseous formaldehyde is made by heating paraformaldehyde, a solid substance obtained by the evaporation of formalin, p. 213.

2. The distillation of calcium formate. Small quantities of formaldehyde may be obtained by heating calcium formate in a dry hard-glass tube,

$$(H.COO)_2Ca = H_2CO + CaCO_3.$$

This reaction should be compared with Reaction 3, p. 199.

CHEMICAL PROPERTIES, CONSTITUTION AND USES
OF FORMALDEHYDE

1. Oxidation of formaldehyde. On oxidation, formaldehyde is converted to formic acid,

$$\begin{array}{c} H \\ \diagdown \\ \diagup \\ H \end{array} C=O + O = \begin{array}{c} H \\ \diagdown \\ \diagup \\ HO \end{array} C=O.$$

Formaldehyde thus behaves similarly to acetaldehyde, which yields acetic acid on oxidation. Formic acid, however, is very readily oxidised to carbon dioxide and water,

$$H.COOH + O = CO_2 + H_2O,$$

whereas acetic acid is stable towards oxidising agents. Hence, oxidising agents, such as potassium permanganate or potassium dichromate in acid solution, which yield acetic acid on reaction with acetaldehyde, convert formaldehyde to carbon dioxide and water. Hydrogen peroxide or iodine in strongly alkaline solution, however, convert formaldehyde quantitatively to sodium formate, according to the equations,

$$2HCHO + 2NaOH + H_2O_2 = 2HCOONa + 2H_2O + H_2,$$
$$HCHO + 3NaOH + I_2 = HCOONa + 2NaI + 2H_2O.$$

2. Action as a reducing agent. The reducing properties of formaldehyde are more powerful than those of acetaldehyde. In the course of its reducing actions, formaldehyde is oxidised to formic acid which, unless formaldehyde is present in excess, is further oxidised to carbon dioxide and water. Like acetaldehyde, formaldehyde in aqueous solution reduces an ammoniacal solution of silver oxide to metallic silver, and Fehling's solution to cuprous oxide. Formaldehyde also reduces an aqueous solution of mercuric chloride to a white precipitate of mercurous chloride, which may turn grey on further reduction to metallic mercury,

$$2HgCl_2 + H_2O + HCHO = HCOOH + 2HCl + Hg_2Cl_2,$$
$$Hg_2Cl_2 + H_2O + HCHO = HCOOH + 2HCl + 2Hg.$$

Formaldehyde in alkaline solution reduces bismuth salts to metallic bismuth, in neutral solution it reduces ferric chloride to iron, and in acid solution it reduces auric chloride to gold.

3. Condensations in which formaldehyde resembles acetaldehyde. Formaldehyde resembles acetaldehyde in the manner in which it undergoes condensation with hydrogen cyanide, hydroxylamine, phenylhydrazine, alcohols in the presence of acids, and Grignard reagents. These condensations are described under Reactions 7, 8, 10, 11, 12, and 13 of acetaldehyde, p. 203. The equations represent the corresponding reactions of formaldehyde if a hydrogen atom is substituted for the methyl group in the acetaldehyde molecule. It should be noted that a primary alcohol is formed when formaldehyde reacts with a Grignard reagent. The bisulphite compound of formaldehyde, and formaldehyde phenyl hydrazone, are freely soluble in water and thus resemble the corresponding compounds of acetaldehyde ; formaldoxime is known only in solution. *Methylal* is formed when formaldehyde reacts with methyl alcohol in the presence of acids ; it is best obtained by boiling formalin with methyl alcohol and a little sulphuric acid. The change is reversible : when methylal is distilled with dilute sulphuric acid, it yields an aqueous solution of methyl alcohol and formaldehyde,

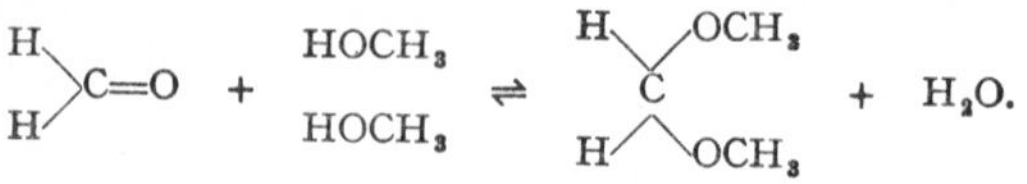

$$\begin{array}{c} H \\ \diagdown \\ \diagup \\ H \end{array} C=O \ + \ \begin{array}{c} HOCH_3 \\ HOCH_3 \end{array} \ \rightleftharpoons \ \begin{array}{c} H \diagdown \diagup OCH_3 \\ C \\ H \diagup \diagdown OCH_3 \end{array} \ + \ H_2O.$$

Methylal is a liquid with a pleasant odour, B.P. 42°. It is readily soluble in water. It is used in medicine as a soporific.

4. Condensations in which formaldehyde behaves differently from acetaldehyde. Formaldehyde *differs completely from acetaldehyde* in its reactions with ammonia, and with sodium or potassium hydroxide solution.

(i) *Reactions with ammonia, and with ammonium chloride.* If a mixture of formalin and excess of dilute ammonia solution is allowed to stand and is then evaporated to dryness, ammonia being kept in excess all the time, hexamethylene tetramine is obtained,

$$6CH_2O \ + \ 4NH_3 \ = \ (CH_2)_6N_4 \ + \ 6H_2O.$$

The structure of the hexamethylene tetramine is probably

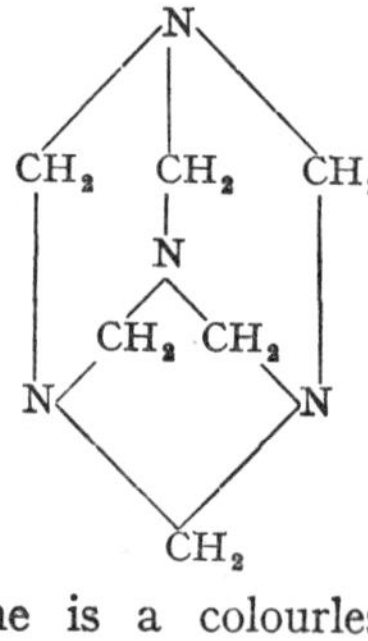

Hexamethylene tetramine is a colourless crystalline substance which sublimes at 260°. It is soluble in water, and it may be re-crystallised from ethyl alcohol. If heated with dilute sulphuric acid it is decomposed to formaldehyde and ammonium sulphate,

$$(CH_2)_6N_4 \ + \ 6H_2O \ + \ 2H_2SO_4 \ = \ 6CH_2O \ + \ 2(NH_4)_2SO_4.$$

It is used as a urinary antiseptic, in the treatment of cholecystitis, and in the manufacture of plastics. If formalin is slowly heated with a solution of ammonium chloride, methylamine hydrochloride is obtained,

$$2HCHO \ + \ NH_4Cl \ = \ CH_3NH_3.Cl \ + \ HCOOH.$$

If a larger proportion of formalin is used and the temperature is higher, dimethylamine hydrochloride and ultimately trimethylamine hydrochloride are formed,

$$4HCHO + NH_4Cl = (CH_3)_2NH_2.Cl + 2HCOOH,$$
$$6HCHO + NH_4Cl = (CH_3)_3NH.Cl + 3HCOOH.$$

(ii) *Reaction with sodium or potassium hydroxide solution. Cannizzaro's reaction.* If formaldehyde is warmed with an aqueous solution of sodium or potassium hydroxide, a mixture of methyl alcohol and sodium or potassium formate is obtained. Methyl formate is probably formed as an intermediate product, and this compound then undergoes hydrolysis

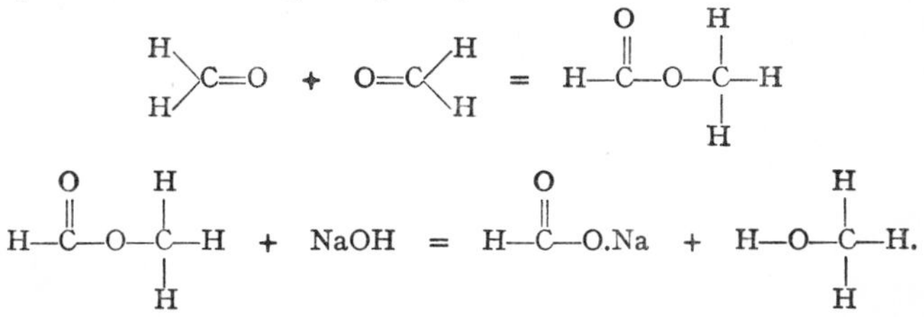

This reaction is of interest because of its similarity to the reaction of benzaldehyde with potassium hydroxide, yielding a mixture of benzyl alcohol and potassium benzoate, p. 430.

Polymerisation. Formaldehyde polymerises with great readiness. In this property it resembles acetaldehyde, but the products of polymerisation of formaldehyde and acetaldehyde are not precisely analogous. The mechanism of the polymerisation of formaldehyde may depend on the setting up, in the presence of water, of an equilibrium between formadehyde and the unstable methylene glycol, thus,

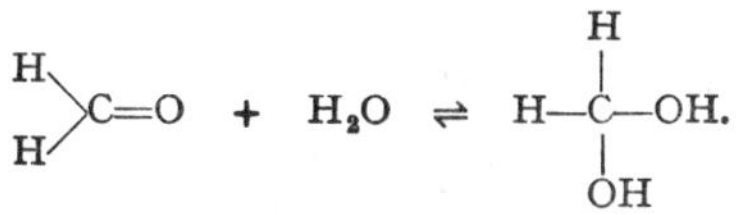

The molecules of methylene glycol may then unite, with the elimination of the elements of water to form chains or rings, thus

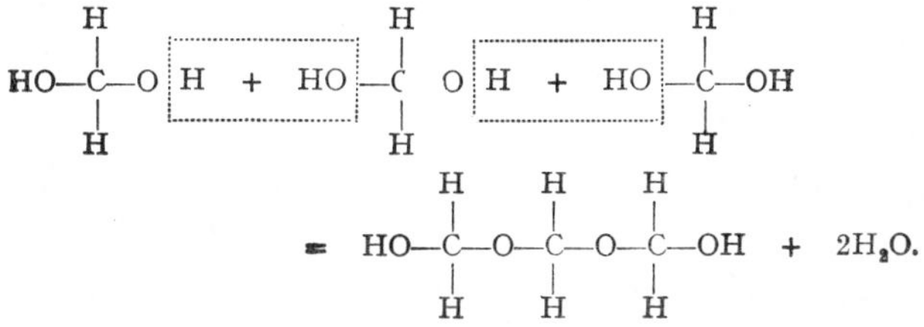

(i) *Polymerisation to paraformaldehyde.* Paraformaldehyde is obtained as a white powder when an aqueous solution of formaldehyde is evaporated. It melts between 150° and 160°, and is soluble in warm water. Its composition and molecular structure are uncertain ; its molecules may consist of long chains of alternate carbon and oxygen atoms produced by the intermediate formation and polymerisation of methylene glycol. Paraformaldehyde yields gaseous formaldehyde when heated.

(ii) *Polymerisation to trioxymethylene.* Trioxymethylene is produced by the polymerisation of gaseous or liquid formaldehyde in the presence of traces of water, acids or alkalis. It is a colourless crystalline substance, M.P. 60–64°, freely soluble in water. It is volatile. It sublimes at 46° undecomposed, and its vapour density indicates a molecular formula $(CH_2O)_3$. It has no aldehydic properties, and its constitution may be

$$\begin{array}{c} H_2 \\ C \\ O \diagup \quad \diagdown O \\ | \qquad \quad | \\ H_2C \diagdown \quad \diagup CH_2 \\ O \end{array}$$

When trioxymethylene is strongly heated it decomposes into pure gaseous formaldehyde ; if traces of water are present trioxymethylene is formed again on cooling.

(iii) *Polymerisation to formose.* If a dilute aqueous solution of formaldehyde is shaken with excess of an aqueous suspension of calcium hydroxide, allowed to stand for half an hour, filtered, and then allowed to stand for several days, the solution contains a mixture of sugars known as formose, some of which have the molecular formula $C_6H_{12}O_6$. Among them is α-acrose, or *dl*-fructose. This reaction is of interest because it may be related to the process by which plants convert carbon dioxide into sugars by photosynthesis.

Uses of formaldehyde. The vapour of formaldehyde, produced by the action of heat on paraformaldehyde, is used as a disinfectant. A 1 per cent. aqueous solution is used in medicine as an internal antiseptic : stronger solutions are used for sterilising surgical instruments. Formalin is also used for preserving biological and anatomical specimens. It renders gelatine insoluble in water.

Formaldehyde has an important use in the production of plastics, including the well-known commercial material " Bakelite ". " Bakelite " is obtained by heating phenol with formalin and ammonia at 80–90°, and subsequently evaporating the solution. Plastics are also made from formaldehyde and urea, and from formaldehyde and thiourea.

Formaldehyde is useful in chemical processes for introducing the methyl group into molecules of other compounds. Substances which may be used in this way are described as methylating agents. The action of formaldehyde in replacing the hydrogen atoms in ammonium chloride by methyl groups has been mentioned on p. 212.

Constitution of formaldehyde. The molecular formula of formaldehyde is H_2CO. If the structural formula is to contain atoms of carbon, oxygen and hydrogen exerting their normal valencies, it can be written in one way only, thus

$$\begin{array}{c} H \\ \diagdown \\ \diagup \\ H \end{array} C=O.$$

This structural formula is confirmed by the relation of formaldehyde to methyl alcohol, from which it is readily formed by the removal of two atoms of hydrogen from the molecule,

$$\begin{array}{c} H \\ | \\ H-C-OH \\ | \\ H \end{array} - H_2 = \begin{array}{c} H \\ \diagdown \\ \diagup \\ H \end{array} C=O.$$

This structure is further confirmed by the reactions of formaldehyde which are analogous to those of acetaldehyde (p. 211).

Tests for formaldehyde.

An aqueous solution of formaldehyde

(i) reduces ammoniacal silver oxide solution in the cold to metallic silver,

(ii) reduces Fehling's solution to cuprous oxide on warming,

(iii) colours Schiff's reagent pink ;

but it does *not*

(iv) form a resin with sodium hydroxide solution,

(v) give a red colour with alkaline sodium nitroprusside solution,

(vi) undergo the iodoform reaction.

These tests have been described under " acetaldehyde ", p. 208, which responds to all of them. Formaldehyde reacts with sodium bisulphite, with phenylhydrazine, and with hydroxylamine, but the products of these reactions are so highly soluble in water that they cannot be used for the identification of formaldehyde.

The reactions mentioned above do not provide any positive test for distinguishing formaldehyde from acetaldehyde.

The colour reaction between formaldehyde and pyrogallol

in acid solution may be used for this purpose. A freshly prepared solution of pyrogallol is mixed with the solution of formaldehyde, and excess of concentrated hydrochloric acid is added. In a few minutes a white precipitate is formed, which rapidly turns pink, and then a deep magenta red. If this test is carried out on acetaldehyde a white precipitate is produced which gradually changes to a pale yellow ; there is no pink or red precipitate.

The *concentration* of formaldehyde in formalin may be determined by adding a measured volume of the dilute formalin solution to a measured volume of standard iodine solution, which must be in excess.[*] Sodium hydroxide solution is then added until the colour of the iodine is almost discharged. After 10 minutes the solution is acidified with hydrochloric acid which liberates the excess iodine. This iodine is determined by titration against standard sodium thiosulphate solution. The iodine used in the oxidation of the formaldehyde to formic acid is the difference between the quantity originally added and that found by the titration.

CHLORAL

Chloral, or trichloracetaldehyde, $CCl_3.CHO$, is derived from acetaldehyde by the substitution of chlorine atoms for the three hydrogen atoms in the methyl group. Chloral is a colourless, oily liquid with a pungent odour. Sp. Gr. 1·512 at 20°, M.P. −57·5°, B.P. 97·7°. It reacts with water to yield chloral hydrate, which is readily soluble in water.

Principal reactions in which chloral is produced

1. The action of chlorine on acetaldehyde. Chloral is obtained when chlorine is passed into acetaldehyde containing calcium carbonate in suspension,

$$\underset{\underset{H}{|}}{\overset{\overset{H}{|}}{H-C}}-C\overset{H}{\underset{O}{\diagdown}} + 3Cl_2 = \underset{\underset{Cl}{|}}{\overset{\overset{Cl}{|}}{Cl-C}}-C\overset{H}{\underset{O}{\diagdown}} + 3HCl.$$

The calcium carbonate is added to neutralise the hydrochloric acid as fast as it is formed. If the acid were allowed to accumulate during the reaction it would convert the chloral to metachloral (see below).

2. The action of chlorine on ethyl alcohol. This reaction is employed in the manufacture of chloral. Chlorine is passed into absolute alcohol containing ferric chloride as a catalyst, for several days. The mixture is at first cooled, and finally heated to 100°. The product obtained when the heated mixture is finally cooled is a white solid mass of chloral alcoholate,

$$Cl_3C-\underset{\underset{OC_2H_5}{|}}{\overset{\overset{H}{|}}{C}}-OH$$

[*] The equation for the oxidation of formaldehyde by iodine in alkaline solution is given on p. 211.

The equations for the sequence of reactions which occur are given on p. 494. The chloral alcoholate is mixed with concentrated sulphuric acid and distilled. Chloral is liberated

$$CCl_3-\overset{\overset{\displaystyle H}{|}}{\underset{\underset{\displaystyle OC_2H_5}{|}}{C}}-OH + H_2SO_4 = CCl_3-C\overset{\displaystyle H}{\underset{\displaystyle O}{\diagdown}} + C_2H_5HSO_4 + H_2O,$$

and may be purified by distillation. It may also be purified by conversion to chloral hydrate (see below), a crystalline substance, which is recrystallised from water, and then decomposed with the liberation of chloral by distillation with concentrated sulphuric acid.

Chemical properties of chloral. Chloral is a stable compound ; it is unaffected by concentrated sulphuric acid at 100°. It undergoes the following chemical reactions.

1. Reaction with water, yielding chloral hydrate. If a small quantity of water is added to chloral, heat is evolved and colourless crystals of chloral hydrate are formed,

$$CCl_3-C\overset{\displaystyle H}{\underset{\displaystyle O}{\diagdown}} + H_2O = CCl_3-\overset{\overset{\displaystyle H}{|}}{\underset{\underset{\displaystyle OH}{|}}{C}}-OH.$$

2. Reaction with alkalis, giving chloroform. Chloral is hydrolysed by boiling aqueous alkalis to yield chloroform and a salt of formic acid. For example, sodium hydroxide yields chloroform and sodium formate.

$$CCl_3.CHO + NaOH = CHCl_3 + H.COONa.$$

3. Oxidation, and action as a reducing agent. Chloral reduces an ammoniacal solution of silver oxide to metallic silver, and Fehling's solution, on warming, to cuprous oxide. In these reactions chloral is oxidised to trichloroacetic acid. Fuming nitric acid also oxidises chloral to trichloroacetic acid,

$$CCl_3-C\overset{\displaystyle H}{\underset{\displaystyle O}{\diagdown}} + O = CCl_3-C\overset{\displaystyle OH}{\underset{\displaystyle O.}{\diagdown}}$$

4. Reduction, giving acetaldehyde. Chloral may be reduced to acetaldehyde by treatment with a mixture of zinc and hydrochloric acid,

$$CCl_3.CHO + 3H = CH_3.CHO + 3HCl.$$

5. Condensations. Chloral exhibits many of the condensation reactions of acetaldehyde. It combines with ammonia to give chloral-ammonia, $CCl_3.CH.OH.NH_2$, with hydrogen cyanide to form chloral cyanhydrin, $CCl_3.CH.OH.CN$, and with sodium bisulphite to give a bisulphite compound, $CCl_3.CH.OH.OSO_2.Na$.

6. Polymerisation of chloral. In the presence of a small quantity of an acid, which acts catalytically, chloral readily polymerises to a white amorphous solid known as *metachloral*. Metachloral is insoluble in water; it is converted to chloral on heating to 180°. On treatment with alkalis or with nitric acid, metachloral behaves similarly to chloral, and yields chloroform and trichloroacetic acid respectively.

Tests for chloral. Chloral answers several of the tests which are primarily applied for acetaldehyde. It reduces ammoniacal silver oxide solution to a silver mirror, it reduces Fehling's solution to cuprous oxide, and it colours Schiff's reagent pink. It may readily be distinguished from acetaldehyde by its reaction with aqueous alkalis yielding chloroform, and by the separation of crystalline chloral hydrate on the addition of a little water. Since chloral is readily hydrolysed to chloroform by alkalis, it gives the isocyanide reaction, p. 154.

CHLORAL HYDRATE

Chloral hydrate is obtained in the form of massive colourless monoclinic prisms, M.P. 52°, B.P. 97·5°, by the action of a small quantity of water on chloral. The reaction is noticeably exothermic

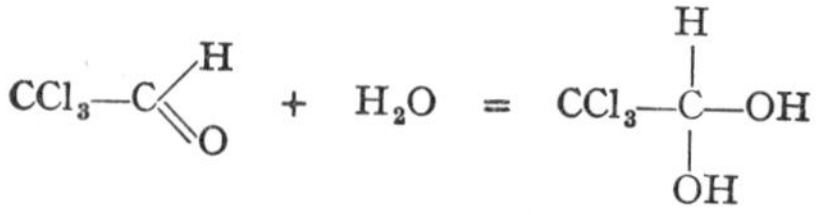

$$CCl_3-C{\overset{H}{\underset{O}{}}} + H_2O = CCl_3-\overset{H}{\underset{OH}{C}}-OH$$

Chloral hydrate is readily soluble in water, alcohol, and many other organic solvents. Chloral hydrate is a rare example of a compound in which two hydroxyl groups are attached to the same carbon atom. Normally the group $>C{\overset{OH}{\underset{OH}{}}}$ dissociates into water and a carbonyl group as soon as it is formed,

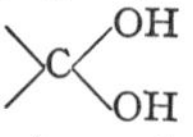

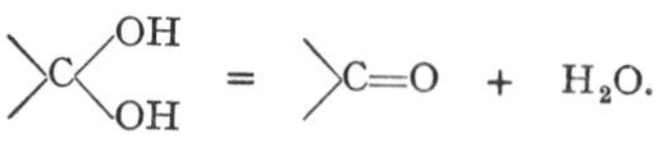

$$>C{\overset{OH}{\underset{OH}{}}} = >C=O + H_2O.$$

The instability of the group $>C{\overset{OH}{\underset{OH}{}}}$ is mentioned on p. 151. When heated alone, chloral hydrate partly dissociates into chloral and steam. If a few crystals of chloral hydrate are shaken with concentrated sulphuric acid at room temperature, the mixture becomes very cold, and an oily layer of chloral collects on the upper surface of the acid,

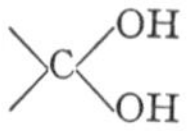

$$CCl_3.CH(OH)_2 = CCl_3.CHO + H_2O.$$

If the mixture is heated, the vapour of chloral distils and may be condensed and collected.

Many of the chemical reactions of chloral hydrate are similar to the corresponding reactions of chloral. For example, both chloral hydrate and chloral (i) undergo hydrolysis by alkalis to yield chloroform, (ii) give the isocyanide reaction, (iii) reduce ammoniacal silver oxide solution to metallic silver, (iv) reduce Fehling's solution, on warming, to cuprous oxide, and (v) undergo oxidation with concentrated nitric acid to yield trichloroacetic acid. Chloral hydrate, however, does not give a pink colour with Schiff's reagent, and it does not form a bisulphite compound. In these two respects it differs from chloral.

Chloral hydrate reacts with potassium cyanide in aqueous solution to form dichloroacetic acid,

$$CCl_3.CH(OH)_2 + KCN = CHCl_2.COOH + HCN + KCl.$$

Chloral hydrate is used as a hypnotic, normally in admixture with potassium bromide.

CHAPTER XIII

THE ALIPHATIC KETONES

ACETONE

THE aliphatic ketones may be theoretically derived from the aldehydes by the substitution of an alkyl group for the hydrogen atom in the aldehyde group, $-C\begin{smallmatrix}\diagup H \\ \diagdown\!\!\diagdown O\end{smallmatrix}$. The substitution of the methyl group for the hydrogen atom in the aldehyde group of acetaldehyde gives dimethyl ketone, or acetone.

$$CH_3-C\begin{smallmatrix}\diagup H \\ \diagdown\!\!\diagdown O\end{smallmatrix} \qquad\qquad CH_3-\underset{\underset{O}{\|}}{C}-CH_3$$

acetaldehyde — acetone

Acetone is a colourless, mobile liquid, B.P. 56·5°. Its specific gravity at 20° is 0·792. It possesses a characteristic sweetish odour. It is miscible in all proportions with water, alcohol, and ether.

PRINCIPAL REACTIONS IN WHICH ACETONE IS PRODUCED

1. The interaction of acetylene and steam. If a mixture of acetylene and steam is passed over a catalyst consisting of zinc vanadate and magnesium vanadate heated to 420°, acetone is produced. The yield is 80–90 per cent.

2. The oxidation of iso-propyl alcohol. The oxidation of iso-propyl alcohol, p. 173, may be carried out either in aqueous solution by means of sodium dichromate and sulphuric acid, or in the vapour phase by passing a mixture of the alcohol vapour and oxygen over finely divided copper at 500°, or over platinum black at 250–300°, or over zinc oxide at 320°. Industrially, iso-propyl alcohol is converted to acetone and hydrogen by passage over a catalyst at a high temperature.

3. The distillation of calcium acetate. If dry powdered calcium acetate is heated it yields acetone vapour, which may be condensed and collected; calcium carbonate remains as a residue,

$$(CH_3.COO)_2Ca \;=\; CH_3.CO.CH_3 \;+\; CaCO_3.$$

3a. The catalytic decomposition of acetic acid vapour. If acetic acid vapour is passed over a catalyst at 300–400° it is converted to a mixture of acetone, steam and carbon dioxide. The catalyst may be finely divided metallic copper, or the oxide of aluminium, thorium, zinc or cadmium. The reaction is clearly a modification of Reaction 3.

4. The fermentation of starch. Starch may be fermented by the bacterium *Clostridium acetobutylicum*. A culture of this organism is added to maize mash, which is then kept at 37·5° for two or three days. The starch is converted to sugars having the molecular formula $C_6H_{12}O_6$, and the sugars undergo further decomposition to yield n-butyl alcohol, acetone, carbon dioxide, hydrogen and water, roughly in accordance with the equation :

$$3C_6H_{12}O_6 = 2C_4H_9OH + CH_3.CO.CH_3 + 7CO_2 + 4H_2 + H_2O.$$

The hydrogen obtained in this process, after the separation of the carbon dioxide by liquefaction, is very pure and may be used in catalytic hydrogenation processes.

5. The ketonic hydrolysis of ethyl acetoacetate. If ethyl acetoacetate is boiled with dilute alcoholic potassium hydroxide solution, it is hydrolysed to acetone, carbon dioxide (which forms potassium carbonate with the potassium hydroxide) and ethyl alcohol,

$$CH_3.CO.CH_2.COOC_2H_5 + HOH = CH_3.CO.CH_3 + CO_2 + C_2H_5OH.$$

This method is important because it is the simplest example of a general method for synthesising ketones by the hydrolysis of ethyl acetoacetate and its derivatives (p. 460).

It should be noted that Reactions 2 and 3 of those enumerated above are parallel to Reactions 2 and 3 for the preparation of acetaldehyde given on p. 199.

Laboratory preparation of acetone. Acetone is one of the starting-points for the preparation of other organic substances, and, therefore, it is manufactured on a large scale. It is not usually made in the laboratory, but, as an exercise, acetone may be obtained by the dry distillation of calcium acetate. About 10 gm. of calcium acetate are placed in a hard-glass tube fitted with a cork and downward delivery tube. The tube is tapped gently to ensure a clear passage for the evolved gases and heated in a Bunsen flame. The crude acetone is collected in an ice-cold receiver, and well shaken with a saturated solution of sodium bisulphite. The white crystals obtained are filtered off, and distilled with a saturated rolution of sodium carbonate. The acetone evolved is collected, dried over fused calcium chloride, and redistilled.

Industrial preparation of acetone. Acetone is made on an industrial scale by (i) the interaction of acetylene and steam, Reaction 1, (ii) the fermentation of starch, Reaction 4, and (iii) the catalytic dehydrogenation of iso-propyl alcohol, Reaction 2, obtained from the propylene in natural gas, or in the gases formed during the cracking of petroleum (p. 475).

CHEMICAL REACTIONS, CONSTITUTION AND USES OF ACETONE

1. Oxidation of acetone, giving acetic acid and carbon dioxide. Acetone is oxidised only by powerful oxidising agents, such as alkaline potassium permanganate solution or chromic acid. The products of oxidation are acetic acid, carbon dioxide and water,

$$CH_3.CO.CH_3 \ + \ 2O_2 \ = \ CH_3.COOH \ + \ CO_2 \ + \ H_2O.$$

Acetone, however, is not a reducing agent. Neither Fehling's solution, nor ammoniacal silver oxide solution are reduced by it, and it may be distilled unchanged from a neutral solution of potassium permanganate. Such a distillation is often used for the preliminary purification of acetone.

2. Reduction of acetone. (i) Reduction giving iso-propyl alcohol and pinacol. Acetone may be reduced to iso-propyl alcohol. The reduction in aqueous solution is effected by sodium amalgam, or electrolytically ; in the vapour phase it is brought about by passing a mixture of acetone vapour and hydrogen over freshly reduced nickel at 120°,

$$\begin{array}{c} CH_3 \\ \diagdown \\ \diagup \\ CH_3 \end{array} C{=}O \ + \ H_2 \ = \ CH_3{-}\underset{\underset{H}{|}}{\overset{\overset{CH_3}{|}}{C}}{-}OH.$$

Iso-propyl alcohol is not the only product obtained when acetone is reduced in aqueous solution ; a considerable proportion of pinacol, or tetramethylethylene glycol, is formed at the same time,

$$O{=}\underset{\underset{CH_3}{|}}{\overset{\overset{CH_3}{|}}{C}} \ + \ 2H \ + \ \underset{\underset{CH_3}{|}}{\overset{\overset{CH_3}{|}}{C}}{=}O \ = \ HO{-}\underset{\underset{CH_3}{|}}{\overset{\overset{CH_3}{|}}{C}}{-}\underset{\underset{CH_3}{|}}{\overset{\overset{CH_3}{|}}{C}}{-}OH.$$

Pinacol is a solid, M.P. 38°. When heated with dilute hydrochloric acid or sulphuric acid it undergoes an interesting intramolecular change, with the elimination of a molecule of water, yielding pinacolone, or trimethyl acetone,

$$CH_3{-}\underset{\underset{OH}{|}}{\overset{\overset{CH_3}{|}}{C}}{-}\underset{\underset{OH}{|}}{\overset{\overset{CH_3}{|}}{C}}{-}CH_3 \ = \ CH_3{-}\underset{\underset{O}{||}}{C}{-}\underset{\underset{CH_3}{|}}{C}{-}CH_3 \ + \ H_2O.$$

(ii) Reduction giving propane. Clemmensen reaction. Acetone is reduced to propane by treatment with amalgamated zinc in the presence of concentrated hydrochloric acid for two or three hours,

$$CH_3.CO.CH_3 + 4H = CH_3.CH_2.CH_3 + H_2O.$$

3. Action with phosphorus pentachloride. Phosphorus pentachloride reacts with acetone, yielding 2:2-dichloropropane,

CH₃\
    C=O   +   PCl₅ = CH₃—C——Cl + POCl₃.\
CH₃

(structure: 2:2-dichloropropane with CH₃ and Cl on central carbon)

4. Halogenation. Chlorine reacts with acetone, replacing the hydrogen atoms in the methyl groups, giving first monochloroacetone, $CH_2Cl.CO.CH_3$, M.P. 119°, and ultimately hexachloroacetone, $CCl_3.CO.CCl_3$. Bromine reacts with acetone to yield ultimately $CHBr_2.CO.CBr_3$, but iodine replaces only two atoms in the molecule to give $CH_2I.CO.CH_2I$.

5. The chloroform and iodoform reactions. When acetone is added to an aqueous suspension of bleaching powder, a vigorous reaction occurs, leading to the formation of chloroform and calcium acetate. This reaction has been described and explained on p. 152.

When a solution of sodium hypochlorite is added to a mixture of acetone and aqueous potassium iodide solution containing sodium hydroxide, a precipitate of iodoform is obtained. This reaction is described on p. 156. As a test for acetone it is mentioned on p. 227.

Condensations. Like acetaldehyde, acetone readily undergoes condensation reactions (p. 202). Acetone does not condense with an alcohol to form a compound corresponding to acetal, and at normal temperatures it gives complex compounds with ammonia, but otherwise its condensation reactions are parallel to those of acetaldehyde. The more important of these reactions are described below.

6. Condensation with sodium bisulphite, giving a bisulphite compound. If acetone is shaken with a concentrated aqueous solution of sodium bisulphite, a white precipitate is formed with the evolution of heat ; on cooling, the suspension turns almost solid. The white precipitate is the acetone bisulphite compound formed according to the equation,

CH₃\
    C=O   + NaHSO₃ = CH₃—C—OH\
CH₃   O.SO₂.Na

If the sodium bisulphite compound is distilled with sodium carbonate solution, acetone is regenerated,

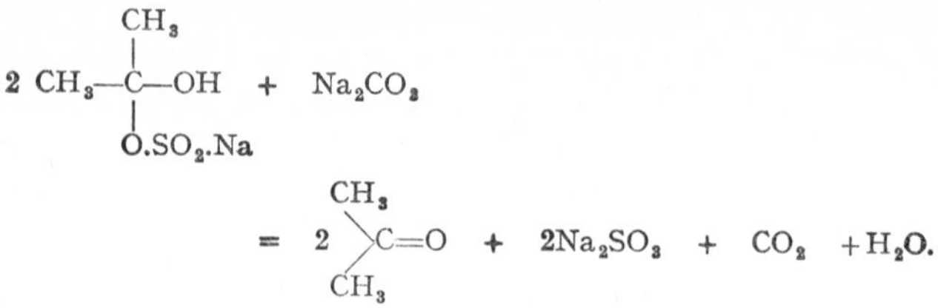

$$2\ CH_3-\underset{\underset{O.SO_2.Na}{|}}{\overset{\overset{CH_3}{|}}{C}}-OH\ +\ Na_2CO_3$$

$$=\ 2\ \underset{CH_3}{\overset{CH_3}{\diagdown}}C=O\ +\ 2Na_2SO_3\ +\ CO_2\ +H_2O.$$

7. Condensation with hydrogen cyanide, giving acetone cyanhydrin. Hydrogen cyanide reacts with acetone to yield acetone cyanhydrin, a colourless liquid, B.P. 82° at 23 mm.,

$$\underset{CH_3}{\overset{CH_3}{\diagdown}}C=O\ +\ HCN\ =\ CH_3-\underset{\underset{CN}{|}}{\overset{\overset{CH_3}{|}}{C}}-OH.$$

Acetone cyanhydrin may be conveniently prepared by the action of sodium cyanide on the addition compound of acetone and sodium sulphite,

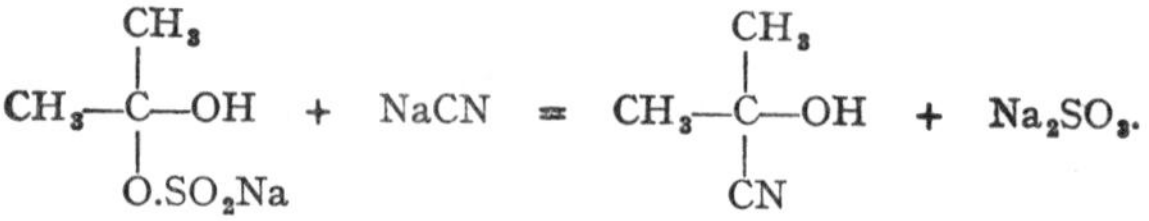

$$CH_3-\underset{\underset{O.SO_2Na}{|}}{\overset{\overset{CH_3}{|}}{C}}-OH\ +\ NaCN\ =\ CH_3-\underset{\underset{CN}{|}}{\overset{\overset{CH_3}{|}}{C}}-OH\ +\ Na_2SO_3.$$

8. Condensation with ammonia. At $-65°$ acetone reacts with ammonia to yield acetone ammonia,

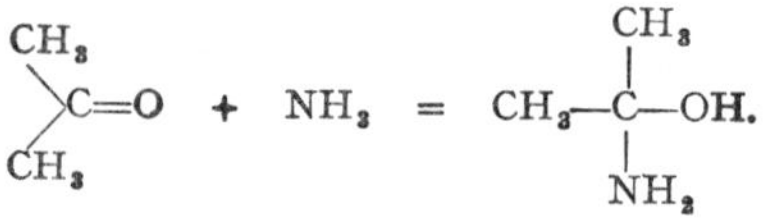

$$\underset{CH_3}{\overset{CH_3}{\diagdown}}C=O\ +\ NH_3\ =\ CH_3-\underset{\underset{NH_2}{|}}{\overset{\overset{CH_3}{|}}{C}}-OH.$$

The reaction between acetone and ammonia under these conditions is similar to that between acetaldehyde and ammonia at room temperature. If, however, acetone is saturated with ammonia, and the solution is kept for some weeks at room temperature, a considerable proportion of the acetone is converted into diacetonamine,

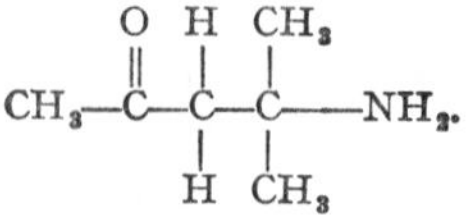

$$CH_3-\underset{\underset{H}{|}}{\overset{\overset{O}{||}}{C}}-\underset{\underset{CH_3}{|}}{\overset{\overset{H}{|}}{C}}-\overset{\overset{CH_3}{|}}{C}-NH_2.$$

Diacetonamine may be regarded as an additive product of mesityl oxide (see below) and ammonia,

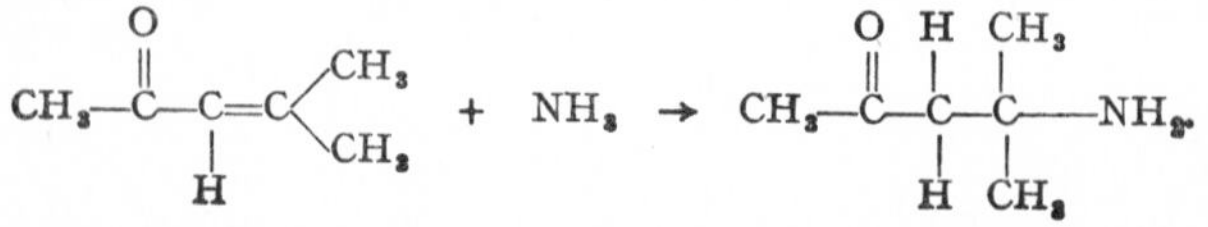

$$CH_3-\underset{}{\overset{\overset{O}{||}}{C}}-\underset{\underset{H}{|}}{C}=C\underset{CH_3}{\overset{CH_3}{\diagup}}\ +\ NH_3\ \rightarrow\ CH_3-\underset{}{\overset{\overset{O}{||}}{C}}-\underset{\underset{H}{|}}{\overset{\overset{H}{|}}{C}}-\underset{\underset{CH_3}{|}}{\overset{\overset{CH_3}{|}}{C}}-NH_2.$$

9. Condensation with hydroxylamine, giving an oxime.
Acetone reacts with hydroxylamine to yield an oxime, acetoxime.

$$\begin{array}{c} CH_3 \\ \diagdown \\ \diagup \\ CH_3 \end{array} C{=}O \ + \ H_2NOH \ = \ \begin{array}{c} CH_3 \\ \diagdown \\ \diagup \\ CH_3 \end{array} C{=}NOH \ + \ H_2O.$$

Acetoxime is best prepared by adding acetone, in small quantities at a time, to an aqueous solution of hydroxylamine hydrochloride made alkaline with sodium hydroxide, while the temperature is kept below 25°. Acetoxime crystallises, contaminated with sodium chloride. It is purified by solution in petroleum, in which sodium chloride is insoluble. The acetoxime is crystallised from the solution after the sodium chloride has been filtered off. Acetoxime melts at 60°, and very readily sublimes. It is used for identifying acetone. When acetoxime is distilled with dilute sulphuric acid, acetone is liberated,

$$\begin{array}{c} CH_3 \\ \diagdown \\ \diagup \\ CH_3 \end{array} C{=}NOH \ + \ H_2SO_4 \ + \ H_2O \ = \ \begin{array}{c} CH_3 \\ \diagdown \\ \diagup \\ CH_3 \end{array} C{=}O \ + \ H_2NOH.H_2SO_4.$$

Pure acetone may be made by this reaction.

10. Condensation with phenylhydrazine, giving acetone phenylhydrazone. Acetone phenylhydrazone is formed by the reaction between acetone and phenylhydrazine dissolved in dilute acetic acid,

$$\begin{array}{c} CH_3 \\ \diagdown \\ \diagup \\ CH_3 \end{array} C{=}O \ + \ H_2N.NHC_6H_5 \ = \ \begin{array}{c} CH_3 \\ \diagdown \\ \diagup \\ CH_3 \end{array} C{=}N.NHC_6H_5 \ + \ H_2O.$$

Acetone phenylhydrazone forms colourless crystals, M.P. 16°; it is, however, soluble and difficult to isolate.

11. Condensation with a Grignard reagent, giving a tertiary alcohol. Acetone unites with a Grignard reagent to give an intermediate product which may be hydrolysed to yield a tertiary alcohol. For example, acetone reacts with phenyl magnesium bromide to yield dimethyl phenyl carbinol, thus,

$$\begin{array}{c} CH_3 \\ \diagdown \\ \diagup \\ CH_3 \end{array} C{=}O \ + \ C_6H_5MgBr \ = \ \begin{array}{c} CH_3 \quad OMgBr \\ \diagdown \diagup \\ C \\ \diagup \diagdown \\ CH_3 \quad C_6H_5 \end{array}$$

$$\begin{array}{c} CH_3 \quad OMgBr \\ \diagdown \diagup \\ C \\ \diagup \diagdown \\ CH_3 \quad C_6H_5 \end{array} \ + \ HCl \ = \ \begin{array}{c} CH_3 \quad OH \\ \diagdown \diagup \\ C \\ \diagup \diagdown \\ CH_3 \quad C_6H_5 \end{array} \ + \ MgBrCl.$$

H   D.C.

12. Condensation of two or more molecules of acetone with one another.

(i) In the presence of barium hydroxide, two molecules of acetone condense thus,

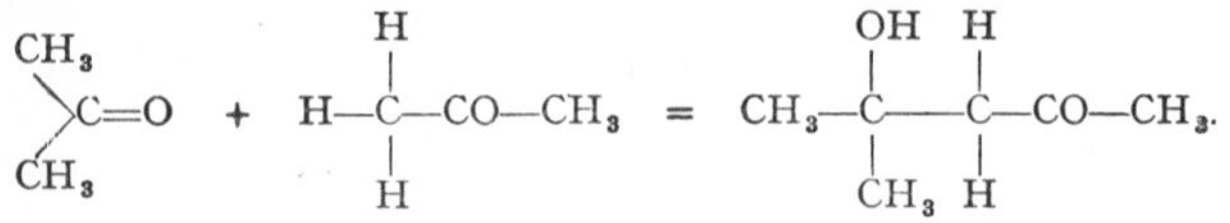

$$\begin{array}{l}CH_3\\ \!\!\!\!\!\!\!\!\diagdown C{=}O\\ CH_3\end{array} + \begin{array}{c}H\\ |\\ H{-}C{-}CO{-}CH_3\\ |\\ H\end{array} = \begin{array}{cc}OH & H\\ | & |\\ CH_3{-}C{-}\!\!-\!\!C{-}CO{-}CH_3.\\ | & |\\ CH_3 & H\end{array}$$

This reaction is similar to the aldol condensation of acetaldehyde. It is the only polymerisation reaction exhibited by acetone.

(ii) If acetone is saturated with dry hydrogen chloride it yields a mixture of mesityl oxide, B.P. 138°, and phorone, M.P. 28°, B.P. 198°. Mesityl oxide is formed according to the equation,

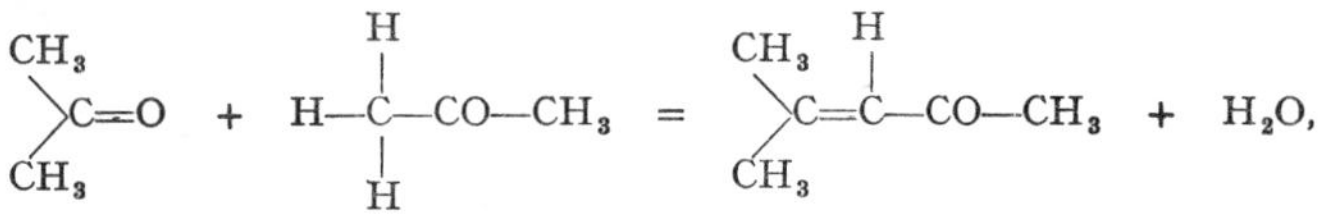

$$\begin{array}{l}CH_3\\ \!\!\!\!\!\!\!\!\diagdown C{=}O\\ CH_3\end{array} + \begin{array}{c}H\\ |\\ H{-}C{-}CO{-}CH_3\\ |\\ H\end{array} = \begin{array}{c}CH_3\;\;H\\ \!\!\!\!\!\!\!\!\diagdown C{=}C{-}CO{-}CH_3\\ CH_3\end{array} + H_2O,$$

and phorone is formed from mesityl oxide by a further condensation, thus

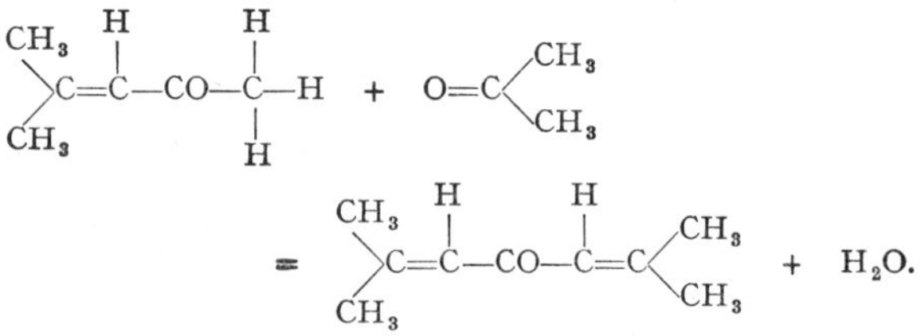

$$\begin{array}{cc}CH_3\;H & H\\ \!\!\!\!\!\!\!\!\diagdown C{=}C{-}CO{-}C{-}H & + \;O{=}C\!\!\diagup^{CH_3}_{\diagdown CH_3}\\ CH_3| & \\ H &\end{array}$$

$$= \begin{array}{c}CH_3\;\;H\;\;\;\;H\\ \!\!\!\!\!\!\!\!\diagdown C{=}C{-}CO{-}C{=}C\!\!\diagup^{CH_3}_{\diagdown CH_3}\\ CH_3\end{array} + \;H_2O.$$

Mesityl oxide shows the same relation to acetone, as crotonaldehyde to acetaldehyde. Both mesityl oxide and phorone regenerate acetone when heated with dilute sulphuric acid.

(iii) If acetone is distilled with 80 per cent. sulphuric acid, mesitylene (trimethylbenzene) is obtained,

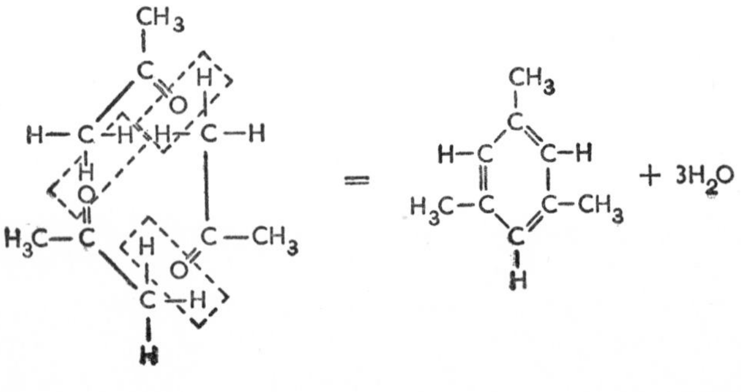

$$= \begin{array}{c}CH_3\\ |\\ C\\ H{-}C\diagup\;\;\diagdown C{-}H\\ \||\\ H_3C{-}C\;\;\;\;C{-}CH_3\\ \diagdown C\diagup\\ |\\ H\end{array} + \;3H_2O$$

Constitution of Acetone. The molecular formula of acetone is C_3H_6O. Acetone does not react with sodium. With phosphorus pentachloride it yields a compound with the molecular formula $C_3H_6Cl_2$, in which two atoms of chlorine have taken the place of the oxygen atom in the original molecule of acetone. These reactions, by comparison with those of ethyl alcohol and acetaldehyde, show that the oxygen atom in acetone is present in a carbonyl group, and not in a hydroxyl group. The presence of a carbonyl group in the acetone molecule is confirmed by the reactions of acetone with hydrocyanic acid, sodium bisulphite, hydroxylamine, and phenylhydrazine, in all of which its behaviour is analogous to that of acetaldehyde.

On this evidence the molecular structure of acetone may be either

$$H_3C—\overset{\overset{\displaystyle O}{\|}}{C}—CH_3 \quad \text{or} \quad CH_3.CH_2.C\overset{\displaystyle H}{\underset{\displaystyle O}{\diagup}}$$

The second formula is that of an aldehyde, and it cannot be assigned to acetone, which fails to show the reducing actions characteristic of an aldehyde ; it reduces neither Fehling's solution, nor ammoniacal silver oxide solution. When acetone is reduced by sodium amalgam and water, it yields a secondary alcohol, isopropyl alcohol, and not a primary alcohol which would be formed from an aldehyde. Acetone is, therefore, assigned the constitution $CH_3.CO.CH_3$.

Uses of acetone. Acetone is chiefly useful as a solvent for other organic compounds. Acetylene is stored in solution in acetone under pressure. Cordite is made by forcing through a die a mixture of gun-cotton and nitroglycerin made pasty with acetone and a little vaseline. The acetone is subsequently removed by evaporation, and the paste sets to a horn-like mass which is safe to handle. Acetone, since it is not attacked by a neutral solution of potassium permanganate, may be used as a solvent for organic compounds which are to be oxidised by potassium permanganate. Acetone is used as the starting-point for the preparation of iodoform and chloroform.

Tests for acetone.

1. The iodoform reaction. The iodoform reaction is shown more readily by acetone than by any other substance. The test is carried out by adding 5 c.c. of 10 per cent. potassium iodide solution and 5 c.c. of freshly prepared sodium hypochlorite solution to 1/2 c.c. of acetone. The mixture is well shaken in the cold, and a yellow precipitate of iodoform separates. This reaction is also given by many other compounds (see p. 156).

2. The sodium bisulphite reaction. This reaction has already been described under Reaction 6, p. 223. Formaldehyde and acetaldehyde do not respond to this test, as their bisulphite compounds are too soluble to be precipitated. Benzaldehyde and salicylaldehyde respond to the test, but acetophenone and benzophenone do not do so.

3. Schiff's reaction. A magenta colour is very slowly developed when acetone is shaken with Schiff's reagent, p. 209.

4. The formation of acetoxime. See Reaction 9, p. 225.

5. The nitroprusside test. The Legal test. If a small quantity of acetone is mixed with a little freshly prepared sodium nitroprusside solution, and excess of dilute sodium hydroxide solution is added, a red coloration is obtained. Acetaldehyde and acetophenone also respond to this test.

6. The dinitrobenzene test. If a little *m*-dinitrobenzene is added to acetone, followed by excess of sodium hydroxide solution, and the mixture is well shaken, a violet coloration is produced which slowly fades. Acetophenone also responds to this test.

Tests 5 and 6 are given by ketones which contain the group

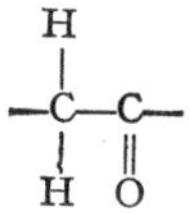

$$-\overset{\displaystyle H}{\underset{\displaystyle H}{\overset{|}{\underset{|}{C}}}}-\overset{\displaystyle }{\underset{\displaystyle O}{\overset{}{\underset{\parallel}{C}}}}-$$

Acetone is not a reducing agent, and therefore it precipitates neither silver from ammoniacal silver oxide solution, nor cuprous oxide from Fehling's solution.

CHAPTER XIV

THE FATTY ACIDS

THE fatty acids are derived from the paraffins by the oxidation of a methyl group : one of the three hydrogen atoms in the methyl group is replaced by a hydroxyl group, and the other two hydrogen atoms are replaced by an oxygen atom. The relation between acetic acid and ethane is shown by their structural formulae,

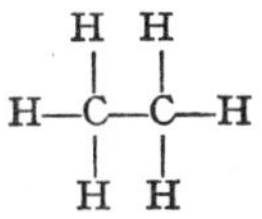

ethane 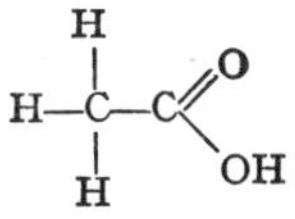   acetic acid

The oxidation of ethane to acetic acid takes place in three stages :

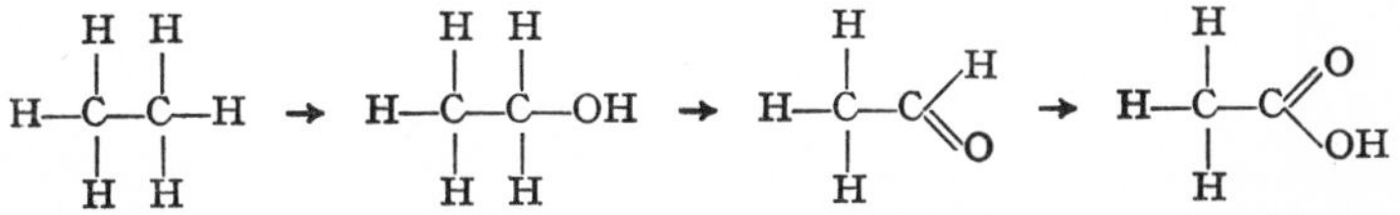

ethane   ethyl alcohol   acetaldehyde   acetic acid

The first stage, the oxidation of ethane to ethyl alcohol, can be experimentally realised only indirectly, by brominating ethane to ethyl bromide (p. 137), and hydrolysing this compound to ethyl alcohol (p. 140). The second and third stages may be directly carried out in the laboratory ; ethyl alcohol vapour is converted to acetaldehyde when it is mixed with air and passed over heated metallic silver (Reaction 2, p. 199), and acetaldehyde is oxidised to acetic acid by passing the vapour, mixed with air, over vanadium pentoxide (Reaction 1, p. 201).

The group $-C\overset{\displaystyle O}{\underset{\displaystyle OH}{}}$ is known as the *carboxyl group*. It represents the final state of oxidation of the methyl group before its disintegration into carbon dioxide and water. The hydrogen atom of the group is ionisable, and the group, therefore, confers acidic properties on any molecule in which it is present. The group $CH_3-C\overset{\displaystyle O}{}$ which represents the acetic acid molecule from which the —OH group has been detached, is known as the *acetyl group*. In general, the group $R-C\overset{\displaystyle O}{\diagup}$ which is related to the fatty acid $R-C\overset{\displaystyle O}{\underset{\displaystyle OH}{\diagup}}$ where R is an alkyl group such as methyl or ethyl, is known as the *acyl group.*

A list of a few members of the fatty acid series is given in Table XIV.

TABLE XIV

Name	Formula	M.P.	B.P.
Formic acid	H.COOH	8·3°	101°
Acetic acid	$CH_3.COOH$	17°	118°
Propionic acid	$C_2H_5.COOH$	−22°	141°
Butyric acid	$CH_3.(CH_2)_2.COOH$	− 8°	164°
iso-Butyric acid	$(CH_3)_2.CH.COOH$	−47°	155°
Palmitic acid	$CH_3.(CH_2)_{14}.COOH$	64°	
Stearic acid	$CH_3.(CH_2)_{16}.COOH$	69°	

The simplest member of the fatty acid series is formic acid, but acetic acid is chosen for detailed description, as it is a more typical member of the series.

ACETIC ACID

Pure acetic acid is a colourless liquid with a freezing point only just above room temperature. In cold weather, therefore, it solidifies to a colourless crystalline solid. If the acid is contaminated with water or other impurities, the melting point is lowered, and it does not solidify in cold weather. A relatively high temperature of solidification, therefore, is an indication that the acid is pure, and " glacial acetic acid " has come to be used to describe acetic acid of a high state of purity. Acetic acid has a sharp characteristic " vinegar odour ". It volatilises in steam. It is miscible in all proportions with water, and with alcohol and ether. It dissolves sulphur, iodine, and many organic compounds. Its density at 20° is 1·05.

PRINCIPAL REACTIONS IN WHICH ACETIC ACID IS PRODUCED

1. The hydrolysis of acetonitrile. When a mixture of aceto-nitrile (a liquid, B.P. 82°, soluble in water) and a dilute aqueous solution of sodium hydroxide is boiled for about 30 minutes in a flask fitted to a water reflux condenser, ammonia and sodium acetate are formed,

$$CH_3.C{\equiv}N \ + \ NaOH \ + \ H_2O \ = \ CH_3.COONa \ + \ NH_3.$$

To obtain the acetic acid from the products of the hydrolysis, the flask is detached from the condenser, and the contents are boiled for a few minutes to expel the ammonia. The solution is cooled and acidified with sulphuric acid until it is acid to litmus paper. The solution is then distilled, and the steam and acetic acid which volatilise (acetic acid is volatile in steam) are condensed to give an aqueous solution of acetic acid. Acetonitrile may also be hydrolysed by acids. The reaction is very slow if hydrochloric acid is used ; 70 per cent. sulphuric acid causes rapid hydrolysis.

2. The hydrolysis of acetanilide. If acetanilide is boiled with 70 per cent. sulphuric acid for 20 minutes in a flask fitted to a reflux water condenser, aniline hydrogen sulphate and acetic acid are formed,

$$C_6H_5-N\begin{array}{c}H\\CO.CH_3\end{array} \quad + \quad H_2O \quad + \quad H_2SO_4$$

$$= \left[C_6H_5-N\begin{array}{c}H\\H\\H\end{array}\right]HSO_4 \quad + \quad CH_3COOH.$$

If the solution is slightly diluted and distilled, an aqueous solution of acetic acid may be collected. The hydrolysis is an example of a general reaction by which the acetyl derivative of a hydroxyl compound (such as an alcohol, a sugar, or phenol) or of an amino compound (such as an amine or aniline) may be converted to the original compound and acetic acid. Solutions of alkalis may be used as hydrolytic agents for this purpose, but hydrolysis is much slower in alkaline than in acid solution.

3. The oxidation of ethyl alcohol. Ethyl alcohol is oxidised to acetic acid under the conditions mentioned under Reaction 8, p. 164. In the manufacture of vinegar, which is essentially a dilute aqueous solution (4–6 per cent.) of acetic acid, the alcohol, in malt wash or wines of inferior quality, is oxidised to acetic acid by atmospheric oxygen in the presence of enzymes produced by *Bacterium aceti*, *Mycoderma aceti*, or *Micrococus aceti*.

4. The oxidation of acetaldehyde. Acetaldehyde may be oxidised to acetic acid by the methods mentioned under Reaction 1, p. 201. Acetic acid is obtained on a large scale by the oxidation of acetaldehyde by air in the presence of manganese acetate, p. 490.

5. The reaction between carbon monoxide and sodium methoxide. At a temperature of 180° sodium methoxide absorbs carbon monoxide to form sodium acetate,

$$CH_3ONa \quad + \quad CO \quad = \quad CH_3.COONa,$$

which yields acetic acid on distillation with dilute sulphuric acid.

Laboratory preparation of acetic acid. Acetic acid is an article of commerce, and its preparation in the laboratory is rarely necessary.

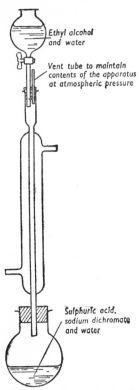

Ethyl alcohol and water

Vent tube to maintain contents of the apparatus at atmospheric pressure

Sulphuric acid, sodium dichromate and water

FIG. 48. Apparatus for the preparation of acetic acid.

As an exercise, an aqueous solution of acetic acid may be obtained by the oxidation of ethyl alcohol with a mixture of sodium dichromate and dilute sulphuric acid. The acid solution of sodium dichromate (say, 50 c.c. of water, 33 c.c. of concentrated sulphuric acid, and 35 gm. of sodium dichromate) is placed in a flask fitted to a reflux condenser, from the top of which a mixture of 15 c.c. of ethyl alcohol and 60 c.c. of water is added drop by drop from a dropping funnel, Fig. 48. The action is vigorous. When all the alcohol has been added, and the reaction has subsided, the flask is heated on a water-bath for 15 minutes. It is then detached from the reflux condenser, and refitted to the condenser for a simple distillation, Fig. 14, p. 57. The mixture is distilled until 80 c.c. of distillate have been collected. The distillate is an aqueous solution of acetic acid, probably containing some acetaldehyde.

Industrial preparation of acetic acid. Acetic acid is manufactured from acetaldehyde by the process mentioned under Reaction 4 above, and described on p. 490.

Glacial acetic acid. Pure acetic acid is known as *glacial acetic acid*. It is so called because it is crystalline at room temperature, whereas impure acetic acid has a lower freezing point.

Glacial acetic acid is prepared by boiling an impure sample of acetic acid with potassium permanganate solution in a flask fitted to a reflux condenser. The acetic acid is unaffected by the potassium permanganate, but other organic compounds which may be present are oxidised to carbon dioxide and water. When the oxidation has continued for some time, a little sulphuric acid is added, and the acetic acid is distilled from the solution. The acetic acid in the distillate is converted to sodium acetate by neutralisation with sodium carbonate, and the solution is evaporated to dryness. The heating is continued until the water of crystallisation in the sodium acetate crystals is expelled. The dehydrated sodium acetate is then distilled with concentrated sulphuric acid. Pure anhydrous acetic acid distils over and crystallises on standing. It is hygroscopic, and during storage access of water must be prevented.

CHEMICAL PROPERTIES, CONSTITUTION AND USE
OF ACETIC ACID

Chemical properties. Acetic acid is a very stable substance. It is not easily decomposed by heat, and it is unattacked by dehydrating agents, by oxidising agents, or by reducing agents. It is unaffected by hot concentrated sulphuric acid, by potassium permanganate solution, or by chromic acid, but it will burn in air when heated nearly to its boiling point. It is also unaffected by reducing agents such as sodium amalgam or zinc and hydrochloric acid, and the vapour is unchanged when passed with hydrogen over heated freshly reduced nickel. Although acetic acid is a stable substance, it undergoes many reactions, of which the more important are those with alkalis, the halogens, the phosphorus halides and alcohols.

1. Reactions with alkalis. Acetic acid is a weak monobasic acid. It reacts with metallic oxides, hydroxides and carbonates to yield acetates,

$$CH_3.COOH + NaOH = CH_3.COONa + H_2O,$$

and with ammonia or ammonium carbonate to yield ammonium acetate,

$$(NH_4)_2CO_3 + 2CH_3.COOH = 2CH_3.COONH_4 + H_2O + CO_2.$$

An account of the principal salts of acetic acid is given on pp. 236 to 239.

2. Chlorination. Chlorine reacts with boiling acetic acid in sunlight, or in the presence of a catalyst such as iodine, sulphur or phosphorus, to produce monochloroacetic acid,

$$CH_3.COOH + Cl_2 = CH_2Cl.COOH + HCl.$$

If the chlorination is continued, the second hydrogen atom in the methyl group is replaced by chlorine, giving dichloroacetic acid $CHCl_2.COOH$, and ultimately trichloroacetic acid, $CCl_3.COOH$ is produced.

3. Reaction with phosphorus pentachloride, phosphorus trichloride, phosphorus oxychloride, or thionyl chloride, giving acetyl chloride. A vigorous reaction takes place when phosphorus pentachloride is added to anhydrous acetic acid. Hydrogen chloride, phosphorus oxychloride and acetyl chloride are formed,

$$CH_3.C{\overset{O}{\underset{OH}{}}} + PCl_5 = CH_3.C{\overset{O}{\underset{Cl}{}}} + POCl_3 + HCl.$$

This reaction takes place almost quantitatively; there are no side reactions similar to those leading to the formation of ethoxy derivatives of phosphorus which occur during the formation of ethyl chloride by the action of phosphorus pentachloride on ethyl alcohol, p. 146.

Phosphorus oxychloride, phosphorus trichloride, and thionyl chloride react similarly according to the equations,

$$3CH_3.COOH \quad + \quad POCl_3 \quad = \quad 3CH_3.COCl \quad + \quad H_3PO_4,$$
$$3CH_3.COOH \quad + \quad PCl_3 \quad = \quad 3CH_3.COCl \quad + \quad H_3PO_3,$$
$$CH_3.COOH \quad + \quad SOCl_2 \quad = \quad CH_3.COCl \quad + \quad SO_2 \quad + \quad HCl.$$

Experimental details for the reaction of phosphorus trichloride on acetic acid are given on p. 247.

4. Esterification. Acetic acid reacts with ethyl alcohol to form ethyl acetate, a typical member of the class of esters,

$$CH_3.C{\overset{O}{\underset{OH}{}}} \quad + \quad C_2H_5OH \quad \rightleftharpoons \quad CH_3.C{\overset{O}{\underset{OC_2H_5}{}}} \quad + \quad H_2O.$$

The reaction is reversible, and proceeds to completion only if the products are removed from the sphere of action. Concentrated sulphuric acid, or gaseous hydrogen chloride, may be employed to catalyse this reaction, and also to promote the forward reaction by removing the water which is formed. For further discussion of this reaction, see p. 256.

Constitution of acetic acid. The empirical formula of acetic acid is $(CH_2O)_x$. The molecular weight, based on the determination of its vapour density, on the depression of the freezing point of its aqueous solution, and on the analysis of its silver salt, is 60. The molecular formula of acetic acid in the vapour and in aqueous solution is, therefore, $C_2H_4O_2$.

Acetic acid is formed by the direct oxidation of acetaldehyde, a reaction which proceeds with facility. On the assumption that it is the aldehydic group which is thus readily oxidised, acetic acid must be assigned the structural formula

$$H{\overset{H}{\underset{H}{\diagup}}}C{-}C{\overset{O}{\underset{OH}{}}},$$

in which the two carbon atoms, as in the molecule of acetaldehyde, are directly linked by a single covalent bond.

This structure is confirmed by :

(i) the action of sodium hydroxide on acetic acid, by which one atom of hydrogen in the molecule of the acid is replaced by an atom of sodium ; one hydrogen atom in the molecule is thus shown to be ionisable, and is therefore differentiated from the other three,

$$\text{H}_2\text{C—C}\begin{smallmatrix}\text{O}\\\text{OH}\end{smallmatrix} + \text{NaOH} = \text{H}_2\text{C—C}\begin{smallmatrix}\text{O}\\\text{ONa}\end{smallmatrix} + \text{H}_2\text{O,}$$

(ii) the action of chlorine on acetic acid, by which three hydrogen atoms in the molecule of the acid are replaced by atoms of chlorine,

$$\text{H}_2\text{C—C}\begin{smallmatrix}\text{O}\\\text{OH}\end{smallmatrix} + 3\text{Cl}_2 = \text{Cl}_2\text{C—C}\begin{smallmatrix}\text{O}\\\text{OH}\end{smallmatrix} + 3\text{HCl.}$$

After the most prolonged action by chlorine not more than three hydrogen atoms in the molecule are replaced by chlorine, and one hydrogen atom remains which is still replaceable by sodium. The hydrogen atoms replaceable by chlorine are, therefore, the three hydrogen atoms in the methyl group.

This discussion establishes that the molecule of acetic acid contains one hydroxyl group, one methyl group, and that the two carbon atoms are directly linked to one another ; there is no direct evidence of the existence of a carbonyl group, $>C=O$, in the molecule. Acetic acid does not react with hydrocyanic acid, with phenyl hydrazine, nor with the other reagents which characteristically attack aldehydes and ketones (pp. 203, 223), and it can be neither oxidised nor reduced. If the carbonyl group is present in the molecule of acetic acid its normal properties are profoundly modified. The explanation of the inertness of the carbonyl group in certain compounds has already been given on p. 24 in terms of the theory of resonance. According to this theory acetic acid consists of the two forms

$$\text{CH}_3\text{—C}\begin{smallmatrix}\text{O}\\\text{OH}\end{smallmatrix} \quad \text{and} \quad \text{CH}_3\text{—C}\begin{smallmatrix}\bar{\text{O}}\\\text{OH}\end{smallmatrix}$$

in resonance. For the purposes of descriptive organic chemistry, however, it is sufficient to regard the molecular formula of acetic acid as $CH_3.COOH$, bearing in mind that the carboxyl group, —COOH, reacts as a whole, and that the carbonyl group which this representation shows it to contain is inactive.

The molecular weight of acetic acid dissolved in benzene and certain other organic solvents is 120. In these solvents the acid is dimeric and has the molecular formula $(CH_3.COOH)_2$.

Uses of acetic acid. Acetic acid is used in the manufacture of acetates, acetic anhydride, indigo, acetate artificial silk ; for coagulating rubber latex ; in curing meat and fish ; as vinegar ; for making acetone.

It is also valuable as a solvent. Since it is not attacked by oxidising agents, it is used as a solvent for other organic compounds which are to be oxidised. For example, anthraquinone, a compound of great technical importance in the manufacture of dyes, including alizarin and indanthrene, may be made by boiling together anthracene and chromium trioxide in glacial acetic acid.

Tests for acetic acid. Acetic acid may be recognised by the following tests :

1. The odour of the free acid is characteristic.

2. The acid is soluble in, and neutralises, a solution of sodium hydroxide or sodium carbonate.

3. If neutral ferric chloride solution is added to a solution of acetic acid neutralised * by ammonia, or by sodium hydroxide solution, a deep red coloration is produced. On boiling the solution, the deep red colour is replaced by a brown precipitate of basic ferric acetate. Formic acid solution behaves similarly, giving a red coloration and a precipitate of basic ferric formate.

4. If a small quantity of acetic acid is warmed with a little ethyl alcohol and a few drops of concentrated sulphuric acid for about one minute, ethyl acetate is formed. If the mixture is cooled and then poured into a few c.c. of water in a test-tube, the odour of bad apples, characteristic of ethyl acetate, may be noticed.

5. Acetic acid does not reduce solutions of potassium permanganate, mercuric chloride, or ammoniacal silver oxide. It is thus easily distinguished from formic acid.

THE ACETATES

Sodium acetate, $CH_3.COONa$. Sodium acetate is obtained by neutralising acetic acid with sodium carbonate. The solution so obtained is evaporated to crystallising point, when crystals of the tri-hydrate $CH_3.COONa,3H_2O$, separate. When the tri-hydrate is gently heated in an open dish, it first melts in its water of crystallisation. As water is driven off the salt solidifies again, and finally fuses. If the melt is stirred to avoid charring, all the water of crystallisation may be removed and the pure andydrous salt obtained. The anhydrous salt is hygroscopic.

* For the success of this test it is essential that the solution should be neutral. If the solution is acid the production of the red colour is inhibited ; if it is alkaline, a brown precipitate of ferric hydroxide is formed. Neutral ferric chloride solution is made by adding dilute sodium hydroxide solution drop by drop to ferric chloride solution until a faint but permanent precipitate is obtained. The solution is filtered and the clear filtrate is used. A neutral solution of ammonium acetate is made by adding ammonia solution to a solution of acetic acid until it is just alkaline to litmus paper. A piece of unglazed porcelain is added, and the solution is boiled until the odour of ammonia is completely removed. It is then ready for use.

Anhydrous sodium acetate is an important reagent in organic chemistry. When heated with soda-lime it yields methane. By action with phosphorus oxychloride or thionyl chloride it is converted to acetyl chloride, p. 247, and if acetyl chloride is treated with a further quantity of sodium acetate, acetic anhydride is obtained. Acetic anhydride may also be made from sodium acetate by heating it with sulphur trioxide and sodium sulphate under reduced pressure. Anhydrous sodium acetate is used in Perkin's reaction, p. 460, and in acetylation, p. 254.

In aqueous solution sodium acetate reacts with silver nitrate solution, to yield crystals of sparingly soluble silver acetate. Electrolysis of the aqueous solution of sodium acetate yields ethane, hydrogen, and sodium carbonate in solution, p. 110.

Potassium acetate, $CH_3.COOK$. Normal potassium acetate forms colourless deliquescent crystals. The reactions of this salt are parallel to those of sodium acetate. An acid potassium acetate is also known, having the constitution $CH_3.COOK,CH_3.COOH$. The existence of the acid potassium acetate is related to the tendency of acetic acid to assume the dimeric form, $(CH_3.COOH)_2$, in the pure state, and also when dissolved in benzene or other non-dissociating solvents.

Ammonium acetate, $CH_3.COONH_4$. This salt is a colourless solid, readily soluble in water. It evolves ammonia when treated with sodium hydroxide solution *in the cold*, leaving sodium acetate in solution.

One of the most important reactions of ammonium acetate is its conversion to acetamide when heated,

$$CH_3.C{\overset{O}{\underset{O.NH_4}{}}} = CH_3.C{\overset{O}{\underset{NH_2}{}}} + H_2O.$$

In practice, however, it is usual to make ammonium carbonate and glacial acetic acid the starting-point for this reaction. For further details see p. 254.

Calcium acetate, $(CH_3.COO)_2Ca$. This salt is made by neutralising acetic acid with milk of lime (a suspension of calcium hydroxide in water) and evaporating the solution. It forms colourless crystals containing one molecule of water of crystallisation,

$$(CH_3.COO)_2Ca, H_2O.$$

These crystals are very soluble in water.

When calcium acetate is heated alone it decomposes, yielding calcium carbonate and acetone, p. 220. When a mixture of calcium acetate and calcium formate is heated, acetaldehyde is liberated, p. 199.

Calcium acetate is used in the preparation of acetone, and in the preparation of ferric acetate and aluminium acetate.

Silver acetate, $CH_3.COOAg$. Silver acetate is precipitated as colourless lustrous plates when silver nitrate solution is added to a concentrated solution of sodium acetate. It is sparingly soluble in cold water. As ordinarily prepared, it darkens on exposure to light. It is used for preparing alkyl acetates by reaction with alkyl halides. For example, if an ethereal solution of ethyl bromide and silver acetate is warmed, silver bromide is precipitated and ethyl acetate remains in solution,

$$C_2H_5Br + CH_3.COOAg = AgBr + CH_3.COOC_2H_5.$$

It has already been explained that the formation of the alkyl acetate is a necessary intermediate stage in the hydrolysis of certain alkyl halides to the corresponding alcohols, p. 148.

Copper acetate, $(CH_3.COO)_2Cu,H_2O$. The crystals of the hydrated salt are a dark greenish blue. They are made by dissolving cupric oxide or cupric carbonate in a boiling aqueous solution of acetic acid, evaporating the solution on a water-bath, and allowing it to crystallise. *Verdigris*, $(CH_3.COO)_2Cu,Cu(OH)_2$ is a basic acetate of copper made by leaving sheet copper in contact with vinegar. It is used as a pigment. *Schweinfurt green, Paris green,* or *Emerald green* is an insoluble double salt of cupric acetate and cupric meta-arsenite, $(CH_3.COO)_2Cu,3Cu(AsO_2)_2$. It is made by mixing the constituent salts. It was formerly used as a pigment, but its use for this purpose has been discarded because in certain circumstances it may liberate the poisonous gas arsine.

Ferric acetate and **aluminium acetate** are important in the dyeing of cotton fabrics. Cotton consists of the chemically inert substance cellulose, to which dyestuffs cannot be fixed. Cotton fabrics to be dyed are, therefore, steeped in a solution containing calcium acetate and either ferric sulphate or aluminium sulphate. When the fabric is removed and heated, the ferric or aluminium acetate which has been formed within the fibres is decomposed to an insoluble precipitate of basic ferric or aluminium acetate, which is firmly retained in the cotton. The dye can then be applied, and it attaches itself to the insoluble basic salts, and thus is held on to the fabric indirectly. Insoluble substances used to fix dyestuffs in this manner are known as *mordants*.

FORMIC ACID

Formic acid is a colourless liquid, M.P. 9°, B.P. 101°, with a pungent odour. It blisters the skin. It is hygroscopic and is miscible in all proportions with water. It is also completely miscible with alcohol, ether and many other organic solvents.

PRINCIPAL REACTIONS IN WHICH FORMIC ACID IS PRODUCED

1. The hydrolysis of hydrogen cyanide. Ammonium formate is always present in an aqueous solution of hydrogen cyanide which has been standing for some time. The course of the hydrolysis may be thus,

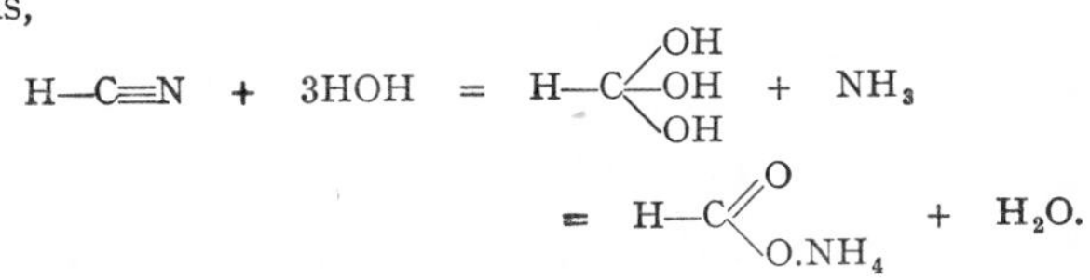

$$H-C\equiv N \ + \ 3HOH \ = \ H-C{\overset{OH}{\underset{OH}{\big<}}}OH \ + \ NH_3$$

$$= \ H-C{\overset{O}{\underset{O.NH_4}{\big<}}} \ + \ H_2O.$$

2. The hydrolysis of ethyl isocyanide. When ethyl isocyanide (a liquid, B.P. 79°) is heated with a dilute mineral acid in a flask fitted to a reflux condenser, a mixture of ethylamine and formic acid is obtained,

$$C_2H_5NC \ + \ H_2O \ = \ C_2H_5NH_2 \ + \ H.COOH.$$

It should be noted that ethyl isocyanide is *not* hydrolysed by boiling alkalis.

3. The hydrolysis of chloroform or iodoform. If chloroform or iodoform is mixed with alcoholic sodium hydroxide solution and heated in a small flask fitted to a reflux condenser, sodium formate is obtained,

$$CHCl_3 \ + \ 4NaOH \ = \ H.COONa \ + \ 3NaCl \ + \ 2H_2O.$$

4. The oxidation of methyl alcohol. If the vapour of methyl alcohol mixed with air is passed over platinum black at ordinary temperatures formic acid is produced, p. 169,

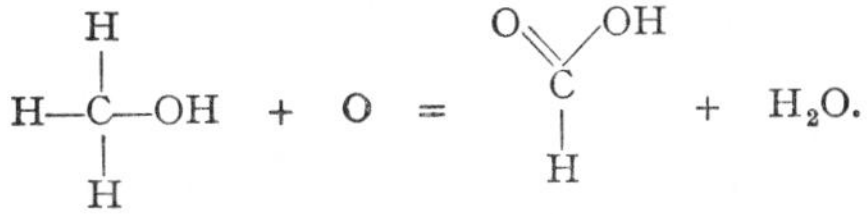

$$H-\overset{\displaystyle H}{\underset{\displaystyle H}{\overset{|}{\underset{|}{C}}}}-OH \ + \ O \ = \ \overset{O}{\underset{\displaystyle H}{\overset{\diagdown}{\underset{|}{C}}}}{\diagup}^{OH} \ + \ H_2O.$$

5. The action between carbon monoxide and potassium or

sodium hydroxide. At a temperature of 100° potassium hydroxide and carbon monoxide unite to give potassium formate,

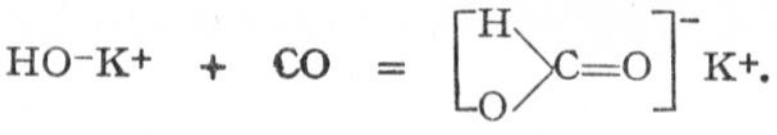

$$HO^-K^+ \;+\; CO \;=\; \left[\begin{array}{c} H \\ O \end{array} \!\!\!\!\!>\!\!C\!=\!O \right]^- K^+.$$

This reaction may be demonstrated in two ways in the laboratory.

(*a*) A tube containing carbon monoxide and a small piece of potassium hydroxide is sealed and heated in a water-bath. At the end of a few hours little carbon monoxide remains, and the solid in the tube is a mixture of potassium formate and unchanged potassium hydroxide.

(*b*) The inside of a large flask is moistened all over with potassium hydroxide solution, and the flask is filled with carbon monoxide and heated on a water-bath. The absorption of the carbon monoxide leads to a gradual fall of pressure inside the flask which can be followed if the flask is attached to a manometer. Sodium formate can be obtained also by passing carbon monoxide over soda-lime under pressure at 200°.

6. The action of anhydrous glycerol on crystalline oxalic acid. If a mixture of anhydrous glycerol, $CH_2OH.CHOH.CH_2OH$, and crystalline oxalic acid, $COOH.COOH,2H_2O$, is heated in a distilling flask to about 120°, a mixture of formic acid and steam distils over and may be collected ; carbon dioxide is evolved at the same time and passes out of the apparatus. The chemical reactions which occur may be summarised as the elimination of carbon dioxide from oxalic acid,

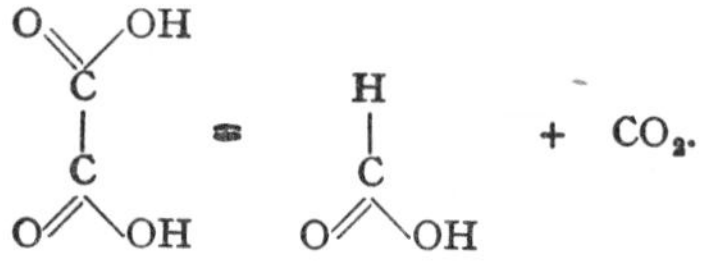

This change, however, occurs indirectly through the formation of glyceryl monoxalate which deco poses to glyceryl monoformate. The glyceryl monoformate is then hydrolysed to formic acid and glycerol ; the glycerol is thus set free to take part in the cycle again. These reactions may be represented by equations, thus :

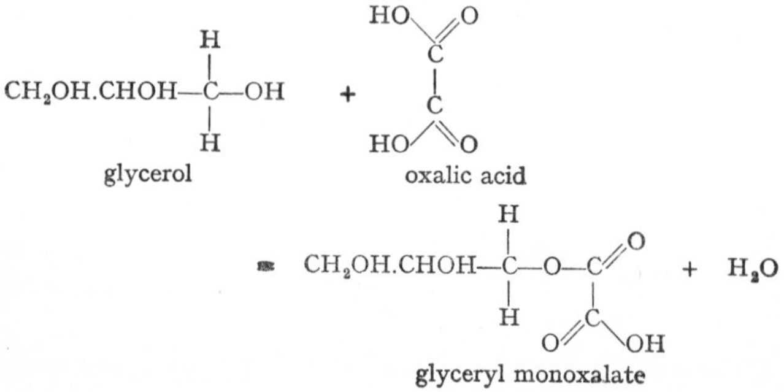

$$CH_2OH.CHOH\!-\!\underset{\underset{H}{|}}{\overset{\overset{H}{|}}{C}}\!-\!O\!-\!\underset{\underset{O}{\overset{}{C}}\diagdown_{OH}}{\overset{\diagup\!\!O}{C}} \;=\; CH_2OH.CHOH\!-\!\underset{\underset{H}{|}}{\overset{\overset{H}{|}}{C}}\!-\!O\!-\!\underset{\underset{H}{|}}{\overset{\diagup\!\!O}{C}} \;+\; CO_2$$

glyceryl monoxalate   glyceryl monoformate

$$CH_2OH.CHOH\!-\!\underset{\underset{H}{|}}{\overset{\overset{H}{|}}{C}}\!-\!O\!-\!\underset{\underset{H}{|}}{\overset{\diagup\!\!O}{C}} \;+\; H_2O$$

$$=\; CH_2OH.CHOH\!-\!\underset{\underset{H}{|}}{\overset{\overset{H}{|}}{C}}\!-\!OH \;+\; HO\!-\!\underset{\underset{H}{|}}{\overset{\diagup\!\!O}{C}}$$

glycerol   formic acid

Laboratory preparation of formic acid. Formic acid is made in the laboratory by means of the reaction between glycerol and oxalic acid, which has just been described. The glycerol is heated at 175° to 180° in an open dish for 5 minutes to ensure dehydration. 50 c.c. of the de-hydrated glycerol are placed in a distilling flask, and 40 gm. of powdered crystalline oxalic acid are added. The bulb of a thermometer is placed *in the mixture* and the flask is connected to a water condenser, Fig. **49.**

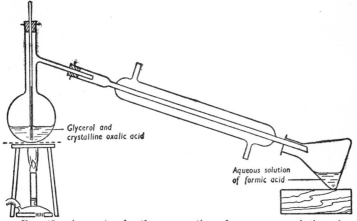

Glycerol and crystalline oxalic acid

Aqueous solution of formic acid

FIG. 49. Apparatus for the preparation of an aqueous solution of formic acid.

The flask is heated until the thermometer reads 110–120°. The evolution of carbon dioxide is marked by effervescence. When this ceases, the flask is cooled to 70–80°, another 40 gm. of oxalic acid are added, and the heating to 120° is repeated. An aqueous solution of formic acid collects as the distillate. The yield of formic acid may be greatly increased by subjecting the contents of the distilling flask to steam distillation, which facilitates the hydrolysis of glyceryl monoformate.

Anhydrous formic acid is obtained through the intermediate preparation of lead formate. The aqueous solution of formic acid is neutralised with lead carbonate, and the solution of lead formate thus prepared is filtered, evaporated, and crystallised. The crystallised lead formate is then put into the inner tube of a water condenser. One end of the condenser tube is connected to an apparatus generating hydrogen sulphide ; the other end of the tube is connected to a receiver closed with a calcium chloride tube, Fig. 50. Hydrogen sulphide is passed

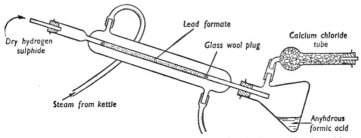

FIG. 50. Apparatus for the preparation of anhydrous formic acid from lead formate.

through the inner tube of the condenser while steam is passed through the jacket. The lead formate is converted to lead sulphide and formic acid collects in the receiver. The formic acid is redistilled over lead formate to eliminate dissolved hydrogen sulphide. Anhydrous formic acid may also be made either (*a*) by carefully adding finely powdered sodium formate to the theoretical quantity of concentrated sulphuric acid at 0°, and distilling off the liberated formic acid under reduced pressure, or (*b*) by distilling a mixture of sodium formate and sodium hydrogen sulphate. Care should be taken to avoid inhaling any carbon monoxide that might be liberated in these experiments.

Industrial preparation. Formic acid is manufactured by the action of carbon monoxide on soda-lime at 200°, see Reaction 5 above.

CHEMICAL PROPERTIES OF FORMIC ACID AND THE FORMATES

Formic acid is less stable than acetic acid. It undergoes thermal decomposition more easily, it is decomposed by warm concentrated sulphuric acid, and it is a vigorous reducing agent. It is a stronger acid than acetic acid. It neutralises alkalis, and liberates carbon dioxide from carbonates, to produce formates. For example, sodium formate is produced by the reaction,

$$2H.COOH + Na_2CO_3 = 2H.COONa + H_2O + CO_2.$$

Sodium formate is a crystalline deliquescent compound. Other metallic formates can be made by neutralising formic acid with the hydroxide or carbonate of the metal concerned. The formates of lead, silver and mercury are sparingly soluble, and they can be precipitated by adding a soluble salt of the metal to an aqueous solution of sodium formate.

When formic acid is heated alone in a closed tube to 160° it decomposes to carbon dioxide and hydrogen,

$$H.COOH = CO_2 + H_2.$$

The same reaction occurs at room temperature when formic acid is shaken with finely divided platinum. Sodium formate, when heated alone to 390°, breaks down differently and yields sodium oxalate and hydrogen,

$$2H.COONa = \begin{matrix} COONa \\ | \\ COONa \end{matrix} + H_2,$$

but if a mixture of sodium formate and sodium hydroxide is heated, hydrogen and sodium carbonate are formed,

$$H.COONa + NaOH = H_2 + Na_2CO_3.$$

This reaction is comparable to the formation of methane by the action of heat on a mixture of sodium acetate and soda-lime. If calcium formate is heated alone it yields formaldehyde and calcium carbonate, p. 210, but if a mixture of calcium formate and calcium acetate is heated, acetaldehyde is formed, p. 199.

Concentrated sulphuric acid at 0° has little or no action on formic acid. When warmed, however, concentrated sulphuric acid removes the elements of water from formic acid, setting free carbon monoxide,

$$H·COOH = H_2O + CO.$$

Salts of formic acid also liberate carbon monoxide when heated with concentrated sulphuric acid.

Formic acid reduces alkaline potassium permanganate solution in the cold, and an acid solution on warming. It also reduces Fehling's solution to cuprous oxide, and an ammoniacal solution of silver oxide to metallic silver. If a neutral solution of sodium formate is added to a neutral solution of silver nitrate in the cold, a white precipitate of silver formate is produced which slowly decomposes to black silver. The change takes place more rapidly on warming,

$$H.COONa + AgNO_3 = H.COOAg + NaNO_3,$$
$$2H.COOAg = H.COOH + 2Ag + CO_2.$$

If formic acid is shaken with mercuric oxide, mercuric formate is formed in solution, but this decomposes on warming to give a white precipitate of mercurous formate, which subsequently breaks down to carbon dioxide, formic acid and a grey precipitate of metallic mercury. Formic acid, or sodium formate solution, reduces mercuric chloride in warm aqueous solution to a white precipitate of mercurous chloride. If excess of formic acid is present, the mercurous chloride is further reduced to mercury.

Tests for formic acid and the formates

1. When formic acid, or one of its salts, is warmed with concentrated sulphuric acid, carbon monoxide only is evolved, and there is no blackening of the solution. Carbon monoxide is identified by its property of burning with a blue flame ; the absence of carbon dioxide in the gas is proved by the lack of any action with lime-water.* This test distinguishes formic acid from acetic acid, and from oxalic, tartaric and citric acids.

2. Formic acid reduces Fehling's solution, and solutions of potassium permanganate and mercuric chloride, and an ammoniacal solution of silver oxide. These reductions, however, are brought about by many classes of organic compounds. (See p. 208.)

3. An aqueous solution of formic acid is strongly acid. If this solution is neutralised with ammonia, or sodium hydroxide solution, it reacts with neutral ferric chloride solution to give a red coloration and a brown precipitate of basic ferric formate. In similar conditions acetic acid also gives a red coloration and a brown precipitate of basic ferric acetate. This reaction, therefore, cannot be used for distinguishing formic acid from acetic acid, p. 236.

THE HIGHER FATTY ACIDS

Propionic acid, $C_2H_5.COOH$, is a liquid with a sour odour. It is miscible with water in all proportions. It may be made, (i) by the hydrolysis of ethyl cyanide, (ii) by the oxidation of n-propyl alcohol with chromic acid, and (iii) by the reduction of lactic acid with concentrated hydriodic acid, p. 273. It resembles acetic acid in its chemical properties. Chlorination of propionic acid yields α-chloropropionic acid, $CH_3.CHCl.COOH$.

Butyric acid, $CH_3.(CH_2)_2.COOH$. The glycerol ester of butyric acid occurs naturally in butter ; the free acid occurs in rancid butter and in perspiration. Butyric acid is a rancid-smelling liquid,

---

* If a flame is applied to the mouth of the test-tube in which carbon monoxide is being generated by the above reaction, the carbon monoxide does not usually ignite, as it diffuses rapidly away into the air, and its concentration in the tube remains low. The mouth of the test-tube should, therefore, be lightly stoppered with the thumb, so that the tube fills with carbon monoxide. If a flame is applied to the tube when it is full of the gas, a pronounced blue flame is seen, which slowly travels down the tube.

Similar considerations apply to the test for carbon dioxide. The mouth of the tube is lightly stoppered. When the gas has accumulated, the thumb is removed, and the gaseous contents of the tube are " poured " into another tube containing about 5 c.c. of freshly prepared lime-water. A white precipitate of calcium carbonate indicates the presence of carbon dioxide.

soluble in water and alcohol. It is made by the oxidation of *n*-butyl alcohol, or by the fermentation of starch, glucose or lactic acid. The fermentation of glucose may be carried out by dissolving it in water, and adding to the solution rancid cheese (which contains the bacillus which induces the fermentation), and excess of calcium carbonate to keep the solution neutral. Sparingly soluble calcium butyrate separates from solution, and is decomposed to butyric acid and insoluble calcium sulphate by treatment with the calculated quantity of sulphuric acid. Sour milk contains lactic acid, p. 270, which can be converted to butyric acid by treatment with rancid cheese and calcium carbonate.

Iso-butyric acid, $(CH_3)_2CH.COOH$, is made by the oxidation of iso-butyl alcohol, p. 171. It is somewhat more volatile than the normal acid, and is less soluble in water.

Palmitic acid, $C_{15}H_{31}.COOH$, and stearic acid, $C_{17}H_{33}.COOH$, are colourless, odourless solids, waxlike in appearance. They are insoluble in water, but soluble in alcohol and ether. The glycerol esters of these acids are important constituents of animal and vegetable fats. The free acids are obtained by hydrolysing the fats with superheated steam : the product is an aqueous solution of glycerol and an insoluble paste of the acids, which after purification is used for making candles, p. 500.

If the fats are hydrolysed by sodium hydroxide, sodium palmitate and sodium stearate are formed. These salts are *soaps*. Sodium palmitate and sodium stearate belong to a class of substances known as *colloidal electrolytes*. The acid radicals of the soaps have the formulae, $C_{15}H_{31}.COO^-$ and $C_{17}H_{33}.COO^-$, and the paraffin residues render them insoluble in water. When the soap is mixed with water some of the positively charged sodium ions pass into solution, and drag with them into the water the negatively charged acid radical ions. The acid radicals, therefore, pass into the water not as single ions, but as *ionic micelles*, which consist of clusters of the ions combined with molecules of the neutral salts. A soap solution is thus a true solution of Na^+ ions, and a colloidal solution of fatty acid ions and neutral soap molecules. The detergent action of a soap solution is due partly to its low surface tension, and partly to the presence of colloidal particles of organic substances which are able to dissolve other organic compounds.

CHAPTER XV

THE ACID CHLORIDES, ANHYDRIDES, AMIDES, ESTERS AND NITRILES OF THE FATTY ACIDS, AND THE ISONITRILES

CERTAIN important derivatives of the fatty acids are obtained by the replacement of the group —OH in the carboxyl group of the acid by some other group of atoms. In the acid chlorides the —OH group is replaced by an atom of chlorine, in the amides by the group —NH_2, and in the esters by a group such as the ethoxy group —OC_2H_5, or the methoxy group —OCH_3. The acid anhydrides are derived from the acids somewhat differently by the elimination of one molecule of water from two molecules of the acid, see p. 251. In the nitriles the —OH group and the doubly linked oxygen atom in the carboxyl group of the acid are replaced by a single triply linked nitrogen atom, p. 260.

Acid chlorides contain the characteristic group —COCl, amides the group —$CONH_2$, esters the group —COOR, where R is an alkyl radical, most commonly ethyl —C_2H_5 or methyl —CH_3. The fatty acid anhydrides contain the group —CO.O.CO—, and the nitriles the group —CN. Acid chlorides, amides, esters and acid anhydrides all contain the group >CO, but they show none of the reactions of aldehydes and ketones which are characteristic of the group >C=O, in which the oxygen atom is linked to the carbon atom by two covalent bonds. The >CO group, in the carboxyl group —COOH, also shows neither aldehydic nor ketonic properties.

It is explained on p. 235 that although it is convenient to formulate the constitution of the carboxyl group as —$C\!\!\begin{smallmatrix}\diagup O\\ \diagdown OH\end{smallmatrix}$, a complete interpretation of its properties, including the suppression of the normal reactions of the group >C=O, is afforded only by the theory of resonance, p. 24. The lack of ketonic properties of the >CO group in acid chlorides, amides, esters and acid anhydrides is also explained by resonance. As there is no convention for writing formulae to indicate resonance, the >CO group in the compounds described in this chapter is written as though the oxygen atom were linked to the carbon atom by a normal double covalent bond.

DERIVATIVES OF FORMIC ACID

Formic acid gives rise neither to an acid anhydride nor to an acid chloride. A mixture of hydrogen chloride and carbon monoxide, however, in certain reactions behaves as the compound H.COCl. Formamide is made by distilling ammonium formate,

$$H.COONH_4 \ = \ H.CO.NH_2 \ + \ H_2O,$$

and ethyl formate, a liquid, B.P. 55°, is formed by heating ethyl hydrogen oxalate,

$$\begin{array}{c} COOH \\ | \\ COOC_2H_5 \end{array} \ = \ H-C\!\!\begin{array}{c} {}^{\displaystyle O} \\ {}_{\displaystyle OC_2H_5} \end{array} \ + \ CO_2.$$

Formonitrile is an alternative name for the familiar compound hydrocyanic acid (prussic acid), HCN.

The methods of preparation and the reactions of the derivatives of acetic acid described below may be taken to be representative of those of the corresponding derivatives of the higher fatty acids.

DERIVATIVES OF ACETIC ACID

ACETYL CHLORIDE

Acetyl chloride is derived by the replacement of —OH in the carboxyl group of acetic acid by an atom of chlorine,

$$H_3C.C\!\!\begin{array}{c} {}^{\displaystyle O} \\ {}_{\displaystyle OH} \end{array} \qquad\qquad H_3C.C\!\!\begin{array}{c} {}^{\displaystyle O} \\ {}_{\displaystyle Cl} \end{array}$$

acetic acid   acetyl chloride

Acetyl chloride is a colourless liquid, B.P. 55°. It fumes in moist air, and reacts with water forming a mixture of acetic and hydrochloric acids.

Preparation of acetyl chloride. Acetyl chloride is formed by the action of phosphorus pentachloride, phosphorus trichloride, phosphorus oxychloride, or thionyl chloride, on anhydrous acetic acid. The equations for these reactions are given on p. 233.

Acetyl chloride is prepared in the laboratory by the action of phosphorus trichloride on anhydrous acetic acid. The experiment must be conducted in a fume cupboard. A distillation flask is fitted with a tap-funnel and connected to a water condenser leading to a receiver closed by a calcium chloride tube, Fig. 51. 25 gm. of anhydrous acetic acid are placed in the flask, which is cooled by immersion in cold water, and 20 gm. of phosphorus trichloride (a liquid, B.P. 76°) are added drop by drop from the tap-funnel. When the addition of the phosphorus trichloride is complete, the flask is warmed on a water-bath to 40–50° until the evolution of hydrogen chloride slackens. The water-bath is

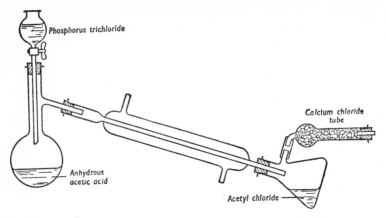

Phosphorus trichloride

Calcium chloride tube

Anhydrous acetic acid

Acetyl chloride

FIG. 51. Apparatus for the preparation of acetyl chloride.

then heated to boiling. The distillate is redistilled from a distilling flask fitted with a thermometer, and the fraction boiling between 53° and 56° is collected.

Chemical properties of acetyl chloride

1. Reaction with anhydrous sodium acetate, giving acetic anhydride. Acetyl chloride reacts vigorously with dry sodium acetate, according to the equation,

$$
CH_3.C\!\!\begin{array}{c}O\\\\Cl\end{array} \ + \ CH_3.C\!\!\begin{array}{c}O.Na\\\\O\end{array} \ = \ CH_3.C\!\!\begin{array}{c}O\\\\O\\\\CH_3.C\end{array}\!\!\begin{array}{c}\\\\\\\\O\end{array} \ + \ NaCl.
$$

This reaction is described in detail on p. 252.

2. Hydrolysis, giving acetic acid. Acetyl chloride reacts vigorously with water,

$$CH_3.COCl \ + \ H_2O \ = \ CH_3.COOH \ + \ HCl,$$

and almost explosively with alkalis,

$$CH_3.COCl \ + \ 2NaOH \ = \ CH_3.COONa \ + \ NaCl \ + \ H_2O.$$

3. Reaction with ammonia, giving acetamide. Acetyl chloride reacts with a concentrated aqueous solution of ammonia to produce acetamide,

$$
CH_3.C\!\!\begin{array}{c}O\\\\Cl\end{array} \ + \ 2NH_3 \ = \ CH_3.C\!\!\begin{array}{c}O\\\\NH_2\end{array} \ + \ NH_4Cl.
$$

4. Reaction with alcohols, phenols, and with primary and secondary amines. Acetylation. Acetyl chloride reacts with compounds such as alcohols and phenols which contain the group —OH, with primary amines which contain the group —NH_2, and with secondary amines which contain the group >NH. The result of these reactions is the replacement of the hydrogen atom in the group —OH, —NH_2, or >NH, by the acetyl group $CH_3.CO.—$. For example, acetyl chloride reacts with ethyl alcohol to give ethyl acetate and hydrogen chloride,

$$CH_3.C{\overset{O}{\underset{Cl}{}}} + HOC_2H_5 = CH_3.C{\overset{O}{\underset{OC_2H_5}{}}} + HCl,$$

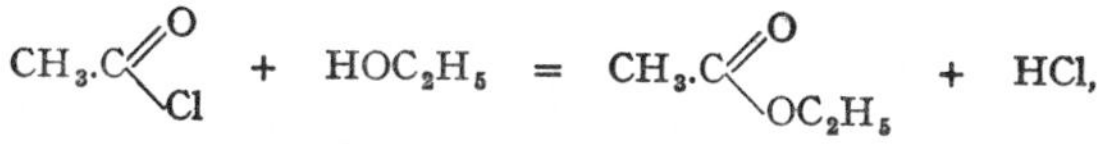

with glycerol to give glyceryl triacetate and hydrogen chloride,

$$
\begin{array}{c}
H \\
| \\
H-C-OH \\
| \\
H-C-OH \\
| \\
H-C-OH \\
| \\
H
\end{array}
+ 3CH_3.COCl =
\begin{array}{c}
H \\
| \\
H-C-O-C{\overset{O}{\underset{CH_3}{}}} \\
| \\
H-C-O-C{\overset{O}{\underset{CH_3}{}}} \\
| \\
H-C-O-C{\overset{O}{\underset{CH_3}{}}} \\
| \\
H
\end{array}
+ 3HCl,
$$

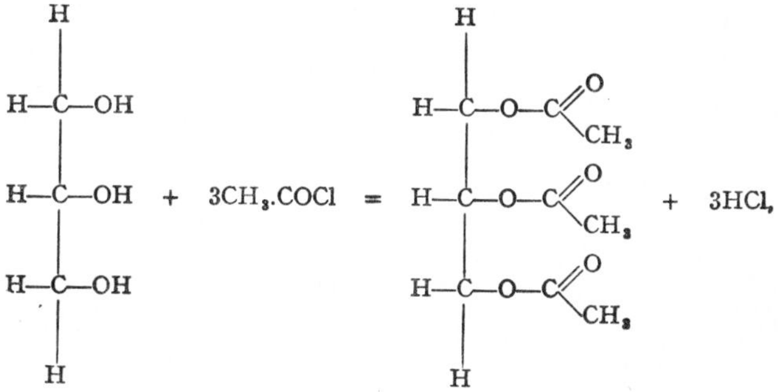

and with ethylamine to give ethyl acetamide and hydrogen chloride,

$$CH_3.C{\overset{O}{\underset{Cl}{}}} + {\overset{H}{\underset{H}{}}}N-C_2H_5 = CH_3.C{\overset{O}{\underset{NC_2H_5}{\underset{H}{}}}} + HCl.$$

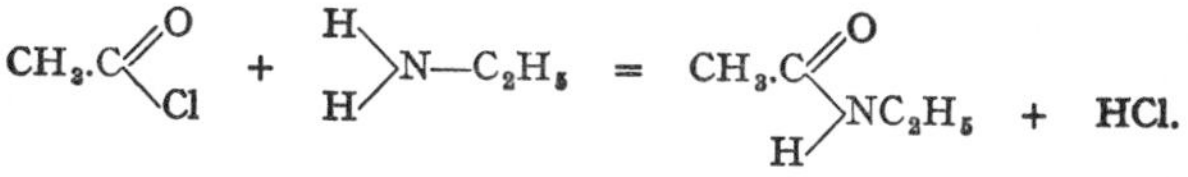

The reaction between acetyl chloride and diethylamine is mentioned on p. 193.

The replacement of the hydrogen atom in a hydroxyl group, or in an amino group, by the acetyl group, $CH_3.CO.—$, is known as *acetylation*; when this change has occurred the original hydroxyl or amino compound is said to be *acetylated*. Acetylation is an important process in experimental organic chemistry, and it is discussed on p. 450.

5. Action with benzene in the presence of aluminium chloride, giving acetophenone. Friedel-Crafts reaction. If acetyl chloride is run slowly from a dropping funnel into a flask containing a mixture of anhydrous aluminium chloride and benzene, hydrogen chloride is evolved and acetophenone is formed,

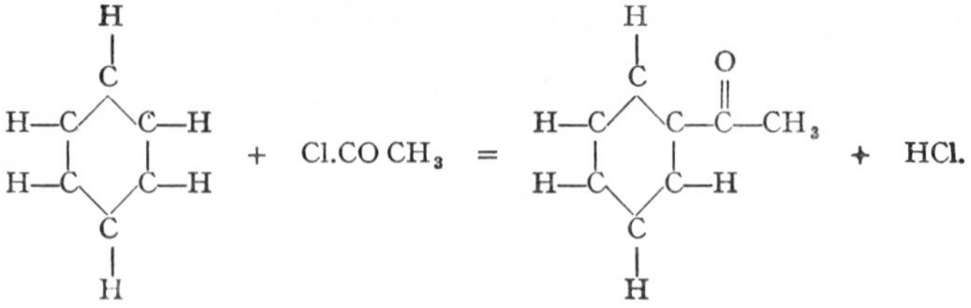

This is an example of a Friedel-Crafts reaction, in which the benzene ring is attacked by the chlorine derivative of a hydrocarbon or a carboxylic acid in the presence of aluminium chloride, which acts as a catalyst.

6. Action with a Grignard reagent, giving a tertiary alcohol. When treated in ethereal solution with ethyl magnesium bromide, for example, acetyl chloride forms an intermediate compound which on hydrolysis with hydrochloric acid yields diethyl carbinol. These reactions, which may be summarised by the equation,

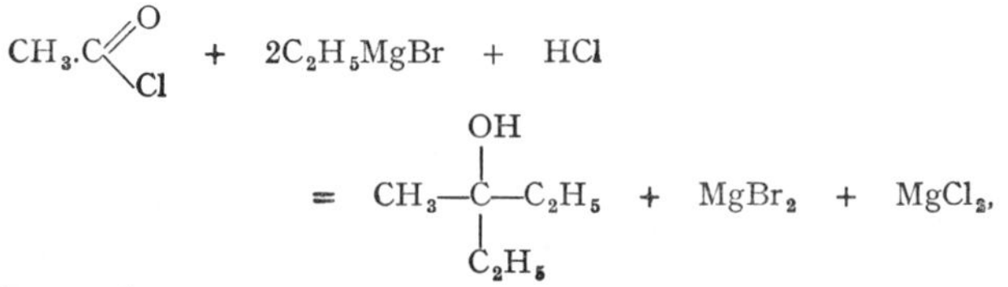

are discussed on p. 458.

Tests for acetyl chloride

1. If 1 c.c. of acetyl chloride is added carefully to 5 c.c. of distilled water, a vigorous reaction occurs, with the evolution of heat, and acetic acid and hydrochloric acid are formed in solution. The solution is divided into two portions. The presence of hydrochloric acid in one portion is confirmed by the silver nitrate test for chlorides; the presence of acetic acid in the other portion is confirmed by the basic ferric acetate for acetates, p. 236.

2. If 1 c.c. of acetyl chloride is added to 1 c.c. of ethyl alcohol and warmed for 1 minute, ethyl acetate is produced. The odour of this ester (bad apples) is best detected by pouring the solution into dilute aqueous sodium carbonate solution, so that any fumes of acetic acid or hydrogen chloride that are present may be absorbed.

3. If 2 c.c. of acetyl chloride are cautiously added to 2 c.c. of aniline in a small flask, a vigorous reaction occurs and solid acetanilide is formed. It is dissolved in just sufficient water to give an almost saturated solution on boiling. When the solution is cooled, crystals of acetanilide, M.P. 114°, are deposited. Acetic anhydride also reacts with aniline to yield acetanilide.

ACETIC ANHYDRIDE

Acetic anhydride is derived by the elimination of a molecule of water from two molecules of acetic acid,

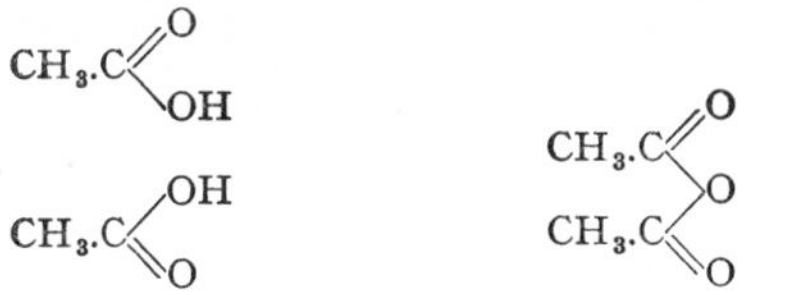

$$CH_3.C\begin{smallmatrix}O\\OH\end{smallmatrix}$$

$$CH_3.C\begin{smallmatrix}OH\\O\end{smallmatrix}$$

acetic acid

$$\begin{matrix}CH_3.C\diagdown^O\\CH_3.C\diagup_O\end{matrix}O$$

acetic anhydride

Acetic anhydride is a colourless liquid, B.P. 139°, with a sharp pungent odour. It is sparingly soluble in cold water, but it rapidly reacts with warm water to give a solution of acetic acid.

Principal reactions in which acetic anhydride is produced

1. The catalytic dehydration of acetic acid. Acetic anhydride may be obtained by passing the vapour of anhydrous acetic acid over dry barium oxide or zinc oxide, heated to 250–300°,

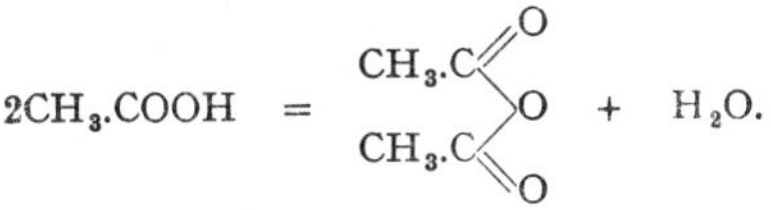

$$2CH_3.COOH = \begin{matrix}CH_3.C\diagup^O\\CH_3.C\diagdown_O\end{matrix}O + H_2O.$$

The products of the reaction are condensed, and acetic anhydride is separated by fractionation from acetic acid in the condensate.

2. The action of acetyl chloride on anhydrous sodium acetate. Acetyl chloride reacts with dry sodium acetate with great readiness, yielding acetic anhydride and sodium chloride,

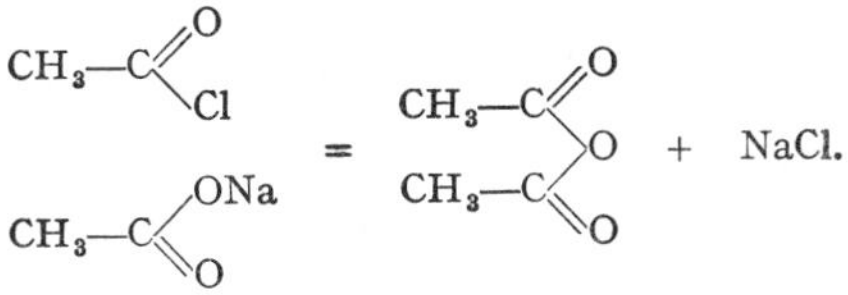

$$\begin{matrix}CH_3—C\diagup^O_{Cl}\\CH_3—C\diagup^{ONa}_O\end{matrix} = \begin{matrix}CH_3—C\diagup^O\\CH_3—C\diagdown_O\end{matrix}O + NaCl.$$

The experimental procedure for carrying out this reaction is described below under " laboratory preparation."

3. The action of anhydrous sodium acetate on phosphorus oxychloride, or on thionyl chloride. Phosphorus oxychloride reacts with anhydrous sodium acetate to yield acetic anhydride, sodium metaphosphate, and sodium chloride,

$$4CH_3.COONa + POCl_3 = 2(CH_3.CO)_2O + NaPO_3 + 3NaCl.$$

Thionyl chloride reacts according to the equation,

$$4CH_3.COONa + 2SOCl_2 = 2(CH_3.CO)_2O + 2SO_2 + 4NaCl.$$

4. The action of acetylene on anhydrous acetic acid in the presence of mercuric sulphate. This reaction, which is used commercially, is described on p. 490.

Laboratory preparation of acetic anhydride. 21 gm. of powdered anhydrous sodium acetate are placed in a small distilling flask cooled in ice-water. 15 c.c. of acetyl chloride are placed in a dropping funnel, of which the stem is inserted into the neck of the distilling flask so that the end is below the side-tube. The acetyl chloride is slowly run on to the sodium acetate, and the liquid mixture is shaken. The flask is then fitted to an air condenser, and heated with a luminous Bunsen flame until no more distillate passes over. The distillate of crude acetic anhydride is redistilled, using an air condenser.

Chemical properties of acetic anhydride

1. Reduction. When acetic anhydride is treated with sodium amalgam, it is reduced to acetaldehyde,

$$CH_3-C\begin{smallmatrix}O\\\\O\end{smallmatrix}\quad CH_3-C\begin{smallmatrix}O\\\\O\end{smallmatrix} \quad + \quad 2H_2 \quad = \quad CH_3.C\begin{smallmatrix}O\\\\H\end{smallmatrix}\quad CH_3.C\begin{smallmatrix}H\\\\O\end{smallmatrix} \quad + \quad H_2O.$$

2. Hydrolysis. Acetic anhydride reacts with warm water to give a solution of acetic acid,

$$(CH_3.CO)_2O \quad + \quad H_2O \quad = \quad 2CH_3.COOH.$$

Its reaction with alkalis to yield, say, sodium acetate, is similar but more vigorous,

$$(CH_3.CO)_2O \quad + \quad 2NaOH \quad = \quad 2CH_3.COONa \quad + \quad H_2O.$$

3. Reaction with ammonia. Acetic anhydride reacts with ammonia to yield a mixture of acetamide and ammonium acetate,

$$CH_3-C\begin{smallmatrix}O\\\\O\end{smallmatrix}\quad CH_3-C\begin{smallmatrix}O\\\\O\end{smallmatrix} \quad + \quad 2NH_3 \quad = \quad CH_3.C\begin{smallmatrix}O\\\\NH_2\end{smallmatrix} \quad + \quad CH_3.C\begin{smallmatrix}O\\\\ONH_4\end{smallmatrix}.$$

4. Acetylation. Like acetyl chloride, acetic anhydride reacts with alcohols and phenols, and with primary and secondary amines. The hydrogen atom in the hydroxyl group of the hydroxy compound, or in the amino group of the amine, is replaced by the acetyl group, $CH_3.CO—$.

(*a*) *Reaction with ethyl alcohol.* If equal volumes of acetic anhydride and ethyl alcohol are boiled together in a flask fitted with a reflux water condenser, the ethyl alcohol is slowly converted to ethyl acetate,

$$CH_3-C{\Large\langle}^O_O \quad CH_3-C{\Large\langle}^O_O \quad + \quad 2C_2H_5OH \quad = \quad 2CH_3.C{\Large\langle}^O_{O.C_2H_5} \quad + \quad H_2O.$$

(b) *Reaction with phenol.* In the presence of sodium hydroxide, the reaction between acetic anhydride and phenol is so rapid that at temperatures just above 0° it may be carried out in aqueous solution. In these conditions sodium phenate is formed by the action of sodium hydroxide on phenol,

$$C_6H_5OH \quad + \quad NaOH \quad = \quad C_6H_5ONa \quad + \quad H_2O,$$

The acetic anhydride attacks the sodium phenate more rapidly than it attacks the water, and phenyl acetate and sodium acetate are formed,

$$C_6H_5ONa \quad + \quad {CH_3-C{\Large\langle}^O \atop CH_3-C{\Large\langle}_O}{\Large\rangle}O \quad = \quad C_6H_5O.CO.CH_3 \quad + \quad CH_3.COONa.$$

In order to carry out the acetylation of phenol by this method, 20 gm. of it are placed in a stout-walled bottle and dissolved in excess (140 c.c.) of ten per cent. aqueous sodium hydroxide solution. 150 gm. of crushed ice are added, followed by 30 c.c. of acetic anhydride. The bottle is corked and shaken vigorously for 5 minutes to complete the reaction. The product is shaken with 10 c.c. of carbon tetrachloride to dissolve the phenyl acetate, and placed in a separating funnel. The lower heavy solution of phenyl acetate in carbon tetrachloride is run off, washed with sodium carbonate solution, and dried over anhydrous calcium chloride. It is then distilled, using an air condenser. The carbon tetrachloride, B.P. 77°, distils over first, followed by the phenyl acetate, B.P. 196°.

(c) *Reaction with aniline.* Acetic anhydride readily reacts with aniline to yield acetanilide,

$$C_6H_5NH_2 \quad + \quad {CH_3-C{\Large\langle}^O \atop CH_3-C{\Large\langle}_O}{\Large\rangle}O \quad = \quad C_6H_5.N{\Large\langle}^H_{CO.CH_3} \quad + \quad CH_3.COOH.$$

The acetylation of aniline is usually carried out by boiling a mixture of 10 c.c. each of acetic anhydride, glacial acetic acid, and aniline for 30 minutes in a small flask fitted to a reflux water condenser. The hot liquid product is then poured into 200 c.c. of cold water which is well stirred. Crystals of crude acetanilide separate, and are filtered off, washed with water and recrystallised from a mixture of equal volumes of acetic acid and water.

Acetic anhydride is generally preferred to acetyl chloride as an acetylating agent because it is not so rapidly affected by moisture.

The acetylating action of acetic anhydride can be moderated by dilution with glacial acetic acid, or promoted by the addition of zinc chloride, or anhydrous sodium acetate.

Tests for acetic anhydride

1. If 1 c.c. of acetic anhydride is added to 5 c.c. of water it will be seen to be almost insoluble. If the solution is warmed, a homogeneous solution is quickly obtained. This solution responds to the tests for acetic acid, p. 236, but not to those for chloride ions ; acetic anhydride may thus be distinguished from acetyl chloride.

2. Ethyl acetate is formed when equal volumes of ethyl alcohol and acetic anhydride are gently warmed together in a test-tube. If the product is poured into dilute sodium carbonate solution so that the odour of acetic acid is destroyed, the odour of ethyl acetate (bad apples) may be detected. Acetyl chloride also responds to this test.

3. If 1 c.c. of aniline is heated with 2 c.c. of acetic anhydride in a small flask on a water-bath for 5 minutes, acetanilide separates as a solid product. It may be recrystallised from hot water, M.P. 114°. Acetyl chloride reacts with aniline similarly, but more vigorously.

ACETAMIDE

Acetamide is derived from acetic acid by replacement of OH in the carboxyl group by $—NH_2$. It may also be regarded as a derivative of ammonia in which one hydrogen atom of the molecule of ammonia is replaced by the acetyl group, $CH_3.CO—$. These alternative methods of regarding the constitution of acetamide are reflected in its amphoteric properties. That acetamide behaves as a very weak base is proved by the isolation of the salts $CH_3.CO.NH_2, HNO_3$ and $(CH_3.CO.NH_2)_2, HCl$, and that it behaves as a weak acid is shown by the existence of the mercuric compound, $(CH_3.CO.NH_2)_2Hg$.

Acetamide forms long colourless crystals, M.P. 82°, B.P. 223°. When recrystallised from acetone it is odourless, but when prepared with the omission of this purification it has an odour of mice which is attributed to the presence of methyl acetamide, $CH_3.CO.NH.CH_3$. It is readily soluble in water and in alcohol.

Acetamide is formed by the action of acetyl chloride or acetic anhydride on ammonia (p. 248 and 252), or by the action of heat on ammonium acetate (p. 237).

Laboratory preparation of acetamide. The dehydration of ammonium acetate is the most suitable method for the preparation of acetamide. In practice it is convenient to start from ammonium carbonate and glacial acetic acid. The glacial acetic acid is present in excess in order to minimise the thermal dissociation of the ammonium acetate into acetic acid and ammonia.

15 gm. of powdered ammonium carbonate are added to 50 c.c. of glacial acetic acid in a round-bottomed flask. When the evolution of carbon dioxide has ceased, a reflux air-condenser is fitted to the flask,

and the contents are boiled for 30 minutes. The dehydration of the ammonium acetate is then complete, and the flask contains acetamide, acetic acid and water. The acetamide is isolated from the mixture by fractional distillation. The air-condenser is removed from the flask and replaced by a column of the type shown on p. 60. A 360° thermometer is fitted to the column, and the side arm is connected to an air condenser. The liquid is distilled very slowly indeed, (to give not more than 1 drop of distillate every 3 seconds) until the temperature reaches 170°, when the residue in the flask is molten acetamide. This is quickly poured out into a small distilling-flask, fitted with a short air condenser, and distilled. The fraction boiling between 215–225° is collected, and crystallised from acetone. The pure acetamide so obtained has M.P. 82°, B.P. 223°, and is odourless.

Chemical properties of acetamide

1. Hydrolysis. Acetamide is hydrolysed by warm sodium hydroxide solution to yield ammonia and sodium acetate,

$$CH_3.C{\overset{O}{\underset{NH_2}{<}}} \ + \ NaOH \ = \ CH_3.C{\overset{O}{\underset{ONa}{<}}} \ + \ NH_3,$$

and by warm dilute sulphuric acid to yield acetic acid and ammonium hydrogen sulphate,

$$CH_3.C{\overset{O}{\underset{NH_2}{<}}} \ + \ H_2O \ + \ H_2SO_4 \ = \ CH_3.C{\overset{O}{\underset{OH}{<}}} \ + \ NH_4.HSO_4.$$

2. Action with nitrous acid, to yield acetic acid and nitrogen. Nitrous acid converts acetamide to acetic acid with the liberation of nitrogen and water. The reaction may be carried out by adding to an aqueous solution of acetamide a concentrated solution of sodium nitrite in dilute acetic acid,

$$CH_3.C{\overset{O}{\underset{NH_2}{<}}} \ + \ HONO \ = \ CH_3.C{\overset{O}{\underset{OH}{<}}} \ + \ N_2 \ + \ H_2O.$$

3. Action with bromine and potassium hydroxide solution, to give methylamine. Hofmann's reaction. If a ten per cent. solution of potassium hydroxide is added to a mixture of acetamide and bromine until the deep red colour changes to a pale yellow, an alkaline solution of bromo-acetamide is obtained. If a concentrated solution of potassium hydroxide is now slowly added to the warm solution of bromo-acetamide, methyl isocyanate is formed, which is immediately hydrolysed to methylamine and potassium carbonate. The equations for this reaction and the experimental procedure for carrying it out are given on p. 190.

Hofmann's reaction is of interest because it affords a means of descending the homologous series. For example, ethyl alcohol may be oxidised to acetic acid, and the acetic acid converted to acetamide. By Hofmann's reaction the acetamide is converted to methylamine, which by reaction with nitrous acid yields methyl alcohol, the alcohol next below ethyl alcohol in the alcohol series.

4. Action with phosphorus pentoxide. When acetamide is distilled with phosphorus pentoxide it loses the elements of water and yields methyl cyanide,

$$CH_3-C{\overset{O}{\underset{NH_2}{}}} = CH_3-C{\equiv}N + H_2O.$$

Constitution of acetamide. The molecular formula of acetamide is C_2H_5ON. It reacts with nitrous acid to yield nitrogen, acetic acid and water. The reaction of nitrous acid with a compound containing the amino group, $-NH_2$, results in the replacement of this group by the hydroxyl group $-OH$. Since the constitution of acetic acid is $CH_3.CO.OH$, it follows that the constitution of acetamide must be $CH_3.CO.NH_2$. This constitution is confirmed by:

(i) the formation of acetamide by the distillation of ammonium acetate;

(ii) the formation of acetamide by the action of ethyl acetate, or acetyl chloride, on ammonia;

(iii) the hydrolysis of acetamide to acetic acid, or its sodium salt, by the action of warm dilute sulphuric acid, or of warm sodium hydroxide solution.

Tests for acetamide. Acetamide does not react with sodium hydroxide solution in the cold, and it is thus distinguished from ammonium acetate, p. 237. When boiled with sodium hydroxide solution, acetamide yields ammonia which is evolved with the steam, and sodium acetate which may be identified in the residual solution.

2. Acetamide gives no reaction with neutral ferric chloride solution. This reaction also serves to distinguish acetamide from ammonium acetate.

ETHYL ACETATE

Ethyl acetate is derived by the replacement of $-OH$ in the carboxyl group of acetic acid by the ethoxy group $-OC_2H_5$.

Ethyl acetate is a colourless liquid, B.P. 77°. It is partially miscible with water, and is miscible with organic solvents in all proportions. It has a characteristic odour of bad apples.

Principal reactions in which ethyl acetate is produced

1. The combination of ethyl alcohol and acetic acid in the presence of a catalyst. Ethyl alcohol combines directly with acetic acid to yield ethyl acetate and water according to the equation,

$$C_2H_5OH + CH_3.COOH \rightleftharpoons CH_3.COOC_2H_5 + H_2O.$$

This reaction is slow and reversible. If it is to be used for the efficient production of ethyl acetate a third substance must be present to increase the rate of the reaction by catalysis, and to displace the equilibrium to the right by facilitating the removal of the water which is formed. The substance which is employed for these purposes is either concentrated sulphuric acid or gaseous hydrogen chloride.

Sulphuric acid acts as a catalyst and dehydrating agent by taking part in the reaction. It combines with the ethyl alcohol to form ethyl hydrogen sulphate which then reacts with the acetic acid to form ethyl acetate ; sulphuric acid is regenerated,

$$C_2H_5OH \quad + \quad H_2SO_4 \quad = \quad C_2H_5HSO_4 \quad + \quad H_2O,$$
$$C_2H_5HSO_4 \quad + \quad CH_3.COOH \quad = \quad CH_3.COOC_2H_5 \quad + \quad H_2SO_4.$$

The reaction is carried out in a flask heated in an oil-bath at 140°. The water and ethyl acetate volatilise and are condensed and collected. The distillate also contains ether which is formed as a by-product in the course of the reaction.[*]

The formation of ether is avoided if the Fischer-Speier method for preparing esters is used. In this method gaseous hydrogen chloride is employed as the catalyst and dehydrating agent. A current of dry hydrogen chloride is passed into a mixture of absolute alcohol and anhydrous acetic acid which is kept gently boiling in a flask fitted to a reflux condenser. The solution is distilled, and the ethyl acetate is separated from water and any unchanged reagents by the procedure described on p. 259.

2. The action of acetyl chloride, or of acetic anhydride, on ethyl alcohol. Ethyl acetate is produced when equal volumes of acetyl chloride and ethyl alcohol are warmed together in a flask fitted to a reflux condenser,

$$CH_3.COCl \quad + \quad C_2H_5OH \quad = \quad CH_3.COOC_2H_5 \quad + \quad HCl.$$

To obtain the ethyl acetate in a reasonably pure state the product is shaken with aqueous sodium carbonate solution to remove hydrochloric acid and excess acetyl chloride, and then with a concentrated solution of calcium chloride to remove excess alcohol. It is finally distilled. The production of ethyl acetate from acetic anhydride and ethyl alcohol is carried out by a similar procedure.

3. The action of silver acetate on ethyl iodide. Ethyl acetate may be made by boiling a suspension of finely powdered silver acetate in ethyl iodide, or by warming an ethereal solution of ethyl

[*] The mechanism of this reaction is further discussed on p. 454.

iodide with silver acetate. The reaction is carried out in a flask fitted to a water reflux condenser,

$$CH_3.COOAg + C_2H_5I = CH_3.COOC_2H_5 + AgI.$$

The conversion of silver acetate to ethyl acetate by this reaction can be carried out very nearly quantitatively.

4. The condensation of acetaldehyde in the presence of aluminium ethylate. Acetaldehyde polymerises to ethyl acetate when passed into aluminium ethylate dissolved in a high boiling solvent. The actual yield is 85 per cent. of the theoretical. This interesting reaction is mentioned on p. 206.

Laboratory preparation of ethyl acetate.

Ethyl acetate is made in the laboratory by the action of acetic acid on ethyl alcohol, Reaction 1, p. 256. Concentrated sulphuric acid is usually employed as the dehydrating agent.

Equal volumes (say 10 c.c.) of ethyl alcohol and concentrated sulphuric acid are mixed in a distilling flask fitted with a tap-funnel and connected to a water condenser, Fig. 52. A few fragments of unglazed

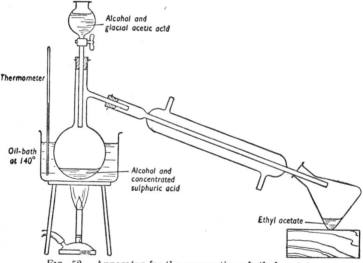

Alcohol and glacial acetic acid

Thermometer

Oil-bath at 140°

Alcohol and concentrated sulphuric acid

Ethyl acetate

Fig. 52. Apparatus for the preparation of ethyl acetate.

porcelain are introduced into the flask, which is then heated in an oil-bath until the temperature of the oil reaches 140°. Under these conditions the alcohol and sulphuric acid react to form ethyl hydrogen sulphate. 70 c.c. of a mixture of equal volumes of ethyl alcohol and glacial acetic acid are placed in the tap-funnel and allowed to run slowly into the flask. The distillation of ethyl acetate soon begins, and the rate of addition of the mixture from the tap-funnel is adjusted to be equal to that at which the distillate condenses. The distillation is continued for

5 minutes after the addition of the alcohol and acetic acid mixture has been completed.

The distillate consists of ethyl acetate mixed with acetic acid, ether, water, unchanged ethyl alcohol, and the reduction products of sulphuric acid. It is placed in a separating funnel and shaken with 25 c.c. of 30 per cent. aqueous sodium carbonate solution to remove acids. The lower aqueous layer is rejected, and the upper layer of ethyl acetate is shaken with a strong solution of calcium chloride (25 gm. of anhydrous calcium chloride in 25 c.c. of water) to remove alcohol. The lower aqueous layer is rejected, and the ethyl acetate is transferred to a small flask containing a few lumps of fused calcium chloride. The mixture is allowed to stand, with occasional shaking, for 20 minutes. The liquid is then filtered and distilled. The distillation must be carried out by placing the distilling flask on a cold water-bath which is gradually warmed. The ether then distils over first at 35–40°, and the ethyl acetate at 74–79°.

Chemical properties of ethyl acetate. Ethyl acetate is a stable compound. It may be distilled without decomposition, and it is neither an oxidising nor a reducing agent. Its principal reactions are described below.

1. Hydrolysis. If ethyl acetate is boiled with water the equilibrium represented by the equation,

$$CH_3.COOC_2H_5 \ + \ H_2O \ \rightleftharpoons \ CH_3.COOH \ + \ C_2H_5OH,$$

is slowly attained. The hydrolysis of ethyl acetate to ethyl alcohol and sodium acetate is rapidly carried out by boiling ethyl acetate with 10 per cent. aqueous sodium hydroxide solution in a flask fitted to a reflux condenser,

$$CH_3.COOC_2H_5 \ + \ NaOH \ = \ C_2H_5OH \ + \ CH_3.COONa.$$

2. Decomposition with hydriodic acid to give ethyl iodide. Ethyl acetate reacts with a concentrated solution of hydrogen iodide to yield ethyl iodide and acetic acid,

$$CH_3.COOC_2H_5 \ + \ HI \ = \ C_2H_5I \ + \ CH_3.COOH.$$

3. Action with ammonia to give acetamide. Ethyl acetate reacts with a concentrated aqueous solution of ammonia, to yield acetamide and ethyl alcohol, both of which remain in solution,

$$CH_3.COOC_2H_5 \ + \ NH_3 \ = \ CH_3.CONH_2 \ + \ C_2H_5OH.$$

4. Action with a Grignard reagent. Ethyl acetate reacts with a Grignard reagent to give a tertiary alcohol. With magnesium phenyl bromide, for example, ethyl acetate yields methyl diphenyl carbinol. The equations representing this reaction are parallel to those representing the formation of triphenyl carbinol from ethyl benzoate, p. 409.

5. Reaction with metallic sodium, to give the sodium derivative of ethyl acetoacetate. If metallic sodium, in the form of slices or wire, is warmed with dry ethyl acetate, the sodium derivative of ethyl acetoacetate is formed. The conversion of ethyl acetate to ethyl acetoacetate is most simply represented as a condensation of two molecules of ethyl acetate with the elimination of a molecule of ethyl alcohol,

$$CH_3.CO \overline{|OC_2H_5} + H|CH_2.COOC_2H_5$$
$$= CH_3.CO.CH_2.COOC_2H_5 + C_2H_5OH.$$

The reactions leading to the formation of the sodium derivative of ethyl acetoacetate are, however, more complex than this ; they are discussed on p. 456.

Uses of ethyl acetate. Ethyl acetate is used as a solvent in the ebullioscopic method for determining molecular weights, and as a general solvent for organic substances.

Tests for ethyl acetate. Ethyl acetate may be recognised by its characteristic odour of bad apples. It undergoes no very distinctive chemical reactions, but the products of its hydrolysis are easily identified. If ethyl acetate is hydrolysed by boiling it with dilute aqueous sodium hydroxide solution in a flask fitted to a reflux condenser, and the contents of the flask are subsequently distilled, ethyl alcohol passes over and may be recognised by the tests described on p. 166. The residue in the distilling flask contains sodium acetate. If it is acidified with sulphuric acid and then distilled, acetic acid will be present in the distillate. Acetic acid may be identified by the tests mentioned on p. 236.

ACETONITRILE

Acetonitrile is derived by the replacement of the group —OH and the doubly linked oxygen atom in the carboxyl group of acetic acid by a triply linked nitrogen atom,

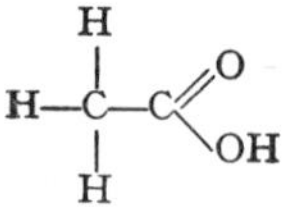

acetic acid 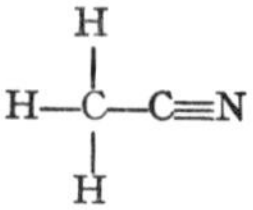   acetonitrile

Acetonitrile may also be regarded either (i) as a derivative of methane, theoretically obtained by the replacement of one hydrogen atom in the methane molecule by the cyanide group —C≡N, or (ii) as an ester derived by the replacement of the —OH group in the molecule of methyl alcohol by the cyanide group. These derivations are indicated by the alternative name *methyl cyanide* which is frequently used for acetonitrile. Acetonitrile is a mobile liquid, B.P. 82°. It possesses a characteristic odour, and is freely soluble in water.

Preparation and chemical properties of acetonitrile.
Acetonitrile is formed when ammonium acetate, or acetamide, is
distilled with a dehydrating agent such as phosphorus pentoxide,

$$CH_3.COONH_4 = CH_3.CN + 2H_2O,$$
$$CH_3.CONH_2 = CH_3.CN + H_2O.$$

It may also be obtained by heating methyl iodide with potassium
cyanide in aqueous alcoholic solution,

$$KCN + CH_3I = CH_3.CN + KI.$$

Acetonitrile is hydrolysed by solutions of either acids or alkalis
(p. 230) in such a way that the —CN group is converted into the
—COOH group,

$$CH_3.CN + NaOH + H_2O = CH_3.COONa + NH_3,$$
$$CH_3.CN + HCl + 2H_2O = CH_3.COOH + NH_4Cl.$$

The behaviour of acetonitrile on hydrolysis is thus different from
that of most esters, which break down to yield an acid and an alcohol.

Acetonitrile is reduced by treatment with zinc and dilute sulphuric
acid, or with sodium and alcohol, to yield the primary amine,
ethylamine,

$$CH_3.CN + 4H = CH_3.CH_2.NH_2.$$

Constitution of acetonitrile. The molecular formula of acetonitrile is C_2H_3N. It is formed by the action of potassium cyanide on
methyl iodide in aqueous alcoholic solution. Since potassium
cyanide is completely ionised, the reaction must occur between the
methyl iodide and the cyanide ion, $\overline{C}\equiv N$, as represented by the
equation :

$$CH_3I + CN^- = CH_3CN + I^-.$$

This reaction shows that the molecule of acetonitrile contains a
methyl group, but it does not show whether the carbon atom or the
nitrogen atom in the cyanide group is attached to the carbon atom
in the methyl group.

The reduction of acetonitrile with sodium and alcohol to yield
ethylamine, and the hydrolysis of acetonitrile by boiling acids or
alkalis to yield acetic acid, show definitely that the carbon atom in
the cyanide group is directly linked to the carbon atom in the methyl
group, and that the constitution of acetonitrile is, therefore,

$$H-\underset{\underset{H}{|}}{\overset{\overset{H}{|}}{C}}-C\equiv N$$

Propionitrile (ethyl cyanide) is a liquid, B.P. 98°, with properties
parallel to those of acetonitrile.

METHYL ISONITRILE

Methyl isonitrile (methyl isocyanide or methyl carbylamine) has the molecular structure $CH_3N^+\equiv C^-$. It is prepared by heating methyl iodide with silver cyanide (cf. p. 142), or by heating methylamine with chloroform and alcoholic potassium hydroxide solution (cf. p. 188). It is a mobile liquid, B.P. 59°, and is sparingly soluble in water. It has an offensive odour and is poisonous.

Methyl isonitrile is not decomposed by boiling sodium hydroxide solution, but if boiled with dilute hydrochloric acid it yields methylamine hydrochloride and formic acid,

$$CH_3NC + 2H_2O + HCl = CH_3NH_2.HCl + H.COOH.$$

Methyl isonitrile may be reduced by hydrogen in the presence of nickel to yield the secondary amine, dimethylamine, p. 182.

The properties of *ethyl isocyanide*, a liquid, B.P. 79°, are similar to those of the methyl compound.

Constitution of methyl isonitrile. The molecular formula of methyl isonitrile is C_2H_3N. Its formation when methyl bromide is heated with silver cyanide,

$$CH_3Br + AgNC = CH_3NC + AgBr,$$

shows that the molecule contains the methyl group. The formation of methyl isonitrile by the action of methylamine on a mixture of chloroform and potassium hydroxide,

$$CH_3NH_2 + 3KOH + CHCl_3 = CH_3NC + 3KCl + 3H_2O,$$

suggests that the nitrogen atom in the isonitrile group is directly attached to the carbon atom of the methyl group. This is further confirmed by :

(i) the hydrolysis of methyl isonitrile by acids (it is not attacked by alkalis) to give methylamine and formic acid,

$$CH_3NC + 2H_2O = CH_3NH_2 + HCOOH,$$

(ii) the reduction of methyl isonitrile by hydrogen in the presence of nickel to give a secondary amine,

$$CH_3NC + 2H_2 = CH_3.NH.CH_3.$$

The constitution of methyl isonitrile is, therefore, $CH_3.NC$.

An attempt to write a formula, using covalencies only, for a molecule of this constitution leads to the structure

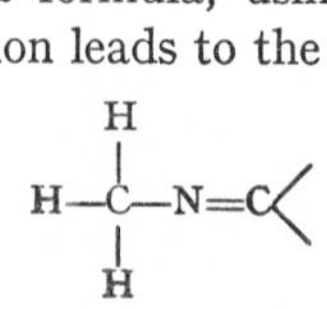

This structure, in which two valencies of the carbon atom in the isonitrile group are unused, is unsatisfactory. If it is expressed in terms of the electronic theory of valency it is represented by the diagram

In this configuration the nitrogen atom controls 8 valency electrons, of which 6 are shared, and the carbon atom controls only 6 electrons. A stable structure may, however, be derived from this unstable structure by establishing a co-ionic bond, p. 18, in addition to the double covalent bond between the nitrogen and carbon atoms. The formation of this bond may be imagined to take place in the following two stages. One of the unshared electrons of the nitrogen atom is transferred to the carbon atom, thus establishing an ionic bond. Each of the two atoms then controls 7 valency electrons, and is thus analogous to an atom of, say, chlorine. An additional covalent bond is then established between the atoms of nitrogen and carbon, by their holding another pair of valency electrons in common. The number of valency electrons in the external quantum shell of each atom then becomes 8. These changes may be represented by the diagrams ;

The stable electron configuration shown in the third diagram is that of methyl isonitrile. It may be written shortly $CH_3.N^+\!\!\equiv\!\!C^-$. The link between the nitrogen atom and the carbon atom consists of three covalent bonds (this group of bonds is exactly similar to the triple bond in the molecule of acetylene) and one ionic bond.

CHAPTER XVI

THE CHLORO-, HYDROXY-, AND AMINO-FATTY ACIDS

In the preceding chapter an account is given of the classes of compounds that may be obtained by the replacement of atoms in the *carboxyl* group of a fatty acid by the chlorine atom, the amino group, or the carbethoxy group. The present chapter deals with the compounds that may be derived by the replacement of one or more hydrogen atoms in the *alkyl* group of a fatty acid by halogen atoms, the hydroxyl group or the amino group. Examples of such compounds are

$$
\begin{array}{ccc}
\overset{\textstyle H}{\underset{\textstyle H}{Cl-C-COOH}} & \overset{\textstyle H}{\underset{\textstyle H}{HO-C-COOH}} & \overset{\textstyle H}{\underset{\textstyle H}{H_2N-C-COOH}} \\
\text{monochloroacetic} & \text{monohydroxyacetic acid} & \text{aminoacetic acid} \\
\text{acid} & \text{or glycollic acid} & \text{or glycine}
\end{array}
$$

The above structural formulae show that these three compounds may also be theoretically derived by the substitution of the carboxyl group for a hydrogen atom in the molecule of methyl chloride, methyl alcohol, or methylamine respectively. The properties of these compounds show that this manner of regarding their constitutions is valid ; monochloroacetic acid, for example, exhibits those properties of acetic acid which are due to the presence of the carboxyl group in the molecule, and those properties of methyl chloride which are due to the presence of the chlorine atom. Similarly, glycine exhibits both the properties of an acid and those of an amine. Certain amino- and hydroxy-fatty acids are of interest because of the parts they play in the chemical processes of living organisms.

THE CHLOROACETIC ACIDS

The chloroacetic acids are derived from acetic acid by the replacement of one or more of the hydrogen atoms in the methyl group by chlorine, thus :

$$
\begin{array}{cccc}
\overset{\textstyle H}{\underset{\textstyle H}{H-C-C}}\diagup^{O}_{OH} & \overset{\textstyle Cl}{\underset{\textstyle H}{H-C-C}}\diagup^{O}_{OH} & \overset{\textstyle Cl}{\underset{\textstyle H}{Cl-C-C}}\diagup^{O}_{OH} & \overset{\textstyle Cl}{\underset{\textstyle Cl}{Cl-C-C}}\diagup^{O}_{OH} \\
\text{acetic acid} & \text{monochloroacetic} & \text{dichloroacetic} & \text{trichloroacetic} \\
& \text{acid} & \text{acid} & \text{acid}
\end{array}
$$

All three chloroacetic acids are obtained by heating acetic acid with chlorine in direct sunlight ; hydrogen chloride is set free in the reactions, as shown, for example, by the equation,

$$CH_3.COOH + Cl_2 = CH_2Cl.COOH + HCl$$

The chloroacetic acids may also be obtained by passing chlorine into boiling acetic acid containing a little iodine to act as a chlorine carrier ; sunlight is not necessary if iodine is present. The catalytic action of the iodine depends on the formation of iodine trichloride, which chlorinates the acetic acid, at the same time breaking down to iodine monochloride, which combines with more chlorine to give iodine trichloride again,

$$CH_3.COOH + ICl_3 = CH_2Cl.COOH + HCl + ICl,$$
$$ICl + Cl_2 = ICl_3.$$

The chlorination of acetic acid may be used as a laboratory method for the preparation of each of the chloroacetic acids. It is difficult, however, to obtain a pure specimen of any one of the chloroacetic acids by this method, and therefore a specific method of preparation for each of the acids is usually chosen.

The chloroacetic acids are monobasic acids, and are stronger acids than acetic acid. They all yield acetic acid when reduced with nascent hydrogen.

MONOCHLOROACETIC ACID

Monochloroacetic acid is a crystalline solid, M.P. 62°, B.P. 189°. It is soluble in water.

Preparation of monochloroacetic acid. Monochloroacetic acid is prepared by the hydrolysis of trichloroethylene, which is made by warming tetrachloroethane, " Westron ", p. 132, with milk of lime,

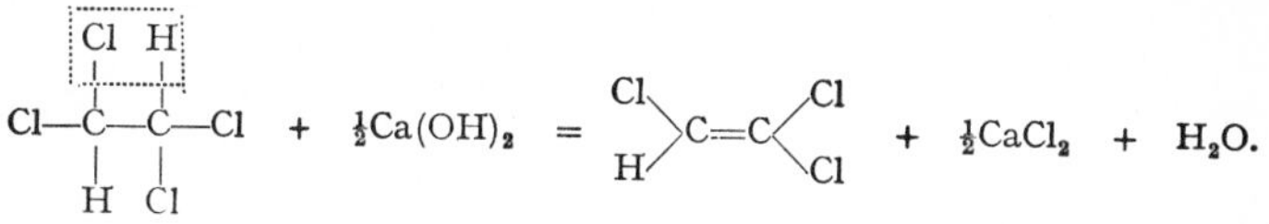

The trichloroethylene is agitated with 90 per cent. sulphuric acid, and monochloroacetic acid is produced,

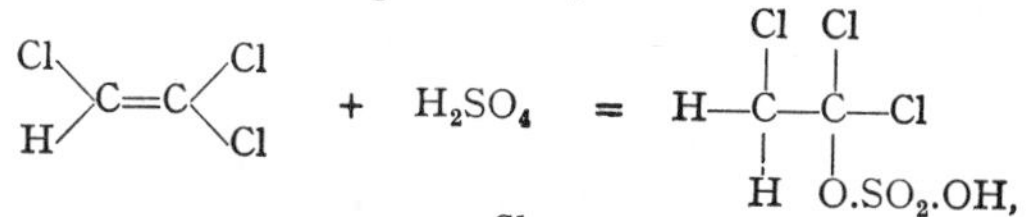

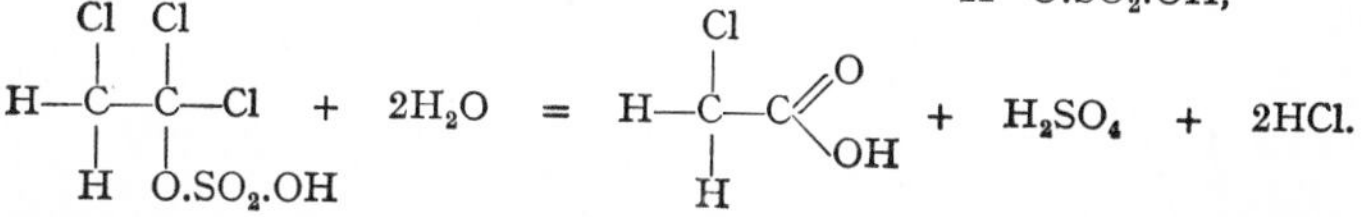

I 2

D.C.

The chloroacetic acid is separated from the mineral acids by distillation *in vacuo*.

Chemical properties of monochloroacetic acid. The chemical reactivity of monochloroacetic acid depends on the presence in the molecule of (i) the carboxyl group, (ii) the chlorine atom.

1. Reactions of monochloroacetic acid in which the carboxyl group alone takes part. Monochloroacetic acid reacts with phosphorus pentachloride to yield chloroacetyl chloride, phosphorus oxychloride, and hydrogen chloride,

$$Cl\text{—}\underset{\underset{H}{|}}{\overset{\overset{H}{|}}{C}}\text{—}C{\overset{O}{\diagdown OH}} + PCl_5 = Cl\text{—}\underset{\underset{H}{|}}{\overset{\overset{H}{|}}{C}}\text{—}C{\overset{O}{\diagdown Cl}} + POCl_3 + HCl.$$

A cold aqueous solution of sodium hydroxide, or sodium carbonate, attacks the carboxyl group of monochloroacetic acid to yield sodium monochloroacetate, according to the equations,

$$CH_2Cl.COOH + NaOH = CH_2Cl.COONa + H_2O.$$
$$2CH_2Cl.COOH + Na_2CO_3 = 2CH_2Cl.COONa + H_2O + CO_2.$$

2. Reactions of monochloroacetic acid in which the chlorine atom takes part. Boiling water attacks the chlorine atom in monochloroacetic acid to yield monohydroxyacetic acid (glycollic acid),

$$Cl\text{—}\underset{\underset{H}{|}}{\overset{\overset{H}{|}}{C}}\text{—}C{\overset{O}{\diagdown OH}} + H_2O = HO\text{—}\underset{\underset{H}{|}}{\overset{\overset{H}{|}}{C}}\text{—}C{\overset{O}{\diagdown OH}} + HCl.$$

Monochloroacetic acid reacts with a hot aqueous solution of sodium hydroxide to form sodium glycollate,

$$Cl\text{—}\underset{\underset{H}{|}}{\overset{\overset{H}{|}}{C}}\text{—}C{\overset{O}{\diagdown OH}} + 2NaOH = HO\text{—}\underset{\underset{H}{|}}{\overset{\overset{H}{|}}{C}}\text{—}C{\overset{O}{\diagdown ONa}} + NaCl + H_2O.$$

In this reaction the sodium hydroxide effects the replacement of the chlorine atom by —OH, and it also reacts with the carboxyl group of the acid to form the sodium salt.

A concentrated aqueous solution of ammonia attacks the chlorine atom in monochloroacetic acid to yield aminoacetic acid (glycine),

$$Cl\text{—}\underset{\underset{H}{|}}{\overset{\overset{H}{|}}{C}}\text{—}C{\overset{O}{\diagdown OH}} + 2NH_3 = H_2N\text{—}\underset{\underset{H}{|}}{\overset{\overset{H}{|}}{C}}\text{—}C{\overset{O}{\diagdown OH}} + NH_4Cl.$$

If potassium monochloroacetate is heated with potassium nitrite in aqueous solution, nitromethane is formed,

$$CH_2Cl.COOK + KNO_2 + H_2O = CH_3NO_2 + KCl + KHCO_3.$$

Monochloroacetic acid is used in the synthesis of indigo.

DICHLOROACETIC ACID

Dichloroacetic acid is a liquid, B.P. 194°. It is made by heating chloral hydrate with potassium cyanide in aqueous solution. The reaction may be summarised by the equation,

$$CCl_3.CH(OH)_2 + KCN = CHCl_2.COOH + HCN + KCl.$$

The course of the reaction may consist of the elimination of the elements of hydrogen chloride from a molecule of chloral hydrate,

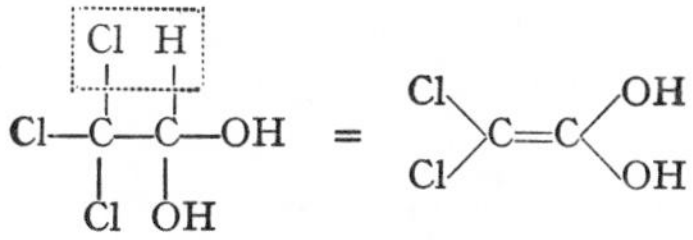

the hydrolysis of the ethylene compound so formed,

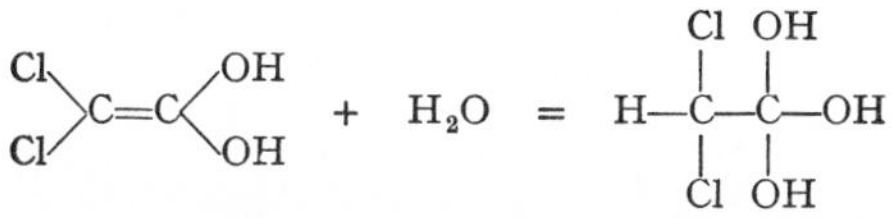

and the elimination of the elements of water from the hydroxyl compound thus produced,

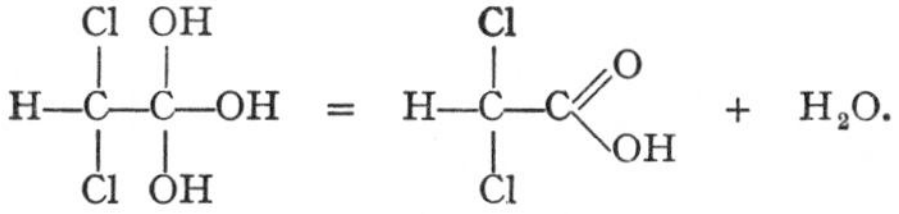

The instability of compounds which contain more than one hydroxyl group attached to the same carbon atom is mentioned on p. 151.

Dichloroacetic acid reacts with hot water under pressure to yield glyoxylic acid,

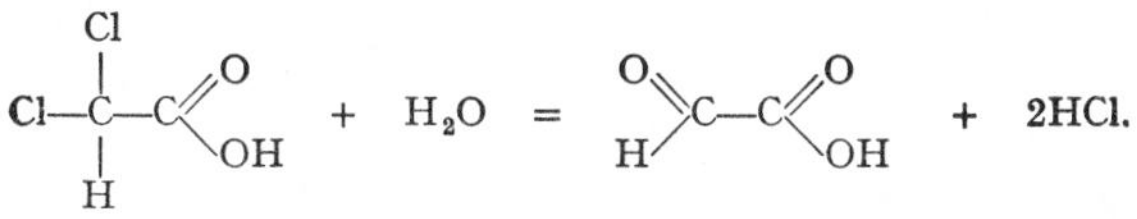

Glyoxylic acid is also produced when silver dichloroacetate is warmed with water. If sodium dichloroacetate, or sodium glyoxylate, is boiled with an aqueous solution of an alkali, a mixture of sodium hydroxyacetate and sodium oxalate is obtained,

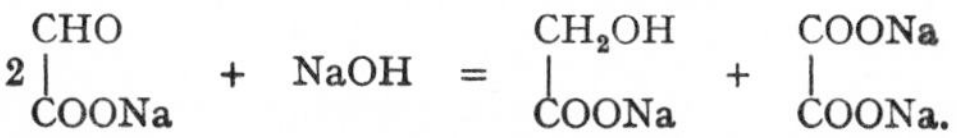

The action of sodium hydroxide on sodium glyoxylate should be compared with the action of potassium hydroxide on formaldehyde, p. 213.

TRICHLOROACETIC ACID

Trichloroacetic acid is a crystalline solid, M.P. $57°$, B.P. $197°$; it has a corrosive action on the skin. It is prepared by oxidising chloral with concentrated nitric acid,

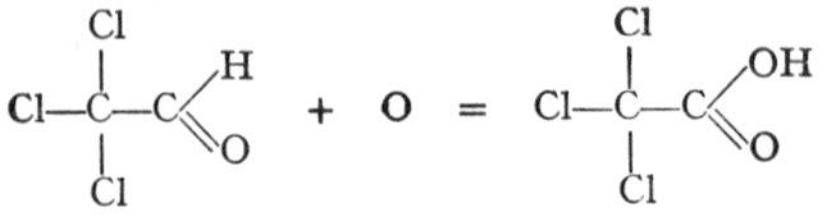

$$\underset{\underset{Cl}{|}}{\overset{\overset{Cl}{|}}{Cl-C-}}C\overset{H}{\underset{O}{<}} \;+\; O \;=\; \underset{\underset{Cl}{|}}{\overset{\overset{Cl}{|}}{Cl-C-}}C\overset{OH}{\underset{O}{<}}$$

Trichloroacetic acid neutralises alkalis to form salts. When it is boiled with excess of sodium or potassium hydroxide, however, it breaks down, forming chloroform and sodium or potassium carbonate,

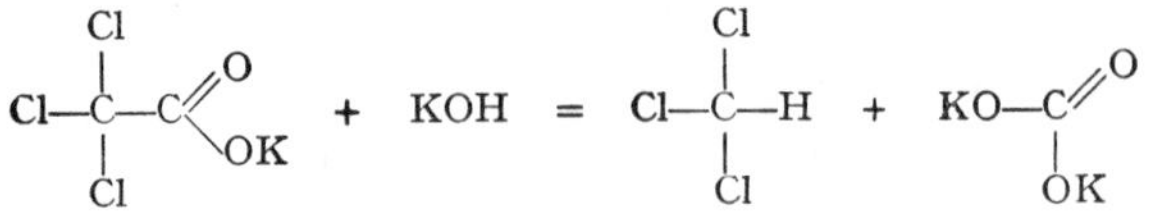

$$\underset{\underset{Cl}{|}}{\overset{\overset{Cl}{|}}{Cl-C-}}C\overset{O}{\underset{OK}{<}} \;+\; KOH \;=\; \underset{\underset{Cl}{|}}{\overset{\overset{Cl}{|}}{Cl-C-}}H \;+\; KO-C\overset{O}{\underset{OK}{<}}$$

It should be noted that the hydrolysis of trichloroacetic acid follows a course which is quite different from the hydrolyses of monochloroacetic acid or dichloroacetic acid. By analogy with the hydrolyses of the other two chloroacetic acids, trichloroacetic acid would be expected to yield oxalic acid as a result of attack by alkalis.

THE HYDROXY-FATTY ACIDS

HYDROXYACETIC ACID (GLYCOLLIC ACID)

Glycollic acid is derived from acetic acid by the replacement of one atom of hydrogen in the methyl group by the hydroxyl group, —OH. It is a hygroscopic crystalline compound, M.P. $80°$. It is soluble in water, alcohol, acetone and ether.

Preparation of glycollic acid

(i) Glycollic acid is formed when monochloroacetic acid is heated with water under pressure,

$$CH_2Cl.COOH \;+\; H_2O \;=\; CH_2OH.COOH \;+\; HCl.$$

It is most conveniently obtained by boiling potassium chloroacetate with water, evaporating to dryness, and extracting the residue with acetone, which dissolves the glycollic acid, but not the potassium chloride.

(ii) Glycollic acid is also formed by the action of nitrous acid on glycine. If a 20 per cent. aqueous solution of sodium nitrite is acidified with a small quantity of dilute acetic acid, and the solution is poured into a cold aqueous solution of glycine, nitrogen is liberated and glycollic acid remains in solution,

$$CH_2NH_2.COOH + HONO = CH_2OH.COOH + N_2 + H_2O.$$

These reactions for the preparation of glycollic acid should be compared with Reactions 2 and 6, p. 159, by which ethyl alcohol may be obtained.

Chemical properties of glycollic acid

Glycollic acid is at once a monobasic acid and a primary alcohol. It forms salts and esters of the types $CH_2OH.COONa$ and $CH_2OH.COOC_2H_5$.

1. Reaction with phosphorus pentachloride. Phosphorus pentachloride attacks both the alcoholic and the carboxylic hydroxyl groups of glycollic acid, thus,

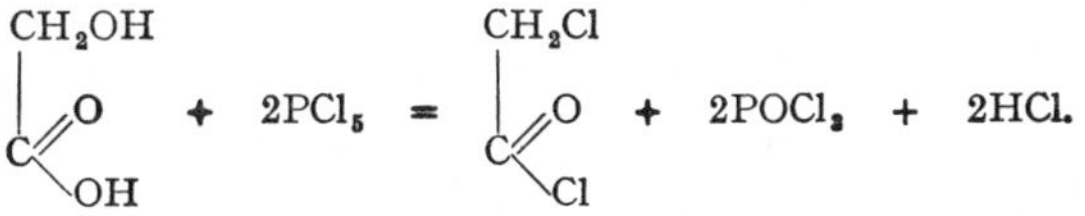

2. Reaction with acetic anhydride. Acetic anhydride attacks only the alcoholic hydroxyl group to yield the acetyl derivative of glycollic acid,

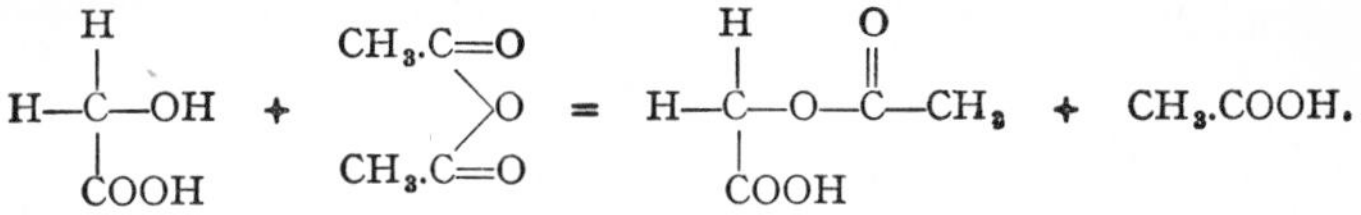

3. Action of heat. If glycollic acid is heated above its melting point under reduced pressure, it condenses to glycollide ; two molecules of the acid take part in this reaction, and the carboxyl group of one reacts with the alcoholic group of the other, thus,

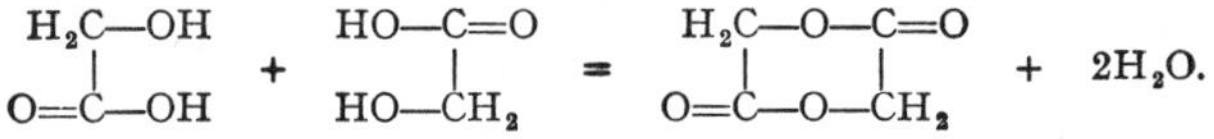

Glycollide may be regarded as an ester, in the formation of which glycollic acid acts both as acid and alcohol. Glycollide is a crystalline solid, M.P. 86°. It is hydrolysed to glycollic acid on boiling with water.

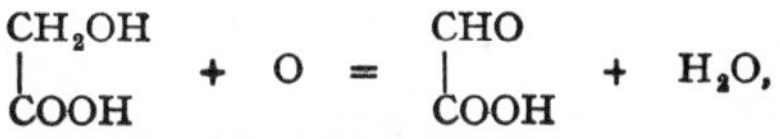

4. Oxidation. On oxidation, the primary alcohol group in glycollic acid is converted first to the aldehyde group, —CHO, to yield glyoxylic acid, and then to the carboxyl group, to yield oxalic acid,

$$\begin{array}{ccc} \text{CHO} & & \text{COOH} \\ | & + \text{ O } = & | \\ \text{COOH} & & \text{COOH.} \end{array}$$

These reactions resemble the oxidation of ethyl alcohol to acetaldehyde and acetic acid, p. 164.

THE HYDROXYPROPIONIC ACIDS

The nature of the hydroxy acid which is obtained by the replacement of a hydrogen atom in the molecule of propionic acid by a hydroxyl group depends on the position of the hydrogen atom which is replaced. Two hydroxy acids may be derived from propionic acid : lactic acid or α-hydroxypropionic acid, and hydracrylic acid or β-hydroxypropionic acid. The relation of these two hydroxy acids to propionic acid is made clear by the structural formulae,

$$\begin{array}{ccc}
\begin{array}{c} \text{H \ H} \\ | \ \ | \\ \text{H—C—C—COOH} \\ | \ \ | \\ \text{H \ H} \end{array}
&
\begin{array}{c} \text{H \ OH} \\ | \ \ | \\ \text{H—C—C—COOH} \\ | \ \ | \\ \text{H \ H} \end{array}
&
\begin{array}{c} \text{OH \ H} \\ | \ \ \ | \\ \text{H—C——C—COOH} \\ | \ \ \ | \\ \text{H \ \ H} \end{array}
\\
\text{propionic acid} & \text{α-hydroxypropionic acid,} & \text{β-hydroxypropionic} \\
& \text{or lactic acid} & \text{acid, or hydracrylic} \\
& & \text{acid}
\end{array}$$

It should be noted that lactic acid contains the secondary alcohol group, $>$CH.OH, and that hydracrylic acid contains the primary alcohol group, $—CH_2.OH$.

LACTIC ACID

Lactic acid occurs naturally in two isomeric forms. One isomer (*dl*-lactic acid) is present in sour milk. It is a crystalline solid, M.P. 18°, but under ordinary laboratory conditions it usually exists as a viscous liquid; its purification is difficult because it condenses to lactide on heating, Reaction 1, p. 272. It has a sour taste and is miscible in all proportions with water, alcohol and ether. The other isomer which occurs naturally (*d*-lactic acid or sarcolactic acid) is present in muscle. The physical properties of these two isomers are different, but their chemical properties are identical. The isomerism of lactic acid is discussed in Chapter XVIII; the present chapter is concerned with the chemical properties of lactic acid.

PRINCIPAL REACTIONS IN WHICH LACTIC ACID IS OBTAINED

1. The replacement of the chlorine atom in α-chloropropionic acid, or the amino group in α-aminopropionic acid, by the group —OH. Lactic acid is formed from α-chloropropionic acid, or from α-aminopropionic acid, by reactions in which the chlorine atom, or the amino group, is replaced by the group —OH. These reactions are identical in principle with those which convert ethyl bromide and ethylamine to ethyl alcohol (p. 159). Thus lactic acid is formed when α-chloropropionic acid is heated with water, dilute aqueous alkalis, or moist silver oxide,

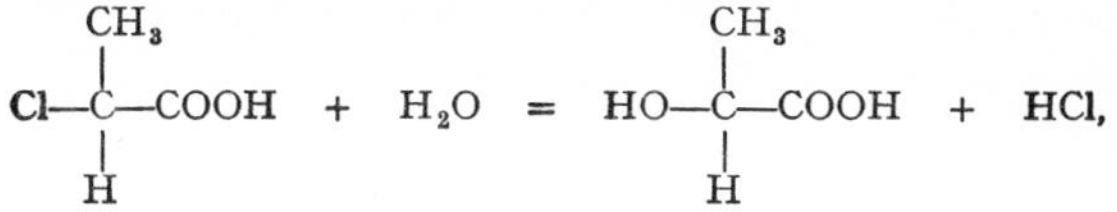

$$\underset{\overset{|}{H}}{\overset{\overset{CH_3}{|}}{Cl\!-\!C\!-\!COOH}} + H_2O = \underset{\overset{|}{H}}{\overset{\overset{CH_3}{|}}{HO\!-\!C\!-\!COOH}} + HCl,$$

and when an aqueous solution of sodium nitrite, acidified with acetic acid, is added to α-aminopropionic acid,

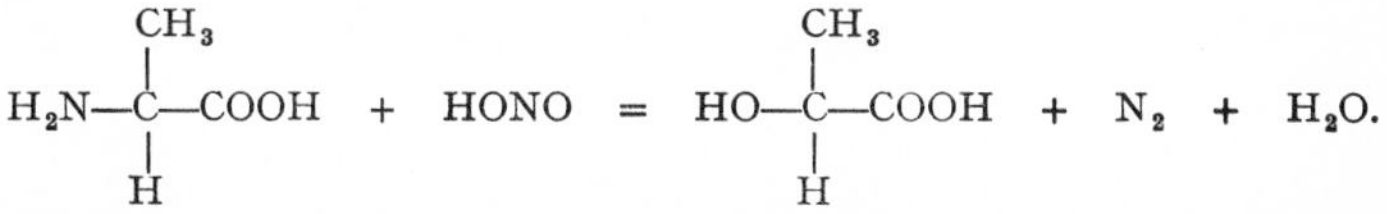

$$\underset{\overset{|}{H}}{\overset{\overset{CH_3}{|}}{H_2N\!-\!C\!-\!COOH}} + HONO = \underset{\overset{|}{H}}{\overset{\overset{CH_3}{|}}{HO\!-\!C\!-\!COOH}} + N_2 + H_2O.$$

2. The reduction of pyruvic acid, $CH_3.CO.COOH$. Pyruvic acid is reduced by the action of sodium amalgam and water to lactic acid,

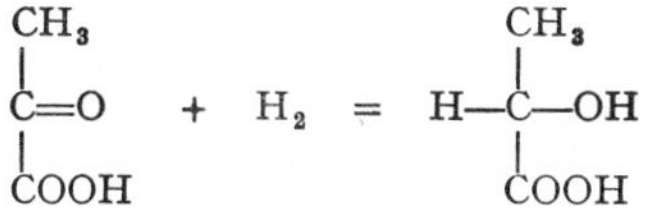

$$\underset{\overset{|}{COOH}}{\overset{\overset{CH_3}{|}}{C\!=\!O}} + H_2 = \underset{\overset{|}{COOH}}{\overset{\overset{CH_3}{|}}{H\!-\!C\!-\!OH}}$$

In this reaction the ketonic group, $>C\!=\!O$, in pyruvic acid is reduced to the secondary alcohol group $>CH.OH$. This process is parallel to the reduction of acetone to iso-propyl alcohol, p. 222.

3. The oxidation of α-propylene glycol. α-propylene glycol is oxidised to lactic acid by nitric acid ; in this reaction the primary alcohol group —$CH_2.OH$ is oxidised to —COOH,

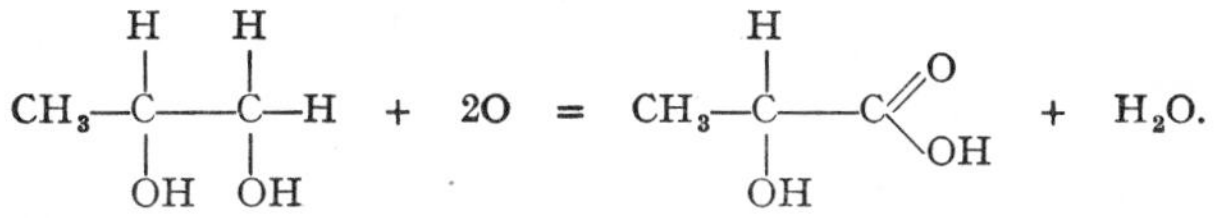

$$\underset{\overset{|}{OH}\ \overset{|}{OH}}{\overset{\overset{H}{|}\ \overset{H}{|}}{CH_3\!-\!C\!-\!-\!C\!-\!H}} + 2O = \underset{\overset{|}{OH}}{\overset{\overset{H}{|}}{CH_3\!-\!C\!-\!-\!C}}\overset{O}{\underset{OH}{\diagdown}} + H_2O.$$

4. The hydrolysis of acetaldehyde cyanhydrin. When acetaldehyde cyanhydrin is boiled with sodium hydroxide solution, ammonia is evolved, and sodium lactate remains in solution,

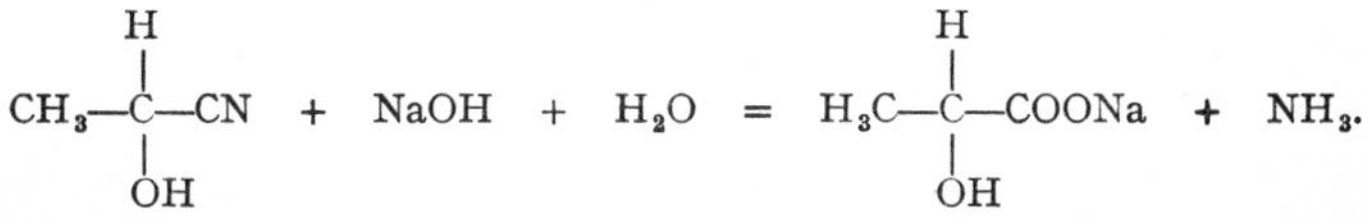

$$\underset{\overset{|}{OH}}{\overset{\overset{H}{|}}{CH_3\!-\!C\!-\!CN}} + NaOH + H_2O = \underset{\overset{|}{OH}}{\overset{\overset{H}{|}}{H_3C\!-\!C\!-\!COONa}} + NH_3.$$

The reaction furnishes important evidence on the structure of lactic acid.

5. Industrial preparation by the lactic fermentation of sugar. Lactic acid is obtained on the technical scale by the action of the lactic ferment on certain sugars, including lactose, a sugar present in milk. The fermentation proceeds best in neutral solution at 37°. Lactose is first hydrolysed to glucose and galactose,

$$C_{12}H_{22}O_{11} + H_2O = C_6H_{12}O_6 + C_6H_{12}O_6$$
$$\text{lactose} \qquad\qquad\qquad \text{glucose} \qquad \text{galactose}$$

which are converted to lactic acid by the enzyme produced by the bacillus *B. acidi lactici*. The neutrality of the solution is preserved by adding zinc carbonate to the solution. As the fermentation proceeds, sparingly soluble zinc lactate separates from the solution. If the zinc lactate is filtered off and treated with a dilute mineral acid, lactic acid is set free in the aqueous solution, from which it may be obtained by repeated extraction with ether.

CHEMICAL PROPERTIES, CONSTITUTION AND USES OF LACTIC ACID

1. Action of heat. In marked contrast to acetic acid (p. 233) lactic acid is an unstable substance. It may be distilled under reduced pressure (B.P. 122°/15 mm.), but when heated alone under normal pressure it condenses to yield lactide,

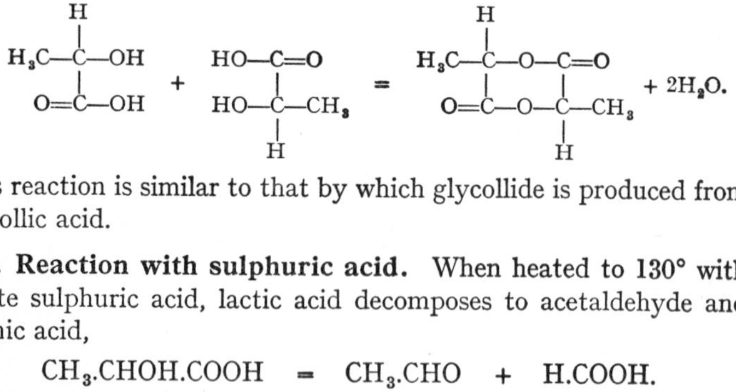

This reaction is similar to that by which glycollide is produced from glycollic acid.

2. Reaction with sulphuric acid. When heated to 130° with dilute sulphuric acid, lactic acid decomposes to acetaldehyde and formic acid,

$$CH_3.CHOH.COOH = CH_3.CHO + H.COOH.$$

When heated with concentrated sulphuric acid it decomposes similarly, but the formic acid is attacked by the sulphuric acid to yield carbon monoxide ; there is also some general oxidation of the organic substances, in which carbon dioxide, sulphur dioxide and carbon are set free.

3. Reaction with phosphorus pentachloride, to yield lactyl chloride. Lactic acid contains the secondary alcohol group, $>CH.OH$, and the carboxyl group, —COOH. When it is treated with phosphorus pentachloride, the —OH groups in the alcohol and in the carboxyl group are both replaced by atoms of chlorine, and lactyl chloride is formed,

$$\begin{matrix} & H & & & & H & & & \\ & | & & & & | & & & \\ H_3C-\!\!\!&C&\!\!\!-OH & + & 2PCl_5 & = & H_3C-\!\!\!&C&\!\!\!-Cl & + & 2POCl_3 & + & 2HCl. \\ & | & & & & | & & & \\ O=\!\!\!&C&\!\!\!-OH & & & & O=\!\!\!&C&\!\!\!-Cl & & & \end{matrix}$$

4. Oxidation. The secondary alcohol group alone is affected by oxidation. Lactic acid, when oxidised with potassium permanganate solution, or with perhydrol (a 30 per cent. aqueous solution of hydrogen peroxide) in the presence of ferric acetate, yields pyruvic acid,

$$\begin{matrix} & CH_3 & & & & CH_3 & & \\ & | & & & & | & & \\ H-\!\!\!&C&\!\!\!-OH & + & O & = & C=\!\!\!&O & + & H_2O. \\ & | & & & & | & & \\ & COOH & & & & COOH & & \end{matrix}$$

This reaction corresponds to the oxidation of iso-propyl alcohol, p. 173.

5. Reactions with the halogen acids. When lactic acid is boiled with a concentrated aqueous solution of hydrogen bromide, it yields α-bromopropionic acid,

$$\begin{matrix} & CH_3 & & & & CH_3 & & \\ & | & & & & | & & \\ H-\!\!\!&C&\!\!\!-OH & + & HBr & = & H-\!\!\!&C&\!\!\!-Br & + & H_2O. \\ & | & & & & | & & \\ & COOH & & & & COOH & & \end{matrix}$$

This reaction corresponds to the action of hydrogen bromide with ethyl alcohol, p. 137. When lactic acid is boiled with a concentrated aqueous solution of hydrogen iodide, however, the acid is reduced to propionic acid

$$CH_3.CHOH.COOH + HI = CH_3.CHI.COOH + H_2O$$
$$CH_3.CHI.COOH + HI = CH_3.CH_2.COOH + I_2.$$

This reaction differs from the action of hydrogen iodide on ethyl alcohol, p. 144.

6. Acid properties of lactic acid. Lactic acid is a monobasic acid (the dissociation constant, $K = 13{\cdot}8 \times 10^{-5}$) which neutralises alkalis to form salts, and combines with alcohols to form esters. Some of the most important salts are sodium lactate, $CH_3.CHOH.COONa$, calcium lactate, $(CH_3.CHOH.COO)_2Ca,5H_2O$, and zinc lactate $(CH_3.CHOH.COO)_2Zn,3H_2O$. These salts are all crystalline, and the zinc salt is sparingly soluble in cold water.

Ethyl lactate, $CH_3.CHOH.COOC_2H_5$, is a neutral liquid which may be distilled without decomposition. It reacts with potassium or sodium to yield metallic derivatives,

$$2\ \underset{\underset{COOC_2H_5}{|}}{\overset{\overset{CH_3}{|}}{H-C-OH}} + 2Na = 2\ \underset{\underset{COOC_2H_5}{|}}{\overset{\overset{CH_3}{|}}{H-C-ONa}} + H_2$$

and with acetyl chloride to yield an acetyl derivative,

$$\underset{\underset{COOC_2H_5}{|}}{\overset{\overset{CH_3}{|}}{H-C-OH}} + CH_3.COCl = \underset{\underset{COOC_2H_5}{|}}{\overset{\overset{CH_3}{|}}{H-C-O-CO.CH_3}} + HCl.$$

Constitution of lactic acid. The empirical formula of lactic acid is CH_2O. Its equivalent determined by the analysis of the silver salt is 90. It is monobasic, and its equivalent, therefore, is identical with its molecular weight. Its molecular formula, therefore, is $C_3H_6O_3$.

The direct reduction of lactic acid to propionic acid by means of hydriodic acid shows that the three carbon atoms in the lactic acid molecule are arranged in the form of a chain.

The presence of a carboxyl group in the molecule of lactic acid is indicated by its reaction with sodium hydroxide to form sodium lactate, and by the formation of the ester, ethyl lactate.

The presence of a hydroxyl group in the molecule is shown by :

(i) the reaction of lactic acid with hydrobromic acid to give bromopropionic acid ;

(ii) the reaction of lactic acid with phosphorus pentachloride to give lactyl chloride ;

(iii) the reaction of sodium lactate with metallic sodium to produce the di-sodium derivative ;

(iv) the reaction of ethyl lactate with acetyl chloride to give ethyl acetyl lactate.

It remains to decide whether the hydroxyl group is attached to the α-carbon atom in the lactic acid molecule (the carbon atom next to the carboxyl group) or to the β-carbon atom

$CH_3.CHOH.COOH$
α-hydroxypropionic acid

$CH_2OH.CH_2.COOH$
β-hydroxypropionic acid

Proof that the lactic acid is α-hydroxypropionic acid is furnished by the formation of lactic acid by the hydrolysis of acetaldehyde cyanhydrin (Reaction 4, p. 271).

It is explained on p. 307 that lactic acid exists in the two optically isomeric forms

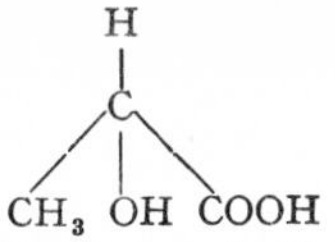

d-lactic, or sarco-lactic acid, obtained from muscle

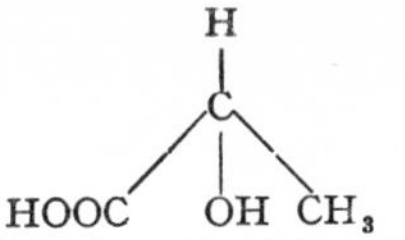

l-lactic acid, obtained artificially

and that a third form, optically inactive by external compensation, may be obtained from sour milk. This inactive form is invariably produced when lactic acid is prepared synthetically from optically inactive reagents.

Uses of lactic acid. Lactic acid is used in tanning, dyeing, and in pharmacy. Ethyl and butyl lactates are used as solvents in the plastics industry.

Tests for lactic acid

1. If a small quantity of lactic acid, or a lactate, is warmed with concentrated sulphuric acid, a brisk effervescence occurs, and the mixture blackens. Carbon monoxide is evolved, mixed with carbon dioxide and sulphur dioxide.

2. Lactic acid responds to the iodoform test, p. 156. To a solution of the acid made alkaline with 10 per cent. sodium hydroxide solution, potassium iodide solution and sodium hypochlorite solution are added. A precipitate of iodoform is formed on shaking in the cold.

HYDRACRYLIC ACID

Hydracrylic acid is a thick sour syrup.

Principal reactions in which hydracrylic acid is produced

Hydracrylic acid is produced by a number of reactions which are parallel to those leading to the formation of lactic acid. Whereas, however, lactic acid is formed by the action of certain reagents on α-derivatives of propionic acid, hydracrylic acid is formed by the action of the same reagents on the corresponding β-derivatives. The reactions mentioned below should be compared with those given under " lactic acid " on p. 270.

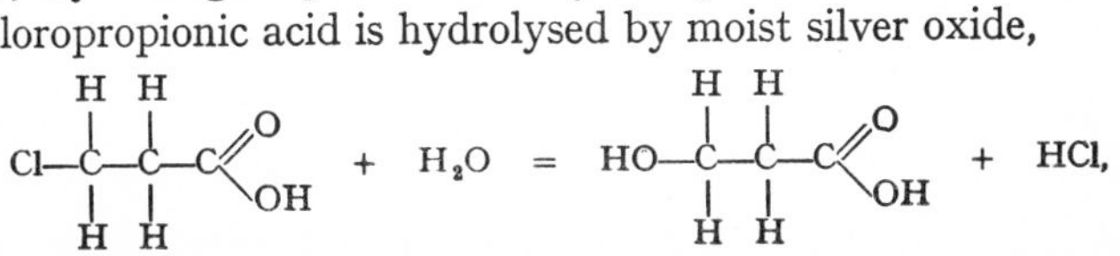

1. The replacement of the chlorine atom in β-chloropropionic acid, or the amino group in β-aminopropionic acid, by the group —OH. Hydracrylic acid is formed when β-chloropropionic acid is hydrolysed by moist silver oxide, or when an aqueous solution of β-aminopropionic acid is treated with a solution of sodium nitrite acidified with dilute acetic acid,

$$\text{HONO} + \text{H}_2\text{N}-\overset{\overset{\displaystyle H}{|}}{\underset{\underset{\displaystyle H}{|}}{C}}-\overset{\overset{\displaystyle H}{|}}{\underset{\underset{\displaystyle H}{|}}{C}}-C\overset{\displaystyle O}{\underset{\displaystyle OH}{}} = \text{HO}-\overset{\overset{\displaystyle H}{|}}{\underset{\underset{\displaystyle H}{|}}{C}}-\overset{\overset{\displaystyle H}{|}}{\underset{\underset{\displaystyle H}{|}}{C}}-C\overset{\displaystyle O}{\underset{\displaystyle OH}{}} + \text{N}_2 + \text{H}_2\text{O}.$$

2. The oxidation of β-propylene glycol.

$$\text{HO}-\overset{\overset{\displaystyle H}{|}}{\underset{\underset{\displaystyle H}{|}}{C}}-\overset{\overset{\displaystyle H}{|}}{\underset{\underset{\displaystyle H}{|}}{C}}-\overset{\overset{\displaystyle H}{|}}{\underset{\underset{\displaystyle H}{|}}{C}}-\text{OH} + 2\text{O} = \text{HO}-\overset{\overset{\displaystyle H}{|}}{\underset{\underset{\displaystyle H}{|}}{C}}-\overset{\overset{\displaystyle H}{|}}{\underset{\underset{\displaystyle H}{|}}{C}}-C\overset{\displaystyle O}{\underset{\displaystyle OH}{}} + \text{H}_2\text{O}.$$

3. The hydrolysis of ethylene cyanhydrin.

Ethylene cyan-hydrin is obtained by the action of potassium cyanide on ethylene chlorohydrin (p. 120) in dilute alcoholic solution,

$$\text{HO}-\overset{\overset{\displaystyle H}{|}}{\underset{\underset{\displaystyle H}{|}}{C}}-\overset{\overset{\displaystyle H}{|}}{\underset{\underset{\displaystyle H}{|}}{C}}-\text{Cl} + \text{KCN} = \text{HO}-\overset{\overset{\displaystyle H}{|}}{\underset{\underset{\displaystyle H}{|}}{C}}-\overset{\overset{\displaystyle H}{|}}{\underset{\underset{\displaystyle H}{|}}{C}}-\text{CN} + \text{KCl.}$$

When ethylene cyanhydrin is boiled with hydrochloric acid, hydra-crylic acid is produced,

$$\text{HO}-\overset{\overset{\displaystyle H}{|}}{\underset{\underset{\displaystyle H}{|}}{C}}-\overset{\overset{\displaystyle H}{|}}{\underset{\underset{\displaystyle H}{|}}{C}}-\text{CN} + 2\text{H}_2\text{O} + \text{HCl} = \text{HO}-\overset{\overset{\displaystyle H}{|}}{\underset{\underset{\displaystyle H}{|}}{C}}-\overset{\overset{\displaystyle H}{|}}{\underset{\underset{\displaystyle H}{|}}{C}}-C\overset{\displaystyle O}{\underset{\displaystyle OH}{}} + \text{NH}_4\text{Cl.}$$

This reaction establishes the constitution of hydracrylic acid.

Chemical properties of hydracrylic acid. Hydracrylic acid is at once a monobasic acid and a primary alcohol. It forms salts with alkalis, and esters with alcohols. The presence of the primary alcohol group in the molecule of hydracrylic acid is revealed by the two following reactions : (i) when hydracrylic acid is heated alone, or with dilute sulphuric acid, it is converted by the loss of water into acrylic acid,

$$\text{H}-\overset{\overset{\displaystyle OH}{|}}{\underset{\underset{\displaystyle H}{|}}{C}}-\overset{\overset{\displaystyle H}{|}}{\underset{\underset{\displaystyle H}{|}}{C}}-\text{COOH} = \overset{\displaystyle H}{\underset{\displaystyle H}{}}{>}C=C{<}\overset{\displaystyle H}{\underset{\displaystyle COOH}{}} + \text{H}_2\text{O},$$

(ii) when hydracrylic acid is treated with chromic acid it is oxidised to malonic acid,

$$\text{H}-\overset{\overset{\displaystyle OH}{|}}{\underset{\underset{\displaystyle H}{|}}{C}}-\overset{\overset{\displaystyle H}{|}}{\underset{\underset{\displaystyle H}{|}}{C}}-\text{COOH} + 2\text{O} = \text{HOOC}-\overset{\overset{\displaystyle H}{|}}{\underset{\underset{\displaystyle H}{|}}{C}}-\text{COOH} + \text{H}_2\text{O}.$$

AMINOACETIC ACID (GLYCINE)

Glycine * is derived from acetic acid by the replacement of one hydrogen atom in the methyl group by the amino group, —NH$_2$.

$$
\begin{array}{cc}
\text{H} & \text{H} \\
| & | \\
\text{H—C—COOH} & \text{H—C—COOH} \\
| & | \\
\text{H} & \text{NH}_2 \\
\text{acetic acid} & \text{glycine}
\end{array}
$$

The molecule of glycine contains the group —COOH, which confers acidic properties, and also the group —NH$_2$, which confers basic properties. An aqueous solution of glycine is neutral to litmus, but glycine gives rise to stable salts of the two types exemplified by sodium aminoacetate, $[CH_2.NH_2.COO]^-Na^+$, and glycine hydrochloride, $[H_3N.CH_2.COOH]^+Cl^-$, analogous respectively to sodium acetate and ammonium chloride. Ammonium aminoacetate is unstable ; glycine itself is obtained by the action of a solution of ammonia on chloroacetic acid, p. 278.

In alkaline aqueous solution the molecule of glycine yields negative ions according to the reaction,

$$H_2N.CH_2.COOH + Na^+ + OH^- = H_2N.CH_2.COO^- + Na^+ + H_2O.$$

In acid solution it combines with a hydrogen ion to produce a positive ion analogous to the ammonium ion, NH_4^+, thus,

$$H_2N.CH_2.COOH + H^+ + Cl^- = H_3N^+.CH_2.COOH + Cl^-.$$

In neutral solution, molecules of glycine undergo both changes to produce ions, thus,

$$H_2N.CH_2COOH \rightleftharpoons H_3N^+.CH_2.COO^-.$$

A compound consisting of ions of this type would exhibit the properties of a compound possessing a high electric moment, p. 21. The high melting point of glycine, 235°, compared with that of acetic acid, 16°, is evidence that glycine has this polar structure. The simple formula for glycine, $NH_2.CH_2.COOH$, however, is normally sufficient for the interpretation of its chemistry. Compounds like glycine, which possess molecules containing both the amino group —NH$_2$ and the carboxyl group —COOH, belong to a class of organic compounds known as the *amino acids*. The amino acids are of great biochemical importance on account of their relation to the proteins. The proteins are the principal constituents of the fleshy parts of the animal body. Only a few of the proteins have been obtained in the crystalline condition. The molecules of the proteins

* Glycine is also known as glycocoll.

are large and complex ; the constitution of any protein has yet to be elucidated. Chemical research on the nature of the proteins has been based on the examination of the simpler substances produced when proteins are subjected to oxidation, fermentation, or hydrolysis. Hydrolysis may be carried out with 25 per cent. sulphuric acid, with baryta water, or with concentrated hydrochloric acid; the final products obtained by any of these methods are amino acids.

Glycine is the simplest member of the series of amino acids. It crystallises in prisms which melt at 235° with decomposition. It is readily soluble in water, but only sparingly soluble in alcohol, and is insoluble in ether. Glycine is produced by the hydrolysis of proteins, and consequently by the hydrolysis of glue or gelatine which contain proteins, and also by the reactions set out below.

Principal reactions in which glycine is produced

1. The action of ammonia on chloroacetic acid. If chloro-acetic acid is dissolved in a concentrated aqueous solution of ammonia at room temperature, aminoacetic acid is obtained.

$$CH_2Cl.COOH \quad + \quad 2NH_3 \quad = \quad CH_2NH_2.COOH \quad + \quad NH_4Cl.$$

To isolate the glycine, the solution is boiled with cupric hydroxide, when a deep blue solution containing the copper derivative * of glycine is produced,

$$2CH_2NH_2.COOH \quad + \quad Cu(OH)_2$$
$$= \quad (CH_2NH_2.COO)_2Cu \quad + \quad 2H_2O.$$

The solution is filtered and crystallised. The deep blue needles of the copper derivative are dissolved in water, and hydrogen sulphide is passed into the solution

$$(CH_2NH_2.COO)_2Cu \quad + \quad H_2S \quad = \quad 2CH_2NH_2.COOH \quad + \quad CuS.$$

The precipitated cupric sulphide is filtered off, and the glycine is obtained by concentrating and crystallising the solution.

* The colour of the aqueous solution of the copper derivative is distinct from that of a solution of a cupric salt, and the carefully neutralised solution does not show the reactions of the cupric ion. The constitution of the copper derivative is therefore probably

The copper atom in the molecule is linked to the oxygen atoms by covalencies, and to the two nitrogen atoms by co-ionic links. This structure is related to that of the cupric ammines (see *General and Inorganic Chemistry*, P. J. Durrant, p. 297).

2. The action of hydrochloric acid on hippuric acid. Hippuric acid or benzoyl glycine, occurs in the urine of herbivora. When heated with hydrochloric acid it yields benzoic acid and glycine hydrochloride,

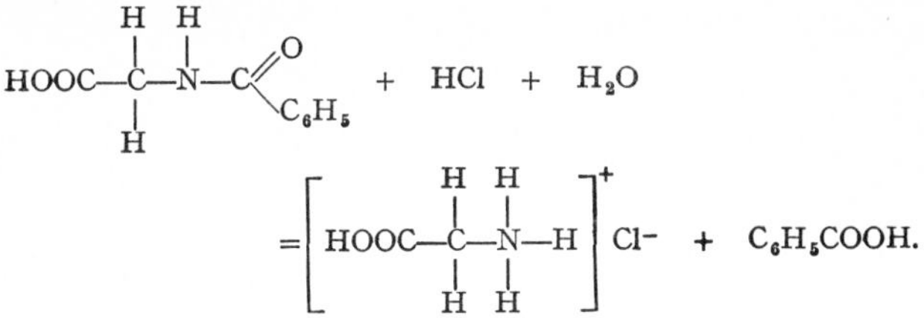

The benzoic acid, which is almost insoluble in cold water, separates when the solution is cooled, and is removed by filtration. The glycine hydrochloride is crystallised from the filtered solution.

3. The action of ethyl chloroacetate on potassium phthalimide, and hydrolysis of the product. Ethyl chloroacetate reacts with potassium phthalimide according to the equation,

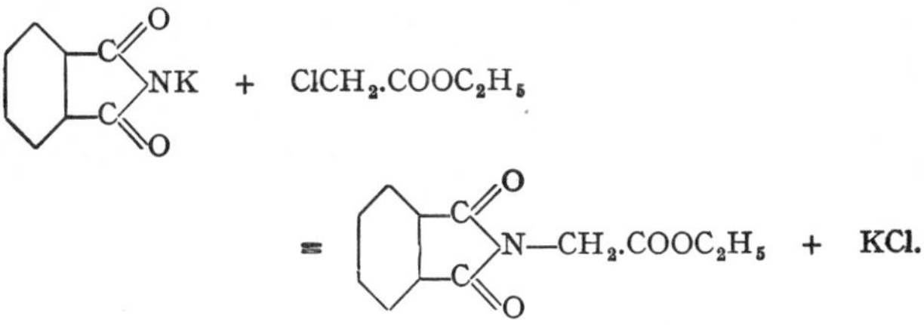

If the phthalimide derivative is treated with hydrochloric acid, phthalic acid and glycine hydrochloride are formed,

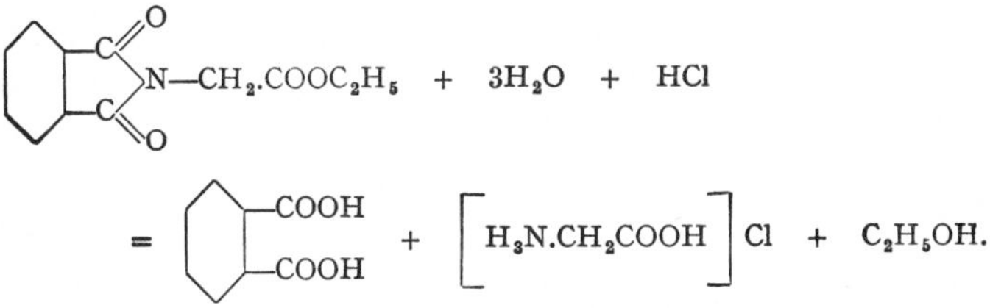

This reaction should be compared with Reaction 2 (c), p. 185.

4. The action of formaldehyde on ammonium chloride and sodium cyanide. Strecker's synthesis. If equimolar proportions of formaldehyde, ammonium chloride and sodium cyanide are allowed to react together in aqueous solution, or in alcoholic solution, the following reactions occur :

(i) hydrogen cyanide, formed by the hydrolysis of sodium cyanide,

$$NaCN + H_2O \rightleftharpoons NaOH + HCN,$$

condenses with the formaldehyde to form formaldehyde cyanhydrin,

$$\underset{H}{\overset{H}{>}}C=O \; + \; HCN \; = \; \underset{H}{\overset{H}{>}}C\underset{CN}{\overset{OH}{<}}$$

(ii) the formaldehyde cyanhydrin combines with ammonia liberated by the action of sodium hydroxide on the ammonium chloride, to form amino-acetonitrile,

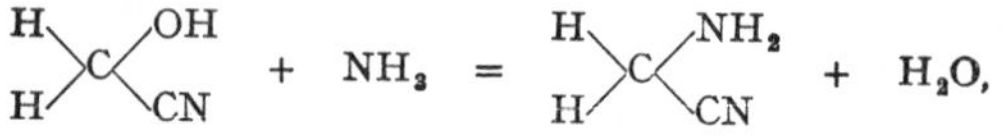

$$\underset{H}{\overset{H}{>}}C\underset{CN}{\overset{OH}{<}} \; + \; NH_3 \; = \; \underset{H}{\overset{H}{>}}C\underset{CN}{\overset{NH_2}{<}} \; + \; H_2O,$$

(iii) the amino-acetonitrile is hydrolysed to glycine,

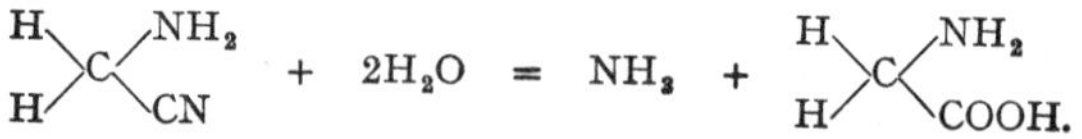

$$\underset{H}{\overset{H}{>}}C\underset{CN}{\overset{NH_2}{<}} \; + \; 2H_2O \; = \; NH_3 \; + \; \underset{H}{\overset{H}{>}}C\underset{COOH}{\overset{NH_2}{<}}.$$

Chemical properties of glycine.

1. Action of heat. When glycine is heated two molecules condense with the elimination of two molecules of water, to yield an anhydride,

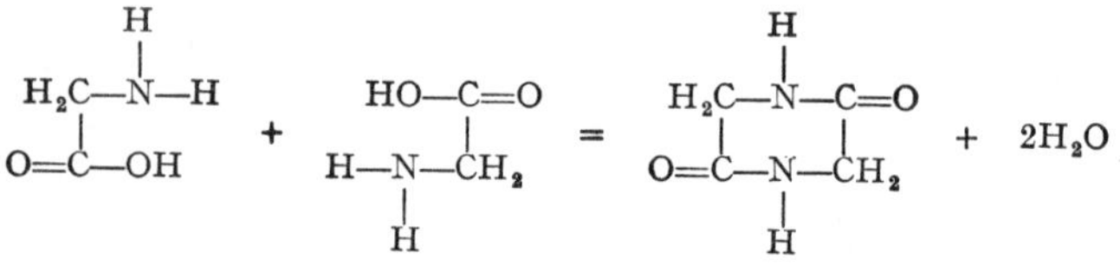

$$
\begin{array}{c}
H \\
| \\
H_2C-N-H \\
| \\
O=C-OH
\end{array}
\; + \;
\begin{array}{c}
HO-C=O \\
| \\
H-N-CH_2 \\
| \\
H
\end{array}
\; = \;
\begin{array}{c}
H \\
| \\
H_2C-N-C=O \\
| \qquad | \\
O=C-N-CH_2 \\
| \\
H
\end{array}
\; + \; 2H_2O
$$

This reaction resembles the production of glycollide from glycollic acid, and of lactide from lactic acid.

2. Decarboxylation. When glycine is heated with barium oxide, it yields monomethylamine,

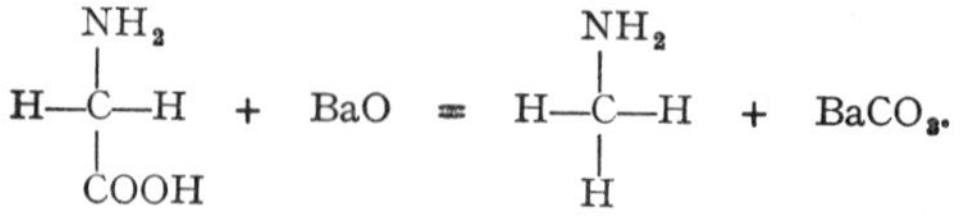

$$
\begin{array}{c}
NH_2 \\
| \\
H-C-H \\
| \\
COOH
\end{array}
\; + \; BaO \; = \;
\begin{array}{c}
NH_2 \\
| \\
H-C-H \\
| \\
H
\end{array}
\; + \; BaCO_3.
$$

This reaction is parallel to the formation of methane by the action of heat on a mixture of sodium acetate and soda-lime, p. 105.

3. Action with nitrous acid, giving glycollic acid. When a solution of sodium nitrite acidified with dilute acetic acid is added to glycine, nitrogen is set free, and glycollic acid is present in the solution,

$$\underset{\substack{| \\ \text{COOH}}}{\overset{\substack{\text{NH}_2 \\ |}}{\text{H—C—H}}} + \text{HONO} = \underset{\substack{| \\ \text{COOH}}}{\overset{\substack{\text{OH} \\ |}}{\text{H—C—H}}} + \text{N}_2 + \text{H}_2\text{O}.$$

4. Action with formaldehyde, giving methylene glycine.
When an aqueous solution of glycine is treated with an excess of a neutral solution of formaldehyde at room temperature, methylene glycine is obtained in solution, rapidly and quantitatively,

$$\underset{\substack{| \\ \text{COOH}}}{\overset{\substack{\text{H} \\ |}}{\text{H—C—NH}_2}} + \text{O=C} \diagup^{\text{H}}_{\diagdown \text{H}} = \underset{\substack{| \\ \text{COOH}}}{\overset{\substack{\text{H} \\ |}}{\text{H—C—N=C}}} \diagup^{\text{H}}_{\diagdown \text{H}}$$

Certain other aldehydes, including benzaldehyde, react similarly with glycine and other amino acids.

This reaction is important because it is the basis of *Sörenson's method* for estimating glycine in solution. An aqueous solution of glycine is neutral to litmus, and therefore it cannot be estimated by titration against sodium hydroxide solution. Methylene glycine, however, is an acid with a dissociation constant roughly equal to that of acetic acid ; it can be titrated against standard alkali solution, using phenolphthalein as indicator. If, therefore, a solution of glycine is treated with excess of formaldehyde solution, and the solution obtained is titrated against standard sodium hydroxide solution, using phenolphthalein as indicator, the titre of sodium hydroxide solution required for neutralisation is equivalent to the quantity of glycine in the solution originally taken.

5. Action with benzoyl chloride, C_6H_5COCl, to give a benzoyl derivative. If a solution of glycine in a dilute aqueous solution of sodium hydroxide is shaken with benzoyl chloride in a stoppered bottle, benzoyl glycine, $C_6H_5CO.NH.CH_2.COOH$, is formed, and is precipitated when the solution is acidified with hydrochloric acid. If 3 : 5 dinitrobenzoyl chloride is used instead of benzoyl chloride, the corresponding glycine derivative,

$$C_6H_3(NO_2)_2.CO.NH.CH_2.COOH,$$

is obtained. It may be crystallised from boiling water. M.P. 179°.

Tests for glycine. Glycine may be recognised by the formation of the dinitrobenzoyl derivative mentioned above, and by the deep blue colour which appears when a solution of glycine is treated with aqueous copper acetate solution, or with precipitated cupric hydroxide.

CHAPTER XVII

ALIPHATIC DIBASIC ACIDS AND THEIR DERIVATIVES

THIS chapter gives an account of carbonic acid, oxalic acid, malonic acid, succinic acid, tartaric acid, and their principal derivatives. All these acids are dibasic, but not all of them belong to the same homologous series.

Carbonic acid, $\begin{smallmatrix}HO\\HO\end{smallmatrix}\!\!>\!\!C{=}O$, is hydroxyformic acid. The acid itself is known only in aqueous solution, but it gives rise to the stable carbonates, which are usually classed as inorganic compounds. The amide of carbonic acid, urea, $\begin{smallmatrix}H_2N\\H_2N\end{smallmatrix}\!\!>\!\!C{=}O$, is an important compound in organic and physiological chemistry.

Oxalic acid, malonic acid and succinic acid are members of the oxalic acid series. Acids in this series are derived by the oxidation of two methyl groups in the molecule of a paraffin. The simplest member of the series is oxalic acid, which is derived by the oxidation of the two methyl groups in ethane. The relation of oxalic acid to ethane and to acetic acid is shown in the following scheme,

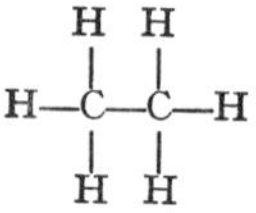

ethane 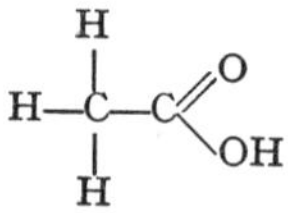   acetic acid 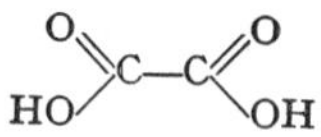   oxalic acid

Malonic acid and succinic acid are derived by the oxidation of the methyl groups in propane and normal butane respectively,

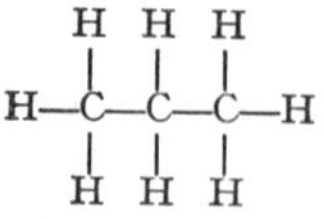

propane 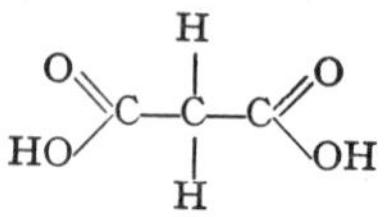   malonic acid

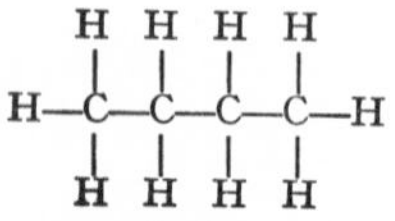

n-butane 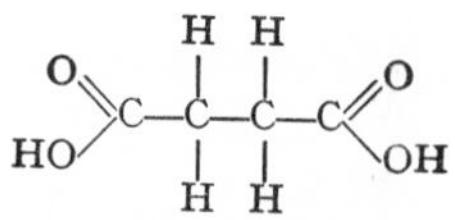   succinic acid

Members of the oxalic acid series are solids which melt, with decomposition, at temperatures approaching 200°. The lower members are readily soluble in water, but they are not volatile in steam. As the molecular weight rises, the acids become less soluble in water and more soluble in ether. With the exception of oxalic acid they are stable towards oxidising agents.

Tartaric acid, HOOC.CHOH.CHOH.COOH, is the dihydroxyl derivative of succinic acid.

UREA

Urea (carbamide) is the amide of carbonic acid,

$$\begin{matrix} HO \\ \diagdown \\ HO \diagup \end{matrix} C{=}O \qquad\qquad \begin{matrix} H_2N \\ \diagdown \\ H_2N \diagup \end{matrix} C{=}O$$

carbonic acid   urea

Urea crystallises in long colourless needles, M.P. 133°. It is soluble in water and in alcohol, but not in ether.

It occurs in the urine of mammals and certain birds and reptiles. It is probably the final decomposition product of the nitrogenous compounds which have taken part in the metabolism of these animals.

To isolate the urea, urine is concentrated and mixed with a hot solution of oxalic acid. Sparingly soluble urea oxalate crystallises and is filtered off. It is mixed with a boiling aqueous suspension of precipitated calcium carbonate which throws down insoluble calcium oxalate, and liberates urea in solution. The calcium oxalate is removed by filtration, and the filtrate is evaporated to dryness on a water-bath. The urea may be recrystallised from ethyl alcohol.

PRINCIPAL REACTIONS IN WHICH UREA IS OBTAINED

1. The action of potassium cyanate on ammonium sulphate. When ammonium cyanate is dissolved in water, it undergoes an intramolecular change by which part of it is converted to urea,

$$NH_4CNO \rightleftharpoons NH_2.CO.NH_2.$$

Equilibrium is reached when about 93 per cent. of the ammonium cyanate is changed to urea. On evaporation urea crystallises, and equilibrium in the solution is thus disturbed in favour of the transformation of more of the ammonium cyanate to urea. When dryness is reached, only urea is present in the residue.

Urea, therefore, may be obtained by evaporating to dryness an aqueous solution containing potassium cyanate and ammonium sulphate,

$$(NH_4)_2SO_4 + 2KCNO = 2NH_4CNO + K_2SO_4.$$

10 gm. of ammonium sulphate and 12 gm. of potassium cyanate are dissolved in 75 c.c. of water in a dish. The dish is placed on a water-bath, and the solution is intermittently stirred while it is evaporated completely to dryness. The solid residue is heated for 10 minutes with 40 c.c. of absolute alcohol in a flask fitted to a reflux condenser. The product is filtered hot, and the filtrate is cooled in ice-water. Colourless crystals of urea then separate.

Urea was first prepared synthetically by Wöhler in 1828. He passed cyanogen into ammonium hydroxide solution, expecting to obtain a mixture of ammonium cyanide and ammonium cyanate, but the product he obtained in fact was a mixture of ammonium cyanide and urea. By this preparation Wöhler demonstrated that an organic compound could be made from inorganic substances without the intervention of " vital force " (see p. 29). The relation between ammonium cyanate and urea, which are distinct compounds possessing identical molecular formulae, was the earliest recognised example of isomerism.

2. The action of ammonia on carbonyl chloride.

$$COCl_2 + 4NH_3 = CO(NH_2)_2 + 2NH_4Cl.$$

This reaction is parallel to that of ammonia on acetyl chloride by which acetamide is obtained, p. 248.

3. The action of dilute sulphuric acid on calcium cyanamide. Calcium cyanamide is obtained by heating calcium carbide with nitrogen to a very high temperature,

$$CaC_2 + N_2 = [N{\equiv}C{-}N]^{--}Ca^{++} + C.$$

In the presence of dilute sulphuric acid calcium cyanamide is hydrolysed to urea, thus,

$$[N{\equiv}C{-}N]^{--}Ca^{++} + 2H^+ + SO_4^{--} = N{\equiv}C{-}NH_2 + Ca^{++}SO_4^{--},$$
$$\text{cyanamide} *$$
$$N{\equiv}C{-}NH_2 + H_2O = H_2N.CO.NH_2.$$

Industrial preparation of urea. Urea is made industrially by the direct action of ammonia on carbon dioxide in the presence of a catalyst at a temperature of about 150°, and a pressure of 70 atmospheres,

$$CO_2 + 2NH_3 = CO(NH_2)_2 + H_2O.$$

CHEMICAL PROPERTIES OF UREA

1. The action of heat on urea. When urea is heated in a test-tube it first fuses, and then decomposes either (i) in accordance with the equation,

$$NH_2.CO.NH_2 = NH_3 + HNCO,$$

* Cyanamide is the amide of cyanic acid, $N{\equiv}C{-}O{-}H$.

yielding ammonia which escapes, and cyanuric acid (a polymer of isocyanic acid, HCNO) which condenses as a sublimate on the cool parts of the tube, or (ii) in accordance with the equation,

$$NH_2.CO.\boxed{NH_2 + H}NH.CO.NH_2 = NH_2.CO.NH.CO.NH_2 + NH_3,$$

yielding ammonia, and biuret which remains as a solid in the tube. If a few drops of an aqueous solution of copper sulphate are added to biuret dissolved in dilute sodium hydroxide solution, a pink coloration is obtained. This pink coloration is given when copper sulphate solution is added to an alkaline solution of a compound which contains in the molecule two —CO—NH— groups linked either to one another, or to the same carbon atom, or to the same nitrogen atom ; among such compounds are the proteins and the peptides, oxamide and malonamide.

2. Action with acids and alkalis. Urea, although its aqueous solution is neutral to litmus, behaves as a weak monacid base in the presence of acids. Urea nitrate, $CO(NH_2)_2.HNO_3$, separates as white crystals when concentrated nitric acid is added to an aqueous solution of urea. Urea oxalate, $2CO(NH_2)_2.(COOH)_2,2H_2O$, is prepared by adding a solution of oxalic acid to a solution of urea. Urea combines with certain metallic oxides and salts to give compounds of which $CO(NH_2)_2.2HgO$, $CO(NH_2)_2.NaCl$ and $CO(NH_2)_2.AgNO_3$ are examples.

3. Action with alkalis ; hydrolysis. When treated with sodium hydroxide solution, urea is hydrolysed to ammonia and sodium carbonate,

$$CO(NH_2)_2 \quad + \quad 2NaOH \quad = \quad 2NH_3 \quad + \quad Na_2CO_3.$$

The reaction proceeds slowly in the cold and rapidly if the solution is heated.

The enzyme urease (which is present in the soya bean) converts urea quantitatively to ammonium carbonate,

$$CO(NH_2)_2 \quad + \quad 2H_2O \quad = \quad (NH_4)_2CO_3.$$

This reaction is used for the accurate estimation of urea in solution.

4. Action with sodium hypobromite. An alkaline solution of sodium hypobromite oxidises urea to nitrogen and carbon dioxide which combines with the sodium hydroxide to form sodium carbonate,

$$CO(NH_2)_2 + 3NaBrO + 2NaOH = Na_2CO_3 + N_2 + 3H_2O + 3NaBr.$$

In practice it is found that the volume of nitrogen evolved is 2–8 per cent. less than the volume calculated from this equation.*

5. Action with nitrous acid. Urea reacts with nitrous acid in the presence of mineral acids to yield nitrogen and carbon dioxide,

$$CO(NH_2)_2 + 2HONO = CO_2 + 2N_2 + 3H_2O.$$

The volume of nitrogen which is evolved, however, is about 30 per cent. less than that calculated from the equation.*

6. Action with dibasic acids to form ureides. If urea is heated at 100° with malonic acid and phosphorus oxychloride, malonylurea, or barbituric acid, is obtained,

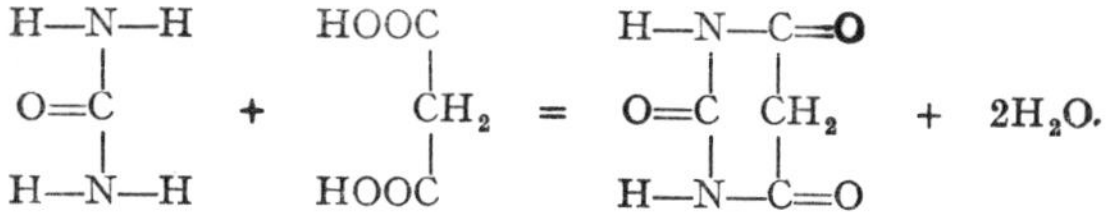

Barbituric acid belongs to the class of compounds known as ureides. The following derivatives of barbituric acid are important hypnotics:

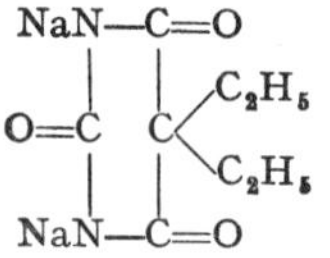

veronal 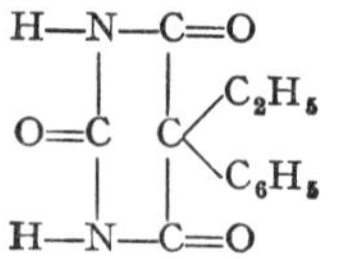   luminal

* No wholly satisfactory explanations of the anomalous reactions of urea with sodium hypobromite and nitrous acid have been put forward. It has been suggested, to explain the low yield of nitrogen, that urea in solution may exist in equilibrium either with ammonium cyanate, thus,

$$CO(NH_2)_2 \rightleftharpoons NH_4CNO$$

or with an isomeric imino compound, thus,

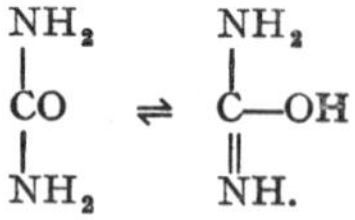

These suggestions are open to the objection that any diminution of the concentration of urea in the solution brought about by oxidation would at once be followed by a reversion of some of the other isomer in order to maintain the equilibrium. This process would continue until all the other isomeric compounds in solution had been converted to urea, and oxidised to nitrogen and carbon dioxide. The existence of such equilibria as those suggested, therefore, would have no effect on the yield of nitrogen from a given quantity of urea.

Some authors hold that the low yield of nitrogen is explained by the conversion of part of the urea to hydrazine. There is considerable evidence that hydrazine is formed when urea is decomposed by sodium hypobromite. If benzaldehyde is present the hydrazone is precipitated. If the reaction is carried out at 0° with only one equivalent of sodium hypobromite, hydrazine is the chief product. Hydrazine, however, is very easily oxidised to nitrogen and water, and it appears unlikely that it could exist in the presence of *excess* of sodium hypobromite.

Uses of urea. Urea is used as a fertiliser. A mixture of urea and thiourea $(CS(NH_2)_2)$ reacts with formaldehyde to produce the plastic *beetle ware*.

Tests for urea

1. **The biuret test.** A small quantity of urea is gently heated in a test-tube until it melts, and the melt re-solidifies. The residue is dissolved in warm sodium hydroxide solution, and 1 drop of dilute copper sulphate solution is added. A pink coloration is obtained. Among other compounds which respond to this test are oxamide and malonamide, see p. 285.

2. **The urease test.** This test depends on the development of alkalinity in a solution of urea treated with urease, which brings about the conversion of urea to ammonium carbonate. The urease test is absolutely specific. 0·2 gm. of urea is dissolved in 5 c.c. of water and 5 drops of the indicator phenol-red and 1 drop of dilute hydrochloric acid are added. The solution is made exactly neutral (pH 7) as follows : It is divided into two portions. To one portion very dilute sodium hydroxide is added until the colour is just red ; the second portion is then added to it until the colour is exactly discharged. This solution is then mixed with 0·1 gm. of jack bean meal in 2 c.c. of water and 5 drops of phenol-red. The mixed solution is allowed to stand at room temperature. The presence of urea is indicated by change of the indicator colour to red.

OXALIC ACID

Oxalic acid crystallises in transparent monoclinic prisms with two molecules of water of crystallisation. The M.P. of the crystals is 101°. The crystals slowly effloresce in air, and water of crystallisation is lost on heating. The hydrated acid becomes anhydrous when carefully heated at 150°. The anhydrous acid sublimes unchanged at slightly higher temperatures, but at 185° it melts with decomposition. The anhydrous acid is hygroscopic and is sometimes used as a dehydrating agent. Oxalic acid is readily soluble in water, moderately soluble in alcohol, and sparingly soluble in ether.

PRINCIPAL REACTIONS IN WHICH OXALIC ACID IS PRODUCED

1. **The hydrolysis of cyanogen.** Ammonium oxalate is present in an aqueous solution of cyanogen which has been standing for some time,

$$\begin{matrix} C\equiv N \\ | \\ C\equiv N \end{matrix} \quad + \quad 4H_2O \quad = \quad \begin{matrix} COONH_4 \\ | \\ COONH_4 \end{matrix}$$

To isolate the free acid, calcium chloride is added to the solution, to precipitate insoluble calcium oxalate. This is filtered off and heated with the requisite quantity of dilute sulphuric acid, which precipitates calcium sulphate, leaving oxalic acid in solution. The calcium sulphate is removed by filtration, the solution is concentrated by evaporation, and the oxalic acid is crystallised.

2. The action of heat on sodium formate. If sodium formate is heated to 390°, hydrogen is evolved and sodium oxalate remains,

$$\begin{matrix} \text{H.COONa} \\ \text{H.COONa} \end{matrix} = \begin{matrix} \text{COONa} \\ | \\ \text{COONa} \end{matrix} + \text{H}_2.$$

Oxalic acid is obtained from sodium oxalate by dissolving it in water, precipitating calcium oxalate, and then proceeding as under Reaction 1.

3. The action of metallic sodium on carbon dioxide under pressure. If metallic sodium is heated with carbon dioxide in a closed vessel to 360° under pressure, sodium oxalate is obtained,

$$2\text{CO}_2 + 2\text{Na} = \begin{matrix} \text{COONa} \\ | \\ \text{COONa.} \end{matrix}$$

4. Oxidation of sucrose. If sucrose (cane sugar, $C_{12}H_{22}O_{11}$) is dissolved in warm concentrated nitric acid, a vigorous reaction occurs with the evolution of copious brown fumes of nitrogen peroxide. When the reaction is over, oxalic acid remains in solution, from which it may be crystallised after the excess of nitric acid has been removed by evaporation. Further details of the procedure are given under " laboratory preparation ". The reaction cannot be represented by a simple equation. It should be noted that aliphatic compounds frequently undergo oxidation by concentrated nitric acid, in such a way that the molecules break down into pairs of carbon atoms yielding oxalic acid. Alcohol, glycol, sugars, fats, and cellulose all undergo this type of oxidation.

5. The action of potassium hydroxide on cellulose. Potassium oxalate is obtained by heating cellulose in the form of sawdust with potassium hydroxide in flat iron pans to 200°. The potassium oxalate is extracted with water, and oxalic acid may be obtained from the solution by precipitating calcium oxalate as explained under Reaction 1 above.

Laboratory preparation of oxalic acid. In the laboratory oxalic acid is most conveniently prepared by the action of concentrated nitric acid on cane sugar. The reaction should be carried out in a good fume-cupboard. 30 gm. of coarsely powdered cane sugar are placed in a 750 c.c. flat-bottomed flask, and 150 c.c. of concentrated nitric acid are added. The flask is warmed on a water-bath until the reaction starts, when it is removed and placed on a wooden block. When the evolution of brown fumes has ceased, the contents of the flask are poured into an evaporating dish, and the flask is washed out with 20 c.c. of nitric acid which is added to the solution in the dish. The dish is heated on the water-bath until the volume of solution is reduced to 25 c.c. 50 c.c. of water are added and the solution is again evaporated until only 25 c.c. are left. The solution is cooled in ice-water when crystals of oxalic acid, $(COOH)_2,2H_2O$, separate. The crystals may be filtered at the pump, recrystallised from a little hot water, and dried between sheets of drying paper. They lose water of crystallisation if heated.

Industrial preparation. Oxalic acid is made on a large scale from sodium formate (p. 487). The method of heating sawdust with fused sodium hydroxide was once used, but it is now obsolete.

CHEMICAL PROPERTIES AND CONSTITUTION OF OXALIC ACID

1. Acid properties. Oxalic acid is a moderately strong dibasic acid which neutralises alkalis to form salts,

$$\begin{matrix} COOH \\ | \\ COOH \end{matrix} + 2NaOH = \begin{matrix} COONa \\ | \\ COONa \end{matrix} + 2H_2O.$$

Oxalic acid also forms the well-defined acid salts, potassium binoxalate, COOH.COOK, and potassium quadroxalate,

$$\begin{matrix} COOK \, COOH \\ | \quad\;\; | \\ COOH,COOH \end{matrix}, \; 2H_2O.$$

Anhydrous oxalic acid combines directly with ethyl alcohol, without the presence of a catalyst, to yield diethyl oxalate,

$$\begin{matrix} COOH \\ | \\ COOH \end{matrix} + 2C_2H_5OH = \begin{matrix} COOC_2H_5 \\ | \\ COOC_2H_5 \end{matrix} + 2H_2O.$$

2. Action of heat. When heated to about 180°, oxalic acid decomposes, yielding carbon dioxide, carbon monoxide, steam, and formic acid. It is probable that the oxalic acid first breaks down into carbon dioxide and formic acid,

$$COOH.COOH = CO_2 + H.COOH,$$

and that some of the formic acid is dehydrated by the unchanged oxalic acid to yield carbon monoxide and steam,

$$H.COOH = CO + H_2O.$$

3. Action with hot sulphuric acid. When oxalic acid is warmed above 95° with concentrated sulphuric acid it decomposes

K   D.C.

into carbon dioxide, carbon monoxide and steam ; there is no charring,

$$COOH.COOH = CO_2 + CO + H_2O.$$

4. Action with hot glycerol. When crystalline oxalic acid is heated with anhydrous glycerol to about 120° it yields a mixture of formic acid, carbon dioxide and steam. The glycerol and oxalic acid first produce glyceryl monoxalate, which loses carbon dioxide to form glyceryl monoformate, which is then hydrolysed to formic acid with the regeneration of glycerol. The equations for these reactions, and the appropriate experimental conditions, have been set out in the description of the preparation of formic acid on p. 240, where it is mentioned that the hydrolysis of the glyceryl monoformate is not completed unless steam is blown into the mixture.

If the glyceryl monoformate is not hydrolysed by steam distillation, but is heated to 220°, it decomposes into allyl alcohol, carbon dioxide and steam according to the equation,

$$
\begin{array}{ccc}
\overset{\displaystyle OH}{\underset{\displaystyle |}{}} & & \overset{\displaystyle OH}{\underset{\displaystyle |}{}} \\
H{-}C{-}H & & H{-}C{-}H \\
| & & | \\
H{-}C{-}OH & = & H{-}C \\
| & & \parallel \\
H{-}C{-}O{-}C{\overset{\displaystyle O}{\diagdown H}} & & C \\
| & & H{\diagup}{\diagdown}H \\
H & &
\end{array}
\quad + \quad CO_2 \quad + \quad H_2O.
$$

5. Oxidation. Oxalic acid is not oxidised either by nitric acid or by chlorine ; it is not attacked by alkaline potassium permanganate solution at all in the cold, and only very slowly on warming. In aqueous solution at 60° in the presence of dilute sulphuric acid it is oxidised quantitatively by potassium permanganate or by manganese dioxide, to carbon dioxide and water,

$$2KMnO_4 + 5(COOH)_2 + 3H_2SO_4$$
$$= K_2SO_4 + MnSO_4 + 10CO_2 + 8H_2O.$$

6. Reduction. Oxalic acid is reduced by nascent hydrogen to glycollic acid,

$$
\begin{array}{l}
COOH \\
| \\
COOH
\end{array}
+ 2H_2 =
\begin{array}{c}
H \\
| \\
H{-}C{-}OH \\
| \\
COOH
\end{array}
+ H_2O.
$$

This is one of the exceptions to the rule that the carboxyl group is not attacked by reducing agents.

7. Oxalic acid and its soluble salts are *poisonous*.

Constitution of oxalic acid. The empirical formula of oxalic acid is CHO_2. The molecular weight cannot be determined by vapour density methods because the anhydrous acid decomposes when heated. The determination of the molecular weight by the method of analysis of the silver salt is also not applicable to oxalic acid, because the silver salt decomposes so violently on heating that loss of silver from the crucible is almost bound to occur. The molecular weight of ethyl oxalate, B.P. 186°, is found to be 146 ; this is the value that would be expected if oxalic were a dibasic acid, and the ethyl ester were formed from it by the replacement of the two hydrogen atoms by ethyl groups. This evidence suggests that the molecular formula of oxalic acid is $C_2H_2O_4$.

The principal evidence for the constitution of oxalic acid is afforded by its relation to ethylene dibromide, the structure of which is established by Reaction 1, p. 149. Ethylene dibromide is hydrolysed by boiling for several hours with aqueous potassium carbonate solution to ethylene glycol,

$$
\begin{array}{c} CH_2Br \\ | \\ CH_2Br \end{array} + K_2CO_3 + H_2O = \begin{array}{c} CH_2OH \\ | \\ CH_2OH \end{array} + 2KBr + CO_2.
$$

If ethylene glycol is oxidised with nitric acid, oxalic acid is obtained,

$$
\begin{array}{c} CH_2OH \\ | \\ CH_2OH \end{array} + 2O_2 = \begin{array}{c} C {\nearrow}^O {\searrow}_{OH} \\ | \\ C {\nearrow}^{OH} {\searrow}_O \end{array} + 2H_2O.
$$

The molecule of oxalic acid, therefore, consists of two carboxyl groups linked by a single covalent bond between the carbon atoms.

Tests for oxalic acid. Oxalic acid may be recognised by the following tests :

1. When oxalic acid is warmed with concentrated sulphuric acid a mixture of carbon dioxide and carbon monoxide is evolved without any charring.

2. A warm solution of potassium permanganate containing sulphuric acid is decolorised by oxalic acid, but alkaline potassium permanganate solution is not decolorised at all in the cold. (This test distinguishes oxalic acid from formic acid.)

3. Calcium chloride solution, when added to a neutral solution of an oxalate, gives a white precipitate of calcium oxalate, which is insoluble in acetic acid but is soluble in dilute hydrochloric acid.

4. Oxalic acid does not reduce mercuric chloride solution or ammoniacal silver oxide solution.

SALTS AND DERIVATIVES OF OXALIC ACID

Potassium oxalate. Normal potassium oxalate crystallises as the monohydrate, COOK.COOK, H_2O. Oxalic acid also forms acid salts with potassium. Potassium binoxalate COOK.COOH occurs naturally in Oxalis Acetosella (wood-sorrel), and in the roots and leaves of rhubarb. Potassium quadroxalate

$$\begin{matrix} COOK & COOH \\ | & | \\ COOH, & COOH \end{matrix}, 2H_2O$$

is known in commerce as " salt of sorrel ". All these potassium salts dissolve in water (the acid salts more readily than the normal) and the solutions exhibit many of the reactions of oxalic acid. Potassium quadroxalate is used in removing iron mould and ink stains, as it converts iron compounds into soluble potassium ferrous oxalate. It is also used in quantitative analysis for standardising potassium permanganate solution. *Potassium ferrous oxalate,*

$$\begin{matrix} COO & COOK \\ | & Fe, | \\ COO & COOK \end{matrix}, H_2O$$

is a reducing agent which is used as a photographic developer.

Silver oxalate,

$$\begin{matrix} COOAg \\ | \\ COOAg, \end{matrix}$$

separates as a sparingly soluble white precipitate when silver nitrate is added to a neutral solution of an oxalate. It explodes when rapidly heated, leaving a residue of silver.

Calcium oxalate,

$$\begin{matrix} COO \\ | & Ca, H_2O, \\ COO \end{matrix}$$

separates as an insoluble white precipitate when neutral calcium chloride solution is added to a neutral or ammoniacal solution of an oxalate. It is insoluble in acetic acid, but soluble in dilute hydrochloric acid.

Ammonium oxalate,

$$\begin{matrix} COONH_4 \\ | & H_2O, \\ COONH_4 \end{matrix}$$

yields oxamide when carefully heated alone,

$$\begin{matrix} O=C-ONH_4 \\ | \\ O=C-ONH_4 \end{matrix} = \begin{matrix} O=C-NH_2 \\ | \\ O=C-NH_2 \end{matrix} + 2H_2O.$$

When it is heated with phosphorus pentoxide, the oxamide decomposes yielding cyanogen.

Diethyl oxalate and *dimethyl oxalate* are made by distilling the product formed when anhydrous oxalic acid is heated with ethyl alcohol or methyl alcohol respectively. These reactions proceed without the assistance of a catalyst,

$$\begin{matrix} COOH \\ | \\ COOH \end{matrix} \;+\; 2C_2H_5OH \;=\; \begin{matrix} COOC_2H_5 \\ | \\ COOC_2H_5 \end{matrix} \;+\; 2H_2O$$

Diethyl oxalate is a liquid, B.P. 186°. It is sparingly soluble in water. Dimethyl oxalate is one of the methyl esters of organic acids which are solid at room temperature. It crystallises in plates, M.P. 54°, B.P. 162°. It is freely soluble in water, but is readily hydrolysed by water to methyl alcohol and oxalic acid. Both diethyl oxalate and dimethyl oxalate are converted to an insoluble precipitate of *oxamide* on shaking with aqueous ammonia solution in a corked flask,

$$\begin{matrix} O{=}C{-}OC_2H_5 \\ | \\ O{=}C{-}OC_2H_5 \end{matrix} \;+\; 2NH_3 \;=\; \begin{matrix} O{=}C{-}NH_2 \\ | \\ O{=}C{-}NH_2 \end{matrix} \;+\; 2HOC_2H_5.$$

Oxamide can also be obtained by carefully heating ammonium oxalate. It is very sparingly soluble both in water and in organic solvents. It sublimes on heating, and has no definite melting point.

Oxamide is hydrolysed by a hot aqueous solution of sodium hydroxide to sodium oxalate and ammonia,

$$\begin{matrix} O{=}C{-}NH_2 \\ | \\ O{=}C{-}NH_2 \end{matrix} \;+\; 2NaOH \;=\; \begin{matrix} O{=}C{-}ONa \\ | \\ O{=}C{-}ONa \end{matrix} \;+\; 2NH_3.$$

Oxamide is also hydrolysed when warmed with concentrated sulphuric acid, but the oxalic acid which is set free is immediately decomposed by the sulphuric acid to carbon monoxide and carbon dioxide, which, with ammonium sulphate, are the ultimate products of the reaction,

$$\begin{matrix} O{=}C{-}NH_2 \\ | \\ O{=}C{-}NH_2 \end{matrix} \;+\; H_2O \;+\; H_2SO_4 \;=\; (NH_4)_2SO_4 \;+\; CO_2 \;+\; CO.$$

If oxamide is treated with an aqueous solution of sodium nitrite acidified with dilute acetic acid, nitrogen is evolved and oxalic acid is left in solution,

$$\begin{matrix} O{=}C{-}NH_2 \\ | \\ O{=}C{-}NH_2 \end{matrix} \;+\; 2HONO \;=\; \begin{matrix} O{=}C{-}OH \\ | \\ O{=}C{-}OH \end{matrix} \;+\; 2N_2 \;+\; 2H_2O.$$

When heated with phosphorus pentoxide, oxamide loses the elements of water and is converted to cyanogen,

$$\begin{matrix} O{=}C{-}NH_2 \\ | \\ O{=}C{-}NH_2 \end{matrix} \quad = \quad \begin{matrix} C{\equiv}N \\ | \\ C{\equiv}N \end{matrix} \quad + \quad 2H_2O.$$

If a small quantity of oxamide is shaken with 10 per cent. sodium hydroxide solution and a few drops of very dilute copper sulphate solution are added, a rose-pink colour is produced. This is an example of the biuret reaction described on p. 287.

MALONIC ACID

Malonic acid crystallises in colourless plates which melt, with decomposition, at 132°. It is readily soluble in water, alcohol and ether.

Preparation of malonic acid. Malonic acid is made by hydro-lysing sodium cyanoacetate with excess of concentrated hydro-chloric acid. The cyanide group is converted to the carboxyl group in accordance with the equation,

$$H_2C\begin{matrix}\diagup CN \\ \diagdown COONa\end{matrix} \quad + \quad 2H_2O \quad + \quad 2HCl$$

$$= \quad H_2C\begin{matrix}\diagup COOH \\ \diagdown COOH\end{matrix} \quad + \quad NH_4Cl \quad + \quad NaCl.$$

The starting-point for the laboratory preparation of malonic acid is monochloroacetic acid. 30 gm. of monochloroacetic acid are mixed with 60 gm. of water in an evaporating dish, and warmed to 55°. Powdered sodium bicarbonate (about 30 gm.) is added until the contents of the dish are just alkaline to litmus. The monochloroacetic acid is thus con-verted to its sodium salt. 24 gm. of powdered potassium cyanide are then added to the solution in the dish, and the temperature is allowed to rise to 90–95°. A vigorous effervescence occurs, and the sodium chloroacetate is converted to sodium cyanoacetate,

$$CH_2Cl.COONa \quad + \quad KCN \quad = \quad CH_2CN.COONa \quad + \quad KCl.$$

The contents of the dish are heated to 135°, and maintained at this temperature for 5 minutes to drive off the water. The dish is allowed to cool, and the solid mixture of potassium chloride and sodium cyano-acetate is chipped out and placed in a conical flask. Excess of hydro-chloric acid is added, and the solution is saturated with gaseous hydrogen chloride. The hydrochloric acid hydrolyses the sodium cyanoacetate to malonic acid, according to the equation given above, and precipitates the sodium and potassium chlorides by common ion action. The clear liquid is decanted from the precipitate, evaporated to dryness on a water-bath, and the malonic acid is obtained from the residue by extraction with ether.

Properties of malonic acid. Malonic acid exhibits the normal properties of a dibasic acid in forming salts and esters. Its most important reaction is its decomposition, when heated above its melting point, into acetic acid and carbon dioxide,

$$H_2C{<}^{COOH}_{COOH} = H_3C.COOH + CO_2.$$

This is an example of a reaction common to all dibasic acids in which the two carboxyl groups are linked to the same carbon atom ; when such an acid is heated, either alone, or in aqueous solution to about 150°, carbon dioxide is eliminated, and a monobasic acid is formed. Further reference to this reaction is made on p. 465.

Diethyl malonate is an important reagent in the synthesis of organic compounds. It is made directly from chloroacetic acid without the isolation of malonic acid. The preparation and properties of diethyl malonate (ethyl malonate) are described on p. 465.

SUCCINIC ACID

Succinic acid is a crystalline solid, M.P. 185°. It crystallises without water of crystallisation. It is sparingly soluble in water, alcohol, and ether. It has an unpleasant taste.

Occurrence and preparation of succinic acid. Succinic acid occurs naturally in amber and in certain plants and animal secretions. If the dark brown oil which is obtained by the distillation of amber is evaporated, a residue of succinic acid is obtained, which may be recrystallised from hot dilute nitric acid.

Succinic acid may be prepared synthetically from ethylene dibromide. Ethylene dibromide is boiled with potassium cyanide in aqueous alcoholic solution, and ethylene dicyanide is formed,

$$\begin{matrix} CH_2Br \\ | \\ CH_2Br \end{matrix} + 2KCN = \begin{matrix} CH_2CN \\ | \\ CH_2CN \end{matrix} + 2KBr.$$

The ethylene dicyanide is then decomposed by hydrolysis with concentrated hydrochloric acid to yield succinic acid and ammonium chloride,

$$\begin{matrix} CH_2.CN \\ | \\ CH_2.CN \end{matrix} + 4H_2O + 2HCl = \begin{matrix} CH_2.COOH \\ | \\ CH_2.COOH \end{matrix} + 2NH_4Cl.$$

Chemical properties of succinic acid. It reacts with alkalis to form succinates, thus

$$\begin{matrix} CH_2.COOH \\ | \\ CH_2.COOH \end{matrix} + 2NaOH = \begin{matrix} CH_2.COONa \\ | \\ CH_2.COONa \end{matrix} + 2H_2O;$$

it may be used as a standard acid in volumetric analysis.

Succinic acid reacts with phosphorus pentachloride to form an acid chloride, succinyl chloride,

$$CH_2.COCl$$
$$|$$
$$CH_2.COCl.$$

It forms acid and neutral esters of the types

$$HOOC.CH_2.CH_2.COOC_2H_5 \text{ and } C_2H_5OOC.CH_2.CH_2.COOC_2H_5$$

respectively. When diethyl succinate is shaken with a concentrated solution of ammonia, a crystalline precipitate of succinamide is obtained. On distillation in a current of ammonia, succinamide yields *succinimide*,

$$\begin{array}{c} CH_2.CONH_2 \\ | \\ CH_2.CONH_2 \end{array} = \begin{array}{c} CH_2.C{=}O \\ | \quad \rangle NH \\ CH_2.C{=}O \end{array} + NH_3.$$

This compound is also obtained when ammonium succinate is distilled.

Succinimide, M.P. 126°, is freely soluble in water. When boiled with water, dilute sulphuric acid or sodium hydroxide, it is hydrolysed to succinic acid, or sodium succinate, with the liberation of ammonia,

$$\begin{array}{c} CH_2.C{=}O \\ | \quad \rangle NH \\ CH_2.C{=}O \end{array} + 2NaOH = \begin{array}{c} CH_2.COONa \\ | \\ CH_2.COONa \end{array} + NH_3.$$

Imides are formed from the amides of dicarboxylic acids in which the carboxyl groups are attached to adjacent carbon atoms. Phthalimide, p. 279, is another example of this class of compound.

Succinic anhydride,

$$\begin{array}{c} CH_2.C{=}O \\ | \quad \rangle O \\ CH_2.C{=}O \end{array}$$

M.P. 120°, is formed when succinic acid is distilled. It is most conveniently made by treating succinic acid with acetic anhydride. The chemical properties of succinic anhydride are similar to those of the anhydrides of the monobasic acids. Anhydrides which are formed by the loss of one molecule of water from *one* molecule of the parent acid, and therefore possess a ring structure like that of succinic anhydride, are known as " inner anhydrides ".

TARTARIC ACID

Tartaric acid is derived from succinic acid by the replacement of one hydrogen atom in each of the two methylene groups in the molecule by a hydroxyl group, thus,

$$\begin{array}{cc} \overset{\text{H}}{\underset{|}{\text{H}}}\ \overset{\text{H}}{\underset{|}{\text{H}}} & \overset{\text{OH}}{\underset{|}{}}\ \overset{\text{OH}}{\underset{|}{}} \\ \text{HOOC--C--C--COOH} & \text{HOOC--C----C--COOH} \\ \underset{\text{H}}{|}\ \underset{\text{H}}{|} & \underset{\text{H}}{|}\ \ \underset{\text{H}}{|} \end{array}$$

succinic acid   tartaric acid

Tartaric acid exhibits the phenomenon of optical isomerism. This subject is discussed in Chapter XVIII where the relations of the various isomeric forms of tartaric acid to one another are explained. In this chapter the general chemistry of tartaric acid is described without reference to its optical isomerism. It is sufficient for the present purpose to note :

(i) that there are four modifications of tartaric acid : dextro-, laevo-, meso-, and racemic ;

(ii) that the modification of tartaric acid obtained from grape juice is dextro-tartaric acid, and that the modification prepared in the laboratory by the methods given below is a mixture of the meso- and the racemic modifications ;

(iii) that the chemical properties of the four modifications of tartaric acid are identical, although their physical properties may differ.

Tartaric acid is a crystalline solid which is readily soluble in water and alcohol, but insoluble in ether. It occurs naturally in grapes and other fruits. Argol is a deposit of impure potassium hydrogen tartrate which is formed during the fermentation of grape juice.

PRINCIPAL REACTIONS IN WHICH TARTARIC ACID IS PRODUCED

1. The hydrolysis of dibromosuccinic acid. Dibromosuccinic acid is made by treating succinic acid with bromine in the presence of red phosphorus,

$$\begin{array}{ccc} \text{CH}_2.\text{COOH} & & \text{CHBr.COOH} \\ | & +\ 2\text{Br}_2\ = & | & +\ 2\text{HBr}. \\ \text{CH}_2.\text{COOH} & & \text{CHBr.COOH} \end{array}$$

The dibromosuccinic acid is then heated with moist silver oxide,

$$\begin{array}{ccc} \text{CHBr.COOH} & & \text{CH.OH.COOH} \\ | & +\ 2\text{AgOH}\ = & | & +\ 2\text{AgBr}, \\ \text{CHBr.COOH} & & \text{CH.OH.COOH} \end{array}$$

and tartaric acid and silver bromide are formed,

2. The hydrolysis of glyoxal dicyanhydrin. Glyoxal combines directly with hydrogen cyanide to form glyoxal dicyanhydrin,

$$\begin{array}{ccc} \overset{\text{O}}{\underset{\|}{}}\ \overset{\text{O}}{\underset{\|}{}} & & \overset{\text{OH}}{\underset{|}{}}\ \overset{\text{OH}}{\underset{|}{}} \\ \text{C--C} & +\ 2\text{HCN}\ = & \text{NC--C----C--CN}. \\ \underset{\text{H}}{|}\ \underset{\text{H}}{|} & & \underset{\text{H}}{|}\ \ \underset{\text{H}}{|} \end{array}$$

If glyoxal dicyanhydrin is boiled with hydrochloric acid, it is hydrolysed to tartaric acid and ammonium chloride,

$$
\begin{array}{l}
\text{H.C.OH.CN} \\
| \\
\text{H.C.OH.CN}
\end{array}
+ \; 2\text{HCl} \; + \; 4\text{H}_2\text{O} \; =
\begin{array}{l}
\text{H.C.OH.COOH} \\
| \\
\text{H.C.OH.COOH}
\end{array}
+ \; 2\text{NH}_4\text{Cl.}
$$

3. Oxidation of maleic and fumaric acids. Maleic and fumaric acids are geometrical isomerides (p. 315). On oxidation with potassium permanganate solution in the presence of sodium carbonate, maleic acid is oxidised to mesotartaric acid, and fumaric acid is oxidised to racemic acid. Both these reactions are illustrated by the equation,

$$
\begin{array}{l}
\text{CH.COOH} \\
\| \\
\text{CH.COOH}
\end{array}
+ \; 2\text{O} \; =
\begin{array}{l}
\text{CH.OH.COOH} \\
| \\
\text{CH.OH.COOH,}
\end{array}
$$

which does not take into account the particular isomeric forms of the molecules taking part. The formation of tartaric acid by the oxidation of maleic and fumaric acids is discussed more fully on p. 318.

4. Industrial preparation of tartaric acid from argol. Argol is impure potassium hydrogen tartrate which is deposited during the fermentation of grape-juice. Argol, which is insoluble in water, is dissolved in boiling hydrochloric acid, and the solution is nearly neutralised with milk of lime. The calcium hydroxide first neutralises the excess of hydrochloric acid, and then reacts with the potassium hydrogen tartrate to precipitate insoluble calcium tartrate while normal potassium tartrate remains in solution,

$$
2
\begin{array}{l}
\text{CH.OH.COOK} \\
| \\
\text{CH.OH.COOH}
\end{array}
+ \; \text{Ca(OH)}_2
$$

$$
=
\begin{array}{l}
\text{CH.OH.COOK} \\
| \\
\text{CH.OH.COOK}
\end{array}
+
\begin{array}{l}
\text{CH.OH.COO} \\
| \\
\text{CH.OH.COO}
\end{array}\!\!\!\!\Big\rangle\text{Ca} \; + \; 2\text{H}_2\text{O.}
$$

The calcium tartrate is separated by filtration, and calcium chloride is added to the filtrate to precipitate calcium tartrate from the normal potassium tartrate,

$$
\begin{array}{l}
\text{CH.OH.COOK} \\
| \\
\text{CH.OH.COOK}
\end{array}
+ \; \text{CaCl}_2 \; =
\begin{array}{l}
\text{CH.OH.COO} \\
| \\
\text{CH.OH.COO}
\end{array}\!\!\!\!\Big\rangle\text{Ca} \; + \; 2\text{KCl.}
$$

This precipitate of calcium tartrate is also collected by filtration. The calcium tartrate from both precipitations is washed with water, and treated with the requisite quantity of dilute sulphuric acid which precipitates calcium sulphate and liberates tartaric acid in solution. The calcium sulphate is removed by filtration, and the solution of tartaric acid is concentrated by evaporation, and crystallised.

CHEMICAL PROPERTIES AND CONSTITUTION OF TARTARIC ACID

Properties. When tartaric acid is heated above 170° it decomposes into a variety of other compounds and free carbon. When heated with concentrated sulphuric acid it also deposits free carbon very rapidly, and a mixture of carbon monoxide, carbon dioxide and sulphur dioxide is evolved from the hot solution.

Tartaric acid is a dibasic acid and gives rise to many well-known normal and acid salts, some of which are described below.

When heated with concentrated hydrobromic acid, tartaric acid yields dibromosuccinic acid,

$$\begin{array}{c} CH.OH.COOH \\ | \\ CH.OH.COOH \end{array} + 2HBr = \begin{array}{c} CH.Br.COOH \\ | \\ CH.Br.COOH \end{array} + 2H_2O,$$

but when tartaric acid is heated witn concentrated hydriodic acid the two hydroxyl groups are reduced to hydrogen, and succinic acid is formed,

$$\begin{array}{c} CH.OH.COOH \\ | \\ CH.OH.COOH \end{array} + 4HI = \begin{array}{c} CH_2.COOH \\ | \\ CH_2.COOH \end{array} + 2H_2O + 2I_2.$$

Tartaric acid is a reducing agent. When warmed with an ammoniacal solution of silver oxide a bright silver mirror is formed on the side of the tube. Tartaric acid reduces an alkaline solution of potassium permanganate, first to green potassium manganate solution, and then to a precipitate of manganese dioxide. If tartaric acid is mixed with a little ferrous sulphate solution, and a few drops of hydrogen peroxide are added,* and then excess of sodium hydroxide, a deep violet or blue colour is obtained. The blue colour is due to the presence of the ferric salt of dihydroxymaleic acid, formed by the oxidation of tartaric acid,

$$\begin{array}{c} CH.OH.COOH \\ | \\ CH.OH.COOH \end{array} + O = \begin{array}{c} C.OH.COOH \\ || \\ C.OH.COOH \end{array} + H_2O.$$

Constitution of tartaric acid. The empirical formula of tartaric acid is $C_2H_3O_3$. It is dibasic. By analysis of its silver salt its molecular formula is shown to be $C_4H_6O_6$.

Tartaric acid is converted to succinic acid when boiled with concentrated hydriodic acid. The constitution of succinic acid is established by its synthesis from ethylene dibromide by the series of reactions described on p. 295.

---

* Hydrogen peroxide in the presence of ferrous sulphate in alkaline solution is known as " Fenton's Reagent ".

The reaction of tartaric acid with hydriodic acid must, therefore, be in accordance with the equation

$$\begin{array}{l} CHOH.COOH \\ | \\ CHOH.COOH \end{array} + 4HI = \begin{array}{l} CH_2.COOH \\ | \\ CH_2.COOH \end{array} + 2H_2O + 2I_2,$$

which shows that tartaric acid is dihydroxysuccinic acid.

Tartaric acid may also be synthesised from glycol (p. 291). Glycol is oxidised with nitric acid under carefully controlled conditions to give glyoxal,

$$\begin{array}{l} CH_2OH \\ | \\ CH_2OH \end{array} + 2O = \begin{array}{l} H{-}C{=}O \\ | \\ H{-}C{=}O \end{array} + 2H_2O.$$

Glyoxal is converted to tartaric acid by the procedure outlined under Reaction 2, p. 297.

Tartaric acid prepared synthetically is always obtained in the optically inactive form. The relation of this form to the two optically active isomerides, *d*- and *l*-tartaric acids, is described on p. 309.

Salts of tartaric acid. Normal potassium tartrate is readily soluble in water ; the hydrated salt which crystallises from the aqueous solution has the constitution, $C_4H_4O_6K_2,\frac{1}{2}H_2O$. Potassium hydrogen tartrate is made by adding excess of tartaric acid to a neutral solution of potassium chloride, or by treating normal potassium tartrate with a mineral acid. It is very sparingly soluble in water, from which it crystallises without water of crystallisation. It is one of the very few sparingly soluble salts of potassium, and it is used as a reagent for testing for this metal. Rochelle salt, $C_4H_4O_6KNa,4H_2O$ is made by neutralising a solution of potassium hydrogen tartrate with sodium carbonate, and crystallising the solution. It is used in the preparation of Fehling's solution, p. 208. Calcium tartrate, $C_4H_4O_6Ca,4H_2O$, is precipitated when a solution of a calcium salt is added to a neutral solution of a tartrate. Calcium tartrate is soluble in potassium hydroxide solution, from which it is reprecipitated by boiling. Tartar emetic, $C_4H_4O_6.K(SbO),\frac{1}{2}H_2O$, is made by heating potassium hydrogen tartrate with antimonious oxide and water. It is soluble in water. It is used as an emetic and as a mordant.

Tests for tartaric acid and the tartrates.

Tartaric acid and its salts may be recognised by the following tests.

(i) They char rapidly when heated alone, and emit an odour of burnt sugar.

(ii) When heated with concentrated sulphuric acid, they rapidly char and evolve a mixture of carbon monoxide, carbon dioxide and some sulphur dioxide.

(iii) In neutral aqueous solution, on warming, they reduce ammoniacal silver oxide solution to a mirror of metallic silver.

(iv) In neutral aqueous solution they give a white precipitate of calcium tartrate when treated with calcium chloride solution in the cold ; this precipitate is soluble in cold potassium hydroxide solution, but it is reprecipitated when the solution is boiled.

(v) When treated with Fenton's reagent (p. 299) they yield a deep violet or blue coloration.

CHAPTER XVIII

OPTICAL AND GEOMETRICAL ISOMERISM

ISOMERISM is defined and briefly discussed in Chapter II (p. 29). Isomerism may be exhibited either, (i) by members of different classes of organic compounds, or (ii) by members of the same class. The physical and chemical properties of isomerides which belong to different classes of compounds are quite distinct. For example, propionic acid, $CH_3.CH_2.COOH$, and methyl acetate, $CH_3.COOCH_3$, are isomerides, but propionic acid, a liquid B.P. 140°, readily soluble in water, has the typical properties of a fatty acid and methyl acetate, a liquid, B.P. 57·5°, sparingly soluble in water, has the typical properties of an ester.

When isomerides are members of the same class of organic compounds, their chemical properties are closely similar, but their physical properties remain distinct. Normal butyl alcohol and iso-butyl alcohol, for example, undergo all the chemical reactions characteristic of primary alcohols, but their boiling points differ by 9°.

normal butyl alcohol   iso-butyl alcohol

It will be seen from the structural formulae that the constitutional difference between normal butyl alcohol and iso-butyl alcohol is determined by the position of a methyl group on the carbon chain in the molecule. In this type of isomerism the variation in constitution of the isomerides is accounted for by a change in the position of a group in the molecule. Such structural differences are adequately represented by means of the conventional molecular formulae drawn in one plane, that of the paper. There are, however, two other types of isomerism between compounds of the same class, *optical isomerism* and *geometrical isomerism*, which can be explained only if the spatial distribution of the valencies of the carbon atom is taken into account. These types of isomerism are two particular cases of *stereoisomerism,* or isomerism which is dependent on the configuration of groups of atoms in space.

The various types of isomerism may thus be classified in the following scheme.

1. Isomerism between members of different classes of compounds.

2. Isomerism between members of the same class of compounds, which may be subdivided into :

(i) Isomerism dependent on the position of a given group in the molecule.

(ii) Isomerism dependent on the configuration of the groups constituting a molecule, which may be further subdivided into:

(*a*) optical isomerism,   (*b*) geometrical isomerism.

OPTICAL ISOMERISM

Modifications of the same chemical compound, which have the same structural formula, and which differ only in the property of rotating the plane of polarised light, are said to show optical isomerism.

POLARISED LIGHT

Experimental evidence shows that light behaves as a transverse wave motion, such as would be obtained if particles of a medium were successively caused to vibrate in directions at right angles to the path along which the wave is travelling.

A rough analogy to the wave motion of light is furnished by the behaviour of a shaken rope. If one end of a horizontally stretched rope is fixed, a sharp jerk of the free end sends a kink travelling along the rope towards the fixed end. The kink can be seen to travel forward, but the particles of the rope are successively displaced sideways in some direction approximately at right angles to the length of the rope. With a little skill the jerk can be so controlled that the particles of the rope can be moved in any given direction, either vertically or horizontally, or in some intermediate direction. In each case the motion of the rope is at right angles to its length ; the kink travels forward, and remains in a vertical plane or in a horizontal plane, or in some intermediate plane.

If the rope is passed through a vertical slit, only kinks in a vertical plane are able to travel through the slit to the fixed end of the rope. If the slit is rotated about the rope into some new position, the only kinks which travel through the slit to the fixed end of the rope are those in the plane in which the slit lies.

Ordinary light behaves as though it were a train of waves formed by the successive displacement of particles which are free to vibrate in all directions at right angles to the path in which the waves are travelling. If the light is passed through a specially constructed prism of Iceland spar, known as a Nicol prism, so-called *plane polarised light* is obtained. This light behaves as a train of waves produced by particles the motion of which is restricted so that they vibrate only in parallel paths which lie in one and the same plane, known as the plane of polarisation. The Nicol prism is known as the *polariser*, and it plays the part of the slit in the rope analogy.

The plane in which the light emerging from the Nicol prism is polarised depends on the orientation of the prism. If a second Nicol prism, known as the *analyser*, is placed along the same axis and given the same orientation as that of the polariser, the plane polarised light will travel through it, but if the analyser is rotated about an axis parallel to the direction of the incident light, the intensity of the light emerging from the analyser is gradually diminished until it is extinguished altogether when the analyser has turned through 90°. With continued rotation the intensity of the emergent light increases again until it reaches a maximum when the analyser has turned through 180°. It passes through another minimum when the analyser has turned through 270°, and finally reaches another maximum when the original orientation has been regained.

If certain substances, which are said to be optically active, are interposed between the polariser and the analyser, the maximum illumination is no longer observed when the analyser is turned through 0° or 180° ; the analyser has to be rotated further before the maximum illumination is obtained. Such optically active substances are said to *rotate the plane of polarised light*. The angle between the positions of maximum illumination obtained with and without the interposition of the optically active substance is known as the *angle of rotation*. The magnitude of the angle of rotation depends not only on the nature, but also on the temperature and the thickness, of the substance interposed between the polariser and the analyser, and also on the wave-length of the light. Monochromatic light from the sodium flame is usually employed.

Certain crystalline substances (both inorganic and organic) are optically active, and their activity has been correlated with the property of *enantiomorphism*. Two objects are said to be *enantiomorphous* when each is the non-superposable mirror image of the other. For example, a left hand and a right hand are enantiomorphous, and so are a left-handed and a right-handed spiral staircase. A left hand cannot be superposed on a right hand ; the parts of the hands correspond if they are placed palm to palm, but if they are similarly orientated, the thumb of one hand falls on the little finger of the other, and so on.

Fig. 53A shows a crystal of barytes (barium sulphate) which possesses a high degree of symmetry. A crystal of this degree of

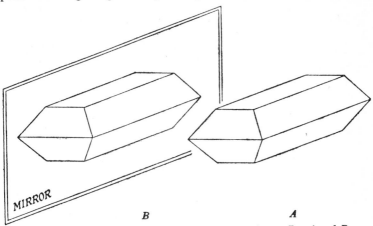

FIG. 53.   A barytes crystal A, and its mirror image B. A and B are superposable, and therefore barytes does not show enantiomorphism.

symmetry is identical with its mirror image, Fig. 53B, and therefore it does not exhibit enantiomorphism.   Figs. 54A and 54B show the

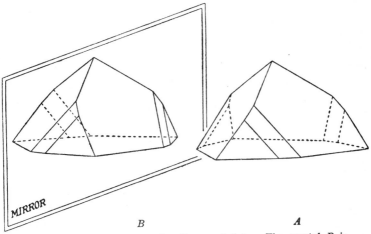

FIG. 54.   Two crystals of sodium periodate.   The crystal B is identical with the mirror image of crystal A.   The crystals A and B are non-superposable, and therefore sodium periodate shows enantiomorphism.

two enantiomorphous crystalline forms of sodium periodate, $NaIO_4,3H_2O$. It will be seen that each crystal may be regarded as the mirror image of the other, and that the two forms are non-superposable ; one is right-handed and the other left-handed.

Crystals of barytes, Fig. 53A, are not optically active. Crystals of sodium periodate are optically active ; the rotatory power of the crystal shown in Fig. 54A is equal in magnitude but opposite in sign to that of the crystal shown in Fig. 54B. This relation between optical activity and enantiomorphism applies universally to all crystals which exhibit these phenomena. It should be noted that crystals are optically active only if they are devoid of certain elements of symmetry. No optically active crystal possesses a plane of symmetry, or a centre of symmetry ; it may, however, possess one or more axes of symmetry.

Sodium ammonium tartrate is an example of an organic compound which exhibits enantiomorphism and optical activity. The two enantiomorphous forms are shown in Fig. 55. A section of

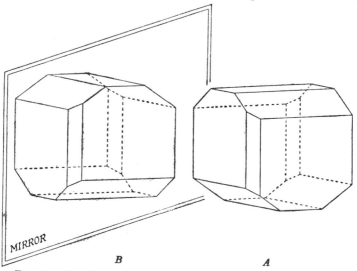

FIG. 55. Enantiomorphous crystals of sodium ammonium tartrate.

the crystal shown in Fig. 55A rotates the plane of polarisation to the right ; an equally thick section of the crystal shown in Fig. 55B cut so that it has the same relation to the axis of the crystal as the section of the crystal shown in Fig. 55A, rotates the plane an equal amount to the left. The crystal shown in Fig. 55A is said to be dextro-rotatory, and that in Fig. 55B laevo-rotatory.

The optical activity of sodium ammonium tartrate, however, is more remarkable than that of sodium periodate, for if crystals of the two forms of sodium ammonium tartrate are dissolved in water the solutions are optically active, whereas a solution of sodium periodate is inactive. The same depths of equally concentrated solutions of each form of sodium ammonium tartrate at the same temperature rotate the plane of polarised light to an equal degree, but in opposite directions. Since the crystal structure of sodium ammonium tartrate is destroyed on solution, the structures of the molecules must be enantiomorphous ; there must be two kinds of molecules of sodium ammonium tartrate related to one another as object to mirror image. Hence it may be concluded that the two molecular structures are non-superposable, and that they possess at the most only axes of symmetry.

Before discussing more closely the molecular structures of the enantiomorphic forms of sodium ammonium tartrate, it is desirable to consider simpler carbon compounds possessing molecular structures which are non-superposable on their own mirror images. The simplest type of such a carbon compound is a derivative of methane in which each of the four hydrogen atoms in the methane molecule is replaced by a different atom or group. The molecule of lactic acid has such a structure :

$$\begin{array}{c} OH \\ | \\ H-C-COOH \\ | \\ CH_3 \end{array}$$

The central carbon atom in the molecule of lactic acid is an example of an asymmetric carbon atom. *An asymmetric carbon atom is one which is linked to four different atoms or groups.*

THE OPTICAL ISOMERISM OF LACTIC ACID

If the molecule of lactic acid is drawn so that it can be seen how the four groups attached to the central carbon atom are distributed in space, it will be observed that there are two possible non-superposable arrangements, of which each is the mirror image of the other :

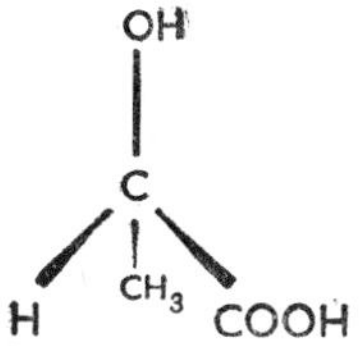

I. laevo-lactic acid 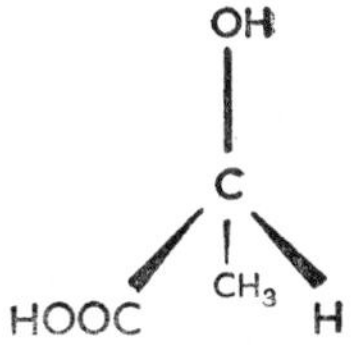   II. dextro-lactic acid

If models of these molecules are constructed it will be seen that no amount of twisting or turning will make molecule I coincident with molecule II. If, however, any two groups in the molecule are made identical, the property of non-superposability is lost and with it the property of optical activity. If, for example, the methyl group in lactic acid is replaced by hydrogen in each of the structures I and II, giving glycollic acid, structure III so obtained is identical with structure IV ; the two molecules are seen to be coincident if one is rotated through 120° about an axis passing through the central carbon atom and the hydroxyl group. Glycollic acid is not optically active.

III. glycollic acid   IV. glycollic acid

Since the only difference between the molecular structures I and II is that one is the mirror image of the other, it would be expected that the chemical and physical properties of dextro-lactic acid and of laevo-lactic acid would be identical. This deduction is confirmed by experiment. Except for their opposite (and equal) effects on polarised light, the two optical isomers of lactic acid are chemically and physically indistinguishable.

d-Lactic acid,* or sarcolactic acid, is present in muscle and is obtained from meat extract. *l*-Lactic acid does not occur naturally. It is prepared from a third modification of lactic acid which is found in sour milk, and which is formed by the lactic fermentation of certain sugars, p. 272. The sour milk acid is not optically active ; it is a molecular compound consisting of equal molecular proportions of *d*-lactic acid and *l*-lactic acid.†

* In this book the prefixes *d*- and *l*- are used as symbols for the prefixes dextro- and laevo- respectively; they therefore indicate the direction in which a solution of an optically active compound rotates the plane of polarised light. This use is in accordance with the convention, suggested by the Committee on Carbohydrate Nomenclature of the American Chemical Society, that the prefixes *d*- and *l*- be used in the manner just mentioned, and that the prefixes *D*- and *L*- be used to indicate the absolute configuration of the groups in an optically active molecule. Consideration of the absolute configuration of groups is outside the scope of this book.

It should be noted, however, that a compound with a *D*-configuration is not necessarily dextro-rotatory, and that to avoid confusion the particular convention adopted in any publication on stereochemistry must be clearly understood.

† The compound of *d*-lactic acid and *l*-lactic acid which is prepared by the lactic fermentation of sugars may be compared to the compound of ferrous

The chemical properties of the sour milk acid are identical with those of d- and l-lactic acid. Its physical properties are different, however, and the numbers of molecules of water present in certain of its crystalline salts are greater than the numbers present in the corresponding salts of d- or l-lactic acid. For example, the constitution of the calcium salt of the sour milk acid is $(C_3H_5O_3)_2Ca, 5H_2O$, and that of d-lactic acid is $(C_3H_5O_3)_2Ca, 4H_2O$; the constitution of the zinc salt of the sour milk acid is $(C_3H_5O_3)_2Zn, 3H_2O$, and that of d-lactic acid is $(C_3H_5O_3)_2Zn, 2H_2O$.

The chemistry of lactic acid is described in Chapter XVI, p. 270. It should be noted that the sour-milk modification is always produced when lactic acid is prepared from reagents which are not optically active. This is a particular case of a generalisation which is mentioned again on p. 311.

THE OPTICAL ISOMERISM OF TARTARIC ACID

Chemical evidence shows the structure of tartaric acid to be

COOH.OH.H.C—C.H.OH.COOH.

Three spatial configurations are possible in a molecule of this structure :

I. mesotartaric acid   II. l-tartaric acid   III. d-tartaric acid

Structure I has a plane of symmetry (indicated by the dotted line) at right angles to the plane of the paper, and the mirror image of this molecule is therefore superposable on the molecule itself. Molecules having the structure I are therefore without effect on polarised light. The compound possessing molecular configuration I is mesotartaric acid. The two carbon atoms which are not part of the carboxyl groups in mesotartaric acid are asymmetric carbon atoms : each is linked to the four different groups, —H, —OH, —COOH,

sulphate and ammonium sulphate which is present in crystals of ferrous ammonium sulphate, $FeSO_4,(NH_4)_2SO_4,6H_2O$. In each case the compound is deposited from solution as a single crystalline species ; the solution, however, behaves as a mixture of the two component compounds.

—CH.OH.COOH. Since the molecule as a whole is optically in-active, the effect of one asymmetric carbon atom on polarised light must be exactly balanced by the effect of the other. Mesotartaric acid is therefore described as an *internally compensated* isomer of tartaric acid.

Configuration II has neither a plane nor any other element of symmetry. Its mirror image is configuration III, on which it is non-superposable. Configurations II and III are those of the optically active tartaric acids, *l*-tartaric acid, and *d*-tartaric acid.

There is a fourth variety of tartaric acid, racemic acid, which exists only in the crystalline state. Crystals of racemic acid contain equal numbers of molecules of *d*-tartaric and of *l*-tartaric acids, together with water of crystallisation ; their composition is repre-sented by the formula $C_4H_6O_6.C_4H_6O_6, 2H_2O$. A solution of racemic acid, therefore, contains molecules of *d*-tartaric acid and of *l*-tartaric acid in equal proportions, and displays no optical activity. Each of the constituent tartaric acid molecules in racemic acid is optically active, but racemic acid itself is inactive because the effect of any one of the constituent molecules is exactly neutralised by the presence of its optical isomer. Since the inactivity is due to the presence of complete molecules of two optical isomerides (and not, as in mesotartaric acid, to the presence of two active groups in the same molecule), racemic acid is said to be *externally compensated*.

The chemical properties of the four modifications of tartaric acid are identical. The physical properties (except for the action on polarised light) of *d*- and *l*-tartaric acids are also identical. The almost complete identity of behaviour of *d*- and *l*-tartaric acids is correlated with the molecular configurations II and III, which exhibit no structural difference, and their only configurational difference is the distinction between an object and its mirror image. The physical properties of mesotartaric acid are different from those of *d*- and *l*-tartaric acids, thus :

	M.P.	*Crystalline forms*	*Solubility in* 100 *gm. of water at* 15°
d- and *l*-	170°, with decomposition	monoclinic prisms	139 gm.
Mesotartaric	143°	rectangular plates (efflorescent)	125 gm.
Racemic acid	anhydrous 206°, with decomposition	rhombic (efflorescent)	20·6 gm.

The configurations of mesotartaric acid, I, and of d-tartaric acid, II, are neither coincident nor are they related to one another as object to mirror image. There is thus a considerable difference between these configurations, which is reflected in the difference in physical properties of the compounds they represent. Racemic acid is an intermolecular compound of d- and l-tartaric acid, and its physical properties differ from those of the separate optical isomers of which it is composed.

If d-tartaric acid is heated with water in a sealed tube to 165°, an intramolecular change occurs which leads to the conversion of one-half of the d-acid to the l-acid. If the solution is evaporated and crystallised, racemic acid is obtained. l-Tartaric acid behaves similarly and also yields racemic acid. This process, by which an optically active isomer is converted to the racemic compound, is known as *racemisation*.

The converse process, by which the two optically active isomers are obtained from racemic acid is known as *resolution*. It is a very important process because the preparation from optically inactive reagents of a compound which is capable of showing optical activity always produces either the racemic or the meso modification.* The optically active isomers must be obtained by resolving the racemic compound.

There are three methods of resolution which are described below.

(i) *Treatment of the racemic compound with a ferment.* Although the optical isomerides are indistinguishable by means of ordinary chemical reactions, nevertheless the chemical processes of living organisms are able to select one isomer in favour of the other. If, for example, racemic acid is exposed to *penicillum glaucum*, the d-isomer is destroyed more quickly than the l-isomer, some of which remains at the end of the experiment.

(ii) *Crystallisation of the components of the racemic compound in enantiomorphic forms.* The crystals of a racemic compound do not display enantiomorphism. Each crystal, however small, contains equal numbers of molecules of the two optical isomers which constitute the racemic compound. Sodium ammonium racemate, for example, crystallises in the habit shown in Fig. 56A. The crystal has a plane of symmetry, and it is identical with its mirror image, Fig. 56B. It may, however, be possible to modify the conditions of

* Such a preparation must involve a change from a more to a less symmetrical molecule, and as the chances of formation of the d- and l-modifica-tions of the less symmetrical molecule are equal, the compound finally ob-tained is optically inactive. This statement is illustrated by the formation of tartaric acid fiom maleic acid or fumaric acid, p. 318.

crystallisation of an aqueous solution of a racemic compound so that the two constituent optical isomerides fail to form crystals of the racemic compound, but yield instead separate enantiomorphic crystals each containing one optical isomeride only. For example, if an aqueous solution of sodium ammonium racemate is crystallised

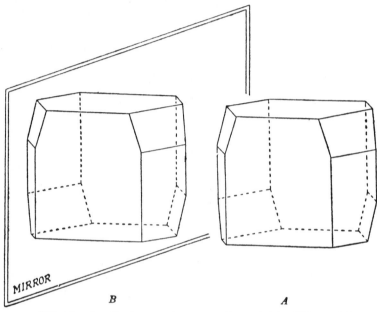

B   *A*

FIG. 56. A sodium ammonium racemate crystal *A*. This crystal is superposable on its mirror image *B*, and hence sodium ammonium racemate does not show enantiomorphism.

above 27°, crystals of the racemate are deposited, Fig. 56. If, however, crystallisation is carried out *below* 27°, the crystals obtained are not those of the racemate, Fig. 56, but a mixture of sodium ammonium *d*-tartrate, Fig. 55A, p. 306, and sodium ammonium *l*-tartrate, Fig. 55B. With the aid of a lens the two enantiomorphic forms of sodium ammonium tartrate may be recognised.

(iii) *Formation of diastereoisomerides.* It has been pointed out in method (ii) that when a solution containing equimolecular proportions of a pair of optical isomerides is crystallised, it produces either crystals of the racemic compound, or a conglomerate of crystals of each of the isomerides according to the conditions. It is, therefore, impossible to separate the *d*- and *l*-isomers constituting a racemic compound by a process of fractional crystallisation. If, however, the two optical isomerides are caused to combine with an optically active isomer of some other compound, two new compounds will be obtained which no longer have configurations related to one another as object to mirror image. Such compounds are known as *diastereoisomerides.*

For example, *d*- and *l*-tartaric acid may be obtained from racemic acid by combining it with an optically active isomeride of the organic base cinchonine ; *d*-cinchonine is usually chosen for this purpose. The relation of the configurations of the two salts obtained may be explained by the following illustration. Suppose the two enantiomorphic modifications of tartaric acid are represented by two enantiomorphic symbols, thus

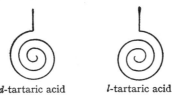

d-tartaric acid   *l*-tartaric acid

and the two enantiomorphic modifications of cinchonine by the symbols,

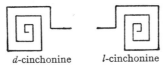

d-cinchonine   *l*-cinchonine

The two diastereoisomerides, *d*-cinchonine *d*-tartrate, and *d*-cinchonine *l*-tartrate, may then be written,

d-cinchonine *d*-tartrate   *d*-cinchonine *l*-tartrate

Inspection shows at once that these salts are not enantiomorphic. Therefore, they do not form a racemic compound, and they do not possess identical physical properties. These salts, therefore, have different solubilities in water, and they may be separated by crystallisation. When each of the salts has been so obtained in a pure condition, it may be reconverted to the corresponding optical isomeride of tartaric acid by treatment with dilute sulphuric acid.

Variations of this method are of general application and it is therefore of great importance.

GEOMETRICAL ISOMERISM

Geometrical isomerism is exhibited by molecules which contain two atoms linked in such a way that they have lost the property of free rotation. Free rotation (p. 50) is a property possessed by all atoms linked by a single bond, whether ionic, covalent or co-ionic.

GEOMETRICAL ISOMERISM OF DICHLOROETHYLENE

The simplest instances of geometrical isomerism are furnished by certain derivatives of ethylene. There are, for example, three dichloroethylenes, $C_2H_2Cl_2$, with boiling points 37°, 60°, and 48·5°. Two of the three isomers may be differentiated by structural formulae, thus :

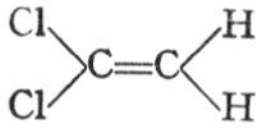

$$\underset{Cl}{\overset{Cl}{\diagdown}} C = C \underset{H}{\overset{H}{\diagup}} \qquad\qquad \underset{H}{\overset{Cl}{\diagdown}} C = C \underset{H}{\overset{Cl}{\diagup}}$$

αα-dichloroethylene, B.P. 37° 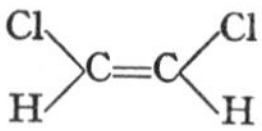　　αβ-dichloroethylene, B.P. 60°

To account for the existence of the third isomer it is necessary to consider the effect of the spatial distribution of the valencies of the carbon atoms in the ethylene molecule. The four covalencies of the carbon atom are directed towards the apices of a regular tetrahedron having the carbon atom at its centre ; the angle between any two covalencies is 109° 28'. This configuration is such that any two

FIG. 57.

valencies of the carbon atom lie in a plane at right angles to that containing the remaining two valencies. Fig. 57 represents a perspective drawing of the valencies of the carbon atom. The valencies a and b lie in the plane of the paper, and the valencies c and d in a plane at right angles to that of the paper. The drawing is intended to show that the valency c is directed upwards towards the reader, whereas the valency d is directed downwards underneath the paper.

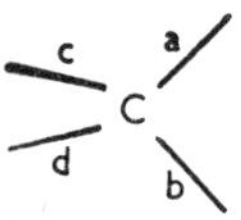

If two carbon atoms are imagined to be brought together so that two covalencies of each come into mutual contact, the arrangement of valencies shown in Fig. 58 is obtained.

The valencies denoted by a, a', b, b', lie in the plane of the paper. The valencies denoted by c, c', are directed upwards above the paper, and the valencies denoted

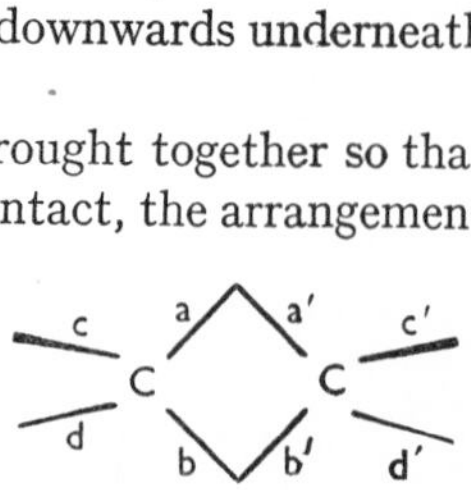

FIG. 58.

by d, d', are directed downwards below the paper. The four valencies, c, d, c', d', all lie in one plane at right angles to that of the paper. Fig. 58 thus represents the configuration of the valencies in the ethylene molecule ; the four valencies, a, a', b, b', represent the double bond.

Inspection of Fig. 58 shows that rotation of one carbon atom with regard to the other about an axis joining them, is impossible without rupture of the double bond.* $\alpha\beta$-Dichloroethylene, therefore, exists in the two isomeric forms,

cis $\alpha\beta$-dichloroethylene, B.P. 60°   *trans* $\alpha\beta$-dichloroethylene, B.P. 48·5°

which are not interconvertible, each possessing its own distinctive physical properties. The third isomer of dichloroethylene is thus accounted for.

The compound in which the two chlorine atoms are adjacent to one another is known as the *cis*-isomeride, and the compound in which the two chlorine atoms are remote from one another as the *trans*-isomeride. This nomenclature is applied generally to geometrical isomerides. The configurations of the *cis*- and *trans*-isomerides of dichloroethylene have been supported by X-ray analysis, by which it has been shown that in the *cis*-compound the distance between the chlorine atoms is 3·6 Å.U. and in the *trans*-compound, 4·7 Å.U.

GEOMETRICAL ISOMERISM OF FUMARIC AND MALEIC ACIDS

Preparation of fumaric acid, maleic acid and maleic anhydride. Fumaric and maleic acids are obtained from malic acid (hydroxysuccinic acid, $COOH.CH_2.CH(OH).COOH$), which is usually prepared from the juice of unripe berries of the mountain ash.

---

* This interpretation of the structure of ethylene derivatives leads to the conclusion that free rotation of the doubly linked carbon atoms is completely eliminated. It is mentioned, however, on p. 316, that maleic acid yields fumaric acid on heating, and that fumaric acid on distillation yields maleic anhydride. Both these reactions require rotation of one of the doubly linked carbon atoms about the double bond, and, therefore, it must be admitted that such rotation is not completely restricted. An interpretation of the nature of the double bond, which permits free rotation in certain conditions, is obtained by the application of wave mechanics to the study of the valency of carbon, but that is outside the scope of this book.

Fumaric acid is obtained by heating malic acid at 130° for a long time.

$$COOH.CH_2.CH(OH).COOH \; = \; COOH.CH{=}CH.COOH \; + \; H_2O.$$
       malic acid   fumaric acid

If malic acid is rapidly heated to a temperature of about 150°, it yields maleic anhydride,

$$COOH.CH_2.CH(OH).COOH \quad = \quad \begin{matrix} HC{-}C{=}O \\ \parallel \qquad \diagdown O \\ HC{-}C{=}O \end{matrix} \quad + \quad 2H_2O.$$
                 malic acid   maleic anhydride

Maleic acid is obtained by treating maleic anhydride with water,

$$\begin{matrix} H{-}C{-}C{=}O \\ \parallel \qquad \diagdown O \\ H{-}C{-}C{=}O \end{matrix} \quad + \quad H_2O \quad = \quad COOH.CH{=}CH.COOH.$$
maleic anhydride   maleic acid (isomeric with fumaric acid)

Interconvertibility of fumaric acid, maleic acid and maleic anhydride. If maleic acid is distilled it is partially converted to maleic anhydride ; if it is treated with cold mineral acids, or is heated to 200° in a sealed tube, it yields fumaric acid. If fumaric acid is heated above 200°, it yields maleic anhydride. Maleic anhydride on treatment with water yields maleic acid only. Fumaric acid can be converted to maleic acid only through the intermediate formation of maleic anhydride. These changes may be summarised in the diagram :

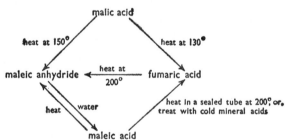

Physical and chemical properties of fumaric and maleic acids. Fumaric acid may be crystallised from hot water as small colourless prisms ; it is sparingly soluble in cold water. It melts at 287°, but, as mentioned above, it yields maleic anhydride vapour when heated above 200°. Maleic acid crystallises in large prisms, and is freely soluble in cold water. It melts at 135°, and if distilled it undergoes conversion to maleic anhydride.

The chemical properties of fumaric acid and maleic acid are

parallel. The products of the reactions of each acid with a given reagent are identical, except that, if the products contain two asymmetric carbon atoms, one acid may give the internally compensated compound and the other the racemic compound. Both acids neutralise bases to form salts of the type, $COONa.CH=CH.COONa$, and their silver salts react with ethyl iodide to form ethyl fumarate and ethyl maleate. Both acids yield succinic acid on reduction with sodium amalgam,

$$COOH.CH=CH.COOH \quad + \quad H_2 \quad = \quad COOH.CH_2.CH_2.COOH,$$

and the racemic modification of bromosuccinic acid when heated with hydrogen bromide,

$$COOH.CH=CH.COOH + HBr = COOH.CH_2.CHBr.COOH,$$

and the racemic modification of malic acid when heated with water to moderate temperatures,

$$COOH.CH=CH.COOH + H_2O = COOH.CH_2.CH(OH).COOH.$$

On treatment with bromine, fumaric and maleic acids yield optically inactive modifications of dibromosuccinic acid,

$$COOH.CH=CH.COOH + Br_2 = COOH.CHBr.CHBr.COOH,$$

and on oxidation with potassium permanganate solution they yield optically inactive modifications of tartaric acid,

$$COOH.CH=CH.COOH \quad + \quad O \quad + \quad H_2O$$
$$= \quad COOH.CH(OH).CH(OH).COOH.$$

Fumaric acid yields racemic acid, and maleic acid mesotartaric acid. This distinction is important for establishing the configurations of fumaric and maleic acids.

The configurations of fumaric and maleic acids.

The similarity of the chemical properties of fumaric and maleic acids shows that these compounds possess the same molecular structure, and the presence of the double bond in the molecule indicates that they are geometrical isomers

$$
\begin{array}{ccc}
\text{H—C—COOH} & & \text{H—C—COOH} \\
\| & & \| \\
\text{H—C—COOH} & & \text{HOOC—C—H}
\end{array}
$$

maleic acid, the *cis*-isomeride   fumaric acid, the *trans*-isomeride

The following two pieces of evidence show that maleic acid should be assigned the *cis*-configuration.

(i) The change from maleic acid to maleic anhydride is reversible, but fumaric acid cannot be formed by heating maleic anhydride with water. Maleic anhydride must have the *cis*-configuration, and its ready conversion to maleic acid must be in accordance with the equation which shows maleic acid as the *cis*-isomeride,

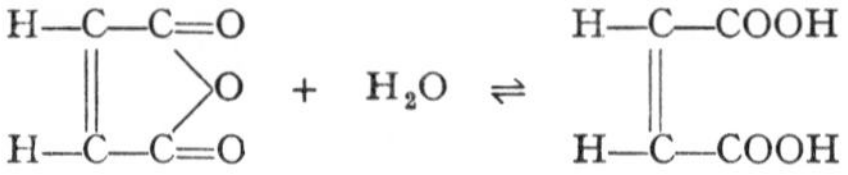
H—C—C=O
O
H—C—C=O
+ H₂O ⇌
H—C—COOH
H—C—COOH

Clearly the *trans*-isomeride could not be formed from maleic anhydride without rotation about the double bond.

(ii) Maleic acid on oxidation with potassium permanganate solution yields mesotartaric acid. Mesotartaric acid has a plane of symmetry. If maleic acid is the *cis*-isomeride its oxidation to mesotartaric acid follows at once if either of the bonds (designated *a* and *b*) in the double linkage is attacked by the oxidising agent, as may be seen from the diagram :

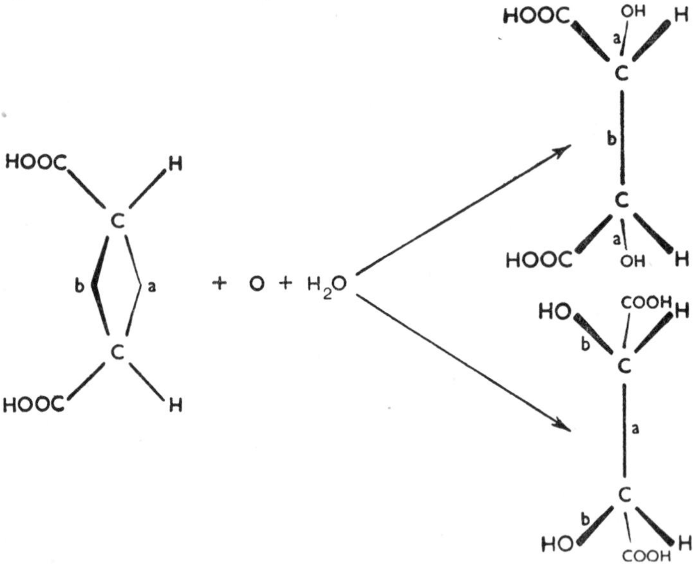
HOOC
H
C
b
a
C
HOOC
H
+ O + H2O
HOOC
OH
H
C
b
C
HOOC
OH
H
HO
COOH
H
C
a
C
HO
COOH
H

If fumaric acid, the *trans*-isomeride, is similarly oxidised, it yields either *d*-tartaric acid or *l*-tartaric acid. The modification of tartaric acid produced depends on the point of attack of the oxidising agent on the double bond : if the linkage *a* is broken *d*-tartaric acid is formed, if the linkage *b* is attacked *l*-tartaric is formed. This is made clear by the diagram :*

* The stereoisomerism of *d*- and *l*-tartaric acid is independent of the orientation of the two central carbon atoms to one another ; in the molecule of tartaric acid there is free rotation about the bond linking these carbon atoms. This is made clear by a comparison of the configurational formulae on this page with those on p. 309.

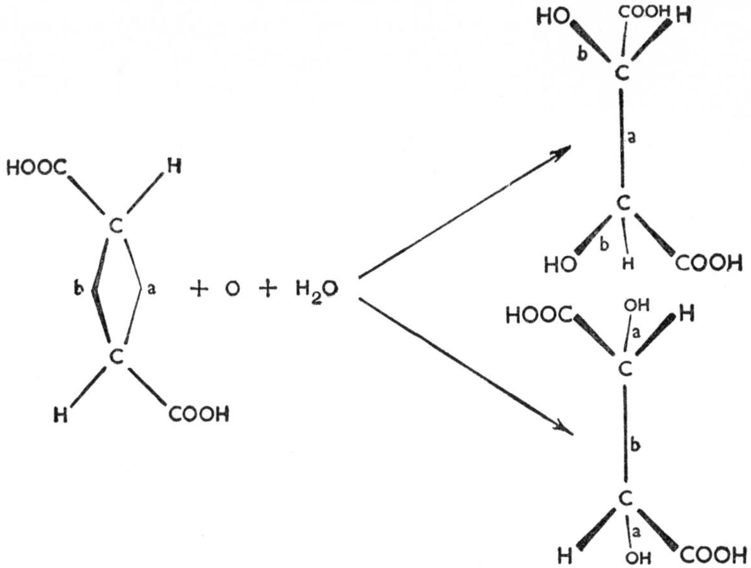

Since the chances of attack on the two linkages *a* and *b* are equal, *d*- and *l*-tartaric acids are produced in equal amounts, and racemic acid is obtained.

Geometrical isomerism is exhibited by many other compounds besides those possessing ethylenic double linkages in the molecule. Carbon atoms lose the property of free rotation on becoming part of a ring structure, and hence such a compound as hexhydroterephthalic acid exists in the two forms :

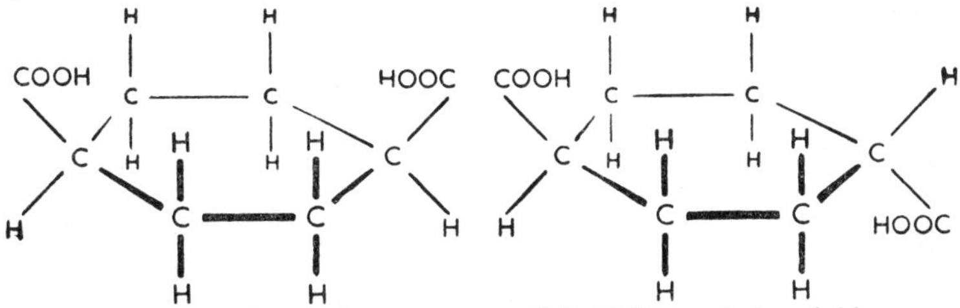

cis. M.P. 162°, soluble   *trans.* M.P. 300°, sparingly soluble

The double bond in geometrically isomeric compounds need not link two carbon atoms. Benzaldoxime, for example, which contains a nitrogen atom doubly linked to a carbon atom, exists in two well-defined isomeric forms :

C_6H_5—C—H
‖
N—OH
syn-benzaldoxime, M.P. 35°

C_6H_5—C—H
‖
HO—N
anti-benzaldoxime, M.P. 125°

CHAPTER XIX

THE POLYHYDRIC ALCOHOLS

GLYCOLS

THE glycols are theoretically derived from the paraffins by the replacement of two hydrogen atoms in the paraffin molecule by hydroxyl groups, thus:

$$
\begin{array}{c}
\text{H} \\
| \\
\text{H—C—H} \\
| \\
\text{H}
\end{array}
\qquad
\begin{array}{c}
\text{OH} \\
| \\
\text{H—C—OH} \\
| \\
\text{H}
\end{array}
$$

methane   methylene glycol

$$
\begin{array}{c}
\text{H} \quad \text{H} \\
| \quad | \\
\text{H—C—C—H} \\
| \quad | \\
\text{H} \quad \text{H}
\end{array}
\qquad
\begin{array}{c}
\text{H} \quad\quad \text{H} \\
| \quad\quad | \\
\text{H—C——C—H} \\
| \quad\quad | \\
\text{OH} \quad \text{OH}
\end{array}
$$

ethane   ethylene glycol

$$
\begin{array}{c}
\text{H} \quad\quad \text{H} \quad\quad \text{H} \\
| \quad\quad | \quad\quad | \\
\text{H—C——C——C—H} \\
| \quad\quad | \quad\quad | \\
\text{OH} \quad \text{OH} \quad \text{H}
\end{array}
$$

$\alpha\beta$-propylene glycol

$$
\begin{array}{c}
\text{H} \quad\quad \text{H} \quad\quad \text{H} \\
| \quad\quad | \quad\quad | \\
\text{H—C——C——C—H} \\
| \quad\quad | \quad\quad | \\
\text{H} \quad \text{H} \quad \text{H}
\end{array}
$$

propane

$$
\begin{array}{c}
\text{H} \quad\quad \text{H} \quad\quad \text{H} \\
| \quad\quad | \quad\quad | \\
\text{H—C——C——C—H} \\
| \quad\quad | \quad\quad | \\
\text{OH} \quad \text{H} \quad \text{OH}
\end{array}
$$

$\alpha\alpha$-propylene glycol

If the glycol molecule contains more than two carbon atoms, the positions of the hydroxyl groups are indicated by denoting the end carbon atoms in the chain as α, and the other carbon atoms in the chain as β, γ, δ, and so on. $\alpha\beta$-butylene glycol is

$$
\begin{array}{c}
\text{H} \quad\quad \text{H} \quad\quad \text{H} \quad\quad \text{H} \\
| \quad\quad | \quad\quad | \quad\quad | \\
\text{H—C——C——C——C—H} \\
| \quad\quad | \quad\quad | \quad\quad | \\
\text{OH} \quad \text{OH} \quad \text{H} \quad \text{H}
\end{array}
$$

and $\beta\gamma$-pentylene glycol is

$$
\begin{array}{c}
\text{H} \quad\quad \text{H} \quad\quad \text{H} \quad\quad \text{H} \quad\quad \text{H} \\
| \quad\quad | \quad\quad | \quad\quad | \quad\quad | \\
\text{H—C——C——C——C——C—H} \\
| \quad\quad | \quad\quad | \quad\quad | \quad\quad | \\
\text{H} \quad \text{OH} \quad \text{OH} \quad \text{H} \quad \text{H}
\end{array}
$$

Methylene glycol has not been isolated, but it is probably present in aqueous solutions of formaldehyde:

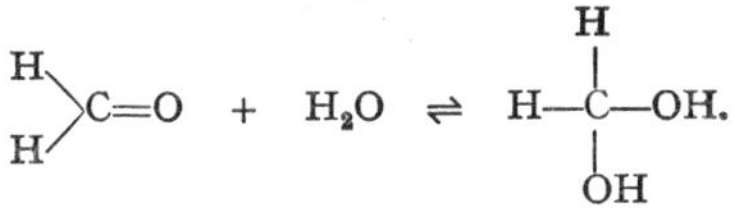

$$\begin{array}{c} H \\ \diagdown \\ \diagup \\ H \end{array} C{=}O \ + \ H_2O \ \rightleftharpoons \ \overset{\displaystyle H}{\underset{\displaystyle OH}{H{-}\overset{|}{\underset{|}{C}}{-}OH.}}$$

The typical member of the series of glycols is ethylene glycol, which is usually referred to as glycol.

ETHYLENE GLYCOL

Ethylene glycol is a colourless, neutral, viscous liquid, M.P. $-11 \cdot 5°$, B.P. $197 \cdot 5°$. It has a sweet taste. It is hygroscopic, and is miscible with water and alcohol in all proportions, but is only sparingly soluble in ether.

PRINCIPAL REACTIONS IN WHICH ETHYLENE GLYCOL IS PRODUCED

1. The oxidation of ethylene. Ethylene glycol is formed when ethylene is shaken with a cold, very dilute, aqueous solution of potassium permanganate made alkaline with sodium carbonate,

$$\begin{array}{c} H \\ \diagdown \\ \diagup \\ H \end{array} C{=}C \begin{array}{c} H \\ \diagup \\ \diagdown \\ H \end{array} \ + \ H_2O \ + \ O \ = \ \overset{\displaystyle H \ \ \ H}{\underset{\displaystyle OH \ \ OH}{H{-}\overset{|}{\underset{|}{C}}{-}\overset{|}{\underset{|}{C}}{-}H.}}$$

2. The hydrolysis of ethylene dibromide. (*a*) Ethylene dibromide may be directly hydrolysed to glycol by treatment with a boiling dilute aqueous solution of potassium carbonate. The reagents are heated together for several hours in a flask fitted to a reflux condenser, and an aqueous solution of glycol and potassium bromide is obtained,

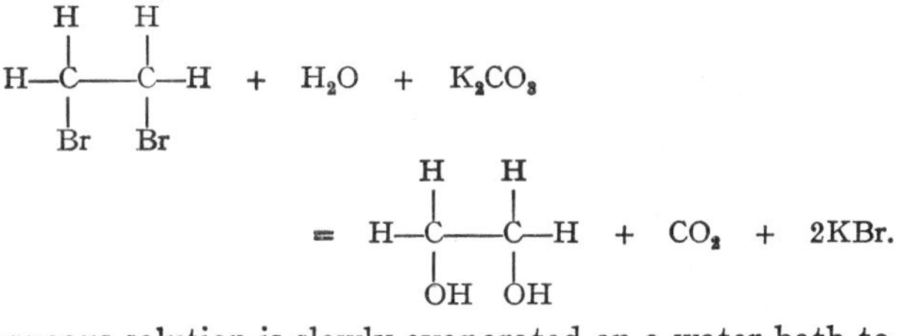

$$\overset{\displaystyle H \ \ \ H}{\underset{\displaystyle Br \ \ Br}{H{-}\overset{|}{\underset{|}{C}}{-}\overset{|}{\underset{|}{C}}{-}H}} \ + \ H_2O \ + \ K_2CO_3$$

$$= \ \overset{\displaystyle H \ \ \ H}{\underset{\displaystyle OH \ \ OH}{H{-}\overset{|}{\underset{|}{C}}{-}\overset{|}{\underset{|}{C}}{-}H}} \ + \ CO_2 \ + \ 2KBr.$$

The aqueous solution is slowly evaporated on a water-bath to expel most of the water. The residue is extracted with a mixture of ether and alcohol which dissolves the glycol, but not the potassium bromide. After filtration, the glycol is obtained from the alcoholic solution by fractional distillation.

(b) Ethylene dibromide may be indirectly converted to glycol by the formation and hydrolysis of glycol diacetate. Ethylene dibromide is first heated with silver acetate and acetic acid to yield glycol diacetate,

$$\begin{array}{c} CH_2Br \\ | \\ CH_2Br \end{array} + 2CH_3.COOAg = \begin{array}{c} CH_2OCO.CH_3 \\ | \\ CH_2OCO.CH_3 \end{array} + 2AgBr,$$

which is then hydrolysed by boiling with a dilute aqueous solution of sodium hydroxide,

$$\begin{array}{c} CH_2OCO.CH_3 \\ | \\ CH_2OCO.CH_3 \end{array} + 2NaOH = \begin{array}{c} CH_2OH \\ | \\ CH_2OH \end{array} + 2CH_3.COONa.$$

3. Industrial preparation. Ethylene glycol is made on the industrial scale from ethylene chlorohydrin, which is obtained by passing a mixture of ethylene and carbon dioxide into a suspension of bleaching powder in water, p. 120. The ethylene chlorohydrin is hydrolysed to glycol by boiling with milk of lime,

$$2\begin{array}{c} CH_2OH \\ | \\ CH_2Cl \end{array} + Ca(OH)_2 = 2\begin{array}{c} CH_2OH \\ | \\ CH_2OH \end{array} + CaCl_2.$$

CHEMICAL PROPERTIES AND USES OF GLYCOL

Properties. Glycol exhibits the typical properties of a primary monohydric alcohol, such as ethyl alcohol, with the difference that in each reaction one molecule of glycol is capable of reacting with two equivalents of the other reagent. Normally, however, the second hydroxyl group in the glycol molecule reacts less readily than the first ; glycol derivatives of the types $CH_2OH.CH_2ONa$ and $CH_2OH.CH_2Cl$ are more easily prepared than those of the types $CH_2ONa.CH_2ONa$, and $CH_2Cl.CH_2Cl$.

1. Reaction with sodium, giving sodium glycol and disodium glycol. Sodium dissolves in glycol at room temperature, giving sodium glycol,

$$2\begin{array}{c} CH_2OH \\ | \\ CH_2OH \end{array} + 2Na = 2\begin{array}{c} CH_2ONa \\ | \\ CH_2OH \end{array} + H_2.$$

If sodium glycol is heated with sodium, disodium glycol is obtained,

$$2\begin{array}{c} CH_2ONa \\ | \\ CH_2OH \end{array} + 2Na = 2\begin{array}{c} CH_2ONa \\ | \\ CH_2ONa \end{array} + H_2.$$

Like sodium ethoxide, sodium glycol and disodium glycol are crystalline and hygroscopic. They are readily decomposed by water with the regeneration of glycol.

2. Reaction with phosphorus halides, giving ethylene dihalides. When glycol is treated with phosphorus pentabromide or phosphorus pentachloride, ethylene dibromide or ethylene dichloride respectively are obtained,

$$\begin{array}{c} CH_2OH \\ | \\ CH_2OH \end{array} + \ 2PCl_5 \ = \ \begin{array}{c} CH_2Cl \\ | \\ CH_2Cl \end{array} + \ 2POCl_3 \ + \ 2HCl.$$

3. Reactions with hydrogen chloride. When hydrogen chloride is passed into glycol at 100°, ethylene chlorohydrin, is formed,

$$\begin{array}{c} CH_2OH \\ | \\ CH_2OH \end{array} + \ HCl \ = \ \begin{array}{c} CH_2Cl \\ | \\ CH_2OH \end{array} + \ H_2O.$$

At higher temperatures, and with excess of hydrogen chloride, ethylene dichloride is produced,

$$\begin{array}{c} CH_2Cl \\ | \\ CH_2OH \end{array} + \ HCl \ = \ \begin{array}{c} CH_2Cl \\ | \\ CH_2Cl \end{array} + \ H_2O.$$

4. Oxidation. The molecule of glycol contains two primary alcohol groups, —CH$_2$OH, either or both of which may be oxidised to the aldehyde group, —CHO, or the carboxyl group, —COOH. The following products may be obtained by the oxidation of glycol with nitric acid :

CH$_2$OH	CH$_2$OH	CHO	CHO	COOH
CHO	COOH	CHO	COOH	COOH
glycollic aldehyde	glycollic acid	glyoxal	glyoxylic acid	oxalic acid

5. Condensation. When heated with ethylene dibromide at 115–120°, ethylene glycol loses water to form condensation products of the type,

$$HO-\overset{\overset{\displaystyle H}{|}}{\underset{\underset{\displaystyle H}{|}}{C}}-\overset{\overset{\displaystyle H}{|}}{\underset{\underset{\displaystyle H}{|}}{C}}-O-\overset{\overset{\displaystyle H}{|}}{\underset{\underset{\displaystyle H}{|}}{C}}-\overset{\overset{\displaystyle H}{|}}{\underset{\underset{\displaystyle H}{|}}{C}}-O-\overset{\overset{\displaystyle H}{|}}{\underset{\underset{\displaystyle H}{|}}{C}}-\overset{\overset{\displaystyle H}{|}}{\underset{\underset{\displaystyle H}{|}}{C}}-OH$$

This condensation is analogous to the formation of paraformaldehyde from formaldehyde, p. 213.

Uses of glycol. Glycol is used as a dielectric in electrical condensers, for preventing ice formation on aeroplane wings, and as the cooling material in liquid-cooled aero-engines. It is an important intermediate product in the manufacture of glycol monoethyl ether, and other ethers and esters which are used in the cellulose industry.

ETHERS AND ESTERS OF GLYCOL

Ethylene chlorohydrin (also known as glycol chlorohydrin) is formed by the action of hydrogen chloride on glycol at 100°, p. 323. It is also formed by the action of an aqueous solution of hypochlorous acid on ethylene, p. 120, and by the action of a mixture of ethylene and carbon dioxide on an aqueous suspension of bleaching powder.

Ethylene chlorohydrin is a liquid, B.P. 130°, immiscible with water. When it is distilled with aqueous potassium hydroxide solution, it yields *ethylene oxide* (see p. 125), a compound which is isomeric with acetaldehyde,

$$\begin{matrix} CH_2Cl \\ | \\ CH_2OH \end{matrix} + KOH = \begin{matrix} CH_2 \\ | \quad \rangle O \\ CH_2 \end{matrix} + KCl + H_2O.$$

Ethylene oxide is a liquid, B.P. 13·5° at 746 mm. It is soluble in water which slowly hydrolyses it to glycol. It reacts with ethyl alcohol to yield *glycol monoethyl ether*,

$$\begin{matrix} CH_2 \\ | \quad \rangle O \\ CH_2 \end{matrix} + \begin{matrix} C_2H_5 \\ | \\ OH \end{matrix} = \begin{matrix} CH_2.OC_2H_5 \\ | \\ CH_2.OH. \end{matrix}$$

When treated with the appropriate proportion of acetic anhydride glycol yields either glycol monoacetate, B.P. 182°, which is soluble in water and alcohol, or glycol diacetate, B.P. 186°, which is soluble in alcohol but only slightly soluble in water.

GLYCEROL

Glycerol * is a trihydric alcohol, theoretically derived from propane by the replacement of one hydrogen atom on each of the carbon atoms in the molecule by a hydroxyl group,

$$\begin{matrix} H & H & H \\ | & | & | \\ H-C-C-C-H \\ | & | & | \\ H & H & H \end{matrix} \qquad \begin{matrix} OH & OH & OH \\ | & | & | \\ H-C-C-C-H \\ | & | & | \\ H & H & H \end{matrix}$$
propane   glycerol

Glycerol, combined with certain higher members of the fatty acid series, occurs naturally in fats. It is obtained by the hydrolysis of fat with the calculated quantity of sodium hydroxide solution. A homogeneous solution is produced, which contains glycerol and the sodium salt of the acids present in the fats. Sodium chloride is added to the solution to cause the sodium salts to separate on the surface as an insoluble curd. The remaining solution consists of an

* Glycerine is a colloquial name for glycerol.

aqueous solution of glycerol and salt. It is filtered, and evaporated to a thick syrup which is distilled under reduced pressure with superheated steam. The mixed vapours are led up columns where the glycerol condenses and the steam passes on.

Glycerol is also obtained by the alcoholic fermentation of cane sugar in the presence of sodium sulphite ; the yield is as high as 20–25 per cent.

As ordinarily prepared, glycerol is a viscous liquid of sp. gr. 1·26. At low temperatures it is crystalline, and it melts at 17°, but it does not readily solidify again on cooling. If it is pure, it boils at 290° without decomposition, but if it is contaminated with even small quantities of salts it decomposes at this temperature yielding acrolein. It is very hygroscopic. It is miscible with water and alcohol in all proportions, but it is insoluble in ether. It has a sweet taste.

CHEMICAL PROPERTIES, CONSTITUTION AND USES OF GLYCEROL

Properties. Glycerol exhibits the properties of a trihydric alcohol, but, as in the case of glycol, reactions in which more than one of the three hydroxyl groups in the molecule are attacked take place only when strong reagents are used, and special attention is paid to the experimental conditions.

1. Reaction with sodium. At room temperature metallic sodium displaces one atom of hydrogen from the molecule of glycerol,

$$2\begin{array}{l} CH_2OH \\ | \\ CHOH \\ | \\ CH_2OH \end{array} + 2Na = 2\begin{array}{l} CH_2ONa \\ | \\ CHOH \\ | \\ CH_2OH \end{array} + H_2.$$

The monosodium derivative of glycerol is hygroscopic and very easily decomposed by water.

2. Reactions with phosphorus halides. Phosphorus pentachloride reacts with glycerol to give glyceryl trichloride,

$$\begin{array}{l} CH_2OH \\ | \\ CHOH \\ | \\ CH_2OH \end{array} + 3PCl_5 = \begin{array}{l} CH_2Cl \\ | \\ CHCl \\ | \\ CH_2Cl \end{array} + 3POCl_3 + 3HCl.$$

If a mixture of white phosphorus, iodine and excess of glycerol is gently warmed in a retort in an atmosphere of carbon dioxide, allyl iodide, B.P. 101°, distils. It is probable that phosphorus tri-iodide is first formed, which reacts with the glycerol to give glyceryl tri-iodide,

$$
\begin{array}{ccc}
CH_2OH & & CH_2I \\
| & & | \\
CHOH & + PI_3 = & CHI + H_3PO_3. \\
| & & | \\
CH_2OH & & CH_2I
\end{array}
$$

The glyceryl tri-iodide then decomposes with the elimination of iodine,

$$
\begin{array}{ccc}
CH_2I & & CH_2 \\
| & & || \\
CHI & = I_2 + & CH \\
| & & | \\
CH_2I & & CH_2I
\end{array}
$$
allyl iodide

If the experiment is carried out using excess of iodine and phosphorus, the allyl iodide is converted to iso-propyl iodide, probably by the reactions :

$$
\begin{array}{ccc}
CH_2 & & CH_2 \\
|| & & || \\
CH & + HI = I_2 + & CH \\
| & & | \\
CH_2I & & CH_3
\end{array}
$$
propylene

$$
\begin{array}{ccc}
CH_2 & & CH_3 \\
|| & & | \\
CH & + HI = & CHI \\
| & & | \\
CH_3 & & CH_3
\end{array}
$$
iso-propyl iodide

3. Reaction with acids, giving esters. A mixture of acetic acid and acetic anhydride reacts with glycerol to yield the three esters :

$$
\begin{array}{ccc}
CH_2OCO.CH_3 & CH_2OCO.CH_3 & CH_2OCO.CH_3 \\
| & | & | \\
CHOH & CHOCO.CH_3 & CHOCO.CH_3 \\
| & | & | \\
CH_2OH & CH_2OH & CH_2OCO.CH_3
\end{array}
$$

glyceryl monoacetate	glyceryl diacetate	glyceryl triacetate
or	or	or
monoacetin	diacetin	triacetin

The number of hydroxyl groups in the glycerol molecule replaced by the acetyl group is governed by the strength of the acetylating mixture, and the temperature at which the reaction takes place.

It should be noted that a special nomenclature is applied to the esters formed by glycerol with organic acids. The name " glyceryl " is omitted, and the suffix " in " replaces the final " ate " in the name of the radical of the organic acid. " Glyceryl diacetate " thus becomes "diacetin", and "glyceryl tripalmitate", an important constituent of animal fats, becomes "tripalmitin".

Concentrated hydrochloric acid (not in excess) at moderately high temperatures converts glycerol to glyceryl monochlorohydrin,

$$\begin{array}{c} CH_2OH \\ | \\ CHOH \\ | \\ CH_2OH \end{array} + HCl = \begin{array}{c} CH_2Cl \\ | \\ CHOH \\ | \\ CH_2OH \end{array} + H_2O.$$

With excess of hydrochloric acid glycerol yields glyceryl αα-dichlorohydrin,

$$\begin{array}{c} CH_2OH \\ | \\ CHOH \\ | \\ CH_2OH \end{array} + 2HCl = \begin{array}{c} CH_2Cl \\ | \\ CHOH \\ | \\ CH_2Cl \end{array} + 2H_2O.$$

Glyceryl trichloride is obtained by the action of phosphorus pentachloride on glycerol or glyceryl dichlorohydrin.

Nitric acid in the presence of sulphuric acid reacts with glycerol to give glyceryl trinitrate, commonly called *nitroglycerin*. Glyceryl trinitrate is made by treating glycerol with a cold mixture of concentrated sulphuric acid and concentrated nitric acid (Sp. Gr. 1·52),

$$\begin{array}{c} CH_2OH \\ | \\ CHOH \\ | \\ CH_2OH \end{array} + 3HNO_3 = \begin{array}{c} CH_2NO_3 \\ | \\ CHNO_3 \\ | \\ CH_2NO_3 \end{array} + 3H_2O.$$

The product of nitration is run into cold water and the glyceryl trinitrate separates as an oil. Glyceryl trinitrate is a heavy oil, Sp. Gr. 1·6, insoluble in water, with a sweetish taste, but no odour. It is sparingly soluble in alcohol and readily soluble in ether. With care, very small quantities of it may be caused to burn quietly when ignited with a flame, but normally it explodes violently when struck or suddenly heated. It is readily hydrolysed to glycerol and sodium nitrate by boiling sodium hydroxide solution,

$$\begin{array}{c} CH_2NO_3 \\ | \\ CHNO_3 \\ | \\ CH_2NO_3 \end{array} + 3NaOH = \begin{array}{c} CH_2OH \\ | \\ CHOH \\ | \\ CH_2OH \end{array} + 3NaNO_3,$$

and when reduced with ammonium sulphide it yields glycerol and ammonia

$$C_3H_5(NO_3)_3 + 12H_2S = C_3H_5(OH)_3 + 3NH_3 + 6H_2O + 12S.$$

Glyceryl trinitrate is the explosive constituent of dynamite, and it is present, mixed with gun-cotton (cellulose nitrate), in blasting gelatine and in cordite. It is used as a medicine in heart disease.

4. Reactions with oxalic acid.

(a) *Formation of formic acid.* If anhydrous glycerol and crystalline oxalic acid are heated to about 120° in a distilling flask, carbon dioxide is evolved, and formic acid distils over. The course of this reaction, and the procedure for carrying it out, are described on p. 240.

(b) *Formation of allyl alcohol.* When anhydrous glycerol and about twice its weight of crystalline oxalic acid are heated to about 230°, glyceryl dioxalate (dioxalin) is formed. It at once decomposes into carbon dioxide and allyl alcohol,

$$
\begin{array}{ccc}
\text{CH}_2\text{OH} & \text{COOH} & \text{CH}_2\text{OC=O} \\
| & | & | \quad | \\
\text{CHOH} \;+\; & \text{COOH} \;=\; & \text{CH OC=O} \;+\; 2\text{H}_2\text{O}. \\
| & & | \\
\text{CH}_2\text{OH} & & \text{CH}_2\text{OH}
\end{array}
$$

$$
\begin{array}{cc}
\text{CH}_2\text{OC=O} & \text{CH}_2 \\
| \quad | & \| \\
\text{CH OC=O} \;=\; & \text{CH} \quad + \; 2\text{CO}_2. \\
| & | \\
\text{CH}_2\text{OH} & \text{CH}_2\text{OH}
\end{array}
$$

Allyl alcohol is a mobile liquid, B.P. 96°, with an irritating odour. It is miscible in all proportions with water, alcohol and ether. The molecule contains an ethylenic linkage and a primary alcohol group. It combines additively with bromine giving glyceryl αβ-dibromohydrin, and it may be oxidised to give acrolein, and acrylic acid,

$$
\begin{array}{ccc}
\text{CH}_2 & & \text{CH}_2\text{Br} \\
\| & & | \\
\text{CH} \;+\; \text{Br}_2 \;=\; & & \text{CHBr} \\
| & & | \\
\text{CH}_2\text{OH} & & \text{CH}_2\text{OH}
\end{array}
$$

$$
\begin{array}{ccccc}
\text{CH}_2 & & \text{CH}_2 & & \text{CH}_2 \\
\| & & \| & & \| \\
\text{CH} & +\text{O} & \text{CH} & +\text{O} & \text{CH} \\
| & \longrightarrow & | & \longrightarrow & | \\
\text{CH}_2\text{OH} & & \text{CHO} & & \text{COOH} \\
& & \text{acrolein} & & \text{acrylic acid}
\end{array}
$$

It reacts with sodium, and forms esters with acids.

5. Oxidation.

The molecule of glycerol contains one secondary and two primary alcohol groups. The secondary alcohol group is capable of being oxidised to the carbonyl group, and each of the primary alcohol groups may be oxidised to the aldehyde or to the carboxyl group. Glycerol, therefore, gives rise to a variety of oxidation products. When glycerol is oxidised with dilute nitric acid it is possible to obtain either glyceric acid,

$$\begin{array}{c} CH_2OH \\ | \\ CHOH \\ | \\ CH_2OH \end{array} + O_2 = H_2O + \begin{array}{c} CH_2OH \\ | \\ CHOH \\ | \\ COOH \end{array} \text{glyceric acid,}$$

or a mixture, known as glycerose, of two isomeric substances, glyceraldehyde and dihydroxyacetone,

$$\begin{array}{c} CH_2OH \\ | \\ CHOH \\ | \\ CH_2OH \end{array} + O_2 = H_2O + \begin{array}{c} CHO \\ | \\ CHOH \quad \text{glyceraldehyde} \\ | \\ CH_2OH \end{array}$$

$$\begin{array}{c} CH_2OH \\ | \\ C{:}O \quad \text{dihydroxyacetone} \\ | \\ CH_2OH \end{array}$$

These substances are the simplest representatives of classes of sugars known as aldoses and ketoses respectively. If glycerose is allowed to stand in dilute aqueous solution of an alkali it polymerises to α-acrose, an optical isomer of fructose.

The unregulated oxidation of glycerol produces a mixture of glycollic, oxalic and carbonic acids.

6. Dehydration. When glycerol is heated with potassium hydrogen sulphate, or phosphorus pentoxide, it loses the elements of water, yielding acrolein. The change proceeds in the following stages

$$\begin{array}{c} CH_2OH \\ | \\ CHOH \\ | \\ CH_2OH \end{array} \xrightarrow{-H_2O} \begin{array}{c} CHOH \\ \| \\ CH \\ | \\ CH_2OH \end{array} \longrightarrow \begin{array}{c} CHO \\ | \\ CH_2 \\ | \\ CH_2OH \end{array} \xrightarrow{-H_2O} \begin{array}{c} CHO \\ | \\ CH \\ \| \\ CH_2. \end{array}$$

Acrolein is a mobile liquid, B.P. 52°. It has an irritating and offensive odour, which may sometimes be detected if meat is baked at too high a temperature. Acrolein undergoes polymerisation very readily, and changes to a solid substance resembling amber in appearance which is a good electrical insulator.

Constitution of glycerol. The empirical formula of glycerol is $C_3H_8O_3$. It is a neutral substance, it reacts with sodium with the liberation of hydrogen, and it contains no unsaturated linkages. It is therefore probable that the oxygen atoms in the molecule are present in hydroxyl groups. This probability is confirmed by the action of glycerol with acetic anhydride to produce glyceryl triacetate. By the method described on p. 98 it can be shown that

330 ORGANIC CHEMISTRY

glycerol contains three hydroxyl groups in the molecule. Hence the constitution of glycerol is,

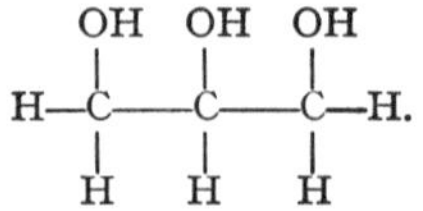

$$\begin{array}{ccc} OH & OH & OH \\ | & | & | \\ H-C-&-C-&-C-H. \\ | & | & | \\ H & H & H \end{array}$$

This constitution is confirmed by the synthesis of glycerol from acetone, of which the constitution has been established, p. 227. Acetone is reduced to iso-propyl alcohol, the alcohol is converted to isopropyl bromide by the action of bromine and phosphorus, and by treatment with alcoholic potassium hydroxide solution the iso-propyl bromide is changed to propylene. These reactions are summarised in the sequence,

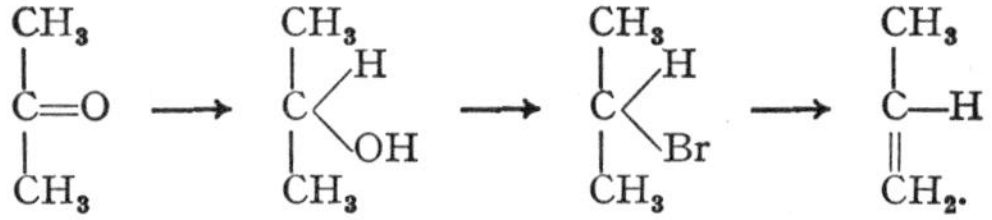

$$\begin{array}{cccc} CH_3 & CH_3 & CH_3 & CH_3 \\ | & | \diagup H & | \diagup H & | \\ C=O \rightarrow & C & \rightarrow C & \rightarrow C-H \\ | & | \diagdown OH & | \diagdown Br & \| \\ CH_3 & CH_3 & CH_3 & CH_2. \end{array}$$

$\alpha\beta$-dibromopropane is prepared from propylene by the direct addition of bromine, and by further bromination $\alpha\alpha\beta$-tribromopropane is obtained,

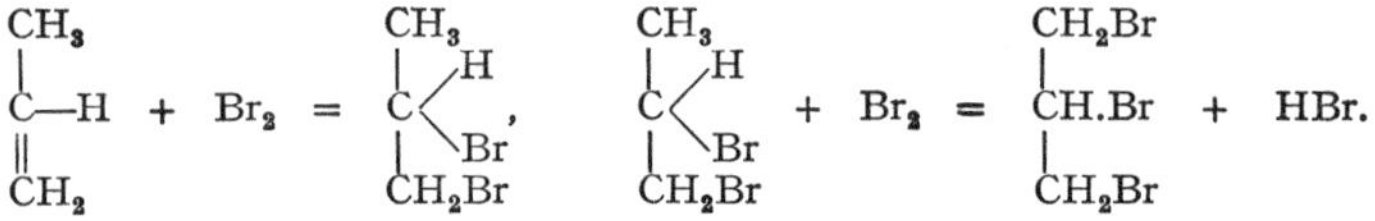

$$\begin{array}{ccccc} CH_3 & CH_3 & CH_3 & & CH_2Br \\ | & | \diagup H & | \diagup H & & | \\ C-H + Br_2 = & C & , \quad C & + Br_2 = & CH.Br + HBr. \\ \| & | \diagdown Br & | \diagdown Br & & | \\ CH_2 & CH_2Br & CH_2Br & & CH_2Br \end{array}$$

By treatment with silver acetate the bromine atoms are replaced by acetate groups, and the acetyl derivative is then hydrolysed with potassium hydroxide to yield glycerol,

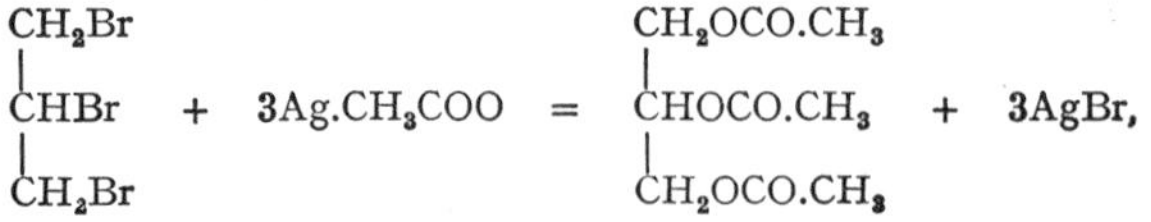

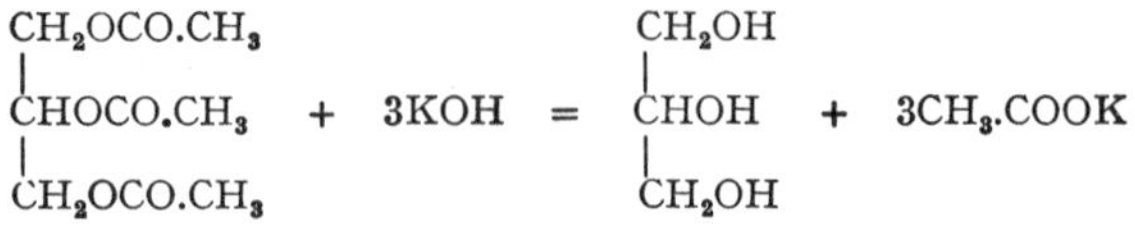

$$\begin{array}{ccc} CH_2Br & & CH_2OCO.CH_3 \\ | & & | \\ CHBr + 3Ag.CH_3COO = & CHOCO.CH_3 + 3AgBr, \\ | & & | \\ CH_2Br & & CH_2OCO.CH_3 \end{array}$$

$$\begin{array}{ccc} CH_2OCO.CH_3 & & CH_2OH \\ | & & | \\ CHOCO.CH_3 + 3KOH = & CHOH + 3CH_3.COOK \\ | & & | \\ CH_2OCO.CH_3 & & CH_2OH \end{array}$$

Uses of glycerol. Large quantities of glycerol are required for the manufacture of glyceryl nitrate (nitroglycerine) which is an important constituent of many explosives. Glycerol is also used as an " antifreeze " and as a food preservative. It is used in medicine as an ointment. Glyceryl monophosphate,

$$CH_2OH.CHOH.CH_2O.PO(OH)_2,$$

is a tonic. Glycerol is combined with phthalic anhydride to make the glyptal series of resinoids which are employed as synthetic finishes.

Test for glycerol. Glycerol may be recognised by the odour of acrolein which is obtained when it is heated with potassium hydrogen sulphate.

CHAPTER XX

CARBOHYDRATES

THE carbohydrates include many compounds, such as sugars, glycogen, inulin, starch and cellulose, which are of the greatest importance in the metabolism and constitution of vegetable and animal organisms. The carbohydrates are so named because they contain, besides carbon, only hydrogen and oxygen in the proportions in which these elements are present in water. The empirical formula of a carbohydrate has the form $C_x(H_2O)_y$. Such a formula, however, bears no relation to the properties or structures of the carbohydrates, and in terms of modern chemistry is quite meaningless.

The carbohydrates are grouped into :

(i) the *monosaccharides*, which contain six or less carbon atoms in the molecule, such as glucose and fructose, both of which have the molecular formula, $C_6H_{12}O_6$;

(ii) the *disaccharides*, which contain twelve carbon atoms in the molecule, such as maltose and sucrose, both of which have the molecular formula, $C_{12}H_{22}O_{11}$;

(iii) the *polysaccharides*, which contain eighteen or more carbon atoms in the molecule, such as starch $(C_6H_{10}O_5)_n$, where n is a large number, probably about 200.

The monosaccharides are further divided into *aldoses* of which the molecules contain an aldehyde group, and *ketoses* of which the molecules contain a ketone group. The systematic class name may also mention the number of carbon atoms in the molecule. For example, glyceraldehyde is an aldotriose, and dihydroxyacetone is a ketotriose ; glucose is an aldohexose, and fructose a ketohexose.

The monosaccharides and disaccharides are crystalline substances which can be assigned definite molecular weights. Their constitutions, although complex, in nearly all cases have been established with certainty. The evidence for the structure of glucose is discussed on p. 341. A brief statement on the constitutions of the carbohydrates mentioned in this chapter is given in the following paragraphs to enable the relationships among these compounds to be understood.

Investigation has shown that the molecules of the disaccharides and polysaccharides are built up of chains consisting of mono-saccharide units linked together by oxygen atoms. Each mono-saccharide unit is a five- or six-membered ring. The α-glucose molecule, for example, has the ring structure

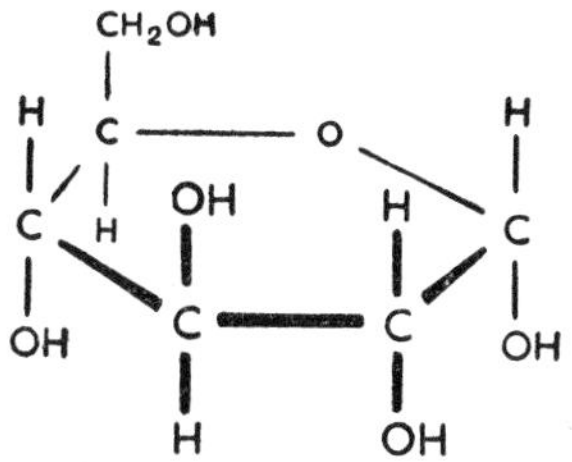

$$CH_2OH$$

α-glucose

The ring of five carbon atoms and one oxygen atom is in a plane at right angles to that of the paper, and it will be seen that certain of the atoms or groups attached to the carbon atoms of the ring are above the plane of the ring, and that others are below it.

The molecule of the disaccharide maltose, for example, consists of two α-glucose ring units linked by an oxygen atom ; it may be theoretically derived by the elimination of a molecule of water from two molecules of glucose, thus

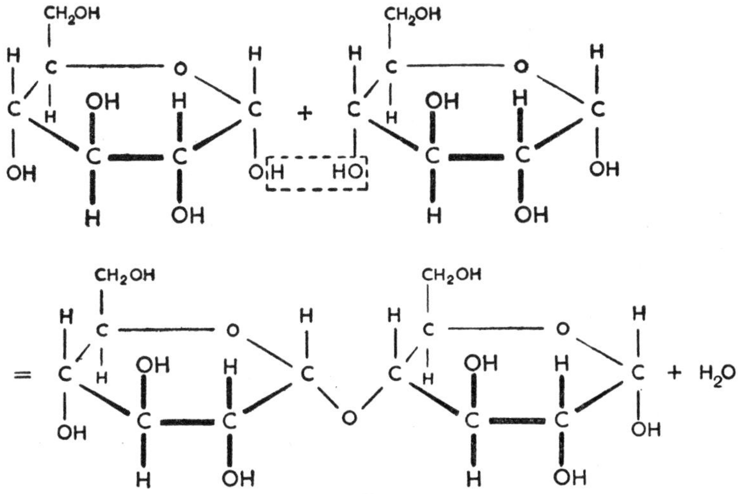

maltose

The molecules of glycogen, dextrin and starch also consist of chains of α-glucose ring units linked by oxygen atoms. The mole-cules of cellubiose and cellulose consist of β-glucose ring units linked

DIAGRAMMATIC REPRESENTATION OF THE STRUCTURES OF CERTAIN CARBOHYDRATES

Key to the diagrams used to represent the structures of certain carbohydrates. The oxygen atom is represented by the symbol o

Name of sugar from which the ring unit is derived	Structural formula of sugar	Structural formula of ring unit*	Symbol representing the structural formula of the ring unit in the diagrams
α-glucose	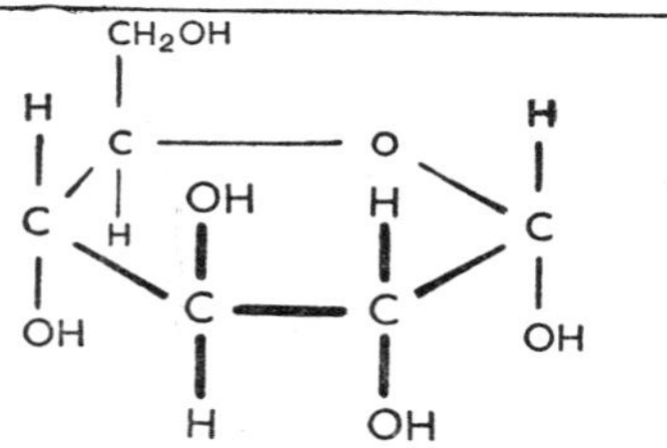	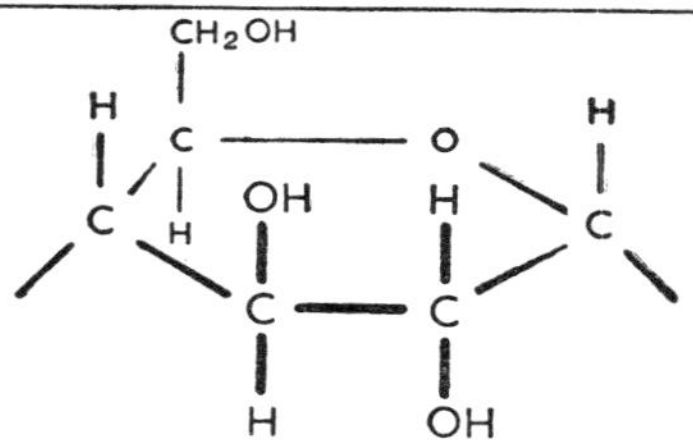	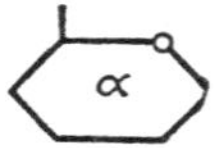
β-glucose	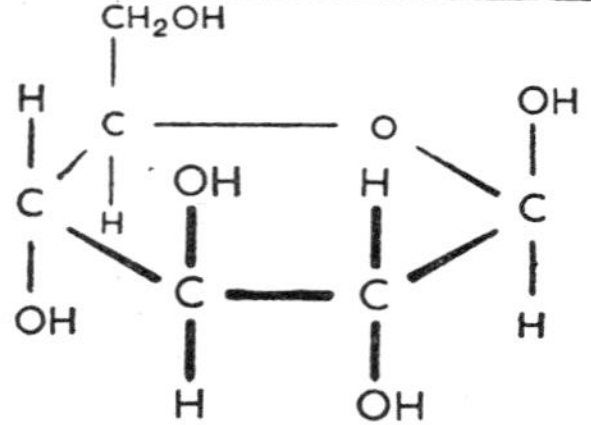	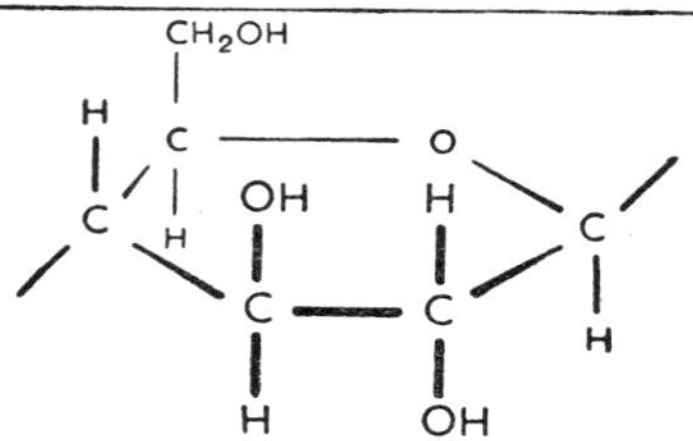	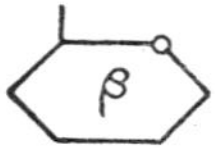
γ-fructose	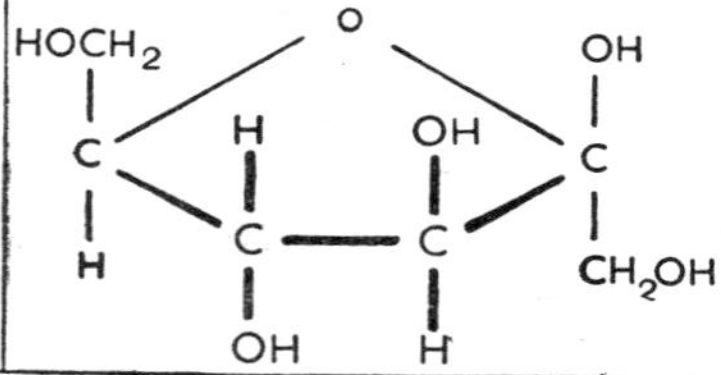	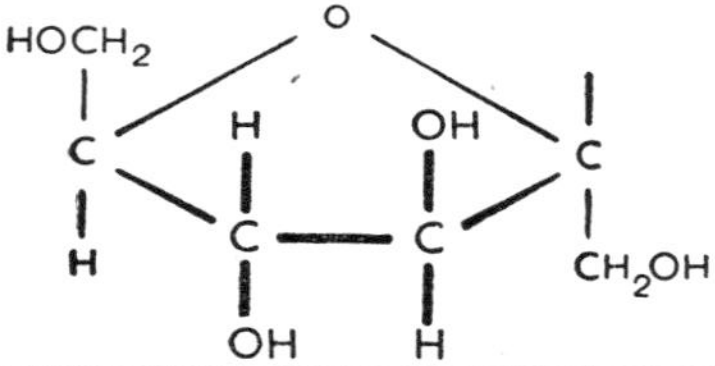	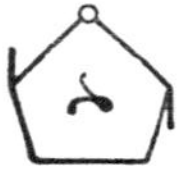

* *When the ring unit is at the end of a chain, the free carbon valency is saturated by an OH group*

by oxygen atoms. The molecule of sucrose consists of one α-glucose ring unit and one γ-fructose ring unit linked by an oxygen atom. The following scheme presents diagrammatically the structures of some of the more familiar carbohydrates.

1. Carbohydrates built up of α-glucose ring units.

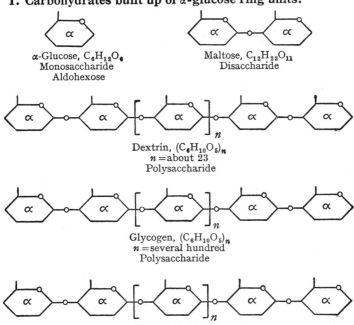

α-Glucose, $C_6H_{12}O_6$
Monosaccharide
Aldohexose

Maltose, $C_{12}H_{22}O_{11}$
Disaccharide

Dextrin, $(C_6H_{10}O_5)_n$
n = about 23
Polysaccharide

Glycogen, $(C_6H_{10}O_5)_n$
n = several hundred
Polysaccharide

Starch, $(C_6H_{10}O_5)_n$
The value of n is uncertain; it is probably about 200.
Polysaccharide

2. Carbohydrates built up of β-glucose ring units.

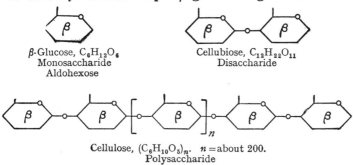

β-Glucose, $C_6H_{12}O_6$
Monosaccharide
Aldohexose

Cellubiose, $C_{12}H_{22}O_{11}$
Disaccharide

Cellulose, $(C_6H_{10}O_5)_n$. n = about 200.
Polysaccharide

3. Sucrose (cane sugar) built up of one α-glucose ring unit and one γ-fructose ring unit.

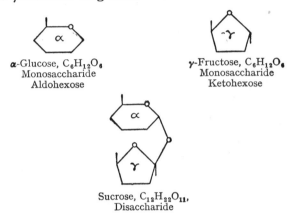

α-Glucose, $C_6H_{12}O_6$
Monosaccharide
Aldohexose

γ-Fructose, $C_6H_{12}O_6$
Monosaccharide
Ketohexose

Sucrose, $C_{12}H_{22}O_{11}$,
Disaccharide

MONOSACCHARIDES

GLUCOSE

Glucose is classified as an aldohexose. Its molecular formula is $C_6H_{12}O_6$. Glucose is known to possess the ring structure shown on p. 333. The ring, however, is readily broken, and in a large number of its chemical reactions glucose behaves as though it possesses an open-chain structure. The opening out of the ring may be assumed to take place by the addition and removal of a molecule of water :

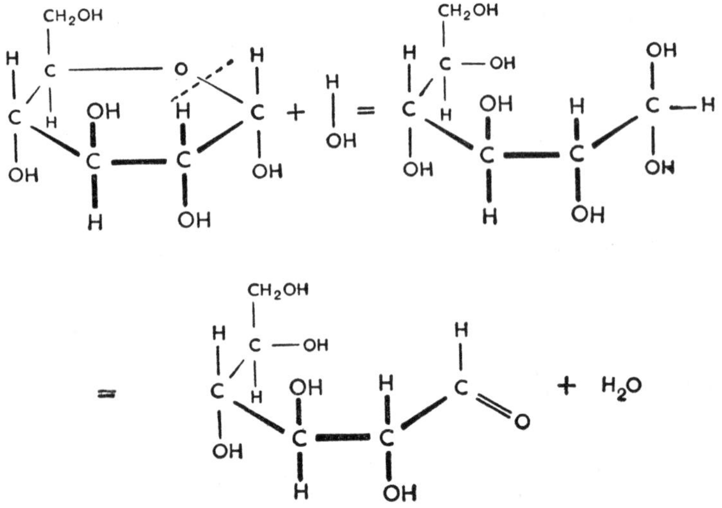

Nearly all the properties of glucose may be explained on the assumption that it is a pentahydroxy aldehyde with the molecular formula

$$\underset{\substack{\displaystyle|\\[-2pt]OH}}{\overset{\substack{H\\[-2pt]|}}{H-C}}-\underset{\substack{\displaystyle|\\[-2pt]OH}}{\overset{\substack{H\\[-2pt]|}}{C}}-\underset{\substack{\displaystyle|\\[-2pt]OH}}{\overset{\substack{H\\[-2pt]|}}{C}}-\underset{\substack{\displaystyle|\\[-2pt]OH}}{\overset{\substack{H\\[-2pt]|}}{C}}-\underset{\substack{\displaystyle|\\[-2pt]OH}}{\overset{\substack{H\\[-2pt]|}}{C}}-C\overset{\displaystyle H}{\underset{\displaystyle O.}{<}}$$

Glucose, M.P. 146°, crystallises from alcohol, or from aqueous solution at 30°, as needles without water of crystallisation ; it crystallises from cold water as the monohydrate, M.P. 86°. Glucose is almost insoluble in absolute alcohol. It dissolves in its own weight of water at room temperature. It is less sweet than sucrose. Glucose is optically active, and its solution is dextrorotatory.

Occurrence. Glucose occurs in considerable amount in grapes. In raisins (which are grapes dried in the sun) the glucose has crystallised as small brown nodules. It is associated with fructose in many sweet fruits, in honey, and in the leaves and roots of many plants.

PRINCIPAL REACTIONS IN WHICH GLUCOSE IS PRODUCED

1. The hydrolysis of starch or sucrose. Glucose is made by the hydrolysis of the more complex carbohydrates, starch and sucrose. When starch is boiled with dilute sulphuric acid it yields a solution of glucose,

$$\underset{\text{starch}}{(C_6H_{10}O_5)_n} + nH_2O = \underset{\text{glucose}}{nC_6H_{12}O_6.}$$

The manufacture of glucose from starch is described on p. 496. When sucrose is boiled with a dilute mineral acid it yields a mixture of glucose and fructose known as " invert sugar ",*

$$\underset{\text{sucrose}}{C_{12}H_{22}O_{11}} + H_2O = \underset{\text{glucose}}{C_6H_{12}O_6} + \underset{\text{fructose}}{C_6H_{12}O_6.}$$

In the laboratory the glucose can be separated from the fructose by carrying out this hydrolysis in alcoholic solution, in which glucose is much less soluble than fructose.

A mixture of 200 c.c. of alcohol diluted with 10 per cent. of water, and 8 c.c. of concentrated hydrochloric acid is maintained at 50°. 75 gm. of sucrose are added in small portions, while the mixture is well stirred. After the mixture has been allowed to stand at 50° for 2 hours it is

---

* As a result of this reaction the specific rotatory power, p. 343, of the cane sugar solution, $[\alpha]_D = +66 \cdot 5°$, changes to that of the solution of the mixture of glucose and fructose, $[\alpha]_D = -20°$. The sign of the angle of rotation of the solution thus becomes inverted. For this reason the action is described as the *inversion of cane sugar*, and the product is known as *invert sugar*.

cooled, and crystallisation is started by seeding with glucose. Crystals of glucose separate in the course of several days, while the more soluble fructose remains in solution. The glucose crystals are collected by filtration and recrystallised from 80 per cent. alcohol.

2. The reduction of gluconolactone. Gluconolactone (see below) is reduced to glucose by the action of sodium amalgam in acid solution,

$$CH_2OH.CHOH.CH.CHOH.CHOH.CO \quad + \quad H_2$$
$$\underline{\quad\quad O\quad\quad}$$
$$= \quad CH_2OH.(CHOH)_4.CHO.$$

CHEMICAL PROPERTIES OF GLUCOSE

1. Oxidation.

(a) Glucose burns in air or oxygen yielding carbon dioxide and water.

(b) When glucose is warmed with concentrated sulphuric acid it is decomposed to yield carbon monoxide, carbon dioxide and free carbon.

(c) When glucose is oxidised with bromine water it yields gluconic acid,

$$CH_2OH.(CHOH)_4.CHO \quad + \quad O \quad = \quad CH_2OH.(CHOH)_4.COOH.$$

Gluconic acid passes spontaneously into gluconolactone,

Gluconolactone is a crystalline compound, soluble in water to give a neutral solution. It may be reduced to glucose. The reduction of a lactone is a reaction of importance because it furnishes a means of obtaining an aldehyde from a hydroxy acid ; the parent acid of the lactone cannot be directly reduced to an aldehyde.

(d) When glucose is oxidised with nitric acid it yields saccharic acid,

$$CH_2OH.(CHOH)_4.CHO \quad + \quad 3O \quad = \quad HOOC.(CHOH)_4.COOH.$$
$$\text{saccharic acid}$$

2. Action as a reducing agent.

(a) Glucose reduces warm solutions of the salts of gold, silver and platinum, precipitating the respective metals.

(b) Glucose precipitates cuprous oxide from boiling Fehling's solution. The concentration of glucose in aqueous solution may be estimated by means of this reaction, p. 346.

3. Reduction. Glucose in aqueous solution is reduced by sodium amalgam to give the hexahydric alcohol, sorbitol,

$$CH_2OH.(CHOH)_4.CHO + H_2 = CH_2OH.(CHOH)_4.CH_2OH.$$

When sorbitol is heated with concentrated hydriodic acid under pressure, it is converted to secondary normal hexyl iodide,

$$CH_3.CH_2.CH_2.CH_2.CHI.CH_3.*$$

4. Reaction with acetic anhydride. When glucose is treated with excess of hot acetic anhydride in the presence of a catalyst such as zinc chloride, all five hydroxyl groups are acetylated,

$$2CH_2OH.(CHOH)_4.CHO + 5(CH_3CO)_2O$$
$$= 2CH_2.OCOCH_3.(CH.OCOCH_3)_4.CHO + 5H_2O.$$

To carry out the acetylation, a mixture of 25 c.c. of acetic anhydride and 1 gm. of zinc chloride is placed in a 100 c.c. round-bottomed flask which is heated on a vigorously boiling water-bath for 5 minutes. 5 gm. of powdered glucose are cautiously added to the mixture, which is heated for 1 hour on the water-bath and then poured into 250 c.c. of cold water. The pentacetyl glucose separates as an oil which slowly crystallises. The crystals are washed with water, drained, and re-crystallised twice from methylated spirit. The pentacetyl glucose so obtained is in the form of colourless crystals, M.P. 110–111°.

5. Fermentation. The enzyme zymase in yeast readily causes the fermentation of glucose, at 20–30°, yielding chiefly ethyl alcohol and carbon dioxide (p. 493).

6. Reaction with metallic hydroxides, giving glucosates. Glucose in aqueous solution reacts with slaked lime to form a soluble compound, $C_6H_{12}O_6,CaO$. This compound is decomposed by carbon dioxide with the liberation of the glucose. Barium hydroxide also reacts with glucose to form a soluble compound which is decomposed by carbon dioxide. The calcium oxide compound of fructose is sparingly soluble, and use is made of this property to separate glucose from fructose.

7. Reaction with phenylhydrazine, giving glucose phenylhydrazone and glucosazone. Glucose reacts with phenylhydrazine to give a soluble phenylhydrazone,

$$\begin{array}{l} H-C=O \\ | \\ H-C-OH \\ | \\ (H-C-OH)_3 \\ | \\ CH_2OH \end{array} + H_2N.NHC_6H_5 = \begin{array}{l} H-C=N.NHC_6H_5 \\ | \\ H-C-OH \\ | \\ (H-C-OH)_3 \\ | \\ CH_2OH \end{array} + H_2O.$$

* Compare the formation of iso-propyl iodide from glycerol, p. 326.

If excess of phenylhydrazine is present, it then oxidises the glucose phenylhydrazone by removing two hydrogen atoms from the secondary alcohol group next to the carbon atom attached to the phenylhydrazine residue, thus,

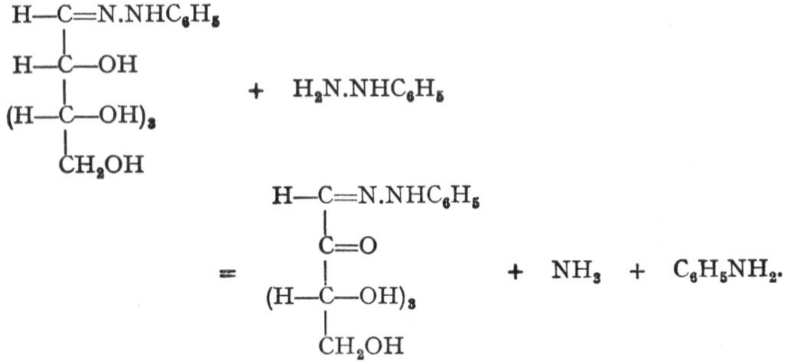

$$
\begin{array}{l}
H-C=N.NHC_6H_5 \\
H-C-OH \\
(H-C-OH)_3 \\
CH_2OH
\end{array}
\quad + \quad H_2N.NHC_6H_5
$$

$$
= \quad
\begin{array}{l}
H-C=N.NHC_6H_5 \\
C=O \\
(H-C-OH)_3 \\
CH_2OH
\end{array}
\quad + \quad NH_3 \quad + \quad C_6H_5NH_2.
$$

Phenylhydrazine then condenses with the carbonyl group thus obtained, giving phenyl glucosazone, a yellow crystalline solid, sparingly soluble in water, M.P. 204°,

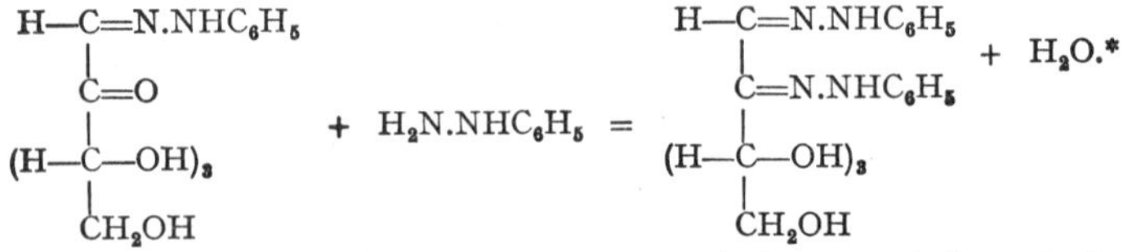

$$
\begin{array}{l}
H-C=N.NHC_6H_5 \\
C=O \\
(H-C-OH)_3 \\
CH_2OH
\end{array}
\quad + \quad H_2N.NHC_6H_5 \quad = \quad
\begin{array}{l}
H-C=N.NHC_6H_5 \\
C=N.NHC_6H_5 \\
(H-C-OH)_3 \\
CH_2OH
\end{array}
\quad + \quad H_2O.*
$$

The formation of the osazone from glucose is best carried out in hot, weakly acid solution; the experimental procedure is described under " Tests for glucose ", p. 345.

If phenyl glucosazone is heated with concentrated hydrochloric acid it is decomposed to yield glucosone and phenylhydrazine hydrochloride,

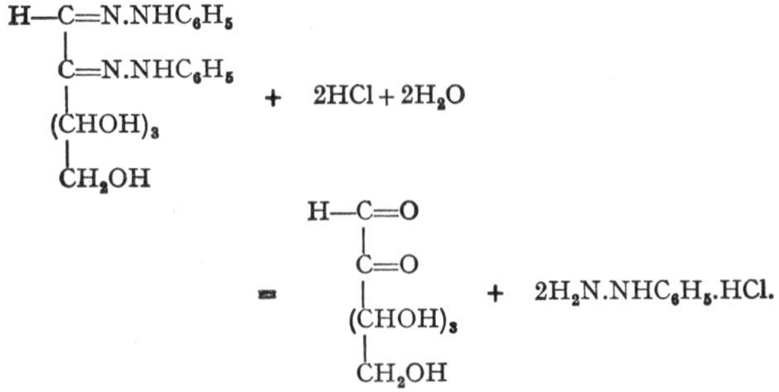

$$
\begin{array}{l}
H-C=N.NHC_6H_5 \\
C=N.NHC_6H_5 \\
(CHOH)_3 \\
CH_2OH
\end{array}
\quad + \quad 2HCl + 2H_2O
$$

$$
= \quad
\begin{array}{l}
H-C=O \\
C=O \\
(CHOH)_3 \\
CH_2OH
\end{array}
\quad + \quad 2H_2N.NHC_6H_5.HCl.
$$

* The equations in this paragraph depict the general course of the reactions leading to osazone formation, but they do not represent the actual mechanism of these reactions. For discussions on the mechanism of the reactions more advanced works should be consulted.

Glucosone may be reduced by zinc dust and acetic acid to yield fructose,

$$
\begin{array}{ccc}
\text{H—C=O} & & \text{H} \\
| & & | \\
\text{C=O} & & \text{H—C—OH} \\
| & \text{+ H}_2 = & | \\
\text{(CHOH)}_3 & & \text{C=O} \\
| & & | \\
\text{CH}_2\text{OH} & & \text{(CHOH)}_3 \\
& & | \\
& & \text{CH}_2\text{OH}
\end{array}
$$

This method of forming fructose from glucose is an example of a general method for converting an aldose to the corresponding ketose through the intermediate formation of the osazone and the osone.

8. Reaction with hydrogen cyanide, giving the hydroxy cyanide. Glucose reacts with hydrogen cyanide in the manner characteristic of an aldehyde, thus,

$$
\text{CH}_2\text{OH.(CHOH)}_4.\text{C}\!\!\begin{array}{c}\diagup\text{H}\\\diagdown\text{O}\end{array} + \text{ HCN } = \text{ CH}_2\text{OH.(CHOH)}_4.\text{C}\!\!\begin{array}{c}\diagup\text{H}\\-\text{OH}\\\diagdown\text{CN.}\end{array}
$$

If the product of this reaction is hydrolysed, and the hydroxy acid so obtained is converted to the lactone (p. 338), and the lactone is reduced, an aldose containing 7 carbon atoms in the molecule is formed,

$$
\begin{array}{ccc}
\text{H} & & \text{H} \\
| & & | \\
\text{HO—C—CN} & \longrightarrow & \text{HO—C—COOH} \\
| & & | \\
\text{(CHOH)}_4 & & \text{(CHOH)}_4 \\
| & & | \\
\text{CH}_2\text{OH} & & \text{CH}_2\text{OH}
\end{array}
$$

$$
\begin{array}{ccc}
\text{O=C} \!\!\!-\!\!\!-\!\!\!-\!\!\!-\!\!\!| & & \\
| & & \text{O=C—H} \\
\text{(H—C—OH)}_2 \quad \text{O} & & | \\
\longrightarrow \quad | \qquad\qquad | & \longrightarrow & \text{(H—C—OH)}_5 \\
\text{H—C} \!\!\!-\!\!\!-\!\!\!-\!\!\!-\!\!\!| & & | \\
| & & \text{CH}_2\text{OH.} \\
\text{(CHOH)}_2 & & \\
| & & \\
\text{CH}_2\text{OH} & &
\end{array}
$$

By this means it is possible to ascend the series of the aldoses.

THE CONSTITUTION OF GLUCOSE

Evidence for the open-chain structure. The quantitative analysis of glucose shows that the empirical formula is CH_2O ; its molecular weight determination by the depression of the freezing point of water shows that the molecular formula is $C_6H_{12}O_6$.

By the method of acetylation, p. 98, the molecule of glucose is shown to contain five hydroxyl groups. The condensations of glucose with hydrogen cyanide and with phenylhydrazine show that the molecule contains a carbonyl group. The oxidation of glucose to gluconic acid or saccharic acid, both of which contain six carbon atoms in the molecule, show that the carbonyl group is part of an aldehyde group. The reduction of glucose to sorbitol, and the reaction of sorbitol with hydrogen iodide to give *n*-secondary hexyl iodide (2-iodohexane), shows that the six carbon atoms in the glucose molecule must be arranged as an unbranched chain. Kiliani has shown that the compound obtained by the action of hydrocyanic acid on glucose (Reaction 8, p. 341) may be hydrolysed to the corresponding acid, and that if this acid is treated with excess of phosphorus and iodine all the —OH groups are replaced by hydrogen atoms to yield normal heptylic acid, $CH_3.(CH_2)_5.COOH$. Kiliani's reaction furnishes conclusive evidence that the carbon chain in the molecule of glucose is unbranched.

All these reactions are explained if glucose is assigned the structural formula :

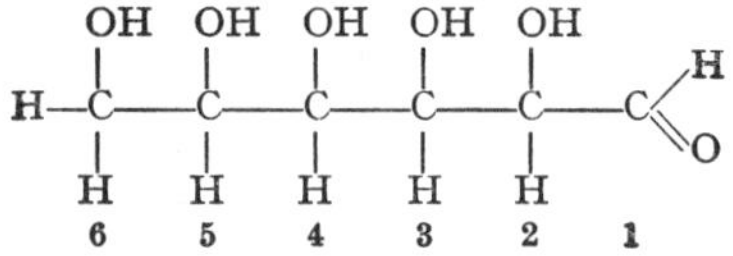

Each of the carbon atoms, 2, 3, 4, 5, is an asymmetric carbon atom, and it can be shown that there should be sixteen different configurations of this structure, each corresponding to one of sixteen isomeric compounds. All these are known, and their particular configurations have been determined. The tetrahedral configuration of the groups attached to a carbon atom requires that the chain of six carbon atoms in glucose should have the form of a partial ring. The open-chain formula for the molecule of glucose should therefore be written :

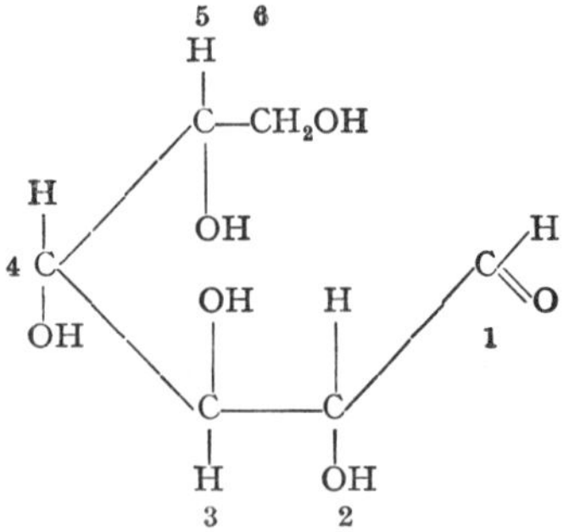

α- and β-glucose. There are two isomeric forms of glucose, designated α-glucose and β-glucose, which cannot be accounted for by the principles of optical isomerism applied to open-chain compounds. α-glucose is prepared by the crystallisation of glucose at room temperature from solution in acetic acid containing a little water. β-glucose is made by crystallisation from pure acetic acid at the temperature of a boiling water bath. The existence of these isomers was deduced from a quantitative study of the optical activity of aqueous solutions of glucose.

Specific rotatory power. In the discussion of the relation between optical activity and molecular structure (Chapter XVIII, p. 302) no account is taken of the magnitude of the angle of rotation ; the argument is complete if it is known whether the aqueous solution of a given substance is optically active or not. Each optically active compound has its own specific rotatory power, which may be used for its identification. The symbol for specific rotatory power is $[\alpha]_{\lambda}^{t}$, where t is the temperature, and λ is the wave length of the light employed ; if the D-line of the sodium spectrum is used the symbol becomes $[\alpha]_{D}^{t}$. For a liquid,

$$[\alpha]_{D}^{t} = \frac{\alpha}{ld}$$

where α is the angle of rotation, l is the thickness of the liquid in *decimetres*, and d is its density.

Most measurements of rotatory power are made on solutions, in which case for sodium light,

$$[\alpha]_{D}^{t} = \frac{\alpha v}{lp}$$

where p is the number of grams of the compound in v c.c. of solution, and α and l have the same significance as before. The nature of the solvent has a marked effect on the rotatory power of a given solute, and it must always be stated in the record of an experiment. Experiments are commonly made on aqueous solutions at 20°. The actual angle of rotation for a solution of an optically active compound is given by

$$\alpha = \frac{lp}{v} [\alpha]_{D}^{t}.$$

α is thus proportional to the concentration of the solution and to its thickness.

The ring structure of glucose. An aqueous solution of α-glucose possesses a specific rotatory power, $[\alpha]_{D} = +110°$. An aqueous solution of β-glucose has a rotatory power, $[\alpha]_{D} = +17·5°$. These two forms, α- and β-glucose, must be different because their rotatory powers are different, but it should be noted that they are not optical isomers because their rotatory powers are neither equal in magnitude nor opposite in sign. An aqueous solution of either isomeride on standing attains a rotatory power of $[\alpha]_{D} = +52·5°,$* thus showing that each isomeride spontaneously changes into the other, so that an equilibrium mixture is finally attained.

On account of this instability it has not been possible to study the constitution of α- and β-glucose directly, but the nature of their

---

* The change of the rotatory power of a sugar solution on standing is known as *mutarotation.*

isomerism may be inferred from the constitution of their methyl derivatives which are obtained by heating anhydrous glucose with anhydrous methyl alcohol containing about 5 per cent. of hydrogen chloride at 65° for some time. Ordinary glucose (which is a mixture of α- and β-glucose) gives rise to α-monomethyl glucoside, M.P. 165°, $[\alpha]_D = +159°$, and to β-monomethyl glucoside, M.P. 105°, $[\alpha]_D = -34°$. These compounds do not spontaneously change into one another, they do not show the common condensation reactions of aldehydes (p. 202), and they are not reducing agents. Their properties are accounted for by assigning them ring structures derived from glucose by the scheme * :

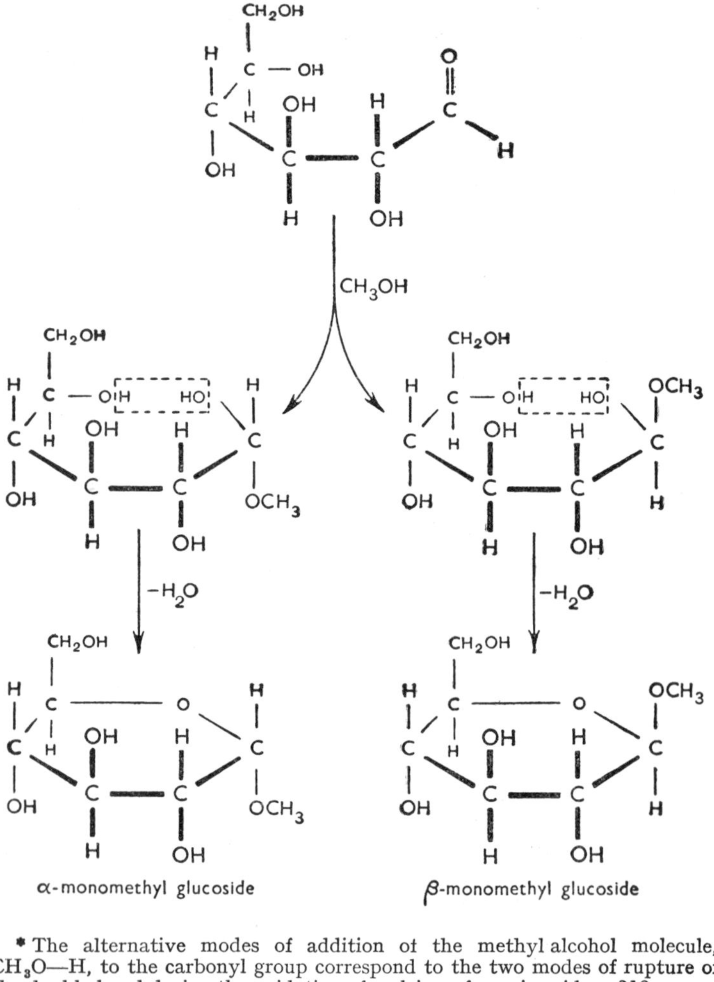

α-monomethyl glucoside   β-monomethyl glucoside

* The alternative modes of addition of the methyl alcohol molecule, CH_3O—H, to the carbonyl group correspond to the two modes of rupture of the double bond during the oxidation of maleic or fumaric acid, p. 318.

α- and β-monomethyl glucosides are geometrical isomers (p. 314). In one case the hydrogen atom attached to carbon atom 1 is above the plane of the ring and the methoxy group is below the plane of the ring, and in the other case these positions are reversed. The configurations of α-glucose and β-glucose correspond to those of the monomethyl glucosides ; the positions occupied by the H and OH groups attached to carbon atom 1 in these two sugars are thus :

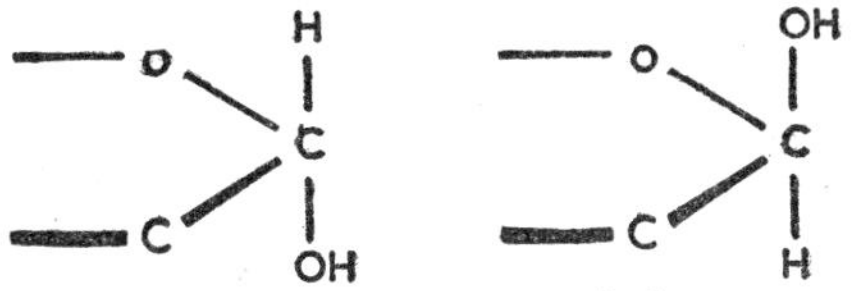

α-glucose   β-glucose

The simplest compound having a molecular structure based on a ring of five carbon atoms and one oxygen atom is 1 : 2 pyran

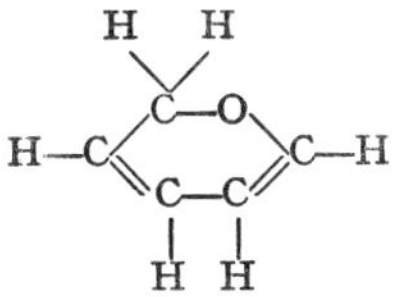

The ring structure of glucose is therefore described as the pyranose form. The pyranose form of glucose is important because it is the unit out of which the more complex carbohydrates are built up. The molecule of starch, for example, contains a chain of about 200 glucopyranose units.

Tests for glucose.

(i) Glucose responds to the two following tests which are given by all carbohydrates :

(a) if glucose is warmed with concentrated sulphuric acid it chars, and carbon monoxide, carbon dioxide and sulphur dioxide are evolved ;

(b) if a 10 per cent. solution of sodium hydroxide is boiled with glucose it is turned yellow, and an odour of caramel is emitted ;

and to a third test which is given by the familiar carbohydrates with the exception of sucrose and starch :

(c) Molisch's test. If 0·1 gm. of glucose dissolved in 2 c.c. of water is mixed with 2–3 c.c. of a 20 per cent. solution of α-naphthol in alcohol, and 2 c.c. of concentrated sulphuric acid are gently poured down the inside of the test-tube to form a layer under the mixture, a deep violet coloration is produced where the two liquids meet.

(ii) Glucose forms an osazone when warmed with phenylhydrazine (Reaction 7, p. 339). Either phenylhydrazine itself, or phenylhydrazine hydrochloride may be used as the reagent.

(a) Formation of glucosazone using phenylhydrazine. **2 gm. of** glucose are dissolved in 10 c.c. of water. 4 c.c. of phenylhydrazine dissolved in 4 c.c. of glacial acetic acid are added, and the mixed solution is heated in a boiling water-bath. The yellow osazone begins to crystalise after 20 minutes heating. After heating for another 30 minutes the tube is cooled, and the crystals are filtered off and washed, first with water and then with a little methylated spirit. The glucosazone is recrystallised from methylated spirit in which it is only slightly soluble.

(b) Formation of glucosazone using phenylhydrazine hydrochloride. About 0·5 gm. of phenylhydrazine hydrochloride and 1 gm. of sodium acetate and a few drops of glacial acetic acid are added to 20 c.c. of a 1 per cent. solution of glucose. Crystals of the osazone appear after heating for about 20 minutes, and may be purified as described in (a) above.

Glucosazone forms characteristic crystals which may be recognised, and distinguished from those of other osazones, by examination under a microscope. It should be noted that fructose yields glucosazone when treated with excess of phenylhydrazine (p. 349) ; under parallel conditions, however, glucosazone is more rapidly formed from fructose than it is from glucose, and this difference may be used to distinguish between the two sugars.

(iii) Glucose reduces an ammoniacal solution of silver oxide to a mirror of metallic silver, and Fehling's solution to cuprous oxide. Fructose and many other organic compounds react similarly with these oxidising agents, see p. 208.

(iv) *Rapid furfural test.* This test is a modification of Molisch's test. Concentrated hydrochloric acid is used instead of sulphuric acid, and it is then found that the rate of formation of the violet coloration depends on the nature of the carbohydrate under examination. The rapid furfural test furnishes a reliable test for distinguishing between glucose and fructose. An alcoholic solution of α-naphthol is mixed with an aqueous solution of the sugar, 6–8 c.c. of concentrated hydrochloric acid are added, and the solution is boiled. If the sugar present is glucose (or lactose or maltose) a violet colour is produced after a delay of about 1 minute. If the sugar is fructose (or sucrose) the violet coloration is produced immediately the solution begins to boil.

Estimation of glucose. The concentration of glucose in aqueous solution may be accurately measured by use of the polarimeter ; this method is clearly inapplicable if the sample of glucose is contaminated with other optically active substances. Glucose may be estimated in solution by titration against Fehling's solution. The titration is conducted by running the glucose solution from a burette into 25 c.c. of Fehling's solution (prepared so that 1 c.c. $\equiv 0 \cdot 0050$ gm. of glucose) maintained just at its boiling point in a white porcelain dish. The end-point is reached when the blue colour of the Fehling's solution completely disappears.

FRUCTOSE

Fructose is classified as a ketohexose. Its molecular formula is $C_6H_{12}O_6$. **Like glucose**, with which it is isomeric, it possesses a ring structure. For many purposes, however, it may be regarded as a pentahydroxy ketone, with the structural formula :

$$\begin{array}{ccccccc}
& H & H & H & H & & H \\
& | & | & | & | & & | \\
H{-}C & {-}C & {-}C & {-}C & {-}C & {-}C{-}H \\
& | & | & | & | & \| & | \\
& OH & OH & OH & OH & O & OH
\end{array}$$

Fructose forms colourless crystals, M.P. 95°. It is more soluble than glucose in alcohol and water. It is about as sweet as glucose. Fructose is optically active, and its aqueous solution is laevo-rotatory. Fructose occurs with glucose in honey and in most sweet fruits.

Methods by which fructose is produced.

1. From sucrose. Sucrose is hydrolysed to a mixture of glucose and fructose known as *invert sugar* on boiling with very dilute sulphuric acid.

To isolate the fructose in invert sugar, 10 gm. of the sugar are dissolved in 50 c.c. of water and the solution is cooled in ice. 6 gm. of slaked lime are stirred into the solution in small quantities at a time. The sparingly soluble lime compound of fructose separates ($C_6H_{12}O_6$,CaO) and is collected on a filter, washed and pressed, suspended in water, and decomposed with carbon dioxide. After removal of the calcium carbonate by filtration, the solution is evaporated to a syrup. The addition of a crystal of fructose causes the syrup slowly to solidify, and the crystals obtained may be recrystallised from alcohol.

2. From inulin. Inulin is a carbohydrate which occurs in place of starch in artichokes and in dahlia tubers. On hydrolysis it yields fructose only,

$$(C_6H_{10}O_5)_n \;+\; nH_2O \;=\; nC_6H_{12}O_6.$$

The hydrolysis is carried out by heating an aqueous solution of inulin containing a few drops of sulphuric acid on a water-bath for 1 hour. The sulphuric acid is then precipitated as barium sulphate by the addition of barium hydroxide, and after filtration the solution is concentrated to a syrup and crystallised by seeding with a crystal of fructose.

Chemical properties of fructose.

1. Oxidation. Fructose burns in air or oxygen, yielding carbon dioxide and water. It is charred when treated with concentrated sulphuric acid, and carbon monoxide, carbon dioxide and sulphur dioxide are evolved.

Under the attack of less vigorous oxidising agents fructose behaves as a ketone, and yields two acids each of which contains less than six carbon atoms in the molecule. Fructose, however, is oxidised very much more readily than a ketone without hydroxyl groups in the molecule. When fructose in aqueous solution is boiled with mercuric oxide it is oxidised to trihydroxybutyric acid and glycollic acid,*

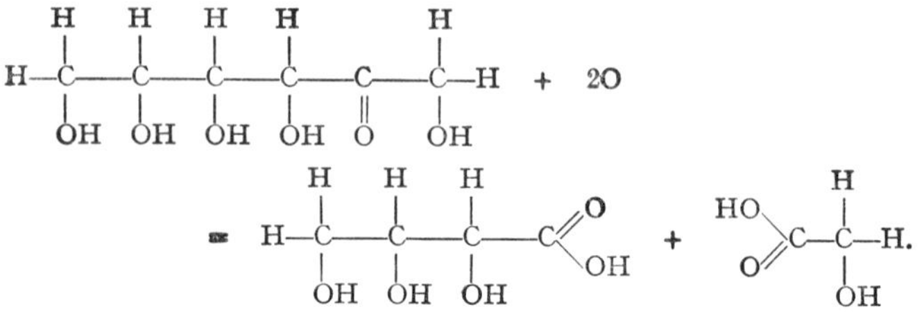

When fructose is oxidised with nitric acid or with bromine water, the molecule is broken down in the same way, but in addition the $-CH_2OH$ group remote from the carbonyl group is also attacked.

The products of these reactions are, therefore, tartaric acid, glycollic acid and water.

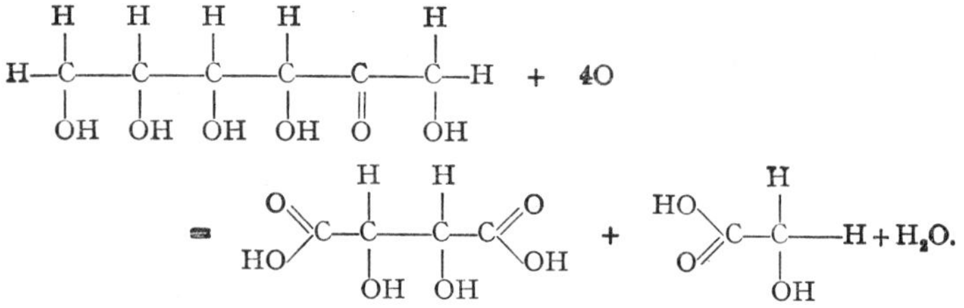

2. Action as a reducing agent. Although fructose is not an aldehyde it is a stronger reducing agent than glucose, and its reducing action on Fehling's solution, and on an ammoniacal solution of silver oxide, is more rapid than that of glucose.

* This reaction is typical of the effect of oxidation on a mixed ketone. If, for example, butyl ethyl ketone is oxidised, the molecule breaks down thus,

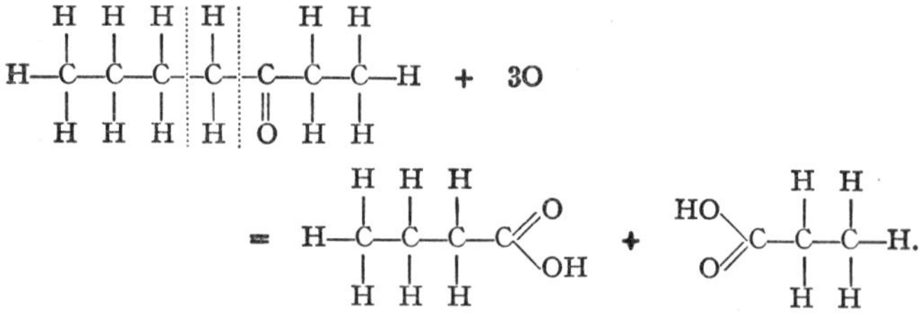

It is seen from the equation that the smaller alkyl group and the carbonyl group yield one fatty acid, propionic acid, and that the $>CH_2$ group of the larger alkyl group next to the carbonyl group is oxidised to the carboxyl group, to yield another fatty acid, butyric acid. The rule that on oxidation of a mixed ketone the carbonyl group remains linked to the smaller alkyl group is known as Popoff's rule. Its application is wide, but not universal.

3. Reduction. Fructose is reduced more easily than glucose by sodium amalgam and water, to yield a mixture of two optically isomeric hexahydric alcohols, mannitol and sorbitol,

$$2C_6H_{12}O_6 + H_2 = C_6H_8(OH)_6 + C_6H_8(OH)_6.$$

4. Reaction with acetic anhydride. When fructose is heated with acetic anhydride and zinc chloride it yields a penta-acetyl derivative,

$$2CH_2OH.(CHOH)_3.CO.CH_2OH + 5(CH_3CO)_2O$$
$$= 2CH_2.OCOCH_3.(CH.OCOCH_3)_3.CO.CH_2.OCOCH_3 + 5H_2O.$$

5. Reaction with metallic hydroxides, giving fructosates. Slaked lime reacts with fructose in aqueous solution to yield the sparingly soluble compound, $C_6H_{12}O_6$,CaO. The use of this compound in the separation of fructose from glucose is mentioned on p. 347.

6. Reaction with phenylhydrazine, giving fructose phenylhydrazone and fructosazone. Fructose reacts with phenylhydrazine to give a soluble phenylhydrazone,

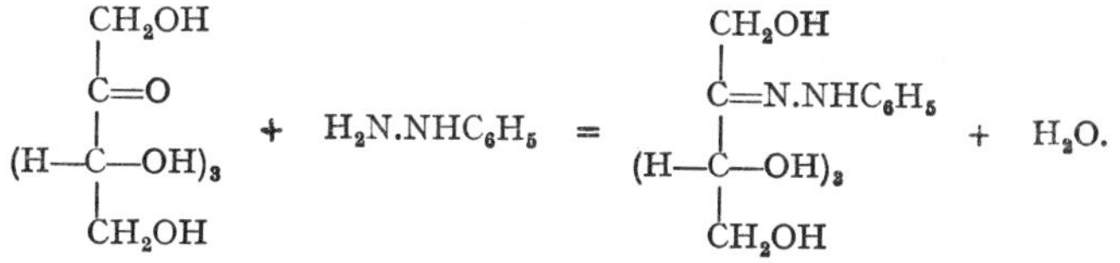

$$\begin{array}{c} CH_2OH \\ | \\ C{=}O \\ | \\ (H{-}C{-}OH)_3 \\ | \\ CH_2OH \end{array} + H_2N.NHC_6H_5 = \begin{array}{c} CH_2OH \\ | \\ C{=}N.NHC_6H_5 \\ | \\ (H{-}C{-}OH)_3 \\ | \\ CH_2OH \end{array} + H_2O.$$

If excess of phenylhydrazine is present, the primary alcohol group next to the hydrazone group is oxidised to an aldehyde group, and this is then attacked by the phenylhydrazine with the formation of fructosazone. The experimental conditions for the reaction of phenylhydrazine with fructose are the same as those described on p. 346 for its reaction with glucose.

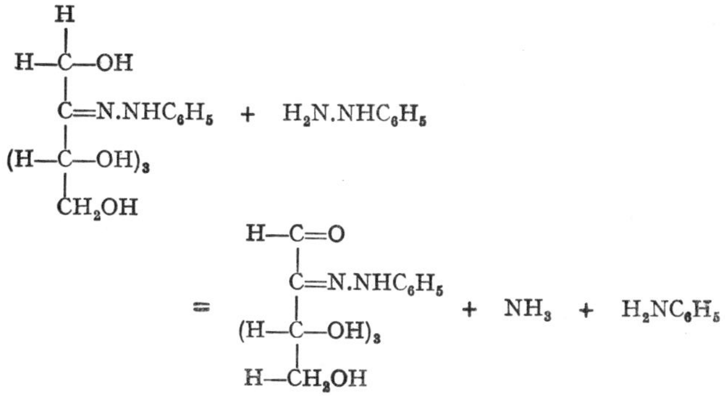

$$\begin{array}{c} H \\ | \\ H{-}C{-}OH \\ | \\ C{=}N.NHC_6H_5 \\ | \\ (H{-}C{-}OH)_3 \\ | \\ CH_2OH \end{array} + H_2N.NHC_6H_5$$

$$= \begin{array}{c} H{-}C{=}O \\ | \\ C{=}N.NHC_6H_5 \\ | \\ (H{-}C{-}OH)_3 \\ | \\ H{-}CH_2OH \end{array} + NH_3 + H_2NC_6H_5$$

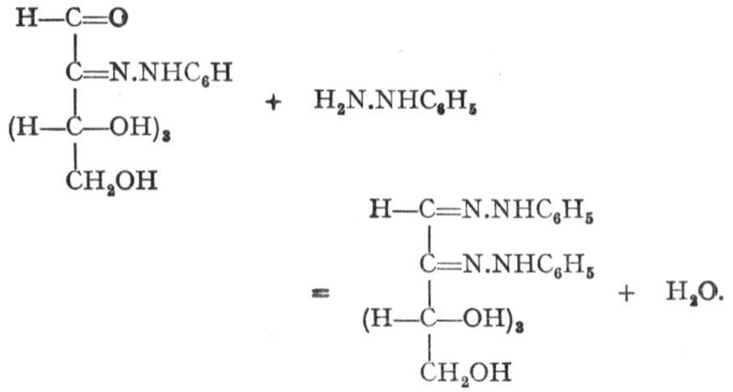

$$\begin{array}{c} H-C=O \\ | \\ C=N.NHC_6H \\ | \\ (H-C-OH)_3 \\ | \\ CH_2OH \end{array} \quad + \quad H_2N.NHC_6H_5$$

$$= \quad \begin{array}{c} H-C=N.NHC_6H_5 \\ | \\ C=N.NHC_6H_5 \\ | \\ (H-C-OH)_3 \\ | \\ CH_2OH \end{array} \quad + \quad H_2O.$$

Fructosazone and glucosazone are identical; the M.P. is 204°. The conversion of fructose to the osazone takes place more rapidly than the similar reaction of glucose. This difference may be used for distinguishing between the two sugars, provided that the two reactions are carried out under strictly parallel conditions.

7. Reaction with hydrogen cyanide, giving a cyanohydrin. Fructose reacts with hydrocyanic acid in the manner characteristic of a ketone, thus :

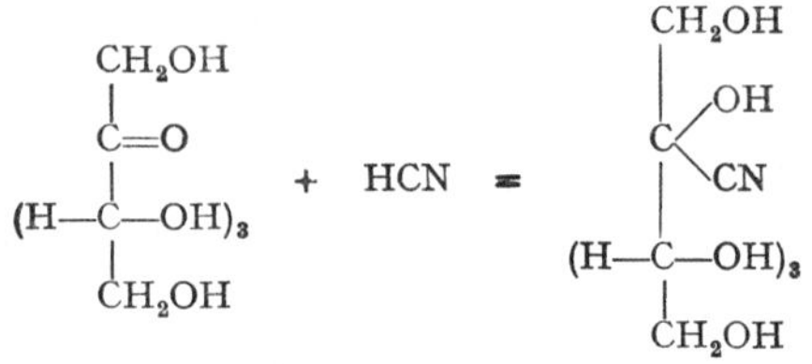

$$\begin{array}{c} CH_2OH \\ | \\ C=O \\ | \\ (H-C-OH)_3 \\ | \\ CH_2OH \end{array} \quad + \quad HCN \quad = \quad \begin{array}{c} CH_2OH \\ | \quad OH \\ C \\ | \quad CN \\ (H-C-OH)_3 \\ | \\ CH_2OH \end{array}$$

8. Fermentation. Fructose ferments with yeast yielding ethyl alcohol and carbon dioxide, the same products as given by glucose.

Constitution of fructose. The chemical reactions of fructose show that it is closely related to its isomer glucose. Like glucose, fructose forms a pentacetyl derivative, and condenses with hydrogen cyanide and phenylhydrazine. On reduction, fructose yields a mixture of mannitol and sorbitol, which on treatment with hydriodic acid yields *n*-secondary hexyl iodide, the identical product obtained by the complete reduction of glucose.

On oxidation, however, fructose yields a mixture of acids, p. 347; this reaction shows that fructose has a ketonic structure in which the carbonyl group is next to one of the carbon atoms at the end of the carbon chain. This evidence is conclusively confirmed by Kiliani's reaction by which fructose is converted to the cyanohydrin, which is hydrolysed to the corresponding acid; this is then reduced to a fatty acid with phosphorus and iodine. The product is methyl-*n*-butyl acetic acid,

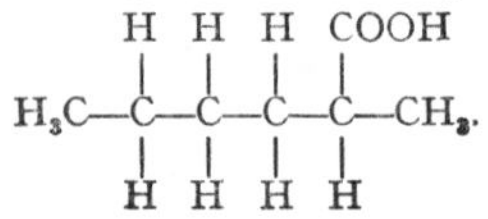

$$\begin{array}{c} H \quad H \quad H \quad COOH \\ | \quad | \quad | \quad | \\ H_3C-C-C-C-C-CH_3. \\ | \quad | \quad | \quad | \\ H \quad H \quad H \quad H \end{array}$$

The cyanohydrin must be formed, therefore, according to the equation,

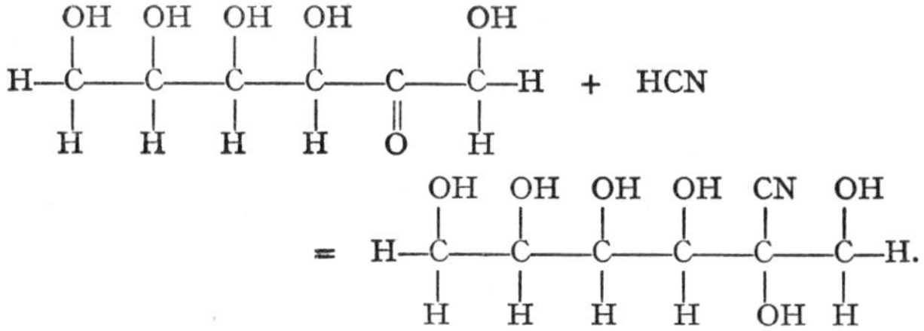

The straight chain formula explains most of the reactions of fructose. Fructose solutions, however, exhibit mutarotation, from which it has been deduced that fructose, as ordinarily obtained, consists of a mixture of the isomeric forms :

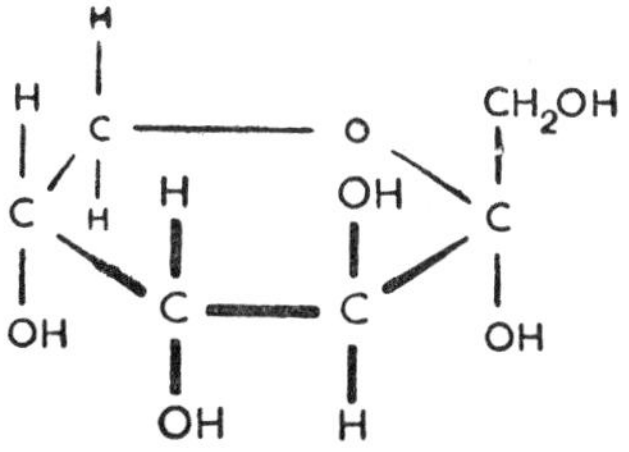

α-fructopyranose 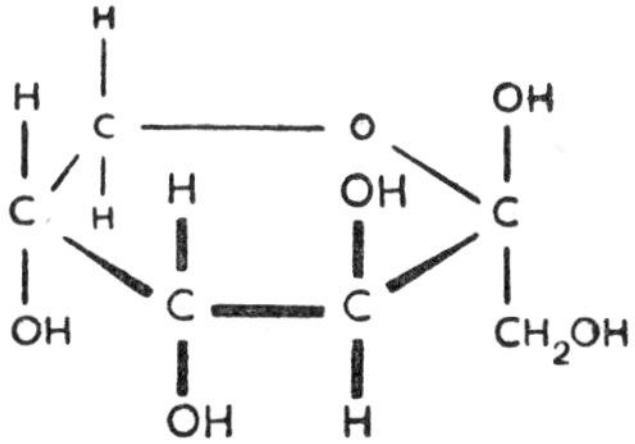   β-fructopyranose

in which the β-form predominates. γ-fructose, p. 334, is an unstable isomeride. It is the form in which a molecule of fructose is condensed with a molecule of α-glucose in sucrose.

Tests for fructose. Fructose responds to all the tests described under " glucose " on p. 345. The most reliable chemical test for distinguishing between fructose and glucose is the " rapid furfural test ".

Fructose is conveniently and conclusively differentiated from glucose by its action on polarised light. Fructose is laevorotatory and glucose is dextrorotatory.

Estimation of fructose. Fructose is estimated in aqueous solution by the use of the polarimeter, or by its action on standardised Fehling's solution. The experimental details for the estimation are exactly the same as those described under the estimation of glucose, p. 346.

DISACCHARIDES

MALTOSE

The structural formula of maltose, $C_{12}H_{22}O_{11}$, is given on p. **333**. Maltose crystallises from aqueous solution in needles containing one molecule of water of crystallisation, $C_{12}H_{22}O_{11},H_2O$. It is obtained by the partial hydrolysis of starch or glycogen by diastase, an enzyme present in germinating barley grain. The chemical reactions in these hydrolyses result in the breaking down of the long chains of glucose ring units in the polysaccharides into the pairs of units which constitute the molecule of maltose (see the scheme on p. **335**).

Chemical properties of maltose. Maltose yields only glucose when hydrolysed by hot dilute hydrochloric acid, or by the enzyme maltase,

$$C_{12}H_{22}O_{11} \quad + \quad H_2O \quad = \quad 2C_6H_{12}O_6.$$

It yields an octa-acetyl derivative when heated with acetic anhydride and zinc chloride, thus showing that the molecule contains eight hydroxyl groups, and it reacts with phenylhydrazine to yield an osazone which may be formulated,

$$
\begin{array}{c}
H \\
| \\
C = N - N \underset{C_6H_5}{\overset{H}{<}} \\
| \\
C_{10}H_{19}O_9 - C = N - N \underset{C_6H_5}{\overset{H}{<}}
\end{array}
$$

The crystals which separate from the hot aqueous solution are characteristic.

Tests for maltose. Maltose is charred by concentrated sulphuric acid, it reduces Fehling's solution and ammoniacal silver oxide solution, and it gives a delayed violet coloration in the rapid furfural test. In these respects it is indistinguishable from glucose. Maltosazone, however, is soluble in hot water (glucosazone is insoluble) and it crystallises in sheaves of flat plates, whereas glucosazone crystallises in needles. Glucosazone and maltosazone may be easily distinguished when examined under a microscope.

SUCROSE (CANE SUGAR)

The molecule of sucrose, $C_{12}H_{22}O_{11}$, consists of one α-glucose ring unit and one γ-fructose ring unit linked together by an atom of oxygen, p. 336.

Sucrose crystallises from aqueous solution in large four-sided monoclinic prisms, as in sugar candy. At room temperature it is soluble in about one-third of its weight of water, but it is almost insoluble in alcohol. It melts at about 160–161°, and if cooled resolidifies to a yellow glassy mass, known as *barley sugar*. At about 200° it loses water and is converted to a brown mass, *caramel*, with a characteristic flavour, which is used for colouring rum, vinegar, gravies, sauces, etc. At higher temperatures cane sugar chars. Sucrose is one of the sweetest of the sugars. It is optically active, and its aqueous solution is dextrorotatory.

Sucrose occurs in ripe sugar cane and in beet-root, and in small quantities in other fruits such as pine-apple and strawberries. It is manufactured from the sugar cane and beet by the processes described on p. 492.

Chemical properties of sucrose.

1. Oxidation. Sucrose burns in air or oxygen, forming carbon dioxide and water. It is oxidised by concentrated nitric acid to oxalic acid. A full account of this reaction is given on p. 288. Sucrose is also oxidised by warm concentrated sulphuric acid. If a strong aqueous solution of sucrose is mixed with an equal volume of concentrated sulphuric acid the mixture becomes hot. It turns black owing to the liberation of carbon, and froths up with the evolution of steam, carbon dioxide and sulphur dioxide.

2. Reaction with acetic anhydride. Sucrose yields an octa-acetyl derivative when boiled with acetic anhydride and fused sodium acetate.

3. Reaction with metallic hydroxides, giving sucrosates. Sucrose in aqueous solution reacts with the hydroxides of calcium, strontium and barium to produce insoluble compounds of the type, $C_{12}H_{22}O_{11},2SrO$. These compounds are readily decomposed when carbon dioxide is passed into their aqueous suspensions. The strontium compound is used for isolating sucrose from non-crystallisable molasses, p. 492.

4. Hydrolysis and fermentation. Sucrose is quantitatively hydrolysed to a mixture of equimolecular proportions of glucose and fructose (invert sugar) by boiling with dilute hydrochloric acid for 10 minutes. If an aqueous solution of sucrose is heated with invertase in faintly acid solution at 50° for about 10 minutes the same reaction occurs. Yeast contains invertase, and therefore, if sucrose is treated with yeast, it is first converted to invert sugar by the invertase, and the invert sugar is then converted to alcohol and carbon dioxide by the zymase. If sodium sulphite is present during the fermentation 20–25 per cent. of the sucrose is converted to glycerol.

Sucrose is not a reducing sugar. It reacts neither with Fehling's solution nor with an ammoniacal solution of silver oxide. Sucrose does not react with phenylhydrazine to form an osazone.

Tests for sucrose. Sucrose responds to Molisch's test, and readily blackens when heated with concentrated sulphuric acid. It does not, however, give a yellow or brown coloration when its solution is boiled with 10 per cent. sodium hydroxide solution. Sucrose responds to the rapid furfural test, and like fructose, yields a violet coloration as soon as the mixed reagents are brought to the boil. After hydrolysis with dilute acids, a solution of sucrose responds to the tests for glucose and fructose.

M   D.C.

POLYSACCHARIDES

GLYCOGEN

The molecule of glycogen contains several hundred α-glucose ring units, p. 335. Glycogen is present in animal organisms as a reserve food material ; its function is the counterpart of that of starch in vegetable organisms. It is found in the liver and to a smaller extent in muscle. It is a white amorphous powder which forms a colloidal solution with water, from which it is reprecipitated by the addition of alcohol. The colloidal solution is dextrorotatory.

A solution of glycogen gives a brownish-red coloration when added to a dilute solution of iodine. This coloration disappears on warming and reappears when the solution cools. Glycogen does not reduce Fehling's solution. Glycogen is hydrolysed to maltose by ptyalin present in the saliva, by glycogenase and by diastase ; when boiled with dilute acids it is quantitatively converted to glucose only.

DEXTRIN

The molecule of dextrin contains about 23 α-glucose ring units, p. 335. Dextrin, together with maltose, is obtained by the action of the enzyme diastase on starch at a temperature of 60–70°, or by heating starch alone *in vacuo* at 120°.

Dextrin is a colourless amorphous powder. It is soluble in water to give a dextrorotatory solution. Dextrin yields a brownish-red coloration with iodine, and it has slight reducing properties. It yields glucose when boiled with dilute acids. Dextrin solution is used as a substitute for gum.

STARCH

The molecule of starch is constructed of a large number of α-glucose ring units linked together by oxygen atoms, p. 335.

Starch is the form in which many plants store reserve material which enables them to continue life and growth in conditions which do not allow the elaboration of sugar by photosynthesis. Starch is present in the grain of rice, barley, wheat and maize, and in the tubers of potatoes and arrowroot. The starch is present in the plant cells as granules. Each plant species has a characteristic form of granule. Potato starch granules, for example, are unsymmetrical, and are marked by striations based on a nucleus or hilum. Starch is produced on an industrial scale from potatoes or grain by the processes described on p. 495.

Properties of starch. Starch granules are insoluble in cold water, but when treated with hot water they swell up and burst. The wall of the granule, starch cellulose, is insoluble and may be filtered off, leaving the contents of the granules, granulose, in solution. The granulose is insoluble in alcohol, which precipitates it from aqueous solution. Precipitated granulose is known as *soluble starch.* It dissolves in cold water. Starch paste is made by mixing ordinary starch with cold water, and pouring the thin paste into boiling water ; the solution is then kept boiling for several minutes.

Starch is composed of two substances, amylose and amylopectin, both of which consist of α-glucose ring units. The molecule of amylose consists of chains of 200–300 α-glucose ring units coiled into close spirals with six glucose units in each coil. The molecule of amylopectin consists of chains of about 30 α-glucose ring units linked in echelon formation.

When boiled with dilute acids starch is converted first into dextrin and then into maltose and glucose ; starch is quantitatively hydrolysed to glucose by boiling with dilute sulphuric acid. When treated with the enzyme diastase at a temperature of 60–70° starch is converted into dextrin and maltose.

Starch does not reduce Fehling's solution, or other solutions of cupric salts, and it does not give an osazone with phenylhydrazine.

Tests for starch. Starch paste gives a deep blue coloration when brought into contact with iodine solution ; the colour disappears on heating, but reappears on cooling again. This reaction of iodine with starch is unique. The solution obtained by hydrolysing starch with hydrochloric acid (50 c.c. of starch solution is boiled with 3 c.c. of concentrated hydrochloric acid for 20 minutes) responds to the tests for glucose.

CELLULOSE

The molecule of cellulose consists of an unbranched chain of about 200 β-glucose ring units, p. 335.

Cellulose is a most important constituent of the cell walls of plants ; it is the material out of which the framework of the plant is constructed. The fibres of cotton, hemp, and flax are rich in cellulose. Pure cellulose may be obtained by repeatedly extracting cotton wool, linen, hemp, flax or good filter paper, with acids to remove inorganic substances. Traces of silica may be removed by treating the product with hydrofluoric acid. The cellulose is then washed with water and dried at 100°.

Properties of cellulose. Cellulose is insoluble in water, alcohol, or ether. It is soluble in a mixture of alkali hydroxide and carbon disulphide, in an aqueous solution of zinc chloride, and in an ammoniacal solution of cupric hydroxide. Some of the processes employed in the manufacture of artificial silk are based on the reprecipitation of cellulose from these solutions.

Cellulose is gelatinised by strong solutions of alkalis. Cotton which has been superficially gelatinised by passage under tension through alkali is said to be " mercerised ". Concentrated sulphuric acid slowly dissolves cellulose. If filter paper, or blotting-paper, is placed in concentrated sulphuric acid for a few seconds, and is then washed with water and dilute ammonia until the acid is removed, it is converted into a tough substance known as parchment paper. This substance resembles parchment in appearance, and it may be used as a semi-permeable membrane to demonstrate osmosis. Cellulose is quantitatively hydrolysed to glucose when it is digested with dilute sulphuric acid under a pressure of 6–7 atmospheres. Cellulose shows the properties of a polyhydric alcohol by forming esters with acetic anhydride or with nitric acid. When it is heated with acetic anhydride at 180°, it yields a white solid compound, cellulose acetate, of which the empirical formula is

$$C_6H_7O_2 (O.CO.CH_3)_3.$$

When cellulose is treated with a mixture of concentrated nitric acid and concentrated sulphuric acid it is converted to cellulose nitrate. If all the hydroxyl groups in cellulose are replaced by the nitrate group the product is gun-cotton ; if the replacement is incomplete collodion cotton is obtained. The manufacture of these important commercial compounds is described on p. 498.

CHAPTER XXI

THE AROMATIC SERIES

COMPOUNDS of the aromatic series contain in the molecule the curious ring of six carbon atoms which is present in benzene. It has proved impossible to explain the structure of this ring in terms of simple Kékulé bonds ; a short account of the current outlook on the structure of benzene is given on p. 367 ; for the purpose of representing chemical changes it is sufficient to write the structural formula of benzene as

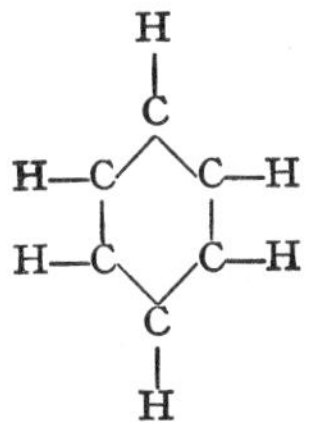

$$
\begin{array}{c}
\text{H} \\
|\\
\text{C} \\
\text{H—C}\diagup\quad\diagdown\text{C—H} \\
|\qquad\qquad| \\
\text{H—C}\diagdown\quad\diagup\text{C—H} \\
\text{C} \\
|\\
\text{H}
\end{array}
$$

In this formula the fourth valency bond of each carbon atom is omitted.

The homologues of benzene are theoretically derived by replacing one of the hydrogen atoms in the benzene molecule by an alkyl group. Toluene, for example, has the structural formula

$$
\begin{array}{c}
\text{H} \\
|\\
\text{C} \\
\text{H—C}\diagup\quad\diagdown\text{C—CH}_3 \\
|\qquad\qquad| \\
\text{H—C}\diagdown\quad\diagup\text{C—H} \\
\text{C} \\
|\\
\text{H}
\end{array}
$$

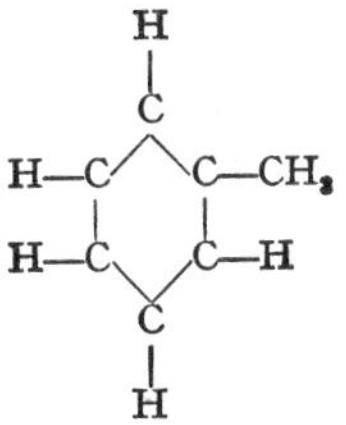

In such a structure the ring of six carbon atoms, and the five hydrogen atoms to which the carbon atoms are directly linked, is known as the *nucleus*,* and the attached alkyl group as the *side-chain*. The term side-chain is usually reserved for alkyl groups, but

---

* The term *nucleus* is also used to denote the positively charged particle at the centre of an atom, p. 2. There is no connection between the use of nucleus in this sense, and its use in aromatic organic chemistry to denote the ring of six carbon atoms and any hydrogen atoms to which they are directly linked.

it may be applied also to other groups containing several atoms, as, for example, —$CONH_2$; single atoms, and simple groups such as —OH, —NO_2 and —COOH, attached to the benzene ring, are not described as side-chains. The group C_6H_5— is known as the *phenyl* group.

ISOMERISM OF BENZENE DERIVATIVES

It has been found that an aromatic compound has no isomerides if it is derived by the replacement of one hydrogen atom in the benzene molecule by the atom of another element, or a particular group of atoms. Compounds such as toluene, chlorobenzene, and nitrobenzene exist in one form only

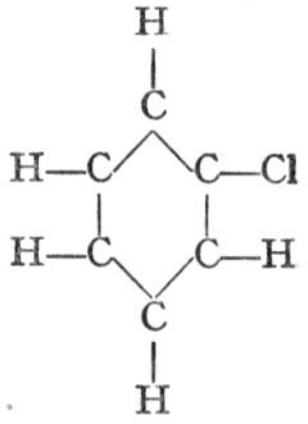

chlorobenzene 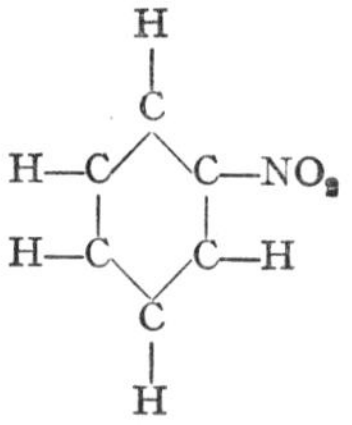   nitrobenzene

If two substituent atoms or groups are introduced into the benzene ring, however, the resulting compounds may be obtained in three isomeric forms. For example, dichlorobenzene exists in the three isomeric forms :

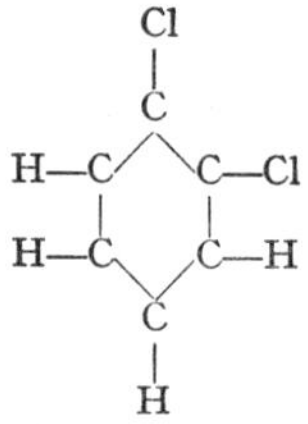

o-dichlorobenzene, *m*-dichlorobenzene, 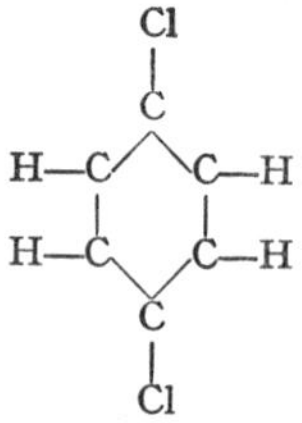 *p*-dichlorobenzene,
or, 1:2-dichloro-   or, 1:3-dichloro-   or, 1:4-dichloro-
benzene   benzene   benzene

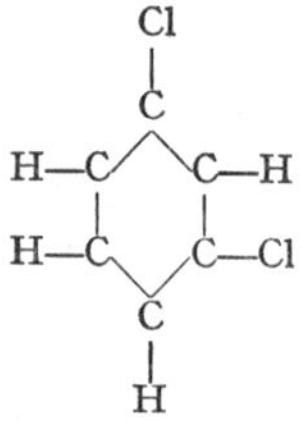

The isomerides are denoted respectively by the prefixes *ortho* (written *o*-) indicating that the two chlorine atoms are attached to adjacent carbon atoms of the nucleus, *meta* (written *m*-) indicating that the two chlorine atoms are attached to carbon atoms which are next but one to one another, and *para* (written *p*-) indicating that the two chlorine atoms are attached to two carbon atoms occupying opposite positions in the nucleus.

An alternative nomenclature may be used, in which the carbon atoms in the nucleus are numbered, and the positions of the substituent atoms or groups are indicated by stating the numbers of the carbon atoms to which they are attached. It should be noted that 1:2-dichlorobenzene and 1:6-dichlorobenzene are identical and correspond to the ortho compound; and that 1:3-dichlorobenzene and 1:5-dichlorobenzene are also identical and correspond to the meta compound. The numerical method of nomenclature is generally used when there are more than two substituent atoms or groups attached to the nucleus.

A compound derived by the replacement of two hydrogen atoms in the benzene molecule by two different atoms or groups also exists in three isomeric forms. For example, the isomerides of chloronitrobenzene are :

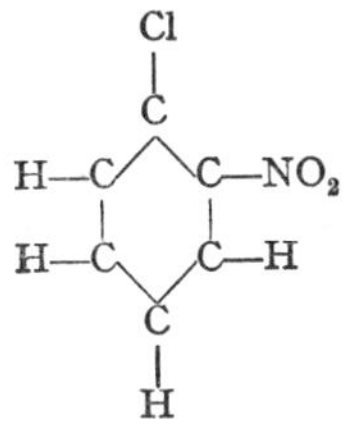

o-chloronitrobenzene 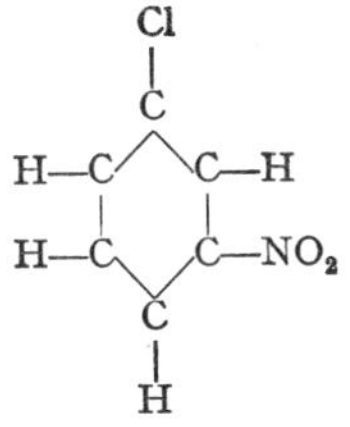   m-chloronitrobenzene 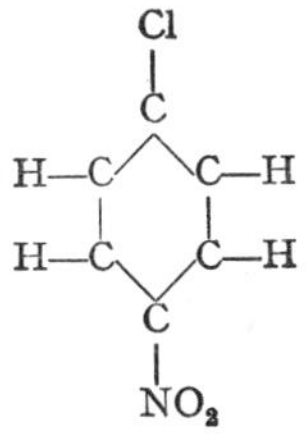   p-chloronitrobenzene

The replacement of three hydrogen atoms in the benzene molecule by identical atoms or groups also produces three isomerides. Trichlorobenzene, for example, exists in the isomeric forms,

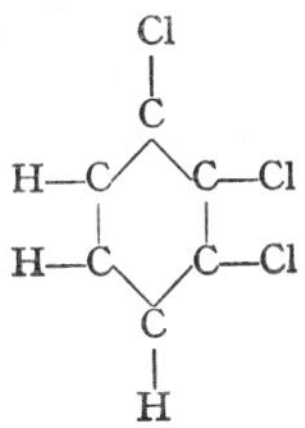

1:2:3-trichlorobenzene 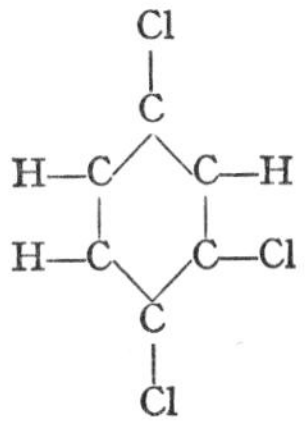   1:3:4-trichlorobenzene 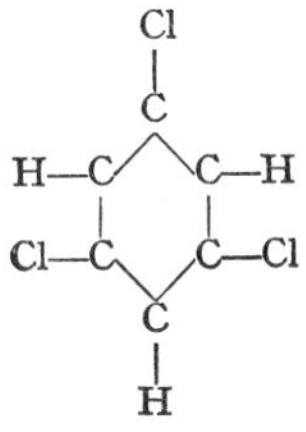   1:3:5-trichlorobenzene

The numbers of isomerides which may be formed by the replacement of hydrogen atoms in the benzene molecule by four or five identical groups, or by combinations of different groups, can be determined by drawing the appropriate structural formulae.

ORIENTATING INFLUENCE OF A SUBSTITUENT GROUP IN THE BENZENE NUCLEUS

When a derivative of benzene formed by the replacement of one hydrogen atom in the benzene molecule by another atom, or group of atoms, is attacked by a reagent capable of introducing a second substituent atom or group of atoms into the nucleus, it is possible to predict which of the three isomerides will be obtained by the use of the following rules :

(i) the position at which a second substituent enters the nucleus is governed only by the nature of the substituent originally present :

(ii) if the substituent originally present in the nucleus is represented by XY, so that the formula of the original benzene derivative is

and if Y is in a higher Group of the Periodic Table than X, or if Y is in the same Periodic Group as X but has a lower atomic weight, then the meta isomeride is obtained ; in all other cases, including the case where XY is a single atom, a mixture of the ortho and para isomerides is obtained.

In accordance with this rule,* among the meta-directing substituent groups are : SO_3H, NO_2, CHO, COOH, $CONH_2$, CN, CCl_3 ; and among the ortho and para directing groups are : Cl, Br, I, OH, NH_2, $NH.COCH_3$, CH_3.

GENERAL PROPERTIES OF AROMATIC COMPOUNDS

Aromatic compounds possess certain characteristic properties which enable them to be differentiated from aliphatic compounds. These properties are mentioned in the following list.

(i) The benzene nucleus in an aromatic compound is attacked by the halogens, by concentrated sulphuric acid, and by concentrated nitric acid in the presence of sulphuric acid, to yield substitution derivatives such as chlorobenzene, C_6H_5Cl, benzene sulphonic acid, $C_6H_5SO_2OH$, and nitrobenzene, $C_6H_5NO_2$. The rate at which the

---

* The rule was devised by Hammick and Illingworth in 1930. It may also be stated in the form : The meta-isomeride is obtained if the component Y of the original substituent group XY is more electronegative than the component X. The orientating influence of a substituent group in the benzene nucleus has been explained in terms of the polarity of the group (p. 23), and the conjugation (p. 125) of the double bonds in the benzene ring. A discussion of this theory is beyond the scope of this book. An account of it is given in the Lecture referred to on p. 23.

substitution reaction proceeds depends on the nature of any sub-stituent groups which may be originally present in the nucleus. In general, ortho and para directing groups promote the reaction, and meta directing groups retard it.

(ii) An aromatic compound containing a halogen atom attached to the benzene nucleus shows little of the varied activity which is exhibited by an alkyl halide * (see ethyl bromide, p. 140), and in consequence the usefulness of such a compound as bromobenzene in preparing other compounds is limited. Bromobenzene, therefore, does not play so prominent a part in aromatic chemistry as ethyl bromide plays in aliphatic chemistry. If, however, one of the groups, COOH, CN, or NO_2, is also present in the nucleus, and is in the ortho or para position with regard to the halogen atom, a compound is obtained which has the reactivity characteristic of an aliphatic compound.

(iii) Benzene and its derivatives may be converted to nitrogen derivatives known as diazo compounds which have no exact counter-part among the aliphatic compounds. The diazo compounds undergo a number of important reactions which are of value in the synthesis of many types of aromatic compounds.

(iv) The benzene nucleus confers slightly acidic properties on compounds in which it is present. Hence phenol, C_6H_5OH, is a weak acid (ethyl alcohol, for comparison, is neutral), and benzoic acid, C_6H_5COOH, is a stronger acid than acetic acid.

(v) The benzene nucleus is very stable towards oxidising agents. When an aromatic compound is treated with an oxidising agent for a long time, any side-chains in the molecule are converted to carboxyl groups, but the nucleus itself is not oxidised. Toluene, for example, when heated with chromium tri-oxide or nitric acid, yields benzoic acid,

$$C_6H_5.CH_3 \quad + \quad 3O \quad = \quad C_6H_5.COOH \quad + \quad H_2O.$$

* It is of interest to note that chloropropylene, $\begin{smallmatrix} CH_3 \\ H \end{smallmatrix} C = C \begin{smallmatrix} H \\ Cl \end{smallmatrix}$ does not show the reactivity of an alkyl halide.

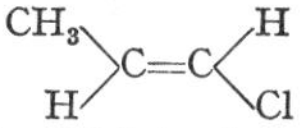

This compound contains the group, C—C=C—Cl, which is also present in chlorobenzene if the formula is written

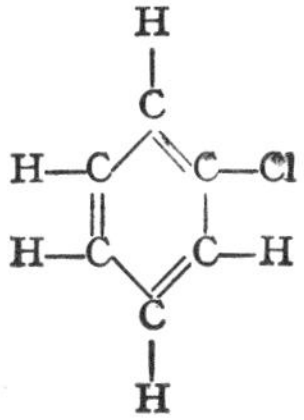

CHAPTER XXII

THE AROMATIC HYDROCARBONS

BENZENE

THE simplest aromatic hydrocarbon is benzene. The structural formula of benzene is written:

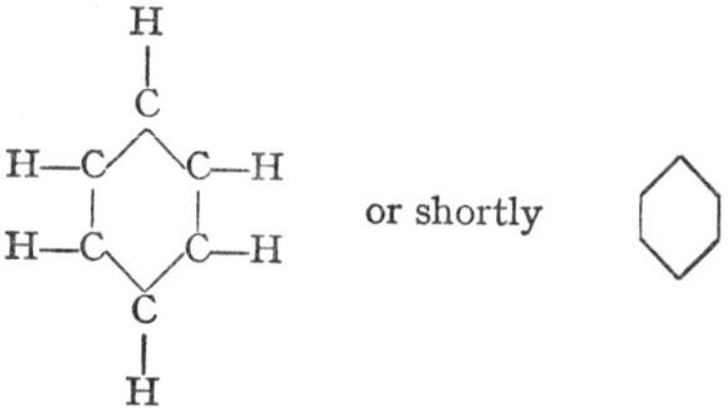

The interesting constitution of benzene is discussed on p. 367.

Benzene is found in certain natural petroleums, and in coal-tar, one of the products of the destructive distillation of coal.

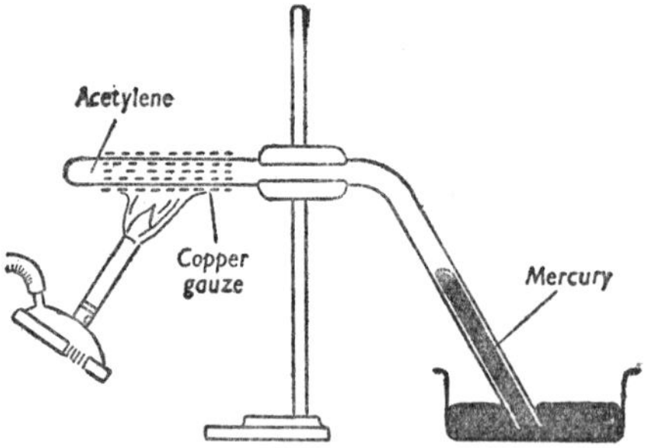

FIG. 59. Apparatus for the polymerisation of acetylene.

Physical properties of benzene. Benzene is a highly refractive mobile liquid, M.P. 5·5°, B.P. 80·5°, Sp. Gr. 0·8799 at 20°. It has a burning taste and a characteristic odour. It mixes with ether and petroleum in all proportions, but it is almost insoluble in water, and is volatile in steam. It is a useful solvent for fats, resins and iodine. It is very inflammable and burns with a luminous flame.

PRINCIPAL REACTIONS IN WHICH BENZENE IS PRODUCED

The following summary shows the chief reactions in which benzene is one of the products. These reactions are of no interest as methods of preparing benzene, because benzene is easily obtainable in large quantities from coal-tar. The reactions, 2, 3, 4 and 5, however, are of great theoretical importance because they illustrate methods by which each of the groups, OH, —COOH, —NH.NH₂, and —N=NCl, linked to the benzene ring, may be replaced by an atom of hydrogen.

1. The polymerisation of acetylene. Acetylene when heated to about 400° at atmospheric pressure polymerises to benzene, p. 134.

$$3C_2H_2 \ = \ C_6H_6.$$

Many other complex hydrocarbons are formed at the same time.

This polymerisation may be demonstrated experimentally by means of the apparatus shown in Fig. 59. The hard glass tube is filled with mercury, and clamped with the open end under the surface of mercury in the trough. Acetylene is passed into the hard glass tube until it is about half full. A portion of the hard glass tube near the closed end is wrapped round with copper gauze which is gently heated with a Bunsen flame. After a short time, drops of oily liquid are seen on the cooler parts of the tube, and when the apparatus is cooled to room temperature, the mercury rises above its original level, thus indicating that the original volume of acetylene has decreased.

2. The action of heat on a mixture of sodium benzoate and soda-lime. If sodium benzoate and soda-lime are well-mixed together, and heated in a hard glass tube, benzene is liberated and sodium carbonate remains as a residue,

$$\bigcirc\!\!-COONa \ + \ NaOH \ = \ \bigcirc \ + \ Na_2CO_3.$$

3. The reduction of phenol with heated zinc dust. If phenol vapour is passed over strongly heated zinc dust, benzene is set free, and the zinc is oxidised to zinc oxide,

$$\bigcirc\!\!-OH \ + \ Zn \ = \ \bigcirc \ + \ ZnO.$$

4. The action of phenylhydrazine on a solution of cupric sulphate or ferric chloride. Phenylhydrazine is quantitatively oxidised to benzene and nitrogen when it is warmed with an aqueous solution of cupric sulphate, Fehling's solution, or ferric chloride,

$$\bigcirc\!\!-NH\!\!-NH_2 \ + \ 2CuSO_4 \ + \ H_2O \ = \ \bigcirc \ + \ Cu_2O \ + \ 2H_2SO_4 + N_2.$$

5. The reduction of a benzene diazonium compound.
(i) *Using ethyl alcohol as the reducing agent.* If a solution of benzene diazonium hydrogen sulphate in absolute ethyl alcohol is

boiled, the benzene diazonium hydrogen sulphate is reduced to benzene and nitrogen, and the alcohol is oxidised to acetaldehyde,

$$\text{C}_6\text{H}_5\text{—N}_2.\text{HSO}_4 \quad + \quad \text{C}_2\text{H}_5\text{OH}$$

$$= \text{C}_6\text{H}_6 \quad + \quad \text{N}_2 \quad + \quad \text{H}_2\text{SO}_4 \quad + \quad \text{CH}_3.\text{CHO}.$$

(ii) *Using an alkaline solution of stannous chloride as the reducing agent.* If an aqueous solution of benzene diazonium chloride is cooled to 0° and made just alkaline with potassium hydroxide, potassium diazotate is formed,

$$\text{C}_6\text{H}_5\text{N}_2\text{Cl} + 2\text{KOH} = \text{C}_6\text{H}_5\text{N}:\text{NOK} + \text{KCl} + \text{H}_2\text{O}.$$

The addition of a strongly alkaline solution of stannous chloride, which may be regarded as a solution of potassium stannite, K_2SnO_2, reduces the potassium diazotate, liberating benzene according to the equation,

$$\text{C}_6\text{H}_5\text{—N}:\text{NOK} \quad + \quad \text{K}_2\text{SnO}_2 \quad + \quad \text{H}_2\text{O}$$

$$= \text{C}_6\text{H}_6 \quad + \quad \text{N}_2 \quad + \quad \text{K}_2\text{SnO}_3 \quad + \quad \text{KOH}.$$

Potassium stannite is more efficient than ethyl alcohol in reducing a benzene diazonium compound to benzene, because it converts a smaller proportion of the diazonium compound to by-products. The intermediate potassium diazotate, however, is liable to explode spontaneously, even in cold aqueous solution.

(iii) *Using a solution of hypophosphorous acid.* This method enables the reduction to be carried out in aqueous solution without risk of explosion,

$$\text{C}_6\text{H}_5\text{N}_2\text{Cl} + \text{H}_3\text{PO}_2 + \text{H}_2\text{O} = \text{C}_6\text{H}_6 + \text{N}_2 + \text{HCl} + \text{H}_3\text{PO}_3.$$

The **industrial production** of benzene is described in Chapter XXX, p. 478.

CHEMICAL PROPERTIES AND CONSTITUTION OF BENZENE

Properties. Benzene is remarkable for its chemical stability. It has no acid properties and no basic properties ; it is attacked neither by boiling concentrated potassium hydroxide solution, nor by hot concentrated hydrochloric acid. It has no oxidising properties, and it is attacked only very slowly indeed by hot solutions of chromic acid, or potassium permanganate. Benzene, however, is far more reactive than a member of the paraffin series such as ethane. It undergoes substitution and additive reactions, in each of which the ring of six carbon atoms present in the molecule persists in the molecule of the product.

Substitution reactions of benzene

1. Reactions with the halogens. In the presence of a halogen carrier, such as iodine or iron, at ordinary temperatures and in the absence of sunlight, chlorine reacts readily with benzene to give chlorobenzene,

$$C_6H_6 \ + \ Cl_2 \ = \ C_6H_5Cl \ + \ HCl.$$

The action may continue, giving rise to further substitution products,

$$C_6H_5Cl \ + \ Cl_2 \ = \ C_6H_4Cl_2 \ + \ HCl,$$

and ultimately to hexachlorobenzene, C_6Cl_6.

Benzene reacts similarly with bromine. Iodine does not react with benzene at ordinary temperatures in any circumstances. At high temperatures, however, iodobenzene is formed if some oxidising agent such as iodic acid is present to remove the hydriodic acid formed in the reaction,

$$C_6H_6 \ + \ I_2 \ = \ C_6H_5I \ + \ HI,$$

which would otherwise reduce the iodobenzene to benzene again, according to the equation,

$$C_6H_5I \ + \ HI \ = \ C_6H_6 \ + \ I_2.$$

2. Reaction with nitric acid, giving nitrobenzene. Concentrated nitric acid reacts with benzene at room temperature to give a very small yield of nitrobenzene,

$$C_6H_6 \ + \ HNO_3 \ = \ C_6H_5NO_2 \ + \ H_2O.$$

A mixture of concentrated sulphuric acid and concentrated nitric acid rapidly converts benzene to nitrobenzene, p. 378.

3. Reaction with concentrated sulphuric acid giving benzene sulphonic acid. Boiling concentrated sulphuric acid in the course of 20–30 hours converts benzene to benzene sulphonic acid,

$$C_6H_6 \ + \ HO.SO_2.OH \ = \ C_6H_5.SO_2.OH \ + \ H_2O.$$

For a detailed account of this reaction, see p. 376.

4. Reaction with methyl chloride in the presence of aluminium chloride, giving toluene. Friedel-Crafts' reaction.

Methyl chloride reacts with benzene in the presence of aluminium chloride, forming toluene and liberating hydrogen chloride,

$$C_6H_6 + CH_3Cl = C_6H_5.CH_3 + HCl.$$

A detailed account of this reaction is given on p. 370.

5. Gattermann's reaction to give benzaldehyde. Benzaldehyde is formed when a mixture of hydrogen chloride and carbon monoxide is passed into benzene containing anhydrous cuprous chloride and anhydrous aluminium chloride. Formyl chloride is probably formed by the interaction of hydrogen chloride and carbon monoxide,

$$HCl + CO = \begin{matrix} H \\ Cl \end{matrix}\!\!\!> C{=}O.$$

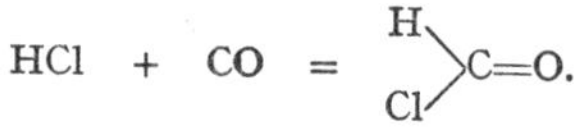

The formyl chloride then reacts with the benzene according to the equation,

$$C_6H_6 + H.CO.Cl = C_6H_5.CHO + HCl.$$

Additive reactions of benzene

6. Addition of hydrogen. If a mixture of hydrogen and benzene vapour is passed over freshly reduced nickel at about 150°, hexahydrobenzene (cyclohexane) is produced,

$$C_6H_6 + 3H_2 = C_6H_{12}.$$

Cyclohexane is a colourless mobile liquid, M.P. 6·4°, B.P. 81°. The properties of cyclohexane are similar to those of the paraffins ; it has no aromatic properties. The molecular structure of cyclohexane is

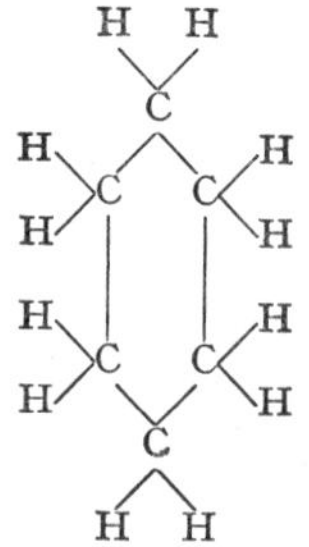

It will be seen that the four valency bonds of each carbon atom in the ring are saturated. The peculiar structure of the original benzene ring has disappeared, and, with it, the typical aromatic properties of benzene.

7. Addition of chlorine. If benzene is treated with chlorine in bright sunlight, and in the absence of halogen carriers, benzene hexachloride is formed,

$$C_6H_6 + 3Cl_2 = C_6H_6Cl_6.$$

When warmed with potassium hydroxide solution, benzene hexa-chloride yields trichlorobenzene and potassium chloride,

$$C_6H_6Cl_6 \ + \ 3KOH \ = \ C_6H_3Cl_3 \ + \ 3KCl \ + \ 3H_2O.$$

Benzene behaves similarly with bromine.

8. Addition of ozone. Benzene forms a tri-ozonide, $C_6H_6(O_3)_3$, which is highly explosive.

Benzene reacts neither with hydrogen iodide, nor with potassium permanganate, and it reacts with sulphuric acid to form substitution compounds only. In these respects benzene differs sharply from ethylene (p. 118).

Constitution of benzene. The analysis of benzene and the determination of its vapour density show that its molecular formula is C_6H_6. If each of the carbon atoms in the molecule is exerting four covalencies, this formula must represent a molecule containing triple or double bonds. If the carbon atoms are arranged in a straight chain, triple bonds must be present, thus,

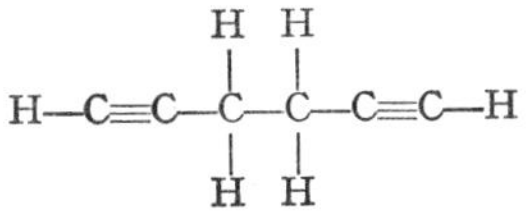

$$\begin{array}{cc} H & H \\ | & | \\ H-C\equiv C-C-C-C\equiv C-H \\ | & | \\ H & H \end{array}$$

If the carbon atoms are arranged in a six-membered ring, three double bonds must be present, thus,

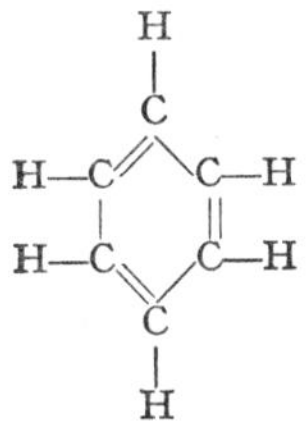

The additive reactions of benzene (Reactions 6, 7 and 8) are in accord with an unsaturated structure. In these reactions the molecule of benzene combines with six atoms of hydrogen, six atoms of chlorine, or with three molecules of ozone. Since, in similar conditions, the molecule of ethylene, which contains one double bond, combines with two atoms of hydrogen or chlorine, and with one molecule of ozone, the additive reactions of benzene furnish strong evidence of the existence of three double bonds in the benzene molecule.

The chemical properties of benzene, however, differ from those of ethylene in certain important respects. Ethylene, besides under-going the three additive reactions just mentioned, also combines additively with the halogen acids, with concentrated sulphuric acid, and it is oxidised to glycol by very dilute potassium permanganate solution. Benzene undergoes none of these reactions. Moreover, it is impossible by any simple chemical reaction to replace a hydrogen atom in the ethylene molecule by some other element or group, to obtain, for example, monochloroethylene, $CH_2\text{=}CHCl$, without simultaneously saturating the double bond. The substitution reactions of benzene (Reactions 1 to 5) show, however, that the replacement of one or more hydrogen atoms in the molecule can be effected without saturating the double linkages.

It has been established by chemical methods :

(i) that the six hydrogen atoms in the benzene molecule occupy equivalent positions ;

(ii) that for any given hydrogen atom in the molecule there are two pairs of symmetrically situated hydrogen atoms ;

(iii) that the replacement of any two adjacent hydrogen atoms in the benzene molecule by chlorine atoms produces the same compound ;

(iv) that three, and only three, isomerides are produced by the replacement by chlorine of any two hydrogen atoms in the molecule.

It has been shown by X-ray diffraction measurements that the six carbon atoms in the benzene molecule are arranged in the form of a regular hexagon, and that the distance apart of any two adjacent carbon atoms is $1\cdot39$ Å. This distance is less than the length, $1\cdot54$ Å, of the C—C bond in diamond and aliphatic compounds, and greater than the length, $1\cdot34$ Å, of the C=C bond in ethylene. This physical evidence thus supports the chemical evidence that the C—C bonds in benzene are different from those in non-aromatic compounds.

The evidence so far brought forward on the structure of the benzene molecule shows :

(i) that the molecule consists of six carbon atoms arranged at the corners of a regular hexagon, and that a hydrogen atom is attached to each carbon atom ;

(ii) that the positions in the molecule occupied by the six carbon atoms are identical ;

(iii) that the benzene ring is unsaturated ;

(iv) that it does not contain triple bonds ;

(v) that if double bonds are present they do not possess the normal properties of the double bond in ethylene.

It is impossible to devise, in terms of normal covalent linkages, a structure for the benzene molecule which is in accord with these facts. Current opinion regards the molecule of benzene as a resonance structure compounded of the two forms :

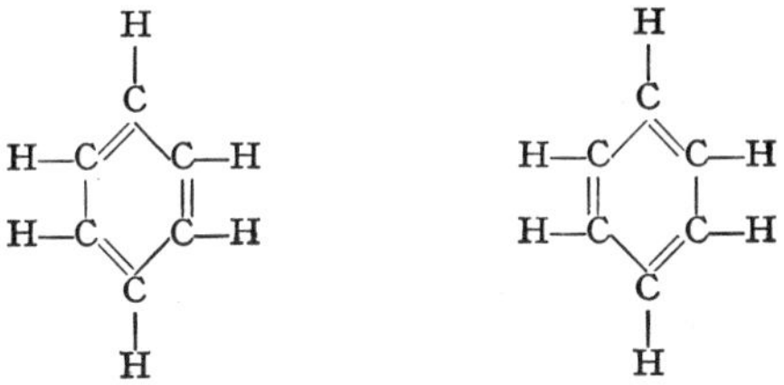

The influence of a substituent group in the benzene nucleus on the position taken up by a second group entering the nucleus (p. 359) suggests, however, that the resonance structure of benzene may give place to an alternating double-bond structure in its derivatives.

Uses of benzene. Benzene is used as a solvent for organic compounds such as resins and fats, and for non-metallic substances such as iodine, sulphur and phosphorus. It is the starting-point for the manufacture of many important compounds including drugs and dyes.

TOLUENE

Toluene is theoretically derived by the replacement of a hydrogen atom in the molecule of benzene by the methyl group, CH_3.

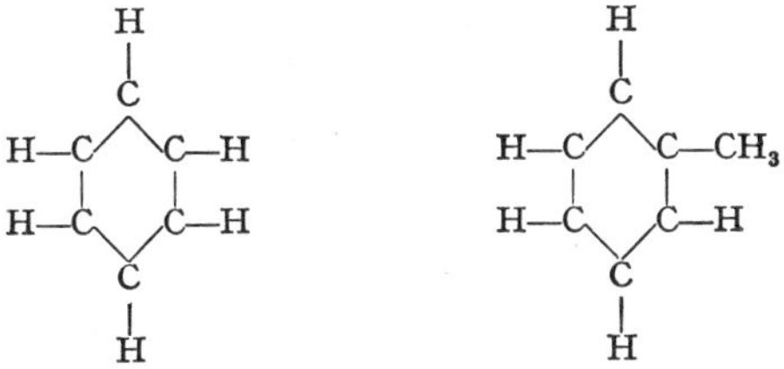

benzene   toluene

Toluene is a mobile liquid, M.P. $-94°$, B.P. $110°$, Sp. Gr. $0·867$ at $20°$. It distils without decomposing and is volatile in steam. It is insoluble in water, but is miscible in all proportions with anhydrous alcohol, ether and petroleum.

Toluene occurs with benzene in coal-tar, and also in certain natural petroleums. It is liberated by the distillation of the resin Tolu balsam, whence the name " toluene " is derived.

PRINCIPAL REACTIONS IN WHICH TOLUENE IS PRODUCED

1. The action of heat on a mixture of sodium methylbenzoate and soda-lime. If a mixture of sodium methyl benzoate and soda-lime is heated in a test-tube, toluene is evolved and sodium carbonate is left,

$$CH_3.C_6H_4.COONa + NaOH = CH_3.C_6H_5 + Na_2CO_3.$$

2. The action of methyl chloride on benzene in the presence of aluminium chloride. Friedel-Crafts' reaction. If a mixture of benzene and methyl chloride is warmed in the presence of aluminium chloride and in the complete absence of water, a reaction occurs which may be summarised by the equation,

$$C_6H_6 + CH_3Cl = C_6H_5.CH_3 + HCl.$$

The mechanism of this reaction is mentioned on p. 458.

To carry out the reaction anhydrous benzene is placed in a flask fitted to a reflux condenser, and about one-third of its weight of special anhydrous aluminium chloride is added. The requisite quantity of dry methyl chloride is passed in, and the mixture is heated on a water-bath until the evolution of hydrogen chloride ceases. The apparatus is then cooled and dismantled. Powdered ice is introduced into the flask to hydrolyse the aluminium compounds, and the product is steam-distilled. The upper layer of the distillate is toluene, which is separated, dried with calcium chloride, and fractionally distilled.

3. The action of metallic sodium on a mixture of methyl iodide and bromobenzene. Fittig's reaction. In ethereal solution methyl iodide and bromobenzene react with metallic sodium to yield toluene and sodium bromide,

$$2Na + CH_3I + C_6H_5Br = CH_3.C_6H_5 + NaBr + NaI.$$

This is one example of a general reaction between a halogen derivative of an aromatic hydrocarbon, an alkyl halide, and metallic sodium. Usually the bromine or iodine aromatic derivative reacts more successfully than the corresponding chlorine compound, and the alkyl iodide gives better results than the chloride or bromide. The experimental details for obtaining toluene by Fittig's reaction are as follows :

22·5 gm. of sodium, pressed as wire, are mixed with 100 c.c. of an-hydrous ether in a 750 c.c. round-bottomed flask fitted to a reflux condenser. A mixture of 34 c.c. of dry bromobenzene and 25·5 c.c. (59·5 gm.) of methyl iodide is poured down the condenser, the top is closed with a calcium chloride tube, and the mixture is shaken thoroughly. The mixture is allowed to stand with occasional shaking for at least three hours. At the beginning of this period the heat of the reaction causes the ether to boil ; at the end a bluish grey sludge has settled on the bottom of the flask together with pieces of undissolved sodium wire. The apparatus shown in Fig. 22, p. 70, is then assembled. The liquid from the 750 c.c. flask is decanted into the dropping-funnel, so as to leave as much of the solid as possible in the flask. The residue is washed with a little ether, and the washings are added to the solution in the dropping-funnel. A little of the ethereal solution from the dropping-funnel is run into the distillation flask which is heated on the water-bath ; the addition of the solution is continued at the rate at which the ether distils. When the distillation of the ether is complete, the apparatus shown in Fig. 16, p. 60, is fitted up, and the crude toluene is fractionated.

4. The reduction of cresol by hot zinc dust. Toluene is obtained when the vapour of cresol (hydroxytoluene) is passed over strongly heated zinc dust,

$$CH_3.C_6H_4.OH \quad + \quad Zn \quad = \quad CH_3.C_6H_5 \quad + \quad ZnO.$$

Industrial preparation of toluene. Toluene is extracted from the " 90 per cent. benzol " obtained by the distillation of coal-tar. A description of the process is given in Chapter XXX, p. 478.

CHEMICAL PROPERTIES AND USES OF TOLUENE

Properties. The reactions of toluene may be divided into those which affect the benzene nucleus and those which affect the side-chain. The benzene nucleus in the molecule of toluene undergoes an additive reaction with hydrogen in the presence of reduced nickel or platinum black to give hexahydrotoluene,

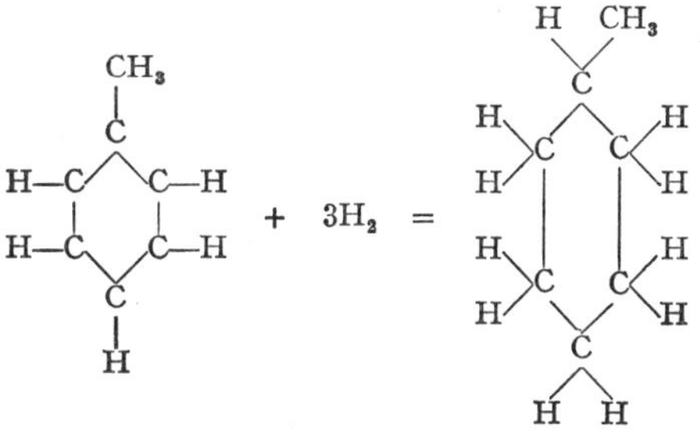

The nucleus in toluene undergoes substitution reactions with concentrated sulphuric acid to yield a mixture of o- and p-toluene sulphonic acids,

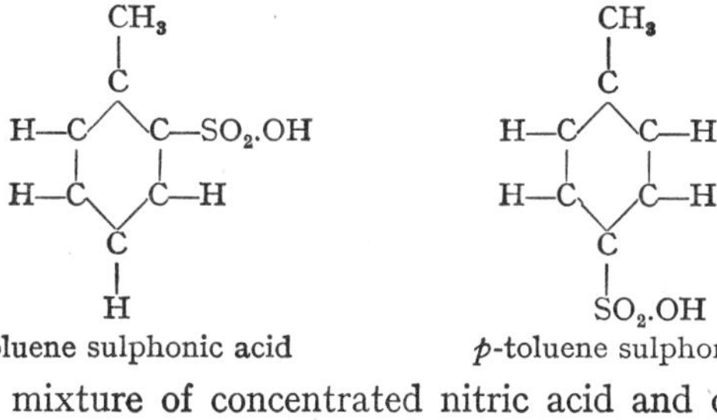

o-toluene sulphonic acid   p-toluene sulphonic acid

and with a mixture of concentrated nitric acid and concentrated sulphuric acid to yield a mixture of *o*- and *p*-nitrotoluene, and ultimately trinitrotoluene.

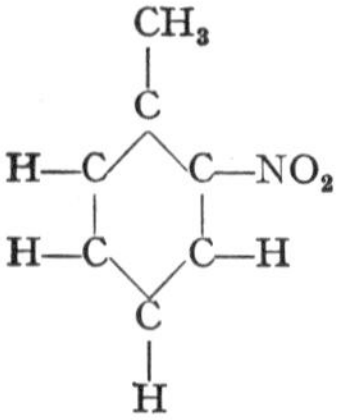

$$CH_3$$

o-nitrotoluene 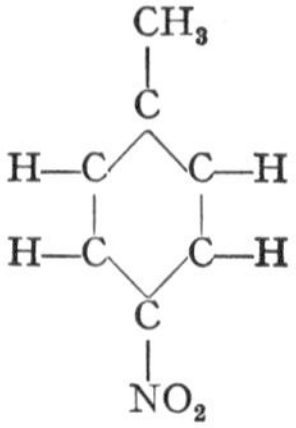   p-nitrotoluene 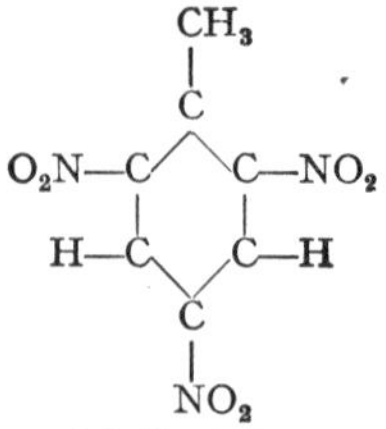   trinitrotoluene

Substitution by chlorine of hydrogen atoms in the *nucleus* takes place if chlorine is passed into toluene at room temperature in the dark, and in the presence of a halogen carrier such as iron filings or iodine. A mixture of *o*- and *p*-chlorotoluene is formed,

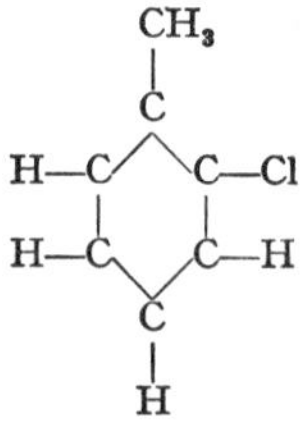

o-chlorotoluene 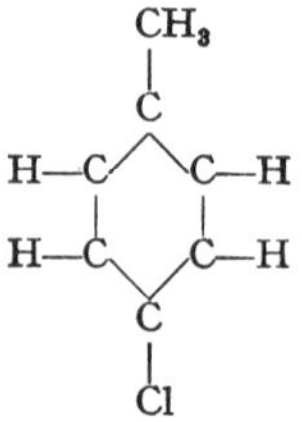   p-chlorotoluene

Chlorination may proceed further to yield di- and tri-chlorotoluenes. If mono-chlorotoluene is to be prepared by the direct chlorination of toluene, the passage of chlorine should be discontinued as soon as the requisite gain in weight has occurred.

If chlorine is passed into toluene boiling in a flask fitted to a reflux condenser, substitution takes place in the *side-chain*, and benzyl chloride is formed, and then successively benzal chloride and benzotrichloride.

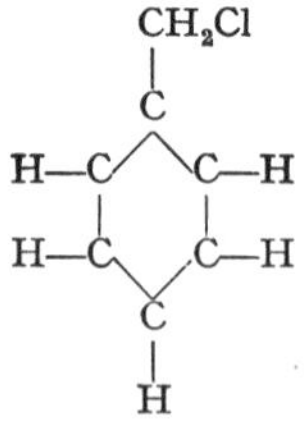

benzyl chloride 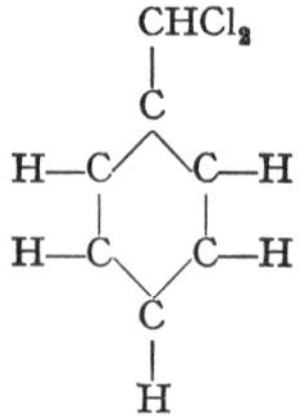   benzal chloride 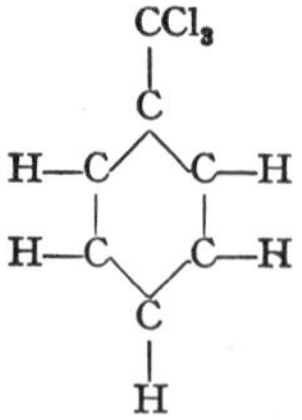   benzotrichloride

The same result is obtained if chlorine is passed into cold toluene exposed to bright sunlight. Bromine reacts similarly with toluene; iodine does not react with toluene.

When toluene is heated with oxidising agents the methyl group is oxidised. Benzaldehyde is first formed and, ultimately, benzoic acid,

$$C_6H_5.CH_3 + 2O = C_6H_5.CHO + H_2O; \quad C_6H_5.CHO + O = C_6H_5.COOH.$$

Chromyl chloride, CrO_2Cl_2, reacts with toluene to yield benzaldehyde (Etard's reaction). An additive compound, $C_6H_5.CH_3(CrO_2Cl_2)$ is first formed, which yields benzaldehyde on treatment with water. Chromium tri-oxide or nitric acid oxidises toluene to benzoic acid. All aromatic compounds containing side-chains are capable of being oxidised to acids, see p. 361.

Uses of toluene. Toluene is used in the manufacture of many other important organic compounds, including trinitrotoluene and saccharin.

CHAPTER XXIII

BENZENE SULPHONIC ACID AND THE NITROBENZENES

BENZENE SULPHONIC ACID

BENZENE sulphonic acid is derived by the replacement of one hydrogen atom in the benzene molecule by the sulphonic group

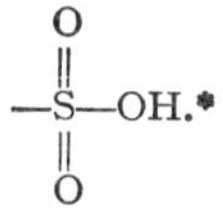

$$\begin{array}{c} O \\ \parallel \\ -S-OH.* \\ \parallel \\ O \end{array}$$

The replacement can be carried out directly by the action of sulphuric acid on benzene,

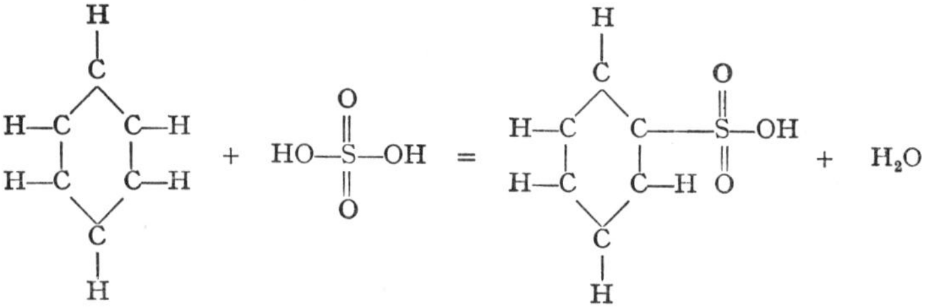

The process by which a hydrocarbon (or one of its derivatives) is changed to a sulphonic acid is known as *sulphonation*. It should be noted that the sulphur atom in the sulphonic group is linked directly to a carbon atom of the benzene nucleus.†

---

* An alternative electronic formula for the sulphonic group is $\begin{array}{c} \bar{O} \\ \mid \\ -\overset{+}{\underset{+}{S}}-OH. \\ \mid \\ \bar{O} \end{array}$

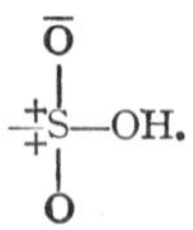

As the experimental evidence is not decisively in favour of one or the other of these formulae the more familiar classical formula is used in this chapter.

† The sulphonic acids are to be distinguished from the esters of sulphuric acid which are of importance in aliphatic chemistry. Ethyl hydrogen sulphate has the constitution

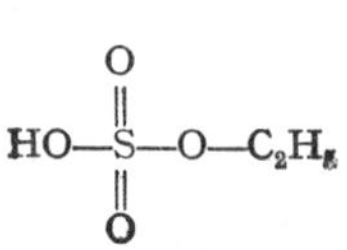

$$\begin{array}{c} O \\ \parallel \\ HO-S-O-C_2H_5 \\ \parallel \\ O \end{array}$$

The hydrogen atom of the sulphonic group separates as a hydrogen ion when benzene sulphonic acid is in aqueous solution,

$$C_6H_5SO_2OH \;\rightleftharpoons\; C_6H_5SO_2O^- \;+\; H^+.$$

Benzene sulphonic acid, therefore, forms a series of salts of the type of sodium benzene sulphonate, $C_6H_5SO_2ONa$.

The sulphonic group is in certain respects analogous to the carboxyl group. The hydroxy group in a sulphonic acid may be replaced by a chlorine atom, to give a sulphonyl chloride, or by an amino group to give a sulphonamide. The relation between benzoic acid, $C_6H_5.COOH$, and benzene sulphonic acid may be seen in a comparison of the formulae of the acids and certain of their derivatives.

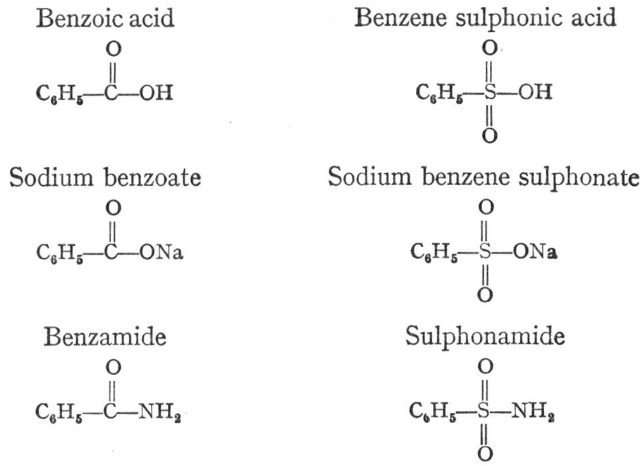

Benzoic acid

$$C_6H_5{-}\overset{\overset{\displaystyle O}{\|}}{C}{-}OH$$

Benzene sulphonic acid

$$C_6H_5{-}\overset{\overset{\displaystyle O}{\|}}{\underset{\underset{\displaystyle O}{\|}}{S}}{-}OH$$

Sodium benzoate

$$C_6H_5{-}\overset{\overset{\displaystyle O}{\|}}{C}{-}ONa$$

Sodium benzene sulphonate

$$C_6H_5{-}\overset{\overset{\displaystyle O}{\|}}{\underset{\underset{\displaystyle O}{\|}}{S}}{-}ONa$$

Benzamide

$$C_6H_5{-}\overset{\overset{\displaystyle O}{\|}}{C}{-}NH_2$$

Sulphonamide

$$C_6H_5{-}\overset{\overset{\displaystyle O}{\|}}{\underset{\underset{\displaystyle O}{\|}}{S}}{-}NH_2$$

and diethyl sulphate the constitution

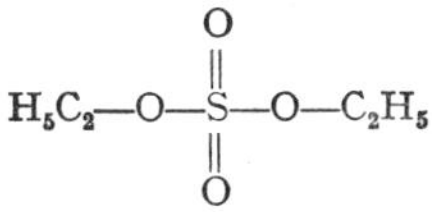

$$H_5C_2{-}O{-}\overset{\overset{\displaystyle O}{\|}}{\underset{\underset{\displaystyle O}{\|}}{S}}{-}O{-}C_2H_5$$

In these compounds the hydrocarbon radical is linked to the sulphur atom through an oxygen atom. The aliphatic analogue of benzene sulphonic acid is ethanesulphonic acid,

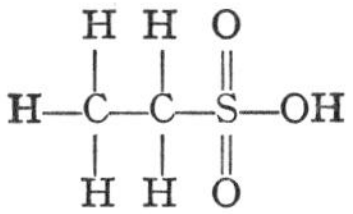

$$H{-}\overset{\overset{\displaystyle H}{|}}{\underset{\underset{\displaystyle H}{|}}{C}}{-}\overset{\overset{\displaystyle H}{|}}{\underset{\underset{\displaystyle H}{|}}{C}}{-}\overset{\overset{\displaystyle O}{\|}}{\underset{\underset{\displaystyle O}{\|}}{S}}{-}OH$$

which is made by oxidising either ethyl hydrogen sulphide, C_2H_5SH, or ethyl thiocyanate, C_2H_5SCN, with nitric acid. Potassium ethyl sulphonate can be made by boiling ethyl iodide with potassium sulphite.

Benzoyl chloride

$$C_6H_5—\overset{\overset{\displaystyle O}{\|}}{C}—Cl$$

Benzene sulphonyl chloride

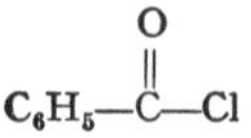

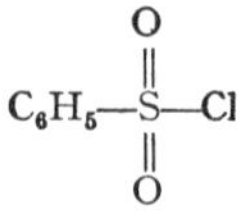

$$C_6H_5—\overset{\overset{\displaystyle O}{\|}}{\underset{\underset{\displaystyle O}{\|}}{S}}—Cl$$

Preparation of benzene sulphonic acid. Benzene sulphonic acid may be prepared by boiling together equal volumes of benzene and concentrated sulphuric acid in a flask fitted to a reflux condenser and heated on a sand-bath. The reaction, which takes twenty to thirty hours, is complete when all the oily drops of benzene have disappeared,

$$C_6H_6 + HO.SO_2.OH = C_6H_5.SO_2.OH + H_2O.$$

The same reaction takes place much more readily if fuming sulphuric acid (sulphuric acid in which 5–8 per cent. of sulphur trioxide is dissolved) is used instead of ordinary concentrated sulphuric acid. The reaction is then carried out experimentally as follows :

120 gm. of fuming sulphuric acid are placed in a flask fitted to a reflux condenser. 30 gm. of benzene are added down the condenser in very small quantities at a time, with continual shaking. Each quantity of benzene is allowed to dissolve before any more is added. The reaction is exothermic, and the flask must be cooled by immersion in cold water. The reaction is complete when all the benzene has been added ; it normally takes no longer than 15 minutes.

The isolation of the benzene sulphonic acid from the excess of sulphuric acid which remains when sulphonation is complete presents difficulties, as the sulphonic acid is highly soluble in water and is non-volatile. Use may be made of the fact that barium benzene sulphonate is soluble in water whereas barium sulphate is insoluble.

The solution resulting from sulphonation is therefore poured into 500 c.c. of water, and the solution is neutralised by the addition of excess of finely powdered barium carbonate made into a cream with water. The mixture is heated and filtered while hot. The barium sulphate and excess of barium carbonate remain on the filter paper. Crystalline barium benzene sulphonate is deposited from the filtrate as it cools. It may be purified by recrystallisation from hot water. Benzene sulphonic acid may be obtained by dissolving a weighed quantity of the pure barium benzene sulphonate in water and adding the exactly equivalent quantity of dilute sulphuric acid. The precipitated barium sulphate is filtered off, and the benzene sulphonic acid is obtained by evaporating the filtrate and allowing the acid to crystallise.

Sodium benzene sulphonate may be prepared directly from the solution obtained by the action of fuming sulphuric acid on benzene. This solution is added very slowly by means of a tap funnel to a saturated solution of common salt (400 c.c.) contained in a beaker standing in ice-water. Sodium benzene sulphonate separates in glistening plates which may be filtered off and washed with a little saturated salt solution.

Properties of benzene sulphonic acid. Benzene sulphonic acid crystallises in colourless hygroscopic plates which have the composition $2C_6H_5SO_2OH, 3H_2O$. It dissolves freely in water and in alcohol, and it is not volatile in steam. It decomposes when heated ; it has no definite melting point and it cannot be distilled.

Benzene sulphonic acid is a strong monobasic acid. It neutralises alkaline hydroxides forming salts,

$$C_6H_5SO_2OH + NaOH = C_6H_5SO_2ONa + H_2O.$$

The metallic salts of benzene sulphonic acid (including the barium salt) are soluble in water.

Benzene sulphonic acid undergoes several reactions which are of general importance. Many of these reactions are best carried out using the sodium salt in place of the free acid.

1. Reaction with superheated acids or steam, giving benzene. If benzene sulphonic acid is heated with hydrochloric acid in a sealed tube, the sulphonic group is replaced by hydrogen,

$$C_6H_5SO_2OH + H_2O = C_6H_6 + H_2SO_4.$$

2. Reaction with alkalis at a high temperature, giving phenol. If solid sodium benzene sulphonate is mixed with a large excess of solid sodium hydroxide (about 8 molar proportions) and a little water in a nickel or silver dish, and heated gradually to about 250°, sodium phenate and sodium sulphite are formed,

$$C_6H_5SO_2ONa + 2NaOH = C_6H_5ONa + Na_2SO_3 + H_2O.$$

Phenol may be obtained from the product by dissolving it in water, acidifying the solution with excess dilute sulphuric acid, and subjecting it to steam distillation.

3. Reaction with potassium cyanide, giving benzonitrile. If potassium benzene sulphonate is fused with potassium cyanide, benzonitrile is formed,

$$C_6H_5SO_2OK + KCN = C_6H_5CN + K_2SO_3.$$

4. Reaction with phosphorus pentachloride, giving benzene sulphonyl chloride. If the theoretical amount of sodium benzene sulphonate is added in small quantities at a time to a weighed quantity of phosphorus pentachloride, benzene sulphonyl chloride is formed,

$$C_6H_5SO_2ONa + PCl_5 = C_6H_5SO_2Cl + POCl_3 + NaCl.$$

It may be isolated by cooling the reaction mixture and pouring it into excess of cold water. The insoluble benzene sulphonyl chloride is separated by means of a funnel, and distilled under reduced pressure. *Benzene sulphonyl chloride* is a colourless oil, M.P. 14·5°, B.P. 120° at 10 mm. pressure. When heated with phosphorus pentachloride it yields chlorobenzene,

$$C_6H_5SO_2Cl + PCl_5 = C_6H_5Cl + POCl_3 + SOCl_2.$$

It is slowly hydrolysed by water and more rapidly by alkalis, thus :

$$C_6H_5SO_2Cl + 2NaOH = C_6H_5SO_2ONa + NaCl + H_2O.$$

It reacts with ethyl alcohol to give ethyl benzene sulphonate,

$$C_6H_5SO_2Cl + C_2H_5OH = C_6H_5SO_2OC_2H_5 + HCl.$$

When shaken with a concentrated aqueous solution of ammonia it gives a precipitate of benzene sulphonamide, which may be crystallised from hot water, M.P. 150°,

$$C_6H_5SO_2Cl + HNH_2 = C_6H_5SO_2NH_2 + HCl.$$

With primary and secondary amines and with phenols benzene sulphonyl chloride undergoes a reaction parallel to the Schotten-Baumann reaction which is described on p. 453.

NITROBENZENE

Nitrobenzene is derived from benzene by the replacement of one hydrogen atom in the molecule by the nitro group, NO_2.

Nitrobenzene is a pale yellow liquid, B.P. 210°, M.P. 5°, Sp. Gr. 1·20 at 20°. Its odour is similar to that of almonds, and is liable to be confused with that of benzaldehyde. Nitrobenzene is almost insoluble in water, but it is markedly hygroscopic. It is volatile in steam. It is miscible with strong nitric acid, and with organic liquids such as benzene, ether and alcohol.

Preparation of nitrobenzene by the nitration of benzene.*
Nitrobenzene is formed by the action of a mixture of concentrated nitric acid and concentrated sulphuric acid on benzene. The reaction may be summarised by the equation,

$$C_6H_6 + HNO_3 = C_6H_5NO_2 + H_2O.$$

The sulphuric acid, however, plays an important part in facilitating the nitration. If benzene is treated with nitric acid alone the yield of

* Nitro compounds are also produced in the following reactions : 1. The action of nitrous acid on diazonium compounds in the presence of cuprous oxide (Sandmeyer). 2. The elimination of the amino group from nitro-anilines. 3. The oxidation of primary aromatic amines. 4. The oxidation of quinone dioxime.

nitrobenzene is small, and numerous by-products are formed. Nitric acid in aqueous solution exists in three forms in equilibrium,

$$H_2O + H\bar{O} + \left[N\underset{O}{\overset{O}{\diagdown}} \right]^+ \rightleftharpoons H_2O + HO-\overset{+}{N}\underset{O}{\overset{\diagup O}{\diagdown}} \rightleftharpoons H_3\overset{+}{O} + \bar{O}-\overset{+}{N}\underset{+O}{\overset{\diagup \bar{O}}{\diagdown}}$$

In dilute solution the equilibrium lies towards the right-hand side of the equation, and the solution possesses oxidising and acidic properties. The action of nitric acid as a nitrating agent probably depends on the presence of the NO_2^+ ion. A high concentration of NO_2^+ ions in nitric acid is favoured by the addition of some other strong acid, which displaces the equilibrium to the left. It has been shown that the facility with which a hydrogen atom in the benzene nucleus is replaced by the nitro group, $—NO_2$, depends on the nature of the group with which the nitro group was originally combined, and that the replacement takes place most easily when the nitrating agent is $HO.SO_2.O.NO_2$. Sulphuric acid, therefore, probably assists nitration by (i) forming $HO.SO_2.O.NO_2$ by reaction with the nitric acid, and (ii) maintaining the strongly anhydrous and acid conditions in which the concentration of NO_2^+ ions is a maximum.

Laboratory procedure for the nitration of benzene. 40 c.c. of concentrated sulphuric acid are slowly added to 35 c.c. of concentrated nitric acid in a 500 c.c. flask cooled by immersion in water. The bulb of a thermometer is immersed in the acid mixture. 29 c.c. of benzene are added * little by little and the contents of the flask are thoroughly mixed after each addition. The temperature of the mixture must not be allowed to rise above 50°. When all the benzene has been added the flask is fitted to a reflux water condenser, and heated at 60° for 45 minutes. During this period the flask is occasionally shaken to mix the acid layer with the oily layer containing nitrobenzene and unchanged benzene.

The contents of the flask are then poured into 300 c.c. of cold water. Nitrobenzene dissolves nitric acid, and to a lesser extent sulphuric acid, and therefore the mixture is vigorously stirred to assist the transference of the acid to the aqueous layer. As much of the upper aqueous layer as possible is decanted from the heavy layer of nitrobenzene, which is separated from the remaining small quantity of aqueous layer by means of a separating funnel. The separated nitrobenzene is washed with its own volume of water, and then with sodium carbonate solution until the evolution of carbon dioxide ceases. It is carefully separated from the aqueous layer and dried over fused calcium chloride. It is then filtered through a fluted filter paper, and distilled using an air condenser.

* On principle, the acid mixture should be added to the benzene, in order to avoid a high local concentration of acid which would be liable to cause the formation of dinitrobenzene. It is difficult, however, to avoid getting acid on the bench and hands if successive small quantities are poured from one vessel to another, and therefore the method described is recommended.

Industrial preparation of nitrobenzene. The method by which nitrobenzene is manufactured is the same in principle as that used for the laboratory preparation. A mixture of concentrated nitric and sulphuric acids is added to benzene in iron vessels fitted with stirrers. The oily product is separated from the aqueous layer containing the acids. After washing it is exposed to a current of steam by which the more volatile benzene is removed.

Chemical properties of nitrobenzene. Nitrobenzene is a neutral substance ; it does not form salts either with acids or with alkalis. The presence of the nitro group does not prevent the benzene nucleus in nitrobenzene from undergoing many of the reactions shown by benzene. Nitrobenzene is converted to dinitrobenzene by a mixture of concentrated nitric and sulphuric acids (p. 382), and it is directly attacked by chlorine and bromine to give *m*-chloro- or *m*-bromonitrobenzene. The nitrogen atom in the molecule of nitrobenzene is firmly attached to the benzene ring ; in none of the reactions of nitrobenzene is the link between the nitrogen atom and the benzene nucleus broken.

The most characteristic reactions of nitrobenzene are those in which the nitro group is attacked by reducing agents. The ultimate reduction product of nitrobenzene, in either acid or alkaline solution, is aniline, $C_6H_5NH_2$,

$$C_6H_5NO_2 + 6H = C_6H_5NH_2 + 2H_2O.$$

In acid solution reduction to aniline proceeds readily, but under special conditions it is possible to isolate an intermediate product, β-phenylhydroxylamine

$$\begin{array}{c} C_6H_5 \\ \diagdown \\ \diagup \hspace{-0.5em} N{-}OH. \\ H \end{array}$$

Another substance, nitrosobenzene C_6H_5NO, which may also be regarded as an intermediate product in the reduction of nitrobenzene to aniline, may be prepared by oxidising β-phenylhydroxylamine with potassium dichromate and dilute sulphuric acid.

When reduction takes place in alkaline solution neither β-phenyl hydroxylamine nor nitrosobenzene can be isolated, but three other substances,

azoxybenzene	azobenzene	hydrazobenzene
$C_6H_5{-}N$	$C_6H_5{-}N$	$C_6H_5{-}N{-}H$
$\parallel$	$\parallel$	$\mid$
$C_6H_5{-}N{-}O$	$C_6H_5{-}N$	$C_6H_5{-}N{-}H$
$+ \ -$		

may be obtained. Their formation may be explained by assuming that nitrosobenzene and β-phenylhydroxylamine are the immediate products of reduction, and that they react together as soon as they are formed to yield azoxybenzene,

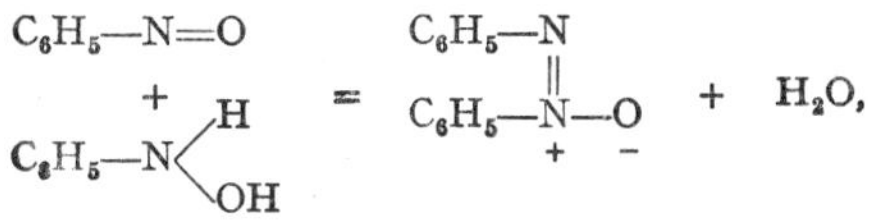

$$C_6H_5-N=O$$
$$+ \quad \text{/H} \quad = \quad C_6H_5-\overset{\|}{N}-O \quad + \quad H_2O,$$
$$C_6H_5-N\langle \quad \text{\textbackslash OH} \qquad \qquad +\quad -$$

which then undergoes further reduction to give azobenzene and hydrazobenzene.

1. Reduction of nitrobenzene in acid solution giving aniline. In the laboratory nitrobenzene is reduced to aniline by the action of tin and hydrochloric acid. Concentrated hydrochloric acid in small quantities at a time is poured on to a mixture of nitrobenzene and granulated tin in a flask fitted to a reflux condenser. When the reaction moderates the flask is heated for a short time on a boiling water-bath. The nitrobenzene is reduced to aniline and the tin is oxidised to stannic chloride, but in the presence of excess hydrochloric acid these products react with the aniline to give aniline chlorostannate.

$$2C_6H_5NO_2 + 3Sn + 12HCl = 2C_6H_5NH_2 + 3SnCl_4 + 4H_2O$$
$$2C_6H_5NH_2 + SnCl_4 + 2HCl = (C_6H_5NH_3)_2SnCl_6.$$

Concentrated sodium hydroxide solution is cautiously added to break down this complex salt,

$$(C_6H_5NH_3)_2SnCl_6 + 8NaOH$$
$$= 2C_6H_5NH_2 + Na_2SnO_3 + 6NaCl + 5H_2O,$$

and the liberated aniline is distilled in steam. Further details of this experiment are given on p. 388.

Under industrial conditions aniline is obtained by heating nitrobenzene with a mixture of iron borings and concentrated hydrochloric acid, p. 389.

2. (i) Reduction of nitrobenzene in alkaline solution, giving azoxybenzene. A mixture of powdered sodium hydroxide (23 gm.), nitrobenzene (18 gm.) and methyl alcohol (120 c.c.) is heated for three hours on a water-bath, with intermittent shaking, in a flask fitted to a reflux water condenser. The reduction of the nitrobenzene proceeds according to the equation,

$$4C_6H_5NO_2 + 3CH_3OH + 3NaOH$$
$$= 2C_6H_5.NO : N.C_6H_5 + 3H.COONa + 6H_2O.$$

When the reaction is over, the excess of methyl alcohol is distilled off, and the residue is poured into cold water (250 c.c.) and acidified with hydrochloric acid. Crude azoxybenzene separates as an oil which solidifies as the solution is stirred. When recrystallised from methylated spirit, azoxybenzene separates as pale yellow crystals, M.P. 36°.

(ii) Reduction of azoxybenzene to azobenzene. Powdered azoxybenzene (8 gm.) and iron filings (25 gm.) are placed in a small distilling flask and thoroughly mixed together by shaking. The side-tube of the distilling flask passes into a boiling tube, Fig. 61.

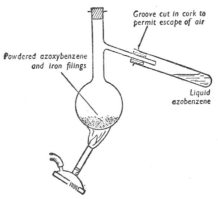

FIG. 61. Apparatus for the reduction of azoxybenzene to azobenzene.

The flask is gently heated with a Bunsen flame and red liquid azobenzene distils. When distillation ceases the azobenzene is shaken with warm dilute hydrochloric acid to extract impurities. The aqueous emulsion of azobenzene is cooled until the globules of azobenzene solidify, and it is then filtered at the pump. After thoroughly washing with water the azobenzene is recrystallised from methylated spirit. It separates as reddish-orange crystals, M.P. 67–68°.

3. Nitration of nitrobenzene, giving *m*-dinitrobenzene.
If nitrobenzene is heated with a mixture of concentrated sulphuric acid and fuming nitric acid, it is converted to *m*-dinitrobenzene. This reaction is described in detail on p. 383.

Tests for nitrobenzene. There are no simple or convenient tests for nitrobenzene. It may be recognised by carrying out on a test-tube scale the reduction to aniline or the nitration to *m*-dinitrobenzene.

(*a*) **Reduction.** 1 c.c. of nitrobenzene is placed in a boiling tube and 5 c.c. of concentrated hydrochloric acid and a few pieces of granulated tin are added. The mixture is warmed while the tube is shaken for about 3 minutes. When all the oil has disappeared the liquid is poured off from the tin into a small conical flask. It is cooled and sufficient

30 per cent. sodium hydroxide solution is added to redissolve the precipitate which first forms. After cooling thoroughly 15 c.c. of ether is added. The ethereal layer is separated in a separating funnel and washed with water. The ether is then evaporated by warming the solution in a basin on a previously heated water-bath in a fume cupboard away from all flames. The residue is aniline which is examined by means of the tests described on p. 395.

(b) **Nitration.** 2 c.c. of concentrated nitric acid and 2 c.c. of concentrated sulphuric acid are mixed together in a boiling tube. 1 c.c. of nitrobenzene is added, and the mixture is heated with constant shaking for a few minutes in a fume cupboard. The product is poured into cold water and solid dinitrobenzene separates. It may be identified by the acetone test, p. 385.

Uses of nitrobenzene. Nitrobenzene is used, under the name of " essence of myrbane " for perfuming cheap soaps, and although poisonous it has been used for flavouring confectionery. It is chiefly important as an intermediate product in the manufacture of aniline from benzene.

DINITROBENZENE

Dinitrobenzene is derived from benzene by the replacement of two hydrogen atoms in the molecule by nitro groups. Dinitrobenzene exists in the three isomeric forms :

o-dinitrobenzene   m-dinitrobenzene   p-dinitrobenzene

In accordance with the rule on p. 360, the nitration of nitrobenzene results chiefly in the formation of m-dinitrobenzene ; about 8 per cent. of o- and p-dinitrobenzene is formed at the same time.

m-DINITROBENZENE

m-dinitrobenzene is a very pale yellow crystalline solid, M.P. 90°. It is insoluble in water and volatile in steam. It is very poisonous.

Preparation of m-dinitrobenzene. m-dinitrobenzene is made by the nitration of nitrobenzene.

20 c.c. of concentrated sulphuric acid are placed in a 150 c.c. flask and 15 c.c. of fuming nitric acid (density 1·5) are carefully added, together with a few pieces of unglazed porcelain. The flask is fitted to a reflux air condenser, and 12 c.c. of nitrobenzene are added down the condenser in quantities of not more than 3 c.c. at a time. After each addition the flask is shaken thoroughly.

The flask is heated on a boiling water-bath for 1 hour with intermittent shaking. Both the flask and the condenser are clamped, as the cork may be attacked and weakened by the acid fumes evolved. The mixture is then poured into about 200 c.c. of cold water. The dinitrobenzene solidifies on stirring. It is filtered at the pump, washed thoroughly with water to remove acid, and drained as completely as possible. The crude dinitrobenzene is heated on a water-bath with 100 c.c. of methylated spirit in a 200 c.c. conical flask fitted to a reflux water condenser. The solution thus obtained is filtered through a small Buchner funnel previously warmed with boiling methylated spirit. When it is cooled, almost colourless crystals of *m*-dinitrobenzene are deposited.* A second crystallisation is usually necessary to remove traces of *o*- and *p*-dinitrobenzene.

Chemical properties of *m*-dinitrobenzene. In *m*-dinitrobenzene, as in nitrobenzene, each nitrogen atom is firmly linked to the benzene ring, and in no chemical reaction of *m*-dinitrobenzene is this link broken. The nitro groups, however, may be reduced to amino groups. By using the calculated quantity of a reducing agent it is possible to reduce one of the nitro groups in the molecule, leaving the other unchanged, and thus to obtain *m*-nitro-aniline,

$$\underset{\text{NO}_2}{\overset{\text{NO}_2}{\bigcirc}} \quad + \quad 6\text{H} \quad = \quad \underset{\text{NH}_2}{\overset{\text{NO}_2}{\bigcirc}} \quad + \quad 2\text{H}_2\text{O}.$$

If excess of the reducing agent is employed, *m*-phenylene diamine is obtained,

$$\underset{\text{NO}_2}{\overset{\text{NO}_2}{\bigcirc}} \quad + \quad 12\text{H} \quad = \quad \underset{\text{NH}_2}{\overset{\text{NH}_2}{\bigcirc}} \quad + \quad 4\text{H}_2\text{O}.$$

Preparation of *m*-nitro-aniline. If *m*-dinitrobenzene is treated with the calculated quantity of stannous chloride and hydrochloric acid it undergoes reduction to *m*-nitro-aniline. The immediate product is a complex compound of nitro-aniline with stannic chloride and hydrochloric acid, from which the free nitro-aniline is liberated by the addition of sodium hydroxide solution. The nitro-aniline may be separated from the mixture by distillation in steam. (Compare the preparation of aniline, p. 381).

The reduction of *m*-dinitrobenzene may also be carried out by passing hydrogen sulphide through a warm alcoholic solution made alkaline with concentrated ammonium hydroxide solution. The passage of the hydrogen sulphide is discontinued when the solution just fails to respond to tests for *m*-dinitrobenzene,

$$\text{C}_6\text{H}_4(\text{NO}_2)_2 + 3\text{H}_2\text{S} = \text{C}_6\text{H}_4(\text{NO}_2)(\text{NH}_2) + 2\text{H}_2\text{O} + 3\text{S}.$$

The most satisfactory method for carrying out the reduction is to warm a dilute suspension of *m*-dinitrobenzene in water with a solution of sodium disulphide, Na_2S_2,

$$\text{C}_6\text{H}_4(\text{NO}_2)_2 + \text{Na}_2\text{S}_2 + \text{H}_2\text{O} = \text{C}_6\text{H}_4(\text{NO}_2)(\text{NH}_2) + \text{Na}_2\text{S}_2\text{O}_3.$$

The *m*-nitro-aniline separates on cooling, and may be obtained as bright yellow crystals, M.P. 114°, by recrystallisation from much hot water.

---

* *o*-dinitrobenzene may be obtained from the mother liquor.

Tests for *m*-dinitrobenzene

(*a*) **The acetone test.** If a few crystals of *m*-dinitrobenzene are dissolved in 1 or 2 c.c. of acetone, and a few drops of aqueous sodium hydroxide solution are added, the solution becomes coloured deep violet. The colour is turned red by acetic acid and is destroyed by mineral acids. This colour reaction may be used as a test for acetone, and for other compounds which either contain the enol group —CH=C—OH or can give rise to it by intra-molecular change (see p. 461).

(*b*) **Reduction followed by the formation of Bismarck brown.** About 1 gm. of *m*-dinitrobenzene is reduced exactly according to the procedure described on p. 382 for the reduction of nitrobenzene. The *m*-phenylene diamine thus obtained is dissolved in about 1 c.c. of dilute hydrochloric acid, the solution is cooled and a few drops of sodium nitrite solution are added. A deep brown solution is formed from which separates a brown precipitate of the dye Bismarck brown.

p-DINITROBENZENE

p-Dinitrobenzene is made by oxidising quinone dioxime with nitric acid,

$$
\begin{array}{c}
\text{NOH} \\
\parallel \\
\text{C} \\
\text{H--C}^{\diagup}\; {}^{\diagdown}\text{C--H} \\
\parallel \quad \parallel \\
\text{H--C}_{\diagdown}\; {}_{\diagup}\text{C--H} \\
\text{C} \\
\parallel \\
\text{NOH}
\end{array}
\;+\; 3\text{O} \;=\;
\begin{array}{c}
\text{NO}_2 \\
\bigcirc \\
\text{NO}_2
\end{array}
\;+\; \text{H}_2\text{O}.
$$

It is a colourless crystalline solid, M.P. 173°. Its chemical properties are analogous to those of *m*-dinitrobenzene. The nitro groups in the molecule may be converted to amino groups by reduction, but there is no reaction by which the links between the nitro groups and the benzene ring may be broken.

o-DINITROBENZENE

o-dinitrobenzene may be obtained from the alcoholic mother liquor from which *m*-dinitrobenzene has been crystallised (p. 384). It is a colourless solid, M.P. 118°. By the action of tin and hydrochloric acid the nitro groups may be reduced to amino groups.

It is possible to sever one of the nitrogen atoms in the *o*-dinitrobenzene molecule from the benzene ring. For example, boiling sodium hydroxide solution reacts with *o*-dinitrobenzene to yield the sodium derivative of *o*-nitrophenol,

$$
\begin{array}{c}
\text{NO}_2 \\
\bigcirc^{\text{NO}_2}
\end{array}
\;+\; 2\text{NaOH} \;=\;
\begin{array}{c}
\text{NO}_2 \\
\bigcirc^{\text{ONa}}
\end{array}
\;+\; \text{NaNO}_2 \;+\; \text{H}_2\text{O},
$$

N

and alcoholic ammonia at moderately high temperatures yields *o*-nitro-aniline,

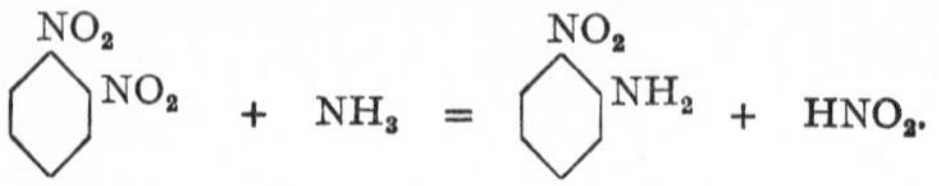

$$\underset{\text{NO}_2}{\bigcirc}\text{NO}_2 \;+\; \text{NH}_3 \;=\; \underset{\text{NO}_2}{\bigcirc}\text{NH}_2 \;+\; \text{HNO}_2.$$

The replaceability of one of the nitro groups in the molecule of *o*-dinitrobenzene by the group —ONa or —NH$_2$ is in striking contrast to the non-replaceability of either of the nitro groups in *m*-dinitrobenzene or *p*-dinitrobenzene.

CHAPTER XXIV

ANILINE

ANILINE is theoretically derived by the replacement of one of the hydrogen atoms in the benzene molecule by the amino group, —NH_2. Its structural formula is

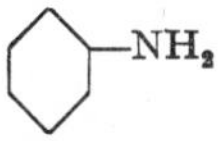

Aniline might also be theoretically derived by the substitution of the phenyl group, —C_6H_5, for one of the hydrogen atoms in the molecule of ammonia. The ammoniacal properties of the residual —NH_2 group are so modified by the presence of the phenyl group, however, that this derivation of the structure of aniline is only of formal interest ; the general behaviour of aniline is most satisfactorily interpreted by regarding it as a derivative of benzene.

Freshly distilled aniline is a colourless oily liquid, M.P. 6·2°, B.P. 182°, density = 1·02 at 20°. On exposure to air and light its colour darkens to yellow-brown and ultimately it becomes almost black. This colour change occurs only in aniline manufactured from benzene obtained from coal tar ; aniline prepared from benzene made from acetylene does not show it. The colour change is due to the oxidation of thiophene (p. 478) which is present in aniline made from coal tar benzene. Aniline has a faint but characteristic odour. It is poisonous. Aniline and water are partially miscible. The solubility of aniline in water is 3·5 per cent., and of water in aniline is 5 per cent. Aniline is volatile in steam. It is soluble in organic solvents.

Reactions in which aniline is produced. Aniline is prepared by the reduction of benzene derivatives in which a nitrogen atom is directly linked to a carbon atom of the nucleus. Among such derivatives are :

Nitrobenzene :

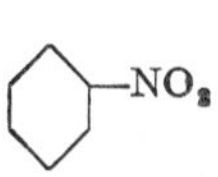

Nitrosobenzene :

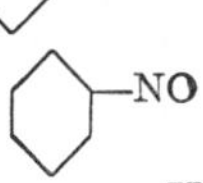

Phenylhydrazine :

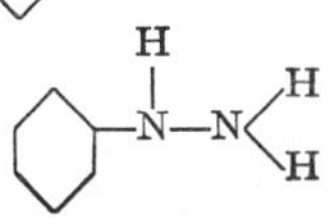

Diazobenzene compounds, such as diazobenzene chloride : $\langle\rangle$—NNCl

Azobenzene : $\langle\rangle$—N:N—$\langle\rangle$

Aniline hydrogen sulphate is formed by the hydrolysis with 70 per cent. sulphuric acid of the acetyl, benzoyl or sulphonyl derivatives of aniline, as shown by the equations :

$$C_6H_5N{\raise1ex\hbox{$\scriptstyle H$}\atop\raise-1ex\hbox{$\scriptstyle COCH_3$}} \quad + \quad H_2O \quad + \quad H_2SO_4$$

acetanilide

$$= \quad [C_6H_5NH_3]HSO_4 \quad + \quad CH_3.COOH$$
aniline hydrogen sulphate   acetic acid

$$C_6H_5N{\raise1ex\hbox{$\scriptstyle H$}\atop\raise-1ex\hbox{$\scriptstyle COC_6H_5$}} \quad + \quad H_2O \quad + \quad H_2SO_4$$

benzanilide

$$= \quad [C_6H_5NH_3]HSO_4 \quad + \quad C_6H_5.COOH$$
benzoic acid

$$C_6H_5N{\raise1ex\hbox{$\scriptstyle H$}\atop\raise-1ex\hbox{$\scriptstyle SO_2.C_6H_4.CH_3$}} \quad + \quad H_2O \quad + \quad H_2SO_4$$

p-toluene sulphonyl aniline

$$= \quad [C_6H_5NH_3]HSO_4 \quad + \quad CH_3.C_6H_4.SO_2.OH$$
p-toluene sulphonic acid

Aniline is liberated when aniline hydrogen sulphate is heated with sodium hydroxide solution.

Laboratory preparation of aniline from nitrobenzene. 25 gm. of nitrobenzene and 50 gm. of granulated tin are placed in a 600 c.c. bolt-head flask fitted to a reflux water condenser. 20 c.c. of concentrated hydrochloric acid are poured down the condenser, and the contents of the flask are shaken. The reaction is vigorous, and it may be necessary to moderate it by immersing the flask in cold water. When the reaction slackens, another 20 c.c. of hydrochloric acid are poured down the condenser, and the process is repeated until 100 c.c. of the acid have been added. The condenser is then removed, and the open flask is heated on a water-bath to complete the reaction. At the end of 20 minutes the odour of nitrobenzene should be scarcely perceptible. At this stage aniline chlorostannate is present,

$$2C_6H_5NO_2 + 3Sn + 12HCl = 2C_6H_5NH_2 + 3SnCl_4 + 4H_2O,$$
$$2C_6H_5NH_2 + SnCl_4 + 2HCl = (C_6H_5NH_3)_2SnCl_6.$$

The flask is cooled in water, and a solution of 75 gm. of sodium hydroxide in 100 c.c. of water is added. A white precipitate of stannic hydroxide is at first thrown down, but is later converted to sodium stannate which dissolves in the aqueous solution. The aniline separates as an oil. The decomposition of aniline chlorostannate to yield aniline is in accordance with the equation :

$$(C_6H_5NH_3)_2SnCl_6 + 8NaOH$$
$$= 2C_6H_5NH_2 + Na_2SnO_3 + 6NaCl + 5H_2O.$$

The flask is fitted up for steam distillation, Fig. 20, p. 65, and the mixture is steam-distilled until about 175 c.c. of distillate have been collected. 30 gm. of powdered sodium chloride are dissolved in the distillate to diminish the solubility of aniline in the aqueous layer, and the distillate is transferred to a large separating funnel. 40 c.c. of ether are added, and the mixture is shaken vigorously to facilitate the partition of aniline between the ethereal and the aqueous layers. The layers are allowed to separate, and the lower aqueous layer is run off into a beaker, and the ethereal layer is poured into a 200 c.c. conical flask. The aqueous layer is extracted with a further 40 c.c. of ether, and the second ethereal solution is added to that in the conical flask. Coarsely powdered potassium hydroxide is added to the ethereal solution, and the corked flask is allowed to stand for some hours until the solution is clear and dry.

Apparatus for the removal of the ether by distillation is assembled, Fig. 22, p. 70. The ethereal solution is filtered through a fluted filter paper into the dropping funnel. About 25 c.c. of the solution are run into the distilling flask which is heated on a previously warmed water-bath ; the remainder of the solution is added as the ether distils. When the distillation of the ether is complete the apparatus is dismantled and the distilling flask is equipped with a thermometer reading to 200°, and fitted to an air condenser. The flask is carefully heated over a wire gauze and the fraction of the distillate boiling at 180–185° is collected.

Industrial preparation of aniline. The industrial preparation of aniline is carried out by heating nitrobenzene with iron borings and hydrochloric acid. When the reaction is over, lime is added to decompose any aniline hydrochloride present, and the aniline is steam-distilled. The equations describing the reduction of nitrobenzene by iron and hydrochloric acid are given on p. 480.

CHEMICAL PROPERTIES OF ANILINE

Reactions of the —NH₂ group in the aniline molecule

1. Action as a base. Aniline is neutral to litmus, but it combines with acids to form salts such as aniline hydrochloride, $(C_6H_5NH_3)Cl$, which is soluble, and aniline sulphate, $(C_6H_5NH_3)_2SO_4$, which is sparingly soluble. The salts of aniline are hydrolysed in aqueous solution, and they are decomposed by alkalis, or by sodium or potassium carbonates. Aniline hydrochloride combines with platinic chloride to give the moderately soluble aniline platinichloride, $(C_6H_5NH_3)_2PtCl_6$, which crystallises in yellow plates.

2. Reaction with ethyl bromide, giving ethyl aniline. Aniline reacts with ethyl bromide to yield ethyl aniline hydrobromide,

$$C_6H_5NH_2 + C_2H_5Br = \left[\begin{matrix} C_6H_5 \\ C_2H_5 \end{matrix} \!\!\! N \!\!\! \begin{matrix} H \\ H \end{matrix} \right] Br.$$

The action of aniline on ethyl bromide, if prolonged, gives diethyl aniline hydrobromide,

$$\left[\begin{matrix} C_6H_5 \\ C_2H_5 \end{matrix} >N< \begin{matrix} C_2H_5 \\ H \end{matrix} \right] Br.$$

Methyl bromide reacts similarly. The alkylanilines, which are important organic substances, are, however, usually prepared by heating under pressure to about 200° a mixture of aniline, the appropriate alcohol, and hydrochloric acid.

3. Reaction with aniline hydrochloride, giving diphenyl-amine. If aniline is heated with aniline hydrochloride in a closed vessel at 260°, diphenylamine and ammonium chloride are formed,

$$C_6H_5NH_2 \ + \ C_6H_5NH_3Cl \ = \ \begin{matrix} C_6H_5 \\ C_6H_5 \end{matrix} >N-H \ + \ NH_4Cl.$$

Diphenylamine is a colourless crystalline compound, M.P. 54°, B.P. 302°. Although it is a derivative of ammonia, it is only a feeble base, and the hydrogen atom attached to the nitrogen atom in the molecule may be replaced by direct action with potassium,

$$2(C_6H_5)_2NH \ + \ 2K \ = \ 2(C_6H_5)_2NK \ + \ H_2.$$

These properties illustrate the acid character which is conferred on a molecule by the presence of the phenyl group.

A solution of diphenylamine in concentrated sulphuric acid is coloured an intense violet by the action of oxidising agents. It is used as a test for nitrates, and as an indicator in the titration of ferrous salts against potassium dichromate solution.

4. Reaction with nitrous acid, giving phenol or a diazonium compound. When aniline hydrochloride is treated with a solution of sodium nitrite warmed to about 50°, phenol, nitrogen and water are formed,

$$C_6H_5NH_2 \ + \ HONO \ = \ C_6H_5OH \ + \ N_2 \ + \ H_2O.$$

This reaction is analogous to that between ethylamine hydrochloride and sodium nitrite. When, however, a solution of aniline hydro-chloride containing excess of hydrochloric acid is treated with sodium nitrite solution between 5° and 10°, a diazonium salt is produced,

$$C_6H_5NH_3Cl \ + \ HONO \ = \ C_6H_5N_2Cl \ + \ 2H_2O.$$

The diazonium salts have no analogues among the aliphatic compounds. They are of great importance in synthetical organic chemistry and are described on p. 396.

5. Reaction with chloroform and an alcoholic solution of potassium hydroxide, giving phenyl isocyanide. Hofmann's carbylamine reaction. If aniline is warmed with chloroform and an alcoholic solution of potassium hydroxide phenyl isocyanide (phenyl carbylamine) is liberated,

$$C_6H_5NH_2 + CHCl_3 + 3KOH = C_6H_5NC + 3KCl + 3H_2O.$$

This compound, in common with other isocyanides, has a marked and disagreeable odour.

6. The acetylation of aniline. Aniline reacts with acetyl chloride and with acetic anhydride to yield acetanilide,

$$C_6H_5NH_2 + CH_3COCl = C_6H_5N\begin{smallmatrix}H\\COCH_3\end{smallmatrix} + HCl,$$

$$C_6H_5NH_2 + \begin{smallmatrix}CH_3C:O\\ \\CH_3C:O\end{smallmatrix}\rangle O = C_6H_5N\begin{smallmatrix}H\\COCH_3\end{smallmatrix} + CH_3COOH.$$

The experimental procedure for the preparation of acetanilide is briefly described on p. 253.

7. The benzoylation of aniline. If a mixture of aniline, aqueous sodium hydroxide solution and benzoyl chloride is shaken for twenty minutes, benzanilide is formed as a white solid,

$$C_6H_5NH_2 + C_6H_5COCl + NaOH$$
$$= C_6H_5N\begin{smallmatrix}H\\COC_6H_5\end{smallmatrix} + NaCl + H_2O.$$

It may be separated from the other products of the reaction by filtration, and recrystallised from methylated spirit. This is an example of the Schotten-Baumann reaction, see p. 453.

8. The sulphonylation of aniline. The Schotten-Baumann reaction may also be carried out by shaking aniline with aqueous sodium hydroxide solution and benzene sulphonyl chloride. Benzene sulphonylaniline is then obtained, according to the equation,

$$C_6H_5N\begin{smallmatrix}H\\H\end{smallmatrix} + C_6H_5.SO_2.Cl + NaOH$$
$$= C_6H_5N\begin{smallmatrix}H\\SO_2.C_6H_5\end{smallmatrix} + NaCl + H_2O.$$

Benzene sulphonylaniline is soluble in sodium hydroxide solution, and therefore it does not separate as the reaction proceeds. It may be isolated in the crystalline form by acidifying the alkaline solution with hydrochloric acid, filtering off the precipitated benzene sulphonylaniline, and recrystallising it from alcohol diluted with one-half of its volume of water.

p-toluene sulphonyl chloride is frequently used as a sulphonylating agent in place of benzene sulphonyl chloride as it is cheaper and more readily available. With aniline it yields p-toluene sulphonylaniline,

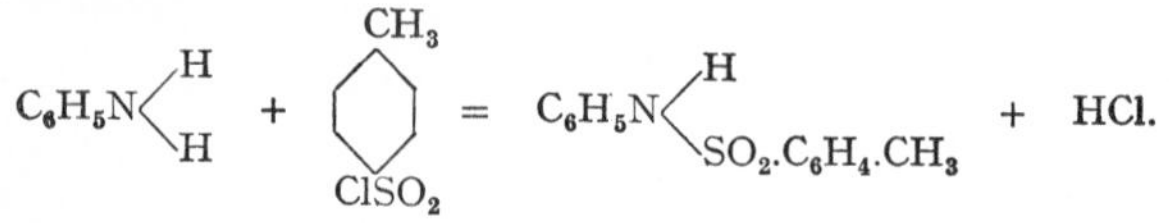

$$C_6H_5N\begin{matrix} H \\ H \end{matrix} + \begin{matrix} CH_3 \\ \bigcirc \\ ClSO_2 \end{matrix} = C_6H_5N\begin{matrix} H \\ SO_2.C_6H_4.CH_3 \end{matrix} + HCl.$$

9. Condensations of aniline with benzaldehyde, and with benzoquinone.

(i) If equal volumes of benzaldehyde and aniline are heated for thirty minutes in a dish on a water-bath, condensation occurs and benzylidene aniline is formed,

$$C_6H_5NH_2 + \overset{H}{\underset{|}{O:C.C_6H_5}} = C_6H_5N:\overset{H}{\underset{|}{C.C_6H_5}} + H_2O.$$

The benzylidene aniline crystallises if the dish is cooled in ice water, M.P. 50°.

(ii) If aniline is added to a solution of benzoquinone in alcohol and the solution is gently warmed, a reddish precipitate of quinone-dianil is formed,

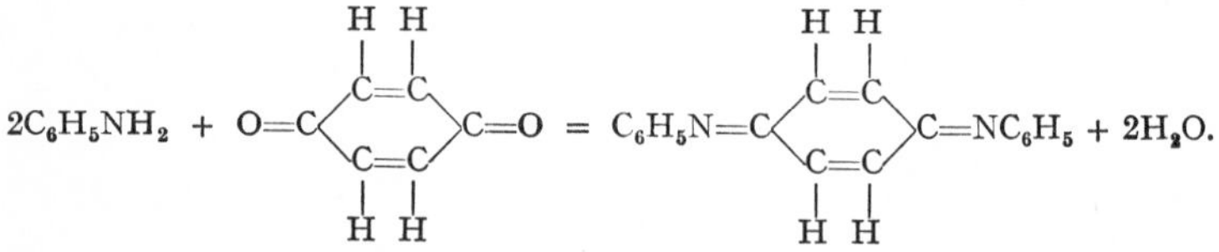

$$2C_6H_5NH_2 + O=C\begin{matrix} \overset{H}{\underset{|}{C}}=\overset{H}{\underset{|}{C}} \\ \underset{|}{C}=\underset{|}{C} \\ H \quad H \end{matrix}C=O = C_6H_5N=C\begin{matrix} \overset{H}{\underset{|}{C}}=\overset{H}{\underset{|}{C}} \\ \underset{|}{C}=\underset{|}{C} \\ H \quad H \end{matrix}C=NC_6H_5 + 2H_2O.$$

10. The coupling of aniline with diazonium salts.
If aniline is added to an aqueous solution of phenyl diazonium sulphate, diazo-aminobenzene is formed,

$$C_6H_5N\begin{matrix} H \\ H \end{matrix} + ClN_2C_6H_5 = C_6H_5N\begin{matrix} H \\ N_2C_6H_5 \end{matrix} + HCl.$$

A reaction of this type between a diazonium salt and an amino compound is known as " coupling ".

Reactions of the nucleus in the aniline molecule

11. Action of the halogens. Chlorine and bromine react with aniline much more readily than they do with benzene. If an aqueous solution of chlorine or bromine is added to an aqueous solution of aniline, or of an aniline salt, a white precipitate of sparingly soluble trichloroaniline or of tribromoaniline is formed immediately,

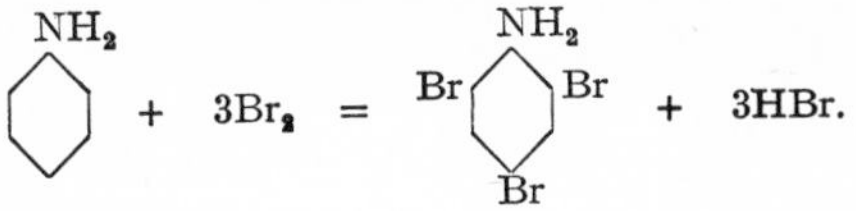

$$C_6H_5NH_2 + 3Br_2 = \text{(tribromoaniline)} + 3HBr.$$

12. The sulphonation of aniline, giving sulphanilic acid. Excess of sulphuric acid reacts with aniline to produce aniline hydrogen sulphate,

$$C_6H_5NH_2 + H_2SO_4 = [C_6H_5NH_3]HSO_4.$$

If the mixture is heated, the aniline hydrogen sulphate is slowly converted to sulphanilic acid,

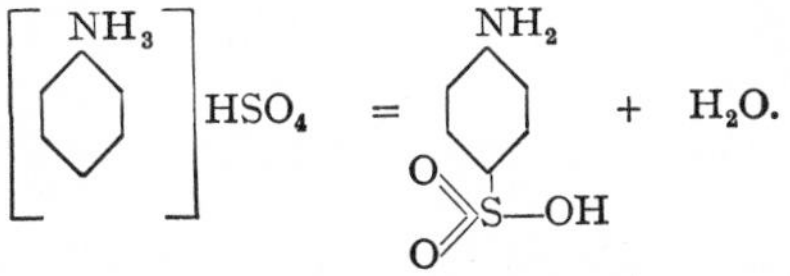

$$[C_6H_5NH_3]HSO_4 = \text{(sulphanilic acid)} + H_2O.$$

This intramolecular change is promoted by the presence of fuming sulphuric acid (concentrated sulphuric acid containing 8–10 per cent. of sulphur trioxide in solution).

The sulphonation of aniline is carried out as follows : 20 c.c. of concentrated sulphuric acid are added to 10 c.c. of aniline in a 150 c.c. conical flask cooled by immersion in water. Aniline hydrogen sulphate is precipitated from the solution in the form of white lumps. 20 c.c. of 10 per cent. fuming sulphuric acid are then added and the mixture is heated in an oil-bath at 180–190° for 1 hour. The product is cooled and poured into 200 c.c. of cold water when crystalline sulphanilic acid separates $NH_2.C_6H_4.SO_3H,2H_2O$. After standing for 5 minutes the sulphanilic acid is filtered at the pump, washed with water and drained. It may be crystallised from about 250 c.c. of boiling water. It should be dried by exposure to air or in an atmospheric calcium chloride desiccator. If placed in a sulphuric acid vacuum desiccator it loses water of crystallisation.

Sulphanilic acid decomposes on heating before its melting point is reached. It is soluble in boiling water, but only slightly soluble in cold water. It does not form salts with acids, but it reacts with sodium hydroxide or with sodium carbonate to give sodium sulphanilate,

$$2NH_2.C_6H_4.SO_3H + Na_2CO_3 = 2NH_2.C_6H_4.SO_3Na + H_2O + CO_2.$$

The constitution of sulphanilic acid is probably

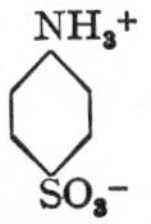

When heated with soda-lime, sulphanilic acid yields aniline,

$$NH_2.C_6H_4.SO_3H + 2NaOH = NH_2.C_6H_5 + Na_2SO_4 + H_2O,$$

a reaction which is reminiscent of the action of soda-lime on sodium acetate.

13. Reaction with nitric acid. Aniline is oxidised and charred by nitric acid ; it is difficult to control the reaction so as to obtain any particular product. Aniline can be nitrated to a mixture of o- and p-nitroanilines by using a very large excess of sulphuric acid in the nitrating mixture. If aniline is to be nitrated, however, it is more satisfactory to convert the aniline to acetanilide,* to nitrate the acetanilide, and to hydrolyse the product to nitroaniline using 70 per cent. sulphuric acid.

14. The oxidation of aniline. Aniline is readily oxidised ; the nature of the products depends on the conditions employed. Most of the oxidation products of aniline are coloured. The effects of adding solutions of bleaching powder, or of ferrous sulphate and hydrogen peroxide, or of ferric chloride are described under " Tests ", p. 395. Aniline black, a black dye of complex structure, is obtained by the controlled oxidation of aniline by sodium dichromate and sulphuric acid. The prolonged oxidation of aniline, or of aniline black, by sodium dichromate and sulphuric acid yields benzoquinone, the typical member of a class of organic substances known as quinones. The constitution of benzoquinone is

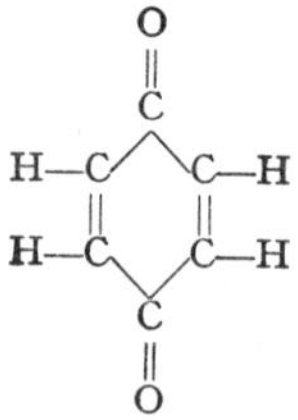

It is an unsaturated cyclic diketone. The ring of six carbon atoms does not possess the characteristic properties of the benzene ring. Benzoquinone is, however, easily converted to true benzene derivatives. On reduction it yields p-dihydroxybenzene, on treatment with phosphorus pentachloride it yields p-dichlorobenzene, and oxidation of the quinone dioxime gives p-dinitrobenzene, p. 385.

Use of aniline. Aniline is an important intermediate compound in the manufacture of certain dyestuffs from benzene.

* For the use of acetylation to diminish the activity of the —NH$_2$ group, see p. 450.

ANILINE

Tests for aniline

1. **The isocyanide reaction.** 1 or 2 drops of chloroform are mixed with 1 or 2 drops of aniline and 2–3 c.c. of alcoholic sodium hydroxide solution are added. The mixture is shaken and gently warmed. The disagreeable odour of phenyl isocyanide is detected.

2. **Diazotization followed by coupling with β-naphthol.** A few drops of aniline are dissolved in 1 c.c. of concentrated hydrochloric acid. The solution is diluted with 3 c.c. of water and cooled in ice, and a few drops of sodium nitrite solution are added. The solution, which contains benzene diazonium chloride, is added to a cold solution of β-naphthol in excess of 10 per cent. sodium hydroxide solution. A brilliant red dye is obtained.

3. **Action of oxidising agents.**
   (a) *Bleaching powder.* If 1 or 2 drops of aniline are shaken with 10 c.c. of water, and a few drops of bleaching powder solution are added, a purple coloration is produced which in a short time turns brown.
   (b) *Hydrogen peroxide and ferrous sulphate in concentrated hydrocholric acid solution.* 1 c.c. of aniline is mixed with 3 c.c. of concentrated hydrochloric acid and 1 c.c. of water is added. When all the aniline hydrochloride has dissolved, a few drops of hydrogen peroxide are added, followed by 1 drop of freshly prepared ferrous sulphate solution. A bright green coloration appears, and later a green dye, emeraldine, is precipitated.
   (c) *Ferric chloride.* If ferric chloride solution is added to a solution of aniline in dilute hydrochloric acid, a pale green coloration is obtained.

4. Aniline may be acetylated or benzoylated and the resulting acetanilide or benzanilide may be identified by means of its melting point.

CHAPTER XXV

THE DIAZO COMPOUNDS

BENZENE DIAZONIUM CHLORIDE

BENZENE diazonium chloride is a salt with a structure analogous to that of ammonium chloride. It is derived from aniline hydrochloride by the substitution of an atom of nitrogen for the three hydrogen atoms directly attached to the nitrogen atom in the ion

$$\left[\begin{array}{c} H \\ | \\ C_6H_5{-}N{-}H \\ | \\ H \end{array} \right]^+$$

The structural formula of the benzene diazonium ion is $[C_6H_5{-}N{\equiv}N]^+$, and in the presence of hydrochloric acid it associates with a chlorine ion to give benzene diazonium chloride $[C_6H_5{-}N{\equiv}N]^+$ Cl^-.

Benzene diazonium chloride undergoes a large number of chemical reactions, and it is, therefore, a substance of the greatest importance in synthetical organic chemistry ; nearly all the simple derivatives of benzene may be prepared using benzene diazonium chloride as the starting-point. In this respect it occupies a position in the chemistry of simple aromatic compounds somewhat similar to that of ethyl bromide in the chemistry of simple aliphatic compounds.

Benzene diazonium salts are not easily obtained in the crystalline condition for two reasons : (a) they are always unstable, and when dry may be dangerously explosive, and (b) they are very soluble in water. The reactions of benzene diazonium salts are normally carried out in aqueous solution.

The preparation and reactions of a solution of benzene diazonium chloride are, therefore, next described. An account of the preparation of crystalline benzene diazonium sulphate is given at the end of the chapter to show that it is possible to isolate a pure specimen of a diazonium compound.

The preparation of an aqueous solution of benzene diazonium chloride

This preparation is carried out by adding an aqueous solution of sodium nitrite to a solution of aniline in hydrochloric acid,

$$NaNO_2 \ + \ HCl \ = \ NaCl \ + \ HNO_2$$
$$[C_6H_5NH_3]^+Cl^- \ + \ HONO \ = \ [C_6H_5N{\equiv}N]^+Cl^- \ + \ 2H_2O.$$

The quantity of hydrochloric acid must be sufficient (a) to liberate nitrous acid from the sodium nitrite which is added, (b) to ensure that throughout the reaction the aniline is present as aniline hydrochloride, (c) to keep the solution acid. If free aniline is present it reacts with the benzene diazonium chloride to give a yellow precipitate of diazo-amino-benzene, p. 401.

$$C_6H_5N_2Cl \quad + \quad HNHC_6H_5 \quad = \quad C_6H_5N_2.NH.C_6H_5 + HCl.$$

The quantity of sodium nitrite added must be slightly in excess of that required just to react with the aniline hydrochloride. Excess leads to the formation of coloured by-products, and a deficiency leaves unchanged aniline in the solution. In practice 1 molar proportion of aniline is dissolved in 3·0 molar proportions of hydrochloric acid, and 1·1 molar proportions of sodium nitrite are added. Throughout the preparation the temperature must be maintained between 5° and 10°. If it rises above 10° the benzene diazonium chloride reacts with water to yield phenol ; if it falls below 5° the reaction between nitrous acid and aniline hydrochloride is arrested. The reaction is exothermic, and the containing vessel must, therefore, be cooled in ice-water.

The conversion of aniline hydrochloride to benzene diazonium chloride is known as *diazotisation* ; the aniline is said to have been *diazotised*. These terms are applied generally in aromatic organic chemistry to the transformation of the amino group in a compound of the type A—NH$_2$ to the diazonium group [A—N≡N]$^+$, where A is an aromatic radical such as phenyl, C$_6$H$_5$, or one of its derivatives.

The practical details are as follows : 15 c.c. of aniline are dissolved in a mixture of 40 c.c. of concentrated hydrochloric acid and 40 c.c. of water in a 250 c.c. conical flask. The flask is immersed in a mixture of ice and water until the thermometer placed in the solution reads 5°. A solution of powdered sodium nitrite * containing 12·5 gm. dissolved in 30 c.c. of water is added, in small quantities of 2–3 c.c. at a time, to the cold aniline hydrochloride solution which is stirred by means of the thermometer. Throughout the addition of the sodium nitrite solution the temperature of the contents of the flask is maintained between 5° and 10°. The reaction is complete when all the sodium nitrite solution has been added, and the solution has been allowed to stand for some minutes at 7° or 8°.

Benzene diazonium chloride is prepared by the diazotisation of aniline immediately before it is required for use. No attempt is made to isolate it from the solution in which it is formed, which is used in all the reactions described below.

* The sodium nitrite must be of good quality, " Sodium nitrite Recryst," in order that the weight shall be an accurate measure of the quantity of NaNO$_2$ taken.

Reactions of benzene diazonium chloride

1. Hydrolysis, giving phenol. If an aqueous solution of benzene diazonium chloride is cautiously warmed, with stirring, to 50–55°, a vigorous evolution of nitrogen occurs and the solution becomes dark in colour,

$$C_6H_5N_2Cl + HOH = C_6H_5OH + N_2 + HCl.$$

The resultant solution contains phenol which may be isolated from the tarry by-products by steam distillation, p. 418.

2. Reaction with potassium iodide, giving iodobenzene. If an aqueous solution of potassium iodide is slowly added, with shaking, to a cold solution of benzene diazonium chloride, a vigorous reaction occurs in which nitrogen is evolved and iodobenzene separates from the solution as a dark heavy oil,

$$C_6H_5N_2Cl + KI = C_6H_5I + N_2 + KCl.$$

The experimental procedure for the preparation of iodobenzene from benzene diazonium chloride is described on p. 410.

It should be noted that the reaction between potassium iodide and benzene diazonium chloride takes place spontaneously without the aid of a catalyst.

3. Reaction with certain cuprous salts, giving bromobenzene, chlorobenzene, or phenyl cyanide. Sandmeyer's reactions.

(a) *Preparation of bromobenzene.* If a solution of benzene diazonium chloride is slowly run into a warm solution of cuprous bromide in hydrobromic acid, nitrogen is evolved and bromobenzene is obtained,

$$C_6H_5N_2Cl + HBr = C_6H_5Br + HCl + N_2.$$

The part played in this reaction by the cuprous bromide is not understood.

(b) *Preparation of chlorobenzene.* If a solution of benzene diazonium chloride is run drop by drop into a solution of cuprous chloride in concentrated hydrochloric acid diluted with its own volume of water and maintained at 60°, nitrogen is evolved and chlorobenzene is formed,

$$C_6H_5N_2Cl + HCl = C_6H_5Cl + HCl + N_2.$$

The mechanism of this change is obscure, but the formation of the addition product, $C_6H_5N_2Cl$, Cu_2Cl_2, which appears momentarily as a yellow precipitate as each drop of the diazotised solution enters the cuprous chloride solution, is doubtless an intermediate stage of the reaction. The production of bromobenzene from benzene diazonium chloride by the analogous reaction described above, suggests that the formation of chlorobenzene does not take place by the simple elimination of two atoms of nitrogen from a molecule of benzene diazonium chloride.

The chlorobenzene is isolated from the other substances present at the completion of the reaction by the procedure described on p. 405.

(c) *Preparation of benzonitrile (phenyl cyanide).* If a solution of benzene diazonium chloride is added to a warm solution of potassium cuprocyanide,* nitrogen is evolved and benzonitrile is formed,

$$4C_6H_5N_2Cl \ + \ K_3[Cu(CN)_4]$$
$$= \ 4C_6H_5CN \ + \ K_3[CuCl_4] \ + \ 4N_2.$$

The resultant solution is distilled in steam, when benzonitrile, together with some phenol and phenyl isocyanide which are formed as by-products, passes into the distillate. The distillate is shaken with ether. The ethereal solution of benzonitrile is shaken with sodium hydroxide solution to remove phenol, and then with dilute sulphuric acid to remove phenyl isocyanide. It is dried over calcium chloride, and the ether is removed (p. 70). The residue of benzonitrile, B.P. 191°, is distilled using an air condenser.

4. Reaction with finely divided copper, giving chlorobenzene. Gattermann's reaction. If copper powder (made by reducing an aqueous solution of cupric sulphate with zinc dust) is added in small quantities at a time to a solution of benzene diazonium chloride cooled in ice-water, a vigorous effervescence of nitrogen occurs, and a mixture of copper powder and chlorobenzene collects on the bottom of the reaction vessel. The upper aqueous layer is discarded, and the residue is steam-distilled. The chlorobenzene in the distillate is extracted with ether, dried over anhydrous calcium chloride, and distilled,

$$C_6H_5N_2Cl \ = \ C_6H_5Cl \ + \ N_2.$$

5. Reduction, giving phenylhydrazine. Benzene diazonium chloride is reduced by a solution of stannous chloride in concentrated hydrochloric acid to yield a precipitate of phenylhydrazine hydrochloride,

$$C_6H_5N_2Cl \ + \ 2SnCl_2 \ + \ 4HCl \ = \ C_6H_5NH.NH_2.HCl \ + \ 2SnCl_4.$$

* A solution of potassium cuprocyanide is made by adding 60 gm. of potassium cyanide dissolved in 100 c.c. of water to 55 gm. of $CuSO_4,5H_2O$ dissolved in 200 c.c. of water. The following reactions occur :

$$CuSO_4 \ + \ 2KCN \ = \ Cu(CN)_2 \ + \ K_2SO_4,$$
$$2Cu(CN)_2 \ = \ Cu_2(CN)_2 \ + \ C_2N_2,$$
$$6KCN \ + \ Cu_2(CN)_2 \ = \ 2K_3[Cu(CN)_4].$$

Phenylhydrazine is liberated from this salt by the action of concentrated sodium hydroxide solution. Phenylhydrazine is a pale yellow crystalline compound. It melts at 23°, and boils with some decomposition at 242°. It is used in organic chemistry for converting aldehydes and ketones to phenylhydrazones, and sugars to osazones, p. 339. Phenylhydrazine may be converted to benzene by oxidation with Fehling's solution, p. 363.

6. Reaction with potassium hydroxide solution. If potassium hydroxide is added to a solution of benzene diazonium chloride, the benzene diazonium ion associates with the hydroxyl ion,

$$[C_6H_5\!-\!N\!\equiv\!N]^+ \ + \ Cl^- \ + \ K^+ \ + \ OH^-$$
$$= \ [C_6H_5\!-\!N\!\equiv\!N]^+OH^- \ + \ K^+ \ + \ Cl^-.$$

A rearrangement of linkages then occurs, thus,

$$[C_6H_5\!-\!N\!\equiv\!N]^+OH^- \ = \ C_6H_5\!-\!N\!=\!N\!-\!OH$$

benzene diazonium hydroxide   diazobenzene hydroxide, or, benzene diazotic acid.

The diazobenzene hydroxide ionises thus,

$$C_6H_5\!-\!N\!=\!N\!-\!OH \ \rightleftharpoons \ [C_6H_5\!-\!N\!=\!N\!-\!O]^- \ + \ H^+,$$

and in the presence of potassium hydroxide it forms the salt potassium benzene diazotate, $[C_6H_5\!-\!N\!=\!N\!-\!O]^-K^+$. This compound is very unstable, and may explode even in cold aqueous solution.

7. Reduction with potassium stannite, giving benzene. When a solution of benzene diazonium chloride, made strongly alkaline with potassium hydroxide, is warmed with an alkaline solution of stannous chloride, nitrogen is liberated and benzene is formed. This reaction is described on p. 364.

8. Reactions with alcohols. If a solution of benzene diazonium hydrogen sulphate in absolute ethyl alcohol is boiled, the diazonium compound is reduced to benzene by the ethyl alcohol which is oxidised to acetaldehyde,

$$C_6H_5N_2HSO_4 + C_2H_5OH = C_6H_6 + CH_3.CHO + N_2 + H_2SO_4.$$

Higher members of the alcohol series react similarly with diazonium compounds. In this reaction the group $-N_2HSO_4$ attached to the benzene nucleus has been replaced by an atom of hydrogen. An $-NH_2$ group attached to the benzene nucleus can thus be replaced by a hydrogen atom, if the original amino compound is converted to a crystalline diazonium compound, which is then reduced by treatment with absolute ethyl alcohol.

If an aqueous solution of benzene diazonium chloride is boiled with ethyl alcohol, part of the diazonium compound is reduced to benzene according to the above equation, and part is converted to phenetole (phenyl ethyl ether) according to the equation,

$$C_6H_5N_2Cl + HOC_2H_5 = C_6H_5OC_2H_5 + N_2 + HCl.$$

If a solution of benzene diazonium hydrogen sulphate in absolute methyl alcohol is boiled, almost the whole of the diazonium compound is converted to anisole (phenyl methyl ether).

9. Reactions with aniline, giving diazoaminobenzene and aminoazobenzene. Benzene diazonium chloride combines with aniline to yield diazoaminobenzene,

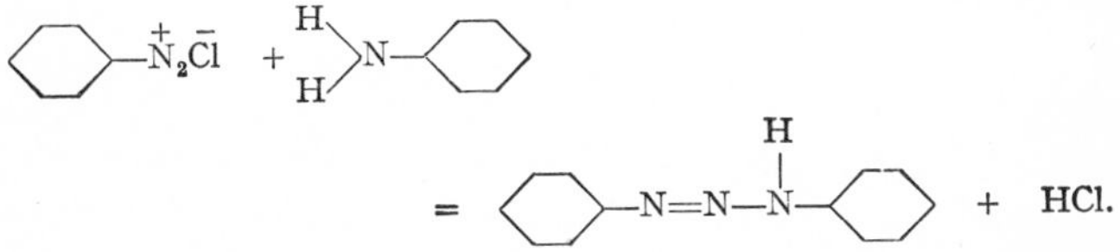

Diazoaminobenzene is a yellow crystalline solid, M.P. 98°, which is insoluble in water and slightly soluble in cold alcohol. It explodes if heated above its melting point. It has already been mentioned that diazoaminobenzene is liable to be formed during the diazotisation of aniline hydrochloride if insufficient hydrochloric acid is present.

If diazoaminobenzene is allowed to stand in contact with hydrochloric acid, or with aniline hydrochloride, a change occurs which is apparently intramolecular, and *aminoazobenzene* is formed,

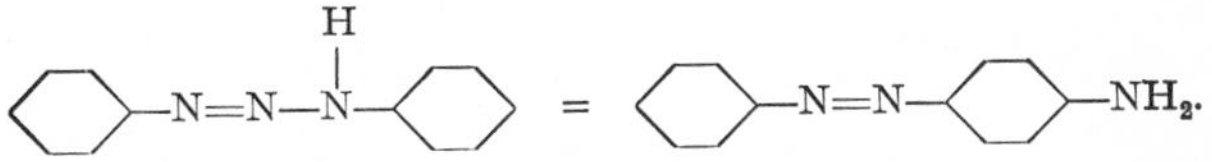

This conversion may be carried out by maintaining a suspension of finely powdered aniline hydrochloride and diazoaminobenzene in aniline at 40° for several hours. The aniline hydrochloride and aniline are then extracted with a mixture of equal volumes of acetic acid and water, in which the aminoazobenzene is insoluble, and the residue is recrystallised from aqueous methylated spirit. Aminoazobenzene is a yellow-brown crystalline substance, M.P. 126°. It is too weak a base to form salts with acetic acid, but it forms a hydrochloride which is a crystalline substance, steel-blue in colour. The difference in colour between the free base and the salt is correlated with the change

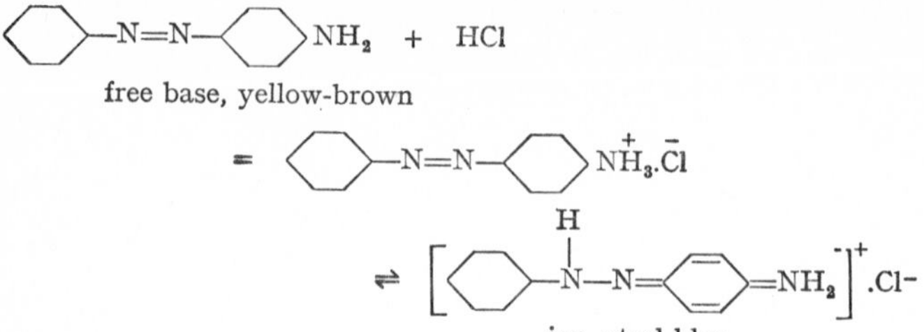

free base, yellow-brown

ion, steel-blue

10. Coupling, to give azo compounds. The condensation of benzene diazonium chloride with another aromatic compound with the elimination of hydrogen chloride is known as *coupling*.

Benzene diazonium chloride couples with :

(i) a *primary* or a *secondary amine* to give a diazo amino compound ; the reaction between benzene diazonium chloride and aniline mentioned in Reaction 9 is an example of a reaction between benzene diazonium chloride and a primary amine ;

(ii) a *tertiary amine* to give an azo compound ; for example, benzene diazonium chloride couples with dimethyl aniline to yield dimethylaminoazobenzene,

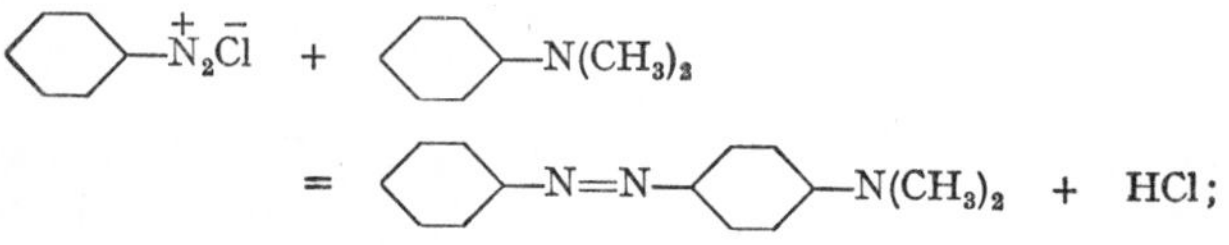

(iii) a *phenol* in alkaline solution ; for example, benzene diazonium chloride couples with phenol in the presence of potassium hydroxide to yield the potassium derivative of hydroxy azobenzene,

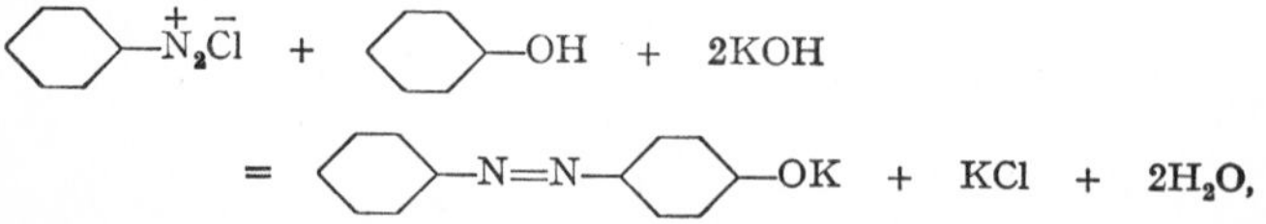

and β-naphthol dissolved in sodium hydroxide solution yields benzene-azo-β-naphthol,

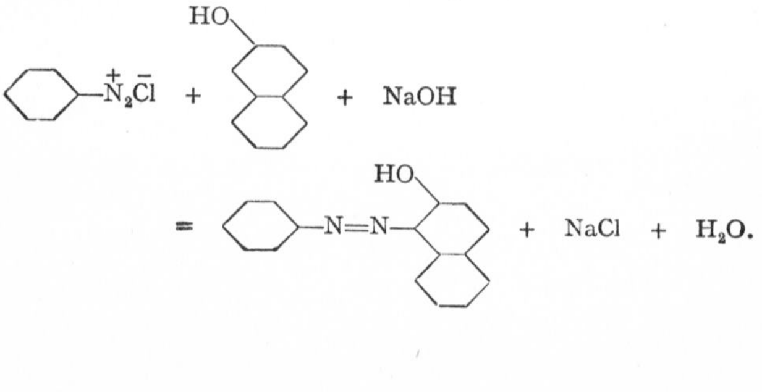

The modification of benzene-azo-β-naphthol shown in the equation then changes into the scarlet isomeric form,

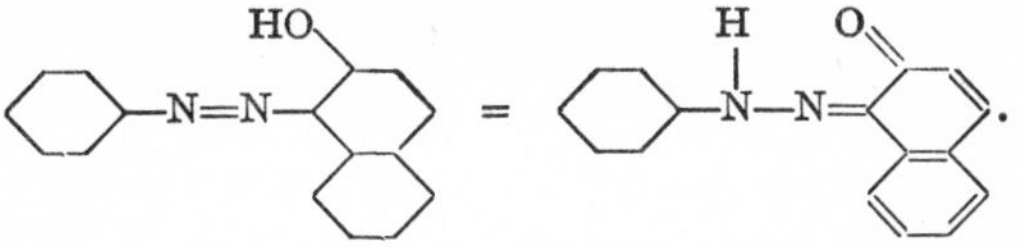

This reaction is used as a test for benzene diazonium chloride, and hence for aniline.

When benzene diazonium chloride couples with a tertiary amino compound, or with a phenol, it attacks the nucleus in the *p*-position with respect to the amino or hydroxy group. If the *p*-position is already occupied by some atom or group other than hydrogen, the diazo compound attacks the *o*-position. If both the *p*-position and the *o*-position are so occupied, no reaction occurs ; coupling does not occur in the *m*-position.

The preparation of crystalline benzene diazonium hydrogen sulphate

This compound is prepared by adding amyl nitrite to a solution of aniline hydrogen sulphate in absolute ethyl alcohol. The diazotisation is carried out in alcoholic solution because the diazonium compound is too soluble in water to be isolated from its aqueous solution. Amyl nitrite is used as the source of nitrous acid because the introduction of sodium nitrite into the solution would cause the precipitation of sodium hydrogen sulphate which is insoluble in ethyl alcohol.

5 gm. of aniline are dissolved in 50 c.c. of absolute ethyl alcohol, and 10 gm. of concentrated sulphuric acid are cautiously added. The temperature of the solution is brought to 30–35°. 6·5 gm. of amyl nitrite are added drop by drop with constant stirring, while the temperature is maintained at 30–35°. When all the amyl nitrite has been added, the solution is kept at about 30° for 10 minutes, and is then cooled in ice-cold water. The pale-green crystals of benzene diazonium hydrogen sulphate which separate are filtered off and washed with alcohol. The colour of the crystals darkens on standing.

An aqueous solution of benzene diazonium hydrogen sulphate may be used for demonstrating the reactions of diazonium compounds. As such compounds are explosive when dry the crystals should not be stored. If not required for immediate use, they should be dissolved in a good quantity of cold water, and the solution poured down the sink.

CHAPTER XXVI

HALOGEN DERIVATIVES OF THE AROMATIC HYDROCARBONS

HALOGEN DERIVATIVES OF BENZENE

THE simplest halogen derivative of benzene is chlorobenzene. The molecule of chlorobenzene contains one atom of chlorine which has replaced an atom of hydrogen in the molecule of benzene. The replacement can be carried out experimentally by passing chlorine into benzene in the presence of a halogen carrier such as iron, until the gain in weight corresponds to the completion of the reaction shown by the equation,

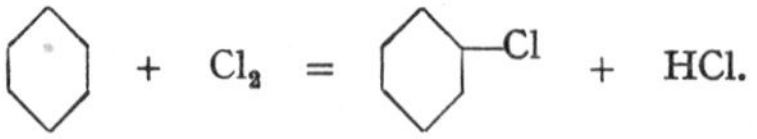

$$\bigcirc + Cl_2 = \bigcirc\!\!-Cl + HCl.$$

The reaction of chlorine on benzene may be continued so that two hydrogen atoms in each benzene molecule are replaced by atoms of chlorine, giving dichlorobenzene, $C_6H_4Cl_2$. Further chlorination produces trichlorobenzene, $C_6H_3Cl_3$, tetrachlorobenzene, $C_6H_2Cl_4$, pentachlorobenzene, C_6HCl_5, and ultimately hexachlorobenzene, C_6Cl_6.

Bromine reacts with benzene to give a corresponding series of products.

CHLOROBENZENE

Chlorobenzene is a colourless, mobile liquid with a pleasant odour, B.P. 132°. It is insoluble in water and volatile in steam. It is soluble in alcohol and ether.

PRINCIPAL REACTIONS IN WHICH CHLOROBENZENE IS PRODUCED

1. The action of chlorine on benzene in the presence of a halogen carrier. If chlorine is passed into benzene in the cold in the presence of a carrier such as iron, iodine, aluminium, antimony, or pyridine, chlorobenzene is formed according to the equation given above. This reaction must be carried out in the absence of direct sunlight, which promotes the union of benzene and chlorine to give additive compounds such as benzene hexachloride, $C_6H_6Cl_6$.

2. The action of heat on a mixture of sodium chlorobenzoate and soda-lime

$$C_6H_4Cl.COONa + NaOH = C_6H_5Cl + Na_2CO_3.$$

3. The action of phosphorus pentachloride on phenol. When phenol is treated with phosphorus pentachloride, chlorobenzene, phosphorus oxychloride and hydrogen chloride are obtained,

$$C_6H_5OH + PCl_5 = C_6H_5Cl + POCl_3 + HCl.$$

4. The action of phosphorus pentachloride on benzene sulphonyl chloride. When a mixture of benzene sulphonyl chloride and phosphorus pentachloride is heated, chlorobenzene, phosphorus oxychloride and thionyl chloride are formed,

$$C_6H_5SO_2Cl + PCl_5 = C_6H_5Cl + POCl_3 + SOCl_2.$$

5. The decomposition of benzene diazonium chloride by copper powder. Gattermann's reaction. If copper powder is added in small quantities at a time to an ice-cold solution of benzene diazonium chloride, nitrogen is evolved and chlorobenzene is formed, p. 399.

$$C_6H_5N_2Cl = C_6H_5Cl + N_2.$$

6. The action of cuprous chloride on benzene diazonium chloride. Sandmeyer's reaction. When a diazotised solution of aniline hydrochloride is gradually added to a solution of cuprous chloride in hydrochloric acid maintained at about 60°, nitrogen is evolved and chlorobenzene is formed. The reaction may be summarised by the equation,

$$C_6H_5N_2Cl = C_6H_5Cl + N_2.$$

The experimental details for carrying out this reaction are described below.

Laboratory preparation of chlorobenzene. Chlorobenzene is most conveniently prepared by the action of cuprous chloride on a solution of benzene diazonium chloride. The preparation of a solution of benzene diazonium chloride is described on p. 397. The cuprous chloride solution is made by dissolving copper sulphate crystals (21 gm. is the appropriate quantity if 15 c.c. of aniline have been diazotised) and sodium chloride (7·5 gm.) in 100 c.c. of water, and passing a brisk stream of sulphur dioxide through the solution while it is maintained at 55–60°. The solution is cooled and the precipitated cuprous chloride is filtered off, washed with a few c.c. of water, and dissolved in a mixture of 20 c.c. of concentrated hydrochloric acid and 20 c.c. of water in a 500 c.c. round-bottomed flask attached to a reflux condenser fitted with a dropping-funnel. The solution of benzene diazonium chloride is placed in the dropping-funnel, and the flask is heated to 60° on a water-bath. The diazotised solution is allowed to run slowly down the condenser into the cuprous chloride solution. As each drop of the diazotised solution enters the solution in the flask a yellow precipitate of $C_6H_5N_2Cl$, Cu_2Cl_2, separates and almost immediately breaks down, yielding nitrogen and chlorobenzene, and regenerating cuprous chloride. Heat is given out by the reaction, and the cuprous chloride solution is maintained at 60° without external heating.

When all the diazo solution has been added, the flask is heated on a boiling water-bath for 30 minutes to complete the reaction. The flask is then detached from the condenser, and its contents are steam-distilled until no more oily drops of chlorobenzene pass over. The heavy chlorobenzene is separated from the water in the distillate, dried over anhydrous calcium chloride, filtered, and distilled from a flask fitted to an air condenser.

Industrial preparation of chlorobenzene. Chlorobenzene is made industrially by passing chlorine into benzene in the cold in the presence of iron which acts as a chlorine carrier. The product is fractionated to separate the chlorobenzene from higher chlorine derivatives of benzene, and from unchanged benzene.*

Chemical properties of chlorobenzene. The constitution of chlorobenzene, C_6H_5Cl, bears a formal resemblance to that of chloroethane, C_2H_5Cl, which suggests that the chemical reactions of these two substances might be similar. In fact, however, there is a marked contrast in their chemical reactivity : unlike chloroethane, *chlorobenzene does not react with* :

(*a*) aqueous solutions of alkalis, or with moist silver oxide ;

(*b*) alcoholic solutions of alkalis ;

(*c*) sodium cyanide ;

(*d*) solutions of silver nitrate, silver nitrite, silver cyanide, or silver acetate ;

(*e*) the sodium derivatives of phthalimide, ethyl acetoacetate, or ethyl malonate ;

(*f*) benzene in the presence of aluminium chloride (the Friedel-Crafts reaction) † ;

(*g*) an alcoholic solution of ammonia.

Chlorobenzene, however, undergoes the following reactions :

I. Reactions affecting the chlorine atom

1. Reduction, giving benzene. Chlorobenzene may, with difficulty, be reduced to benzene by the action of either (i) sodium

---

* For another industrial method of preparing chlorobenzene, see p. 479.

† The chlorine atom in methyl chloride reacts with the phenyl group in chlorobenzene in the presence of aluminium chloride, but the chlorine atom in chlorobenzene does not react with the phenyl group of another aromatic molecule.

amalgam and aqueous alcohol, or (ii) hydrogen iodide in the presence
of red phosphorus at high temperatures,

$$C_6H_5Cl + 2H = C_6H_6 + HCl.$$

2. Reaction with metallic sodium, giving diphenyl. If
chlorobenzene in ethereal solution is allowed to react with metallic
sodium, diphenyl is formed,

$$2C_6H_5Cl + 2Na = C_6H_5.C_6H_5 + 2NaCl.$$

**3. Reaction with methyl iodide in the presence of metallic
sodium. Fittig's reaction.** If a dry mixture of chlorobenzene and
methyl iodide dissolved in anhydrous ether is allowed to stand for
several hours in contact with clean sodium wire, toluene is formed,
p. 370,

$$C_6H_5Cl + ICH_3 + 2Na = C_6H_5.CH_3 + NaCl + NaI.$$

4. Reaction with magnesium in the presence of ether. This
reaction proceeds very slowly to give the Grignard reagent phenyl
magnesium chloride,

$$C_6H_5Cl + Mg = C_6H_5MgCl.$$

The corresponding bromine derivative phenyl magnesium bromide,
is, however, much more readily prepared, and consequently is more
frequently employed as a reagent in synthetical chemistry.

II. Reactions affecting the benzene nucleus

5. Nitration. Chlorobenzene is readily nitrated. In accordance
with the rule on p. 360, nitration produces a mixture of the o- and p-
nitrochlorobenzenes ; m-nitrochlorobenzene must be prepared by
chlorinating nitrobenzene, or by diazotising m-nitroaniline and
decomposing the resulting solution with cuprous chloride.

6. Sulphonation. Chlorobenzene undergoes sulphonation yielding
a mixture of o- and p-chlorobenzene sulphonic acids.

Tests for chlorobenzene. There is no distinctive test for chlorobenzene. It may be nitrated on a test-tube scale. 1 c.c. of chlorobenzene is placed in a boiling-tube and 2 c.c. of concentrated nitric acid
are added, followed by 2 c.c. of concentrated sulphuric acid. The mixture
is gently warmed with shaking for about 4 minutes, and the product is
poured into a beaker containing cold water. An oil separates and
solidifies to a pale yellow crystalline mass with the odour of " bitter
almonds " when the inside of the beaker is scratched with a glass rod.
The crystalline solid is p-nitrochlorobenzene. Bromobenzene, iodobenzene and benzyl chloride behave somewhat similarly.

BROMOBENZENE

Bromobenzene is a colourless liquid, B.P. 156°, density 1·50. It has a faint pleasant odour. Like chlorobenzene it is soluble in alcohol, and ether, but not in water, and is volatile in steam.

Preparation of bromobenzene. Bromobenzene is produced by reactions analogous to those described for chlorobenzene.

Bromobenzene is prepared in the laboratory by the direct bromination of benzene using pyridine as a bromine carrier.

$$C_6H_6 + Br_2 = C_6H_5Br + HBr.$$

The bromine and the pyridine to be used in the reaction should be dry ; the benzene may be dried over anhydrous calcium chloride, and the pyridine over solid potassium hydroxide. The experiment should be conducted in a good fume-cupboard out of direct sunlight. 0·5 c.c. of the pyridine and 34 c.c. of benzene are placed in a flask fitted to a reflux water condenser. The flask is immersed in a cold water-bath and 24 c.c. of bromine are poured down the condenser. A vigorous reaction occurs and hydrogen bromide is evolved. When the evolution of hydrogen bromide slackens, the water-bath is heated to 25–30° for one hour, and finally to 65–70° for a further three-quarters of an hour. The product is a dark coloured liquid, which is transferred to a separating-funnel and shaken with excess of 10 per cent. aqueous sodium hydroxide solution. The lower layer of bromobenzene, which is now colourless, is washed with water, dried over anhydrous calcium chloride, filtered and slowly distilled from a flask fitted to an air condenser. The fraction boiling at 150–160° is collected.* The distillate should be fractionated in order to obtain pure bromobenzene, B.P. 156°.

Chemical properties of bromobenzene. The chemical properties of bromobenzene are closely parallel to those of chlorobenzene. The bromine atom in bromobenzene is comparatively inert, and is detached from the benzene ring only in the Fittig reaction and the Grignard reaction ; bromobenzene may be nitrated and sulphonated.

Use of bromobenzene in Grignard's reaction. A halogen derivative of benzene reacts with metallic magnesium suspended in dry ether to form a Grignard reagent of the general formula, C_6H_5—Mg—Hal, where Hal stands for one atom of halogen. Grignard reagents are used in the synthesis of alcohols, and of many other classes of compounds. If the compound to be synthesised is to contain a phenyl group, the Grignard reagent employed is usually prepared from bromobenzene.

---

* The residue contains *p*-dibromobenzene which may solidify as the flask cools. It is isolated by solution in methylated spirit. The solution is heated with animal charcoal, filtered, and cooled in ice-water. The crystals which separate are colourless and melt at 89°.

The synthesis of triphenyl carbinol, $(C_6H_5)_3COH$, from ethyl benzoate and phenyl magnesium bromide is described below as an example of the procedure for carrying out a Grignard reaction.

The chemical reactions which occur during the synthesis are :

(i) the formation of the Grignard reagent, phenyl magnesium bromide, according to the equation,

$$C_6H_5Br \ + \ Mg \ = \ Mg\Big\langle {}^{C_6H_5}_{Br}$$

(ii) the condensation of the Grignard reagent with the ethyl benzoate to give the intermediate compound, $(C_6H_5)_3COMgBr$, according to the equation,

$$C_6H_5C\Big\langle {}^{O}_{OC_2H_5} \ + \ 2Mg\Big\langle {}^{C_6H_5}_{Br} \ = \ {}^{C_6H_5}_{C_6H_5}\Big\rangle C\Big\langle {}^{OMgBr}_{C_6H_5,} \ + \ Mg(OC_2H_5)Br$$

(iii) the hydrolysis, by dilute sulphuric acid, of the intermediate compound to give triphenyl carbinol, magnesium sulphate and hydrobromic acid,

$$ {}^{C_6H_5}_{C_6H_5}\Big\rangle C\Big\langle {}^{OMgBr}_{C_6H_5} \ + \ H_2SO_4 \ = \ {}^{C_6H_5}_{C_6H_5}\Big\rangle C\Big\langle {}^{OH}_{C_6H_5} \ + \ MgSO_4 \ + \ HBr.$$

2·5 gm. of magnesium turnings are placed in a round-bottomed flask attached to a reflux condenser. All the apparatus must be thoroughly dry, and the top of the condenser is closed with a calcium chloride tube. 15·7 gm. of dry bromobenzene are dissolved in 50 c.c. of anhydrous ether (p. 179), in a small well-corked flask, and about half this solution is added to the magnesium turnings in the round-bottomed flask. If the reaction does not begin on standing or gentle warming, a crystal of iodine is carefully added to the mixture so that it rests on the magnesium metal. The reaction then starts in the neighbourhood of the iodine, and increases in vigour until the ether boils. When the boiling has subsided, the remainder of the bromobenzene solution is added to the magnesium in small quantities at a time. When all the bromobenzene has been added, the flask is heated on a water-bath for a further 15 minutes to ensure that the reaction is completed. At this stage phenyl magnesium bromide has been formed according to Reaction (i).

The flask is then removed from the water-bath, and a solution of 5·2 gm. of dry ethyl benzoate in 15 c.c. of anhydrous ether is added down the condenser in small quantities at a time. When the boiling of the ether has subsided, the flask is heated on the water-bath for a further 15 minutes. At this stage the intermediate compound, $(C_6H_5)_3COMgBr$, has been formed according to Reaction (ii). The mixture is then cooled in ice-water, and the ethereal solution is poured into a mixture of 60 c.c. of dilute sulphuric acid and 100 gm. of crushed ice. Reaction (iii) now takes place. The mixture is stirred well, and the liquid is poured into a separating-funnel where it separates into two layers. The lower aqueous layer, which contains inorganic acids and salts, is run off and rejected. The ethereal layer, which contains the triphenyl carbinol, is washed once with water, and run into a 300 c.c. flask for steam-distillation ; the receiver is a Buchner flask with a piece of rubber tubing fitted to the side-tube and falling below the level of the bench, Fig. 22. 100 c.c. of water are added and the mixture is steam-distilled. The distillate, which contains ether and a few by-products of the reaction, is discarded. Crude triphenyl carbinol solidifies in the distilling flask as soon as it cools. The solid is filtered at the pump, washed with water, dried between layers of filter paper, and recrystallised from methylated spirit. The crystals thus obtained are colourless, M.P. 162°.

IODOBENZENE

Iodobenzene is a colourless liquid, B.P. 188°, density 1·83. On exposure to light it becomes pale yellow. It is insoluble in water and volatile in steam.

Preparation of iodobenzene. There is no strict analogy between the reactions which produce chlorobenzene and bromobenzene and those which produce iodobenzene. Iodine does not react with benzene at ordinary temperatures, even in the presence of a halogen carrier. Iodobenzene, however, may be obtained by heating to a high temperature a mixture of iodine, benzene, and an oxidising agent such as iodic acid (see p. 365). Iodobenzene is prepared from benzene diazonium chloride by the direct action of potassium iodide without the use of a catalyst.

An aqueous solution of benzene diazonium chloride is prepared as described on p. 397 and to this cold solution 35 gm. of potassium iodide dissolved in 50 c.c. of water are slowly added with shaking. The mixture is allowed to stand for 10 minutes after the addition of the potassium iodide solution is complete, and it is then heated on a boiling water-bath for 20 minutes. The crude iodobenzene is then present as a heavy dark oil on the bottom of the reaction vessel,

$$C_6H_5N_2Cl \ + \ KI \ = \ C_6H_5I \ + \ N_2 \ + \ KCl.$$

Some phenol may have been formed by the reaction of the benzene diazonium chloride with water (p. 397). A 10 per cent. solution of sodium hydroxide is added until the solution is just alkaline to litmus, in order to convert the phenol to sodium phenate which is non-volatile in steam. The mixture is then steam-distilled until no more oily drops of iodobenzene come over. The distillate is transferred to a separating-funnel, and the lower layer of iodobenzene is run into a small flask. It is dried over anhydrous calcium chloride, filtered, and distilled using an air condenser.

Chemical properties of iodobenzene. The chemical properties of iodobenzene are, for the most part, closely similar to those of chlorobenzene and bromobenzene. Iodobenzene, however, reacts with chlorine, in a manner which is not paralleled by chlorobenzene or bromobenzene, to form iodobenzene dichloride in which the iodine atom is trivalent,

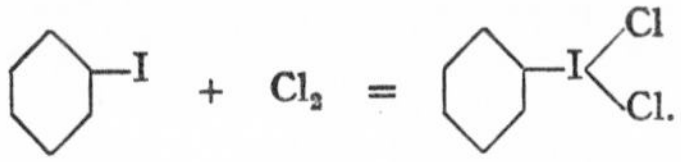

$$\text{C}_6\text{H}_5\text{—I} + \text{Cl}_2 = \text{C}_6\text{H}_5\text{—I}\begin{smallmatrix}\text{Cl}\\\text{Cl.}\end{smallmatrix}$$

Iodobenzene dichloride separates as yellow crystals when a stream of chlorine is passed through an ice-cold solution of iodobenzene in chloroform. On standing it decomposes into p-chloro-iodobenzene and hydrogen chloride,

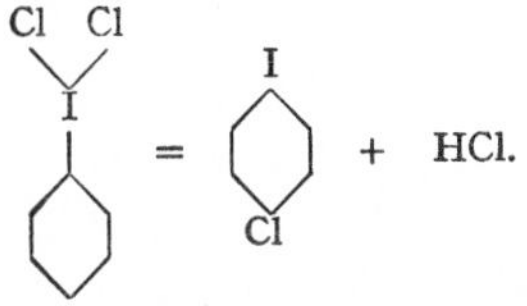

$$= + \text{HCl.}$$

When shaken with a cold aqueous solution of sodium hydroxide, iodobenzene dichloride is converted to the insoluble iodosobenzene,

$$\text{C}_6\text{H}_5\text{ICl}_2 + 2\text{NaOH} = \text{C}_6\text{H}_5\text{IO} + 2\text{NaCl} + \text{H}_2\text{O},$$

which is a base giving rise to the salts, iodosobenzene dinitrate $\text{C}_6\text{H}_5\text{I}(\text{NO}_3)_2$, and iodosobenzene diacetate $\text{C}_6\text{H}_5\text{I}(\text{CH}_3.\text{COO})_2$. On boiling with water iodosobenzene yields iodoxybenzene thus :

$$\text{C}_6\text{H}_5\text{IO} = \text{C}_6\text{H}_5\text{IO}_2 + \text{C}_6\text{H}_5\text{I}.$$

Both iodosobenzene and iodoxybenzene are crystalline substances. When heated they explode without melting.

HALOGEN DERIVATIVES OF TOLUENE

Four isomeric compounds may be obtained by the replacement of a hydrogen atom in the toluene molecule by an atom of chlorine. In three of these isomerides the chlorine atom is directly attached to the nucleus. Their names and structural formulae are

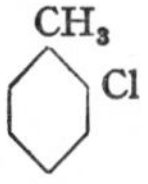

o-chlorotoluene,
B.P. 156°

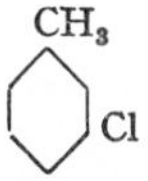

m-chlorotoluene,
B.P. 150°

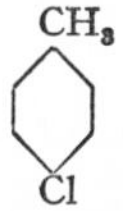

p-chlorotoluene,
B.P. 163°

The remaining isomeride, benzyl chloride, contains the chlorine atom in the side-chain

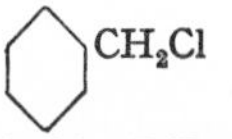

benzyl chloride, B.P. 179°

Benzyl chloride may also be regarded as a derivative of methyl chloride in which one hydrogen atom of the methyl group has been replaced by the phenyl group:

$$H-\underset{\underset{H}{|}}{\overset{\overset{H}{|}}{C}}-Cl \qquad\qquad C_6H_5-\underset{\underset{H}{|}}{\overset{\overset{H}{|}}{C}}-Cl$$

methyl chloride   chlorotoluene or benzyl chloride

It is shown below that the properties of the chlorine atom in benzyl chloride are similar to those of the chlorine atom in methyl and other alkyl chlorides. The properties of the chlorine atom in the chloro-toluenes are similar to those of the chlorine atom in chlorobenzene.

THE CHLOROTOLUENES

o- and *p*-chlorotoluene may be made by chlorinating toluene in the presence of a halogen carrier. The reaction is carried out in the cold and out of direct sunlight. According to the rule on p. 360, substitution occurs in the *o*- and *p*-positions,

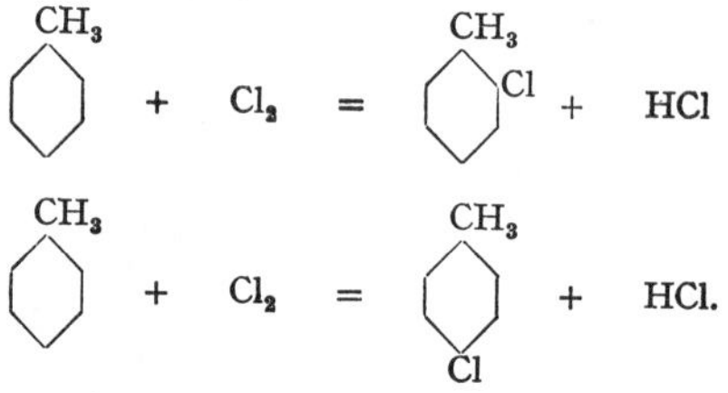

o- and *p*-chlorotoluene may also be obtained from toluene by nitration and sulphonation. The nitration of toluene gives *o*- and *p*-nitrotoluene which may be reduced to *o*- and *p*-toluidine. The toluidines may be converted into the corresponding toluene diazonium chlorides and thence by Sandmeyer's reaction to *o*- and *p*-chlorotoluene. These changes may be recapitulated thus:

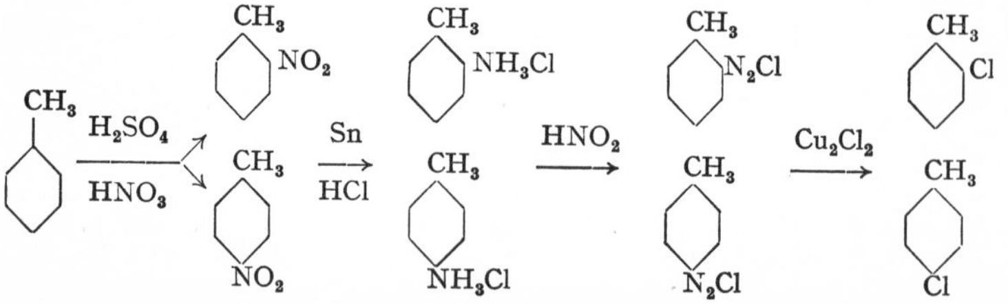

The sulphonation of toluene gives *o*- and *p*-toluene sulphonic acids. The sodium salts of these acids on fusion with sodium hydroxide yield *o*- and *p*-hydroxy toluene (cresol), which may be converted to the corresponding chlorotoluenes by the action of phosphorus pentachloride,

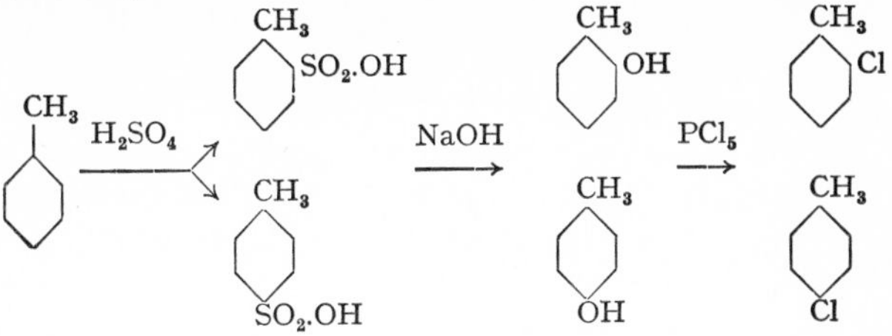

m-Chlorotoluene cannot be obtained directly from toluene because the methyl group in the toluene molecule directs a second substituent either to the o- or the p-position in the benzene ring. It may be made starting from p-nitrotoluene. The nitrotoluene is reduced to p-toluidine by tin and hydrochloric acid,

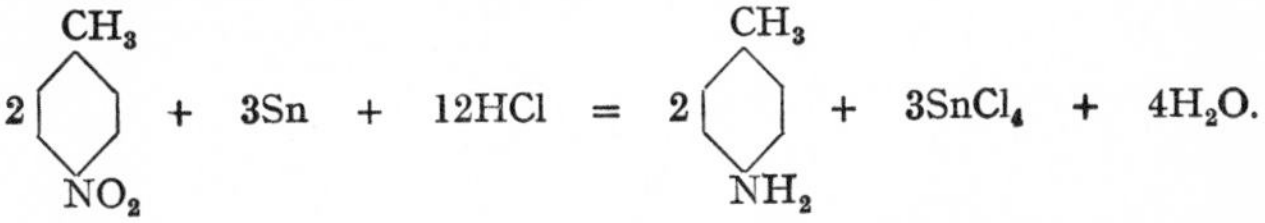

The amino group is then acetylated (in order to prevent its reaction with chlorine *) and the p-acetotoluidide is chlorinated. The chlorine atom enters the o-position with respect to the acetotoluidide group,

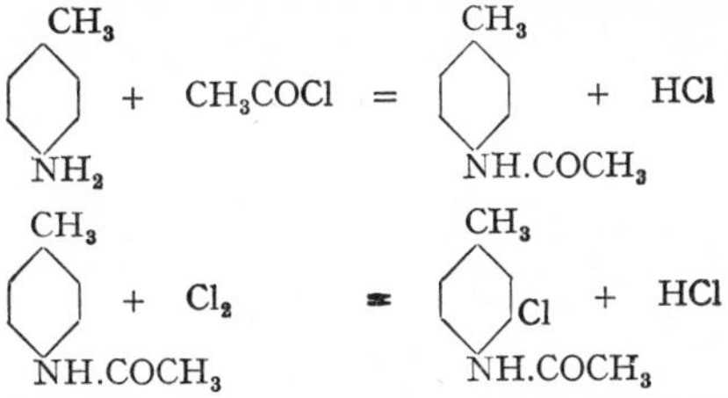

The chloroacetotoluidide is now hydrolysed with 70 per cent. sulphuric acid, the resulting amino compound is diazotised, and the diazo group is reduced to hydrogen by an alkaline solution of sodium stannite,

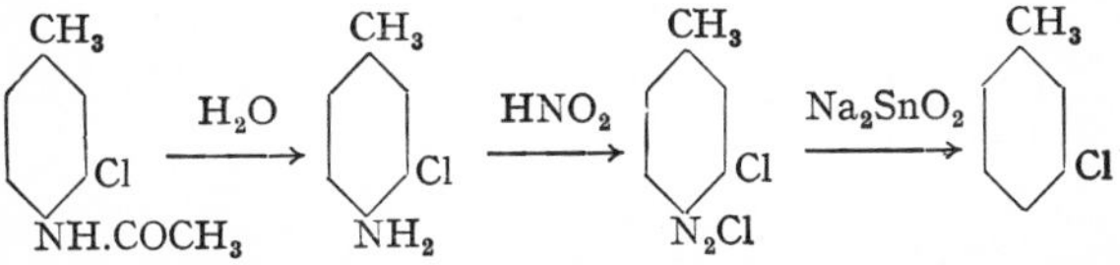

In many respects the properties of o-, m-, and p-chlorotoluene resemble those of the chlorobenzenes. The chlorine atom is inert to water, moist silver oxide, sodium hydroxide, metallic salts such as

* For this use of acetylation, see p. 450.

silver nitrate, and ammonia in alcoholic solution. The chlorine atom is, however, detached from the nucleus and replaced by other groups by the reactions of Fittig or Grignard. The nucleus in chlorotoluene is open to attack by halogenation, nitration or sulphonation.

The presence of the methyl group in chlorotoluene introduces new properties not exhibited by chlorobenzene. On oxidation with alkaline potassium permanganate solution, chlorotoluene is converted to the corresponding chlorobenzoic acid, for example,

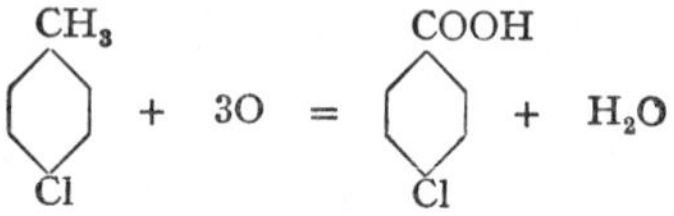

$$\underset{\text{Cl}}{\overset{\text{CH}_3}{\bigcirc}} + 3O = \underset{\text{Cl}}{\overset{\text{COOH}}{\bigcirc}} + H_2O$$

and if chlorine is passed into boiling chlorotoluene in sunlight substitution takes place in the side-chain, giving chlorobenzyl chloride, chlorobenzal chloride, or chlorobenzotrichloride (see below).

The bromo- and iodo-toluenes may be made from the appropriate toluidines by diazotisation and treatment with cuprous bromide, or potassium iodide respectively.

SIDE-CHAIN CHLORINE DERIVATIVES OF TOLUENE

The three side-chain chlorine derivatives of toluene are benzyl chloride, $C_6H_5.CH_2Cl$, benzal chloride, $C_6H_5.CHCl_2$, and benzotrichloride, $C_6H_5.CCl_3$.

BENZYL CHLORIDE, $C_6H_5.CH_2Cl$

Benzyl chloride is prepared by passing chlorine into boiling toluene. A weighed quantity of toluene is placed in a flask fitted to a reflux condenser, Fig. 60. The flask is heated on a sand-bath while exposed to strong sunlight, and a stream of chlorine is passed through the boiling toluene by means of the delivery tube,

$$C_6H_5.CH_3 + Cl_2 = C_6H_5.CH_2Cl + HCl.$$

The reaction is continued until the theoretical gain in weight has taken place. The benzyl chloride in the product is isolated by fractionisation from other chlorine derivatives and from unchanged toluene.

Benzyl chloride may also be obtained by acting upon benzyl alcohol with phosphorus pentachloride,

$$C_6H_5.CH_2OH + PCl_5 = C_6H_5.CH_2Cl + POCl_3 + HCl.$$

Benzyl chloride is a colourless liquid, B.P. 179°. It is insoluble in water, but is miscible with organic liquids.

The properties of benzyl chloride which depend on the presence of the chlorine atom in the molecule are distinct from the properties of the isomeric chlorotoluenes. Benzyl chloride has an unpleasant odour and is lachrymatory; these properties are common to all benzene derivatives with a halogen atom in the side-chain. The chlorine atom has the reactivity characteristic of the chlorine atom in ethyl chloride. Benzyl chloride is hydrolysed by alkalis to benzyl alcohol,

$$C_6H_5.CH_2Cl + NaOH$$
$$= C_6H_5.CH_2OH + NaCl,$$

and it undergoes reactions parallel to those numbered 1–4 and 6–14 on pp. 140–143. Besides undergoing the Grignard reaction it also reacts with alcoholic ammonia and with the sodium derivatives of ethyl acetoacetate, ethyl malonate, and phthalimide. The reactions of the chlorine atom in benzyl chloride show that it is attached to an alkyl group.

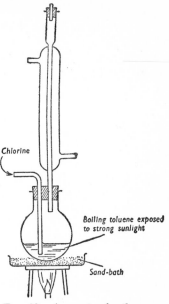

Chlorine

Boiling toluene exposed to strong sunlight

Sand-bath

FIG. 60. Apparatus for the preparation of benzyl chloride.

The presence of the side-chain in the molecule of benzyl chloride does not interfere, however, with the normal reactions of the benzene nucleus. Benzyl chloride may be chlorinated, nitrated and sulphonated. The side-chain is readily oxidised by an alkaline solution of potassium permanganate to give benzoic acid,

$$C_6H_5.CH_2Cl + 2O = C_6H_5.COOH + HCl.$$

It is oxidised to benzaldehyde by cupric nitrate, p. 426.

Tests for benzyl chloride

1. **Aqueous silver nitrate solution.** If 2 c.c. of 10 per cent. aqueous silver nitrate solution are shaken with 1 c.c. of benzyl chloride in the cold, a slight precipitate of silver chloride is obtained. The precipitation rapidly increases on warming.

2. **Nitration.** 1 c.c. of benzyl chloride is placed in a boiling-tube and 2 c.c. of concentrated nitric acid are added followed by 2 c.c. of concentrated sulphuric acid, and the mixture is warmed for a few minutes. p-Nitro-benzyl chloride is formed. The product is poured into cold water, and the nitro compound separates as an oil which solidifies in the course of several minutes.

3. Oxidation. 1 c.c. of benzyl chloride is boiled for 30 minutes in a flask fitted to a reflux condenser with 50 c.c. of saturated aqueous potassium permanganate solution and 2 c.c. of sodium carbonate. The product is acidified with concentrated hydrochloric acid, and sodium sulphite is added to dissolve the brown precipitate of manganese dioxide which has been formed. Benzoic acid separates as white crystals when the solution is cooled.

BENZAL CHLORIDE, $C_6H_5.CHCl_2$

Benzal chloride is formed when benzaldehyde is treated with phosphorus pentachloride,

$$C_6H_5.CHO + PCl_5 = C_6H_5.CHCl_2 + POCl_3.$$

On a large scale it is prepared by the chlorination of toluene. The conditions are the same as those described for the preparation of benzyl chloride, except that the passage of chlorine is continued until the gain in weight of the toluene shows that two atoms of hydrogen per molecule have been replaced by chlorine. Benzal chloride is a liquid, B.P. 206°. It is hydrolysed by water, or by sodium hydroxide, to give benzaldehyde, p. 425.

BENZOTRICHLORIDE, $C_6H_5.CCl_3$

Benzotrichloride is prepared by the chlorination of toluene. It is a liquid, B.P. 213°. When heated with water it yields benzoic acid,

$$C_6H_5.CCl_3 + 2H_2O = C_6H_5.COOH + 3HCl.$$

CHAPTER XXVII

PHENOL

PHENOL, C_6H_5OH, is derived from benzene by the replacement of one hydrogen atom in the molecule by a hydroxyl group.

The properties of the hydroxyl group when it is linked to the benzene ring are not in all respects similar to its properties when it is linked to an alkyl group. Therefore, the class of aromatic compounds to which phenol gives its name is distinct from the class of alcohols. The constitutional difference between an alcohol and a phenol is evident if the Kekulé formulae for benzene and phenol are compared with the formula for an alcohol,

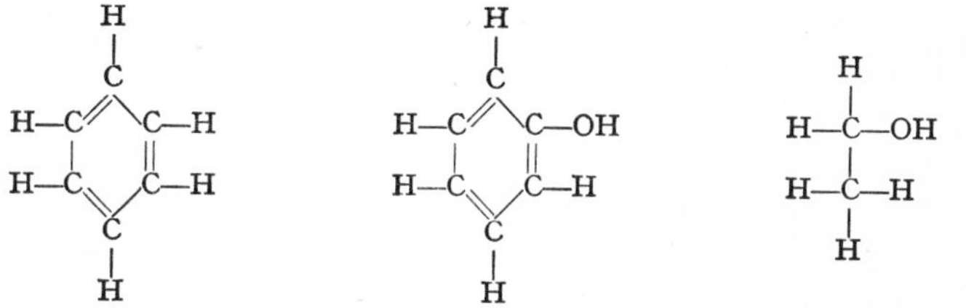

benzene   phenol   ethyl alcohol

It is seen from these formulae that whereas in ethyl alcohol the —OH group is linked to a saturated carbon atom, in phenol the —OH group is linked to a carbon atom which is attached to a neighbouring carbon atom by a double bond.*

Phenol is a colourless crystalline solid, M.P. 41°, which turns pink on exposure to air and light. It may be distilled, B.P. 181·4°, and it is volatile in steam. Phenol is hygroscopic. It is partially miscible with water at room temperature (at 20° a saturated solution of phenol in water contains 72·2 per cent. of phenol, and a saturated solution of water in phenol contains 91·8 per cent. of phenol), but above 68·8° phenol and water are completely miscible. Phenol dissolves freely in organic solvents. It has a characteristic odour (carbolic acid), it is highly poisonous, and it quickly causes blisters if brought into contact with the skin.

* The group —C=C—OH is the *enol* group. It is present in the enolic form of ethyl acetoacetate which, like phenol, gives a characteristic violet coloration with ferric chloride solution.

                 D.C.

PRINCIPAL REACTIONS IN WHICH PHENOL IS PRODUCED

1. The hydrolysis of benzene diazonium chloride. If an aqueous solution of benzene diazonium chloride (prepared as described on p. 397) is gently warmed to 50–55°, nitrogen is evolved, and a dark-coloured solution which contains phenol is obtained,

$$C_6H_5N_2Cl + HOH = C_6H_5OH + N_2 + HCl.$$

The solution is steam-distilled and the distillate extracted with ether. After the ethereal solution has been dried with anhydrous potassium carbonate, the ether is removed by distillation, (p. 70), and finally the phenol is distilled using an air-condenser. For the preparation of phenol, benzene diazonium hydrogen sulphate is used in preference to the chloride, which always yields some chlorobenzene in the side-reaction,

$$C_6H_5N_2Cl = C_6H_5Cl + N_2.$$

2. The fusion of sodium benzene sulphonate with sodium hydroxide. If sodium benzene sulphonate is mixed with a large excess of sodium hydroxide and a little water in a nickel dish and heated gradually to about 250°, sodium phenate and sodium sulphite are formed,

$$C_6H_5SO_3Na + 2NaOH = C_6H_5ONa + Na_2SO_3 + H_2O.$$

The solid product is dissolved in water. The solution is acidified with dilute sulphuric acid to liberate phenol from the sodium phenate, and steam-distilled. The phenol is isolated from the distillate by extraction with ether as described in Reaction 1 above.

3. The action of heat on a mixture of sodium salicylate and soda-lime. If sodium salicylate is ground with soda-lime in a mortar and the mixture is heated in a hard-glass tube, phenol is evolved,

$$NaOH + C_6H_4.OH.COONa = C_6H_5OH + Na_2CO_3.$$

This reaction should be compared with the preparation of methane by heating a mixture of sodium acetate and soda-lime.

Industrial preparation of phenol. Phenol occurs in coal-tar. The phenol of commerce is either obtained directly from coal-tar, or manufactured from benzene by the methods described in Chapter XXX, p. 480.

THE CHEMICAL PROPERTIES OF PHENOL

The chemical reactions of phenol may be classified under three heads : (i) reactions of the hydroxyl group, (ii) reactions of the nucleus peculiar to aromatic hydroxy compounds, (iii) reactions of the nucleus common to most aromatic compounds.

Reactions of phenol in which the hydroxyl group alone takes part

1. The acidic properties of phenol. The phenyl group confers weak acidic properties on the hydroxyl group so that phenol dissociates in aqueous solution,* thus,

$$C_6H_5OH \rightleftharpoons C_6H_5O^- + H^+.$$

Phenol, therefore, dissolves in aqueous solutions of potassium or sodium hydroxide to form potassium or sodium phenate,

$$C_6H_5OH + NaOH = C_6H_5ONa + H_2O.$$

Potassium and sodium phenates are much less easily hydrolysed than the corresponding ethoxides, which can be prepared only in the absence of water, p. 162. The phenates, however, are decomposed by even so weak an acid as carbonic acid, to yield the alkali carbonate and phenol,

$$2C_6H_5ONa + CO_2 + H_2O = 2C_6H_5OH + Na_2CO_3.$$

This reaction is irreversible ; if phenol is mixed with sodium carbonate solution, it dissolves in the water, but it does not attack the sodium carbonate.

2. The formation of phenyl esters. Phenol does not react directly with acids to form esters, but the hydroxyl group in the molecule may be replaced by chlorine by the action of phosphorus pentachloride, to form phenyl chloride,

$$C_6H_5OH + PCl_5 = C_6H_5Cl + POCl_3 + HCl.$$

3. The acetylation of phenol. Phenol can be acetylated by the action of acetyl chloride or acetic anhydride,

$$C_6H_5OH + CH_3.COCl = C_6H_5O.CO.CH_3 + HCl,$$
$$C_6H_5OH + (CH_3.CO)_2O = C_6H_5O.CO.CH_3 + CH_3.COOH.$$

The experimental conditions for the acetylation of phenol using acetic anhydride are described on p. 253.

4. The benzoylation of phenol. Phenol may be benzoylated by the Schotten-Baumann reaction. This reaction is carried out by dissolving 5 gm. of phenol in 70 c.c. of 10 per cent. sodium hydroxide solution contained in a stout glass bottle. 11 gm. of benzoyl chloride are added, and the bottle is corked and shaken vigorously for about 15 minutes. The reaction occurs,

$$C_6H_5CO.Cl + NaOC_6H_5 = C_6H_5CO.OC_6H_5 + NaCl,$$

and the phenyl benzoate separates as an insoluble solid. It is

---

* The feebly acidic properties of phenol justify the older name, " carbolic acid ".

separated by filtration, washed, and crystallised from methylated spirit.

5. Reduction of the hydroxyl group in phenol. When phenol vapour is passed over heated zinc dust it is reduced to benzene,

$$C_6H_5OH + Zn = C_6H_6 + ZnO.$$

(The reduction of phenol to cyclohexanol is mentioned on p. 421.)

Reactions of phenol in which the nucleus behaves in a manner peculiar to aromatic hydroxy compounds

6. The Reimer-Tiemann reaction, by which phenol yields salicylaldehyde or salicylic acid. The reaction between phenol and chloroform in the presence of sodium hydroxide to yield salicyl aldehyde is described on p. 154.

Phenol also reacts with carbon tetrachloride under similar experimental conditions to yield sodium salicylate. The reaction is summarised by the equation,

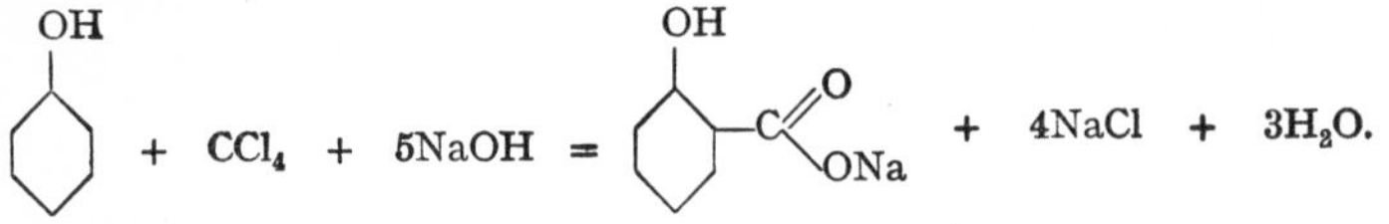

6. Coupling with diazonium salts. The action of phenol on benzene diazonium chloride in the presence of potassium hydroxide yields the potassium derivative of hydroxy azobenzene. This reaction is mentioned on p. 402.

7. Condensation with phthalic anhydride to yield phenolphthalein. If phenol is heated with phthalic anhydride in the presence of concentrated sulphuric acid (which acts as a dehydrating agent) phenolphthalein is obtained.

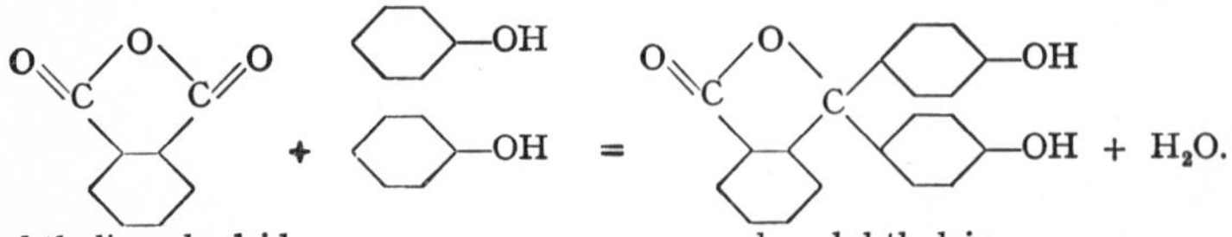

phthalic anhydride   phenolphthalein

In the presence of acids, phenolphthalein is colourless and has the molecular structure shown in the equation. In the presence of alkalis phenolphthalein ionises thus, to give a red coloured anion,

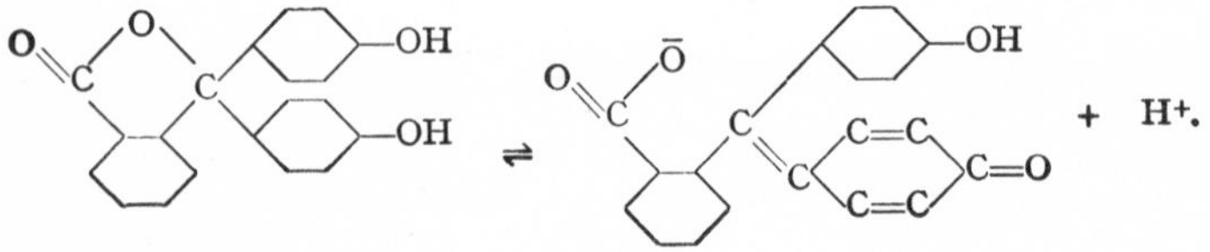

The use of phenolphthalein as an indicator in acidimetry over the pH range 10·0–8·3, depends on this change of constitution and the accompanying colour change.

Reactions of phenol in which the nucleus behaves in a manner common to aromatic compounds

The benzene nucleus in phenol is more ready than benzene itself to combine with the halogens, nitric acid and sulphuric acid.

8. Reduction of phenol to cyclohexanol. When phenol vapour is passed with hydrogen over nickel heated to 150°, cyclohexanol is formed,

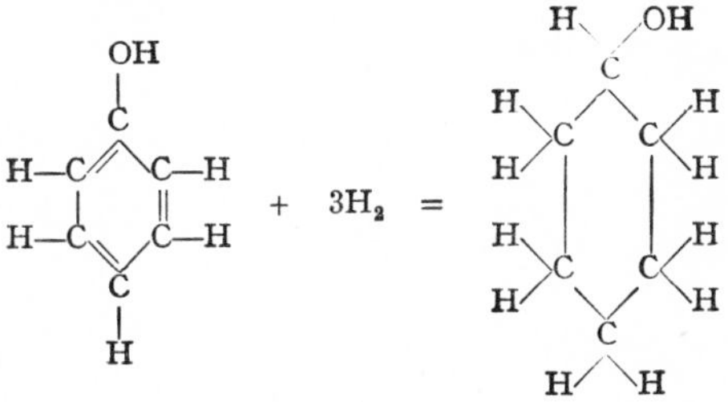

9. Bromination of phenol. When a dilute solution of phenol is shaken with bromine water, a white precipitate of tribromophenol is immediately obtained.

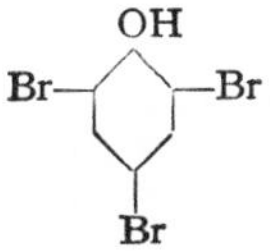

10. Nitration of phenol. Phenol is readily nitrated by nitric acid. A mixture of 1 part of concentrated nitric acid and 3 parts of water reacts with an emulsion of phenol in water at room temperature to give a mixture of o- and p-nitrophenol. The o-nitrophenol is obtained from the product by steam distillation ; the p-compound is extracted with boiling dilute hydrochloric acid from the solid residue left after the steam distillation. Phenol reacts with a mixture of concentrated nitric acid and fairly concentrated sulphuric acid to yield trinitrophenol or picric acid, p. 483.

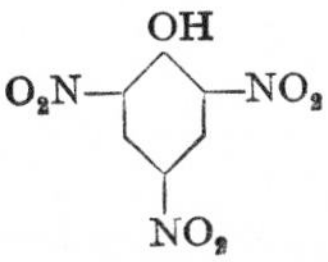

11. Sulphonation of phenol. The mere solution of phenol in concentrated sulphuric acid is enough to bring about sulphonation. At room temperature a mixture of *o*- and *p*-sulphonic acids is produced ; at 90–100° the product is chiefly the *p*-compound.

Uses of phenol. Phenol is used as an antiseptic. Phenol is the starting-point for the manufacture of picric acid, salicylic acid, aspirin, and many types of plastics.

Tests for phenol

1. Liebermann's nitroso reaction. A mixture of 0·5 gm. of phenol and a very small crystal of sodium nitrite is heated very gently in a test-tube for about 20 seconds. The tube is cooled and 2 c.c. of concentrated sulphuric acid are added and mixed with the phenol layer by slowly rotating the tube. After 1–2 minutes a deep green or deep blue colour develops. If the mixture is diluted with water a red solution is obtained, which turns green or blue on the addition of excess sodium hydroxide solution. Certain other hydroxy aromatic compounds give colour reactions when subjected to the above procedure, but resorcinol $(C_6H_4(OH)_2)$ is the only compound besides phenol which shows the colour-sequence green-red-green.

2. If 1 drop of ferric chloride solution is added to an aqueous solution of phenol, a violet or blue coloration is obtained.*

3. If bromine water is added to an aqueous solution of phenol, the brown colour of the bromine disappears, and a white precipitate of tribromophenol is produced.*

4. The formation of a red dye by coupling phenol with a diazonium salt is used as a test for phenol. 2–3 drops of aniline are dissolved in 1 c.c. of concentrated hydrochloric acid and 3 c.c. of water. The solution is cooled in ice, and a few drops of 20 per cent. sodium nitrite solution are added. This solution, which now contains benzene diazonium chloride, p. 397, is added to a cold solution of phenol in excess of sodium hydroxide solution. A red precipitate of an azo dye is obtained.*

5. The preparation of phenolphthalein is used as a test for phenol. About 0·5 gm. of phenol and the same weight of phthalic anhydride are placed in a test-tube and moistened with 2 drops of concentrated sulphuric acid. The contents of the tube are gently fused for about 1 minute. The tube is cooled and excess of 10 per cent. sodium hydroxide solution is added. A red coloration is obtained.*

* Other aromatic hydroxy derivatives, including resorcinol, catechol, the cresols, the naphthols, and salicylic acid respond to these tests. The colour obtained by treatment with ferric chloride, a diazonium salt, or phthalic anhydride usually depends on the nature of the hydroxy compound which is present. For further details a text-book of Practical Organic Chemistry should be consulted.

CHAPTER XXVIII

BENZYL ALCOHOL, BENZALDEHYDE, BENZOIC ACID AND SALICYLIC ACID

BENZYL ALCOHOL

BENZYL alcohol, $C_6H_5.CH_2OH$, may be theoretically derived *either* by the replacement of one hydrogen atom in the side-chain of toluene by the group —OH, *or* by the replacement of one hydrogen atom in the methyl group of methyl alcohol by the phenyl group, —C_6H_5.

Benzyl alcohol is a colourless liquid, B.P. 206°. It is sparingly soluble in water, but is miscible in all proportions with organic solvents.

Principal reactions in which benzyl alcohol is produced

1. The reduction of benzaldehyde. Benzyl alcohol is formed when benzaldehyde is reduced with sodium amalgam and water,

$$C_6H_5.CHO + H_2 = C_6H_5.CH_2OH.$$

2. The condensation of benzaldehyde in the presence of potassium hydroxide. Cannizzaro's reaction. Benzaldehyde condenses in the presence of potassium hydroxide solution to yield a mixture of benzyl alcohol and potassium benzoate, p. 430. Benzyl alcohol is most conveniently prepared in the laboratory by this reaction.

Benzaldehyde is shaken with a cold aqueous solution of potassium hydroxide in a corked glass bottle until a stiff paste is obtained. This is allowed to stand for several hours so that the reaction,

$$2C_6H_5.CHO + KOH = C_6H_5.CH_2OH + C_6H_5.COOK,$$

may be completed. Water is added to dissolve the potassium benzoate, and the benzyl alcohol is extracted with ether. The ethereal solution is dried with anhydrous potassium carbonate, the ether is removed by distillation, p. 70, and the residue of benzyl alcohol is distilled.

3. The hydrolysis of benzyl chloride. If benzyl chloride is boiled with milk of lime or sodium carbonate solution, benzyl alcohol is obtained,

$$2C_6H_5.CH_2Cl + Ca(OH)_2 = 2C_6H_5.CH_2OH + CaCl_2.$$

Benzyl alcohol is made commercially by this reaction.

Chemical properties of benzyl alcohol. The properties of the —OH group in benzyl alcohol resemble those of the —OH group in an aliphatic alcohol. Benzyl alcohol reacts with metallic sodium or potassium to give the metallic derivatives, $C_6H_5.CH_2ONa$ and $C_6H_5.CH_2OK$, which are easily decomposed by water. It reacts with phosphorus pentachloride to give benzyl chloride, and with concentrated acids, acid chlorides or anhydrides to yield esters. It exhibits no phenolic properties. These reactions show that the —OH group in benzyl alcohol is in the side-chain, and not directly attached to the nucleus.

When benzyl alcohol is heated with an oxidising agent, such as dilute nitric acid, or an aqueous solution of cupric nitrate, or an alkaline solution of potassium permanganate, the side-chain in the molecule is oxidised. Benzaldehyde is first formed, and then benzoic acid,

$$C_6H_5.CH_2OH + O = C_6H_5.CHO + H_2O,$$
$$C_6H_5.CHO + O = C_6H_5.COOH.$$

Benzyl alcohol may be reduced to toluene by the action of hydriodic acid in the presence of phosphorus at a temperature of 140°.

Test for benzyl alcohol. There is no simple test for benzyl alcohol. It may, however, be oxidised to benzoic acid which is easily recognised. 0·5 c.c. of benzyl alcohol is boiled for 15 minutes with 25 c.c. of saturated potassium permanganate solution containing 0·5 gm. of sodium carbonate, in a flask fitted to a reflux water condenser. A precipitate of manganese dioxide and a solution of potassium benzoate are obtained. The mixture is acidified with concentrated hydrochloric acid, and the precipitate of manganese dioxide is dissolved by the addition of sodium sulphite solution. On cooling, benzoic acid crystallises and may be identified by the tests given on p. 434. Benzyl chloride and benzaldehyde also give benzoic acid on oxidation, but these compounds are easily identified by the tests given on p. 415 and p. 431.

BENZALDEHYDE

Benzaldehyde is derived by the elimination of two hydrogen atoms from the molecule of benzyl alcohol,

benzyl alcohol   benzaldehyde

Benzaldehyde is a colourless liquid, B.P. 179°, Sp. Gr. 1·05 at 15°. It is sparingly soluble in water, and is volatile in steam. It is miscible in all proportions with ethyl alcohol and ether. It has the characteristic odour of bitter almonds, of which it is the odorific principle.

Benzaldehyde occurs naturally in the compound amygdalin, $C_{20}H_{27}O_{11}N$, which is found in the kernels of the peach and cherry. On hydrolysis with the enzyme emulsin, or with a dilute mineral acid, amygdalin yields benzaldehyde, glucose and hydrogen cyanide.

PRINCIPAL REACTIONS IN WHICH BENZALDEHYDE IS OBTAINED

1. The action of heat on a mixture of calcium benzoate and calcium formate. This is an example of a general method for preparing aldehydes, p. 199.

$$(C_6H_5.COO)_2Ca + (H.COO)_2Ca = 2CaCO_3 + 2C_6H_5.CHO.$$

2. The oxidation of an aromatic compound containing a side-chain. Toluene, benzyl alcohol, benzyl chloride and sodium cinnamate yield benzaldehyde when treated with appropriate oxidising agents.

Toluene is oxidised to benzaldehyde by chromyl chloride, p. 373, or by manganese dioxide in the presence of sulphuric acid, p. 482. Benzyl alcohol, benzyl chloride and sodium cinnamate are oxidised to benzaldehyde by alkaline potassium permanganate solution. Benzaldehyde is prepared in the laboratory by oxidising benzyl chloride with an aqueous solution of cupric nitrate, see below.

3. The reduction of phenyl cyanide. Phenyl cyanide is reduced to phenyl aldimine hydrochloride by the action of a solution of stannous chloride in anhydrous ether saturated with hydrogen chloride,

$$C_6H_5.C{\equiv}N + 3HCl + SnCl_2 = C_6H_5.C\underset{NH.HCl}{\overset{H}{<}} + SnCl_4.$$

The phenyl aldimine hydrochloride and the stannic chloride unite to form an additive compound which separates as a white precipitate. This is filtered off, and decomposed by warm water, which hydrolyses the aldimine hydrochloride to benzaldehyde and ammonium chloride,

$$C_6H_5.C\underset{NH.HCl}{\overset{H}{<}} + H_2O = C_6H_5.C\underset{O}{\overset{H}{<}} + NH_4Cl.$$

4. The hydrolysis of benzal chloride. Benzaldehyde is formed when benzal chloride is boiled with aqueous sodium hydroxide solution,

$$C_6H_5.CHCl_2 + 2NaOH = C_6H_5.CHO + 2NaCl + H_2O.$$

A modification of this reaction is used for the commercial preparation of benzaldehyde, p. 482.

O2   D.C.

5. The reaction of a mixture of carbon monoxide and hydrogen chloride on benzene in the presence of anhydrous aluminium and cuprous chlorides. Gattermann's reaction. This reaction is described on p. 366.

Laboratory preparation of benzaldehyde. Benzaldehyde is prepared on a small scale by the oxidation of benzyl chloride with cupric nitrate.

Benzyl chloride is heated for 6–8 hours with an aqueous solution of cupric nitrate in a flask fitted to a reflux condenser. The benzyl chloride is first hydrolysed to benzyl alcohol,

$$C_6H_5.CH_2Cl \quad + \quad H_2O \quad = \quad C_6H_5.CH_2OH \quad + \quad HCl$$

and the benzyl alcohol thus obtained is then oxidised by the cupric nitrate,

$$2C_6H_5.CH_2OH \quad + \quad Cu(NO_3)_2 \quad + \quad 2HCl$$
$$= \quad 2C_6H_5.CHO \quad + \quad CuCl_2 \quad + \quad N_2O_3 \quad + \quad 3H_2O.$$

The oxides of nitrogen are swept out of the reaction flask by a stream of carbon dioxide, and are thus prevented from oxidising the benzaldehyde to benzoic acid. The benzaldehyde is isolated from the resulting solution by extraction with ether. Sodium bisulphite solution is added to the ethereal solution to precipitate the benzaldehyde as the bisulphite compound, which is filtered from the solution, washed with ether, and distilled with dilute sulphuric acid to regenerate benzaldehyde. The distillate is again subjected to ethereal extraction, the ethereal solution is dried with anhydrous calcium chloride, the ether is removed (p. 70) and the residual benzaldehyde is distilled.

Industrial preparation of benzaldehyde. Benzaldehyde is manufactured in three different ways, (i) directly from benzene by Gattermann's reaction, p. 480, (ii) by the oxidation of toluene with manganese dioxide in the presence of sulphuric acid, p. 482, and (iii) by the hydrolysis of benzal chloride, p. 482.

CHEMICAL PROPERTIES AND USES OF BENZALDEHYDE

The more important reactions of benzaldehyde are described below. It should be noted, (i) that many of the reactions are parallel to those of acetaldehyde with the same reagents, (ii) that reactions of benzaldehyde with ammonia and with sodium hydroxide (Reactions 6 and 10 (*a*)) are different from those of acetaldehyde with these compounds, (iii) that benzaldehyde does not undergo polymerisation to yield substances similar to paraldehyde, metaldehyde, or acetaldehyde resin, (iv) that benzaldehyde undergoes many condensation reactions (Reaction 10) which are not undergone by acetaldehyde.

1. Oxidation. Benzaldehyde is readily oxidised to benzoic acid,

$$C_6H_5.CHO \quad + \quad O \quad = \quad C_6H_5.COOH.$$

The oxidation is brought about by air ; the outside of the stopper of a bottle containing benzaldehyde is usually coated with crystals of benzoic acid. It is necessary to distil benzaldehyde immediately before use if a sample free from benzoic acid is required.

Benzaldehyde reduces an ammoniacal solution of silver oxide to metallic silver, but it reduces Fehling's solution only very slowly.

2. Reduction. On reduction with sodium amalgam and water, benzaldehyde is converted to benzyl alcohol, p. 423.

3. Action with phosphorus pentachloride. Phosphorus penta-chloride reacts with benzaldehyde to produce benzal chloride and phosphorus oxychloride, p. 416.

4. Condensation with hydrogen cyanide to give a cyanhydrin. Hydrogen cyanide reacts with benzaldehyde to give benzaldehyde cyanhydrin, also known as *mandelonitrile*,

$$C_6H_5.C{\overset{H}{\underset{O}{\big<}}} \quad + \quad HCN \quad = \quad C_6H_5.C{\overset{H}{\underset{CN}{\big<}}}OH$$

Mandelonitrile may also be obtained by a reaction given under paragraph 5 below. It is a colourless oil, which dissociates into benzaldehyde and hydrogen cyanide when heated to 170°.

5. Condensation with sodium bisulphite to give a bisulphite compound. An aqueous solution of sodium bisulphite reacts with benzaldehyde to yield the addition compound

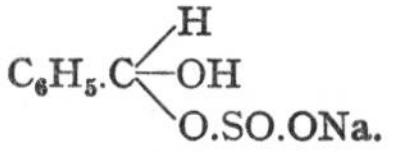

$$C_6H_5.C{\overset{H}{\underset{O.SO.ONa.}{\big<}}}OH$$

This compound is sparingly soluble in water, and it separates as a white crystalline precipitate in the course of the reaction.

Benzaldehyde is liberated again when the bisulphite compound is distilled with dilute sulphuric acid, or with an aqueous solution of sodium carbonate. The decomposition with sodium carbonate proceeds according to the equation,

$$2C_6H_5.CH.OH.SO_3Na \quad + \quad Na_2CO_3$$
$$= \quad 2C_6H_5.CHO \quad + \quad 2Na_2SO_3 \quad + \quad CO_2 \quad + \quad H_2O.$$

When crystals of benzaldehyde sodium bisulphite compound are shaken with a concentrated aqueous solution of sodium cyanide, mandelonitrile is produced,

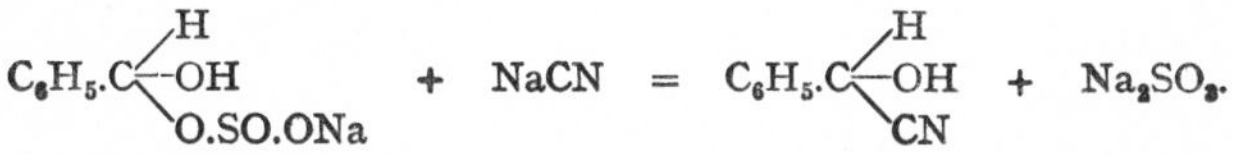

$$C_6H_5.C{\overset{H}{\underset{O.SO.ONa}{\big<}}}OH \quad + \quad NaCN \quad = \quad C_6H_5.C{\overset{H}{\underset{CN}{\big<}}}OH \quad + \quad Na_2SO_3.$$

6. Condensation with ammonia to give hydrobenzamide.

When benzaldehyde is treated with ammonia, colourless crystals of hydrobenzamide, M.P. 160°, are formed,

$$3C_6H_5.CHO + 2NH_3 = (C_6H_5.CH)_3N_2 + 3H_2O.$$

7. Condensation with hydroxylamine to give benzaldoxime.

Benzaldehyde reacts directly with hydroxylamine to yield α-benzaldoxime, M.P. 35°,

$$\begin{matrix} C_6H_5-C-H \\ \parallel \\ O \end{matrix} + H_2NOH = \begin{matrix} C_6H_5-C-H \\ \parallel \\ N-OH \end{matrix} + H_2O.$$

When benzaldehyde reacts with hydroxylamine hydrochloride in alcoholic solution, the geometrical isomeride

$$\begin{matrix} C_6H_5-C-H \\ \parallel \\ HO-N \end{matrix}$$

β-benzaldoxime, M.P. 125°, is formed.

8. Condensation with phenylhydrazine to give a phenylhydrazone.

If equi-molar proportions of phenylhydrazine and benzaldehyde are separately dissolved in ethyl alcohol, and the solutions are mixed, benzaldehyde phenylhydrazone rapidly crystallises as colourless prisms, M.P. 155°,

$$\begin{matrix} H \\ | \\ C_6H_5-C=O \end{matrix} + H_2N.NHC_6H_5 = \begin{matrix} H \\ | \\ C_6H_5-C=N.NHC_6H_5 \end{matrix} + H_2O.$$

Benzaldehyde phenylhydrazone may be prepared on a test-tube scale by the procedure given under " Tests " on p. 431.

9. Reaction with Grignard reagents to give secondary alcohols.

Benzaldehyde reacts with a Grignard reagent, for example, C_2H_5MgBr, to give an intermediate compound, which on treatment with a dilute mineral acid yields a secondary alcohol,

$$\begin{matrix} H \\ | \\ C_6H_5-C=O \end{matrix} + C_2H_5MgBr = \begin{matrix} H \\ | \\ C_6H_5-C-OMgBr, \\ | \\ C_2H_5 \end{matrix}$$

$$\begin{matrix} H \\ | \\ C_6H_5-C-OMgBr \\ | \\ C_2H_5 \end{matrix} + HCl = \begin{matrix} H \\ | \\ C_6H_5-C-OH \\ | \\ C_2H_5 \end{matrix} + MgBrCl.$$

10. Condensation reactions peculiar to aromatic aldehydes.

(a) *Claisen's reaction.** In the presence of dilute sodium hydroxide solution, benzaldehyde condenses with acetaldehyde to give cinnamic aldehyde, the flavouring principle of cinnamon, according to the equation,

$$\underset{\substack{|\\H}}{C_6H_5-C=O} + \underset{H}{\overset{H}{\underset{H}{>}}}C\underset{}{-}\underset{}{\overset{H}{C}}=O = \underset{}{C_6H_5-\overset{H}{C}=\overset{H}{C}-\overset{H}{C}=O} + H_2O.$$

The formation of cinnamic aldehyde from benzaldehyde may be compared with the formation of crotonaldehyde from acetaldehyde, p. 207.

In the presence of sodium hydroxide solution benzaldehyde condenses with acetone to yield dibenzal acetone,

$$C_6H_5-\overset{H}{C}=O + \overset{H}{\underset{H}{>}}C-\overset{O}{\overset{\|}{C}}-\overset{H}{C}\overset{H}{\underset{H}{<}} + O=\overset{H}{C}-C_6H_5$$

$$= C_6H_5-\overset{H}{C}=\overset{H}{C}-\overset{O}{\overset{\|}{C}}-\overset{H}{C}=\overset{H}{C}-C_6H_5 + 2H_2O.$$

(b) *Perkin's reaction.* Benzaldehyde reacts with a mixture of acetic anhydride and anhydrous sodium acetate to form acetyl cinnamic acid,

$$C_6H_5-\overset{H}{C}=O + \overset{H}{\underset{H}{>}}C-\overset{O}{\overset{\|}{C}}-O.CO.CH_3$$

$$= C_6H_5-\overset{H}{C}=\overset{H}{C}-\overset{O}{\overset{\|}{C}}-O.CO.CH_3 + H_2O,$$

* At the present time the study of the mechanisms of condensation reactions is an extremely active field of research. There is general agreement that Claisen's reaction takes place in three stages :

(i) the ionisation of the compound with which the benzaldehyde will react, thus, $H_3C-CHO = H^+ + H_2\bar{C}-CHO$,

(ii) the union of the negative ion so formed with the positive aldehydic carbon atom in the benzaldehyde molecule (see p. 23),

$$\underset{\substack{\|\\O\downarrow}}{C_6H_5-\overset{H}{C}} + -\overset{H}{\underset{H}{C}}-CHO = C_6H_5-\overset{H}{\underset{O}{C}}-\overset{H}{\underset{H}{C}}-CHO,$$

(iii) the elimination of the elements of an OH⁻ ion, which on combination with the H⁺ ion liberated in reaction (i) forms a molecule of water,

$$C_6H_5-\overset{H}{\underset{O}{C}}-\overset{H}{\underset{H}{C}}-CHO + H^+ = C_6H_5-\overset{H}{C}=\overset{H}{C}-CHO.$$

There is also general agreement that the reactions under (b) and (c) proceed in the same manner as Claisen's reaction. The mechanisms of the reactions under (d) and (e), however, are still under discussion.

which may be hydrolysed to sodium cinnamate and sodium acetate by the action of sodium carbonate.

$$C_6H_5-\overset{H}{\underset{|}{C}}=\overset{H}{\underset{|}{C}}-\overset{O}{\underset{||}{C}}-O.CO.CH_3 \ + \ Na_2CO_3$$

$$= \ C_6H_5-\overset{H}{\underset{|}{C}}=\overset{H}{\underset{|}{C}}-\overset{O}{\underset{||}{C}}-ONa \ + \ NaO.CO.CH_3 \ + \ CO_2.$$

The reaction is carried out by mixing benzaldehyde, acetic anhydride, and finely powdered anhydrous sodium acetate in a flask fitted to an air condenser closed with a calcium chloride tube. The mixture is heated in an oil-bath at 180° for 8 hours. It is then poured into water, and aqueous sodium carbonate solution is added until the solution is alkaline. Any unchanged benzaldehyde is expelled from the solution by steam-distillation. The residual solution is cooled, filtered, and acidified with concentrated hydrochloric acid. Cinnamic acid is precipitated. It is filtered off, and recrystallised from aqueous methylated spirit.

(c) *Condensation to benzylidene aniline.* Benzaldehyde condenses readily with aniline in alcoholic solution, to give benzylidene aniline,

$$C_6H_5-\overset{H}{\underset{|}{C}}=O \ + \ \overset{H}{\underset{H}{\diagup}}N-C_6H_5 \ = \ C_6H_5-\overset{H}{\underset{|}{C}}=N-C_6H_5 \ + \ H_2O.$$

Equal volumes of benzaldehyde and aniline are mixed and heated in a dish on a water-bath for 30 minutes. The product is cooled in ice, and the solid benzylidene aniline is crystallised from methylated spirit.

(d) *The benzoin condensation.* When a solution of benzaldehyde in ethyl alcohol is treated with potassium cyanide, the benzaldehyde polymerises to benzoin,

$$C_6H_5-\overset{H}{\underset{||}{\underset{O}{C}}} \ + \ \overset{O}{\underset{||}{\underset{H}{C}}}-C_6H_5 \ = \ C_6H_5-\overset{H}{\underset{|}{\underset{OH}{C}}}-\overset{O}{\underset{||}{C}}-C_6H_5.$$

5 gm. of potassium cyanide are dissolved in 20 c.c. of water and 50 c.c. of ethyl alcohol. The solution is placed in a flask fitted to a reflux condenser. 25 c.c. of benzaldehyde are added, and the mixture is heated for 30 minutes. When the product is cooled the benzoin separates as a solid. It may be recrystallised from methylated spirit. It forms pale yellow crystals, M.P. 137°.

(e) *The Cannizzaro reaction.* If an emulsion of benzaldehyde and aqueous potassium hydroxide solution is allowed to stand for several hours, a mixture of benzyl alcohol and potassium benzoate is obtained. Benzyl benzoate is first formed

$$C_6H_5-\overset{H}{\underset{|}{\underset{H}{C}}}=O \ + \ \overset{O}{\underset{||}{\underset{H}{C}}}-C_6H_5 \ = \ C_6H_5-\overset{H}{\underset{|}{\underset{H}{C}}}-O-\overset{O}{\underset{||}{C}}-C_6H_5,$$

and it subsequently reacts with the potassium hydroxide to form potassium benzoate and benzyl alcohol. The procedure for carrying out this reaction is described under the preparation of benzyl alcohol, p. 423, and, on a test-tube scale, on p. 432.

11. Nuclear reactions of benzaldehyde. Benzaldehyde yields *m*-nitrobenzaldehyde when treated with a mixture of nitric acid and sulphuric acid. *o*- and *p*-nitrobenzaldehyde are made by oxidising *o*- and *p*-nitrocinnamic acids respectively with an alkaline solution of potassium permanganate,

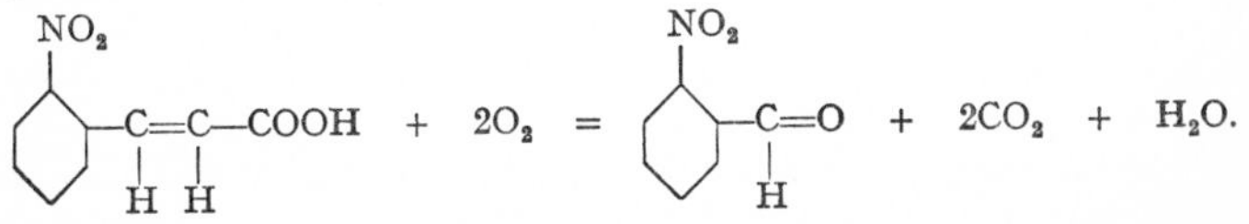

$$NO_2\text{-}C_6H_4\text{-}C{=}C\text{-}COOH \ (H,H) \ + \ 2O_2 \ = \ NO_2\text{-}C_6H_4\text{-}C{=}O \ (H) \ + \ 2CO_2 \ + \ H_2O.$$

The nitro compounds may be reduced to yield the corresponding aminobenzaldehydes. Benzaldehyde may be chlorinated in the presence of a carrier to yield *m*-chlorobenzaldehyde. If chlorine is passed into *boiling* benzaldehyde, substitution takes place in the side-chain, and benzoyl chloride is obtained.

Uses of benzaldehyde. Benzaldehyde is used for flavouring purposes. It is also used in the manufacture of certain dyes, for example, malachite green. Benzaldehyde is condensed with dimethyl aniline in the presence of zinc chloride to form a compound known as the leuco base,

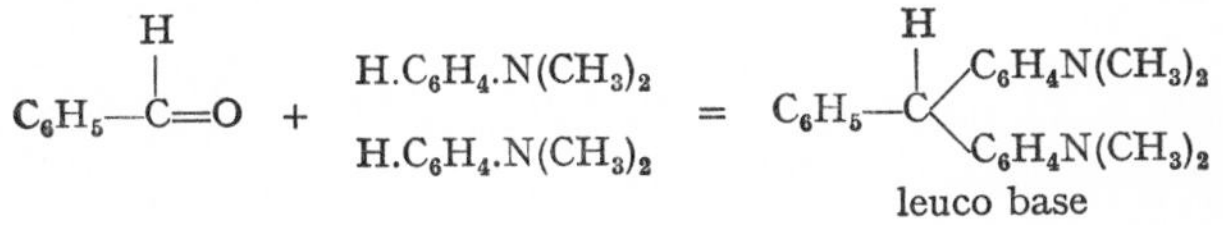

$$C_6H_5\text{-}C{=}O \ (H) \ + \ \begin{matrix} H.C_6H_4.N(CH_3)_2 \\ H.C_6H_4.N(CH_3)_2 \end{matrix} \ = \ C_6H_5\text{-}C(H)\big\langle \begin{matrix} C_6H_4N(CH_3)_2 \\ C_6H_4N(CH_3)_2 \end{matrix}$$

leuco base

The leuco base is oxidised with lead peroxide to the colourless colour base, which on treatment with a warm acid gives the dyestuff

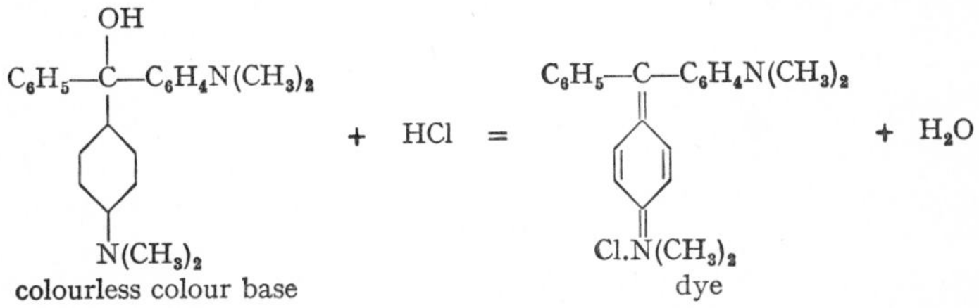

$$C_6H_5\text{-}\underset{\underset{N(CH_3)_2}{|}}{\overset{\overset{OH}{|}}{C}}\text{-}C_6H_4N(CH_3)_2 \ + \ HCl \ = \ C_6H_5\text{-}\underset{Cl.N(CH_3)_2}{C}\text{-}C_6H_4N(CH_3)_2 \ + \ H_2O$$

colourless colour base　　　　　　dye

Tests for benzaldehyde. Benzaldehyde has the characteristic odour of bitter almonds. It reduces an ammoniacal solution of silver nitrate to metallic silver, but it has scarcely any reducing action on Fehling's solution. With Schiff's reagent it produces a pink colour only slowly.

Benzaldehyde may be distinguished from acetaldehyde by the following tests :

(i) The formation of crystalline phenylhydrazone. 0·5 c.c. of phenylhydrazine and 0·5 c.c. of glacial acetic acid are added to 5 c.c. of water. 3 drops of benzaldehyde are added and the mixture is shaken. In a few minutes a flocculent precipitate of benzaldehyde phenylhydrazone is produced. Salicylaldehyde will also give a precipitate under these conditions, but the phenylhydrazones of acetaldehyde, acetone and formaldehyde are too soluble to be thrown down.

(ii) Cannizzaro's reaction. A mixture of 2 c.c. of 30 per cent. sodium hydroxide solution and 1 c.c. of benzaldehyde is warmed gently and stirred for 5 minutes. Water is then added to dissolve the sodium benzoate which is formed, the aqueous solution is decanted from the unchanged benzaldehyde and acidified with hydrochloric acid. A white precipitate of benzoic acid is obtained.

(iii) Oxidation to benzoic acid. Benzaldehyde is oxidised to benzoic acid by warm alkaline potassium permanganate solution. The procedure is described under tests for benzyl chloride, p. 415. Benzaldehyde, benzyl chloride and benzyl alcohol are among the compounds which respond to this test.

BENZOIC ACID

Benzoic acid is derived by the oxidation of the methyl group, —CH$_3$, in the molecule of toluene to the carboxyl group, —COOH.

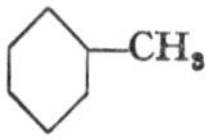

toluene 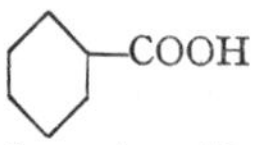   benzoic acid

Benzoic acid crystallises in glistening plates, M.P. 121·5°. It boils at 249°. It sublimes readily, and it is volatile in steam. It dissolves freely in hot water, but only slightly in cold water, and it is therefore easily crystallised from its aqueous solution. It has an irritating odour.

Benzoic acid occurs naturally in gum benzoin, and in various resins. Hippuric acid, the benzoyl derivative of glycine, occurs in the urine of herbivora.

Principal reactions in which benzoic acid is produced

1. The oxidation of toluene, benzyl alcohol, benzyl chloride, or benzaldehyde with dilute nitric acid, chromic acid, or potassium permanganate. These reactions are described on pp. 373, 424, 415, 426 respectively.

2. The hydrolysis of benzotrichloride. When benzotrichloride is boiled with milk of lime, calcium benzoate is obtained,

$$2C_6H_5.CCl_3 + 4Ca(OH)_2 = (C_6H_5.COO)_2Ca + 3CaCl_2 + 4H_2O.$$

The calcium benzoate is treated with hydrochloric acid to precipitate benzoic acid, which is separated by filtration and recrystallised from hot water.

3. Cannizzaro's reaction. This reaction is described on p. 423 as a method of preparing benzyl alcohol. The product of the reaction is a mixture of benzyl alcohol and potassium benzoate. After the benzyl alcohol has been extracted with ether, the potassium benzoate remains in aqueous solution. Addition of hydrochloric acid to the solution liberates benzoic acid, which is recrystallised from hot water.

Preparation of benzoic acid from gum benzoin or hippuric acid

Gum benzoin contains uncombined benzoic acid which may be isolated by sublimation. The preparation of benzoic acid from hippuric acid is described on p. 279.

Chemical properties of benzoic acid

The presence of the carboxyl group in the molecule confers on benzoic acid the same properties as it confers on acetic acid. Benzoic acid is a weak monobasic acid (its dissociation constant is 0·006) which forms salts and esters. When benzoic acid is heated with soda-lime it produces benzene,

$$C_6H_5.COOH + 2NaOH = C_6H_6 + Na_2CO_3 + H_2O.$$

By the action of phosphorus pentachloride or thionyl chloride benzoic acid is converted to benzoyl chloride,

$$C_6H_5.COOH + SOCl_2 = C_6H_5.COCl + HCl + SO_2.$$

Benzoic anhydride, benzamide, and benzonitrile

Benzoic anhydride is made by the action of benzoyl chloride on sodium benzoate,

$$C_6H_5.COCl + C_6H_5.COONa = (C_6H_5.CO)_2O + NaCl,$$

a reaction parallel to that by which acetic anhydride is prepared. Benzamide separates as a solid when benzoyl chloride is shaken with excess of concentrated ammonia solution. It may be recrystallised from hot water to give colourless crystals, M.P. 130°.

Benzonitrile may be obtained by heating benzamide with phosphorus pentoxide. It is also made from potassium benzene sulphonate, p. 377, and from benzene diazonium chloride, p. 399. It is a liquid, B.P. 191°, with an odour resembling that of benzaldehyde. It is hydrolysed by acids or alkalis to benzoic acid ; on reduction it yields benzylamine.

Tests for benzoic acid. The recognition of benzoic acid is important, because benzoic acid is formed when any aromatic compound containing a single side-chain in the molecule is oxidised. Proof of the presence of benzoic acid among the products of oxidation of an aromatic compound, therefore, confirms the existence of a single side-chain in the original compound.

Benzoic acid is much more soluble in hot water than in cold water. It is soluble in sodium hydroxide solution and in sodium carbonate solution.

Benzoic acid yields benzene when heated with soda-lime. About 1 gm. each of benzoic acid and soda-lime is thoroughly mixed in a mortar. The mixture is heated in a hard-glass tube. The benzene evolved is recognised by its odour, and by the smoky flame with which it burns.

A neutral solution of ammonium benzoate (made by boiling a small quantity of benzoic acid with a slight excess of ammonia solution until the odour of ammonia is completely removed) gives a buff precipitate of basic ferric benzoate when added to a neutral solution of ferric chloride.* Hydrochloric acid dissolves this precipitate, but throws down simultaneously a white precipitate of benzoic acid. Cinnamic acid and phthalic acid behave in a precisely parallel manner. The three acids, however, are readily distinguished. Cinnamic acid reduces an alkaline solution of potassium permanganate, and phthalic acid forms bright-red phenolphthalein when it is warmed with phenol and concentrated sulphuric acid and the product is made alkaline with sodium hydroxide solution (p. 422) ; benzoic acid undergoes neither of these reactions.

SALICYLIC ACID

Salicylic acid (*o*-hydroxybenzoic acid), forms colourless needles, M.P. 159°. It is sparingly soluble in cold water and readily soluble in hot water. When heated it sublimes, with some decomposition to phenol and carbon dioxide. It is odourless.

The methyl ester of salicylic acid occurs naturally as oil of wintergreen.

Preparation. Salicylic acid may be prepared by the Reimer-Tiemann reaction in which phenol reacts with carbon tetrachloride in the presence of sodium hydroxide according to the equation,

$$\text{C}_6\text{H}_5\text{OH} + CCl_4 + 5NaOH = \text{(salicylate)} + 4NaCl + 3H_2O.$$

Equi-molar proportions of phenol and carbon tetrachloride are mixed with excess of a concentrated aqueous solution of potassium hydroxide. Sufficient alcohol is added to make a homogeneous solution, and a little

---

* Compare with the similar test for acetic acid, p. 236.

precipitated copper is introduced to act as a catalyst. The solution is heated in a flask fitted to a reflux condenser for 8–10 hours. The product is steam-distilled to remove any unchanged carbon tetrachloride. It is then acidified and extracted with ether. The ether dissolves the salicylic acid and any unchanged phenol. The ethereal extract is boiled with aqueous sodium carbonate solution which reacts with salicylic acid but not with phenol. The salicylic acid is then precipitated from the aqueous solution of sodium salicylate by the addition of hydrochloric acid, and recrystallised from hot water.

On a large scale salicylic acid is prepared by heating sodium phenate with carbon dioxide under pressure at 100°. Sodium phenyl carbonate is obtained as an intermediate product,

$$\text{C}_6\text{H}_5\text{—ONa} \;+\; \text{CO}_2 \;=\; \text{C}_6\text{H}_5\text{—O.CO.ONa}$$

The temperature is then raised to 130°, when the sodium phenyl carbonate undergoes an intramolecular change to yield sodium salicylate, thus,

$$\text{C}_6\text{H}_5\text{—O.COONa} \;=\; \text{C}_6\text{H}_4}\begin{cases}\text{OH}\\ \text{COONa}\end{cases}$$

The sodium salicylate is dissolved in water, and salicylic acid is precipitated from the solution by the addition of hydrochloric acid.

Properties of salicylic acid. The carboxyl group and the hydroxyl group in the molecule of salicylic acid retain many of the properties which they exhibit in benzoic acid and phenol respectively.

Salicylic acid behaves as a dibasic acid towards strong bases ; it reacts with sodium hydroxide and barium hydroxide to form the salts,

$$\left[\text{C}_6\text{H}_4}\begin{cases}\text{COO}\\ \text{O}\end{cases} \right]^{--} 2\text{Na}^+ \quad\text{and}\quad \left[\text{C}_6\text{H}_4}\begin{cases}\text{COO}\\ \text{O}\end{cases} \right]^{--} \text{Ba}^{++}$$

Sodium carbonate, which does not react with phenol, reacts with salicylic acid thus,

$$2\text{C}_6\text{H}_4.\text{OH.COOH} \;+\; \text{Na}_2\text{CO}_3 \;=\; 2\text{C}_6\text{H}_4.\text{OH.COONa} \;+\; \text{CO}_2.$$

In the presence of concentrated sulphuric acid, salicylic acid reacts with methyl alcohol and with ethyl alcohol to form esters. The methyl ester, $\text{C}_6\text{H}_4}\begin{cases}\text{OH}\\ \text{COOCH}_3\end{cases}$, is oil of wintergreen, and may easily be recognised by its characteristic odour. The esters are hydrolysed to the alcohol and sodium salicylate by hot dilute sodium hydroxide solution, but if treated with a cold solution of sodium hydroxide they yield sodium derivatives which react with alkyl halides or with dimethyl sulphate to yield alkyl derivatives, for example, according to the equation,

ethyl *o*-methoxy benzoate

Salicylic acid yields phenol when heated with soda-lime. When reduced with sodium and boiling amyl alcohol the benzene nucleus is attacked and an aliphatic compound, pimelic acid, is obtained,

pimelic acid

Salicylic acid is a powerful antiseptic. It is also used in the manufacture of azo dyes.

Tests for salicylic acid. If salicylic acid is heated with soda-lime, phenol is liberated.

If neutral ferric chloride solution is added to a solution of ammonium salicylate, or to a dilute solution of salicylic acid, a violet coloration is obtained.* The colour is destroyed by mineral acids.

If 0·5 gm. of salicylic acid or one of its salts is heated with 1 c.c. of methyl alcohol and a few drops of concentrated sulphuric acid for 1 minute, methyl salicylate is formed. The odour of oil of wintergreen is most easily detected by pouring the contents of the tube into a few c.c. of cold water in a boiling-tube.

The formation of an azo dye and the formation of a phthalein may be used as tests for salicylic acid in the same way as they are used as tests for phenol, p. 422.

(*a*) *Azo dye formation.* 3–4 drops of aniline are dissolved in 1 c.c. of concentrated hydrochloric acid and diazotised. The resulting solution is poured into a cold solution of salicylic acid in excess of sodium hydroxide solution. A red coloration is obtained. If the solution is acidified with hydrochloric acid, a yellowish-brown precipitate of the azo dye is thrown down.

(*b*) *Phthalein formation.* About 0·5 gm. each of salicylic acid and phthalic anhydride are placed in a test-tube and moistened with 2

---

* Salicylic acid alone of the hydroxybenzoic acids gives a violet coloration with ferric chloride solution ; the *m*- and *p*-hydroxybenzoic acids do not give it.

drops of concentrated sulphuric acid. The contents of the tube are gently fused for about 1 minute. The product is cooled, dissolved in cold water, and excess of sodium hydroxide solution is added. A bright red coloration is obtained. The equations for the reactions which take place in the formation of the phthalein are analogous to those given under Reaction 7 on p. 420.

PHENYL SALICYLATE (" SALOL ")

Phenyl salicylate is prepared by heating a mixture of sodium salicylate, sodium phenate, and phosphorus oxychloride. The reaction which occurs may be regarded as a modification of the Schotten-Baumann reaction. Salicyl chloride, instead of being added to sodium phenate as in the normal procedure for carrying out a Schotten-Baumann reaction, is prepared *in situ* from sodium salicylate and phosphorus oxychloride,

$$C_6H_4.OH.COONa + POCl_3 + 2NaOH$$
$$= NaPO_3 + 2NaCl + C_6H_4.OH.COCl + H_2O.$$
$$C_6H_4.OH.COCl + NaOC_6H_5 = C_6H_4.OH.COOC_6H_5 + NaCl.$$

Phenyl salicylate is a solid, M.P. 42°. It is almost insoluble in water ; its alcoholic solution gives a violet coloration with ferric chloride. It is used in medicine and surgery in place of salicylic acid.

ACETYL SALICYLIC ACID (" ASPIRIN ")

Acetyl salicylic acid forms colourless crystals, M.P. 136°. It is very sparingly soluble in water.

It is made by acetylating salicylic acid with either acetic anhydride,

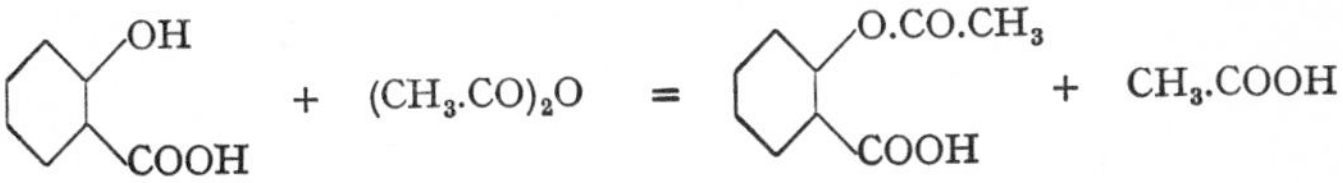

or acetyl chloride,

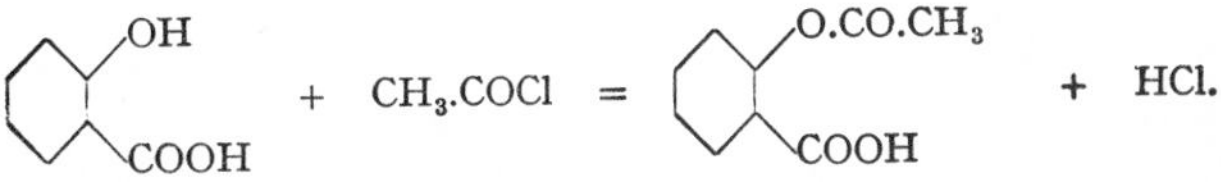

If acetic anhydride is to be used, a mixture of salicylic acid, acetic anhydride and acetic acid is heated for 30 minutes in a flask fitted to a reflux condenser. The product is poured into cold water, the precipitated acetyl salicylic acid is filtered off, washed, and recrystallised from a mixture of equal volumes of water and acetic acid. If acetyl chloride is to be used as the acetylating agent, salicylic acid is dissolved in dry pyridine, and acetyl chloride is added in small quantities at a time, while the solution is shaken and the temperature is not allowed to rise above 60°. When the acetyl chloride has been added, the mixture is heated for 5 minutes to complete the reaction, and poured into cold water. The precipitated acetyl salicylic acid is recrystallised from dilute acetic acid.

Acetyl salicylic acid is hydrolysed to salicylic acid and acetic acid if boiled with 10 per cent. sodium hydroxide solution for 30 minutes. It gives no violet coloration with neutral ferric chloride solution. It is used in medicine as an analgesic for diminishing pain, and as an antipyretic for reducing body temperature.

SALICYLALDEHYDE

Salicylaldehyde (o-hydroxybenzaldehyde) is prepared from phenol by the Reimar-Tiemann reaction, for which the structural equation is,

$$\text{C}_6\text{H}_5\text{—OH} + \text{CHCl}_3 + 3\text{NaOH} = \text{[salicylaldehyde]} + 3\text{NaCl} + 2\text{H}_2\text{O}.$$

Phenol (1 molar proportion) and sodium hydroxide (8 molar proportions), dissolved in a little water, are heated to 70° in a flask fitted with a reflux condenser. Chloroform (2 molar proportions) is slowly added from a tap-funnel fitted to the top of the condenser. The heating is continued for 2 hours. The excess of chloroform is then removed by simple distillation. The residual alkaline solution is acidified with excess dilute sulphuric acid and distilled in steam. The distillate, which contains phenol and salicylaldehyde, is extracted with ether. The ether is distilled off, and the residue is shaken with a strong aqueous solution of sodium bisulphite. The crystalline bisulphite compound is collected by filtration, and decomposed with hot dilute sulphuric acid. The salicylaldehyde in the acid solution is extracted with ether. The ethereal solution is dried with anhydrous sodium sulphate, and, after removal of the ether, the salicylaldehyde is distilled.

Salicylaldehyde is a liquid, B.P. 197°, with a characteristic odour. It is insoluble in water, but it dissolves in sodium hydroxide solution, turning it yellow. Salicylaldehyde added to ferric chloride solution gives an intense violet coloration. When reduced with sodium amalgam and water it yields saligenin (o-hydroxybenzyl alcohol, salicyl alcohol). It is easily oxidised to salicylic acid by an alkaline solution of potassium permanganate, but it reduces neither Fehling's solution nor ammoniacal silver oxide solution. It does not give a colour with Schiff's reagent.

CHAPTER XXIX

A SUMMARY AND DISCUSSION OF SOME OF THE PRINCIPAL REACTIONS IN ORGANIC CHEMISTRY

ONE of the most important fields of research in organic chemistry is concerned with the mechanism of the reactions of organic compounds. In order to explain the mechanism of an organic reaction it is necessary to be able to describe in detail how the valencies linking the atoms in the molecules of the reagents are re-arranged to link the atoms in the molecules of the resultants. In terms of the electronic theory of valency this re-arrangement must be expressed as a process of redistribution of valency electrons. It must be shown how the valency electrons leave certain of the atoms of the reacting molecules, and build up new linkages which hold together the atoms in the molecules of the products.

During the past 20 years much attention has been paid to the detailed mechanism of chemical reactions, but no broad generalisations have emerged to explain, in terms of a few simple principles, the behaviour of molecules undergoing chemical change. Experimental investigation has indeed shown that it is dangerous to attempt to explain the mechanism of a reaction in terms of the " common sense " views of elementary chemistry. For example, it might well be expected that all the alkyl halides would be attacked in the same way by a dilute solution of sodium hydroxide to yield an alcohol and the sodium halide. It has been shown, however, from a study of the rates of the reactions, that the mechanism of the hydrolysis of methyl bromide and ethyl bromide by sodium hydroxide solution differs from that of the hydrolysis of isopropyl bromide and tertiary butyl bromide by the same reagent. To take another example, it might be expected that the mechanism of the formation of an ester from an acid and an alcohol would be parallel to that of the formation of a salt from an acid and a base, as shown by the equation,

$$H^+Cl^- + Na^+OH^- = Na^+Cl^- + H_2O,$$

which indicates that a molecule of water is produced by the combination of the H^+ ion from the acid with the OH^- ion from the base. It has been shown, however, by the esterification of alcohols containing a heavy isotope of oxygen in place of normal oxygen atoms, that esterification proceeds thus :

$$CH_3CO \vdots OH \; + \; H \vdots OC_2H_5 \; = \; CH_3COOC_2H_5 \; + \; H_2O,$$

and that the molecule of water is produced by the combination of the OH group of the acid with the H atom of the hydroxyl group of the alcohol.

The following sections of this chapter contain general accounts of certain types of reactions of organic compounds, and, where possible, comments on the probable mechanisms of these reactions.

OXIDATION

An organic compound undergoes oxidation when hydrogen is removed from the molecule or oxygen is added to it.

Some of the more important types of oxidation reactions are included in Table XV. The principal types of valency change which may be brought about by oxidation are set out in the first column of this table, and examples of specific reactions in which these valency changes occur are given in the third column. The third column also contains a reference to the page (p) and to the number of the paragraph (R) in which the reaction is described. The oxidising agents which have been found most suitable for bringing about a given reaction are stated in the second column. There is no apparent relation between the various types of oxidation reactions and the different oxidising agents which bring them about. The detailed mechanism of oxidation reactions is not understood.

TABLE XV *

Type of reaction	Oxidising agent	Exemplified by the oxidation of
1. 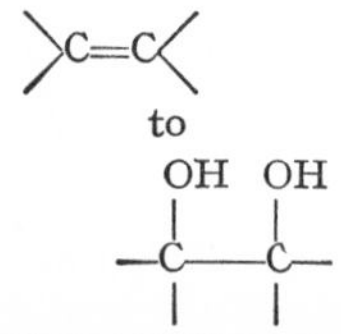 $>C=C<$ to OH OH | | $-C-C-$ | |	A 1 per cent. solution of potassium permanganate containing sodium carbonate	(a) ethylene to glycol, p. 121 ,R. 6 (b) maleic and fumaric acids to mesotartaric acid and racemic acid respectively, p. 318

* The information collected in this table is not to be regarded as exhaustive ; the number of available oxidising agents for any given type of reaction, and the number of examples of reactions, could be greatly increased if space permitted.

Type of reaction	Oxidising agent	Exemplified by the oxidation of
2. H —C—OH H to —C⟨O / H	(i) catalytic dehydrogenation at 300° in the presence of copper or nickel (ii) air at 300°, in the presence of metallic platinum, silver or copper as catalyst (iii) aqueous potassium dichromate solution in the presence of dilute sulphuric acid (iv) a 1 per cent. solution of potassium permanganate containing sodium carbonate	(a) ethyl alcohol to acetaldehyde, p. 163, R. 7 (b) isobutyl alcohol to isobutaldehyde, p. 172 (a) methyl alcohol to formaldehyde, p. 169, (b) ethyl alcohol to acetaldehyde, p. 199, R. 2 (a) ethyl alcohol to acetaldehyde, p. 164, R. 8 (b) isobutyl alcohol to isobutaldehyde, p. 172 benzyl alcohol to benzaldehyde, p. 425, R 2.
3. —C⟨O / H to —C⟨O / OH	(i) air in the presence of manganese acetate or vanadium pentoxide (ii) sodium dichromate or potassium permanganate solution in the presence of dilute acid (iii) Fehling's solution or ammoniacal silver oxide solution (iv) concentrated nitric acid (v) bromine water	acetaldehyde to acetic acid, p. 201, R. 1 acetaldehyde to acetic acid, p. 201, R. 1 (a) acetaldehyde to acetic acid, p. 201, R. 2 (b) chloral to trichloroacetic acid, p. 217, R. 3 (c) benzaldehyde to benzoic acid, p. 427 (Fehling's solution is reduced only very slowly) chloral to trichloroacetic acid, p. 217, R. 3 glucose to gluconic acid, p. 338
4. H —C—OH H directly to —C⟨O / OH	(i) air at room temperature in the presence of platinum black as catalyst (ii) nitric acid	methyl alcohol to formic acid, p. 239, R. 4 (a) α-propylene glycol to lactic acid, p. 271, R. 3 (b) β-propylene glycol to hydracrylic acid, p. 276, R. 2 (c) ethylene glycol to oxalic acid, p. 323, R. 4 (d) glycerol to glyceric acid, p. 328, R. 5 (e) glucose to saccharic acid, p. 338, R. 1 (f) fructose to tartaric acid, p. 348, R. 1 (g) benzyl alcohol to benzoic acid, p. 424

Table XV—*continued*

Type of reaction	Oxidising agent	Exemplified by the oxidation of
	(iii) chromic acid	hydracrylic acid to malonic acid, p. 276
	(iv) bromine water	fructose to tartaric acid, p. 348, R. 1
5. C with H and OH to C=O	(i) oxygen at 500° in the presence of finely divided copper as catalyst	iso-propyl alcohol to acetone, p. 220, R. 2
	(ii) aqueous potassium dichromate solution in the presence of dilute sulphuric acid	iso-propyl alcohol to acetone, p. 173
	(iii) potassium permanganate solution, or perhydrol in the presence of ferric acetate	lactic acid to pyruvic acid, p. 273, R. 4
6. Oxidation of ketones. The nature of the products is predictable by Popoff's rule, p. 348	(i) a solution of potassium permanganate containing sodium carbonate, or a solution of chromic acid	acetone to acetic acid and carbon dioxide, p. 222, R. 1
	(ii) an aqueous suspension of mercuric oxide	fructose to trihydroxybutyric acid and glycollic acid, p. 348, R. 1
7. 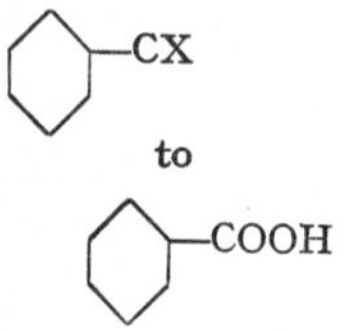 ⬡—CX to ⬡—COOH	a solution of potassium permanganate containing sodium carbonate, or a 1 : 1 solution of nitric acid	(a) toluene * to benzoic acid, p. 373 (b) chlorotoluene to chlorobenzoic acid, p. 414 (c) benzyl chloride to benzoic acid, p. 415 (d) benzyl alcohol to benzoic acid, p. 424

REDUCTION

An organic compound undergoes reduction when hydrogen is added to the molecule or oxygen is removed from it. Some of the more important reduction reactions are included in Table XVI which is constructed on the same lines as Table XV.

* The oxidation of a side-chain consisting of an alkyl group is very slow, and it is usual to chlorinate it to render oxidation easier ; in order to oxidise toluene, for example, it would first be chlorinated to benzyl chloride.

TABLE XVI *

Type of reaction	Reducing agent	Exemplified by the reduction of
1. Alkyl and aryl halides to hydrocarbons	(i) sodium amalgam and water, or moist alcohol and a zinc copper couple, or zinc and dilute hydrochloric acid	(a) methyl iodide to methane, p. 104, R. 1 (b) ethyl iodide to ethane p. 108, R. 1 (c) ethyl bromide to ethane, p. 140, R. 1
	(ii) zinc and dilute hydrochloric acid	(a) chloral to acetaldehyde, p. 217, R. 4 (b) trichloroacetic acid to acetic acid, p. 265
	(iii) sodium amalgam and alcohol	chlorobenzene (with difficulty) to benzene, p. 406, R. 1
	(iv) hydriodic acid and red phosphorus at high temperatures	,,
2. $\diagup C=C \diagdown$ to H H $\mid$ $\mid$ —C—C— $\mid$ $\mid$	(i) hydrogen at room temperature in the presence of platinum black (ii) hydrogen at 150–200° in the presence of nickel	ethylene to ethane, p. 118 (a) ethylene to ethane, p. 118 (b) benzene to cyclohexane, p. 366, R. 6 (c) toluene to hexahydrotoluene, p. 371 (d) phenol to cyclohexanol, p. 421, R. 8
3. —C≡C— to H$\diagdown$ $\diagup$H $\diagup C=C \diagdown$	hydrogen at room temperature in the presence of platinum black, or at 150–200° in the presence of nickel	acetylene to ethylene, p. 132, R. 3
4. —C$\diagup$H $\diagdown$O to H $\mid$ —C—OH $\mid$ H	(i) hydrogen at 150–200° in the presence of nickel (ii) sodium amalgam and water	acetaldehyde to ethyl alcohol, p. 160, R. 4 (a) acetaldehyde to ethyl alcohol, p. 160, R. 4 (b) glucose to sorbitol, p. 339, R. 3 (c) benzaldehyde to benzyl alcohol, p. 423, R. 1
	(iii) zinc and hydrochloric acid (iv) zinc dust and acetic acid	acetaldehyde to ethyl alcohol, p. 201, R. 3 glucosone to fructose, p. 341, R. 7

* The footnote on p. 440 applies, *mutatis mutandis*, to Table XVI. A brief account of lithium aluminium hydride, a recently introduced reducing agent not mentioned in this table, is given on p. 501.

TABLE XVI—*continued*

Type of reaction	Reducing agent	Exemplified by the reduction of
5. $-C-\overset{\overset{O}{\|\|}}{C}-C-$ to $-C-\overset{\overset{OH}{\|}}{\underset{\underset{H}{\|}}{C}}-C-$	(i) hydrogen at 120° in the presence of nickel (ii) sodium amalgam and water	acetone to iso-propyl alcohol, p. 222, R. 2 (*a*) acetone to iso-propyl alcohol, p. 222 (*b*) pyruvic acid to lactic acid, p. 271, R. 2 (*c*) fructose to a mixture of sorbitol and mannitol, p. 349, R. 3
6. 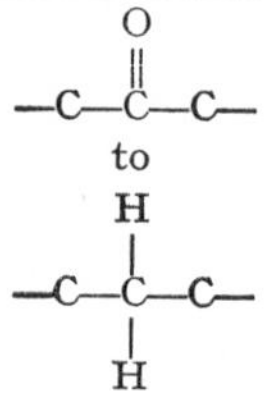 $-C-\overset{\overset{O}{\|\|}}{C}-C-$ to $-C-\overset{\overset{H}{\|}}{\underset{\underset{H}{\|}}{C}}-C-$	amalgamated zinc in the presence of concentrated hydrochloric acid	acetone to propane, p. 222
7. Anhydrides to 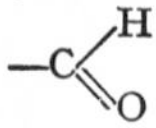 $-C\overset{\nearrow H}{\underset{\searrow O}{}}$	(i) sodium amalgam in acid solution	(*a*) acetic anhydride to acetaldehyde, p. 252, R. 1 (*b*) gluconolactone to glucose, p. 338
8. 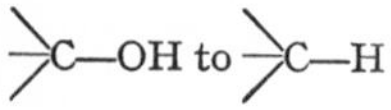 $>C-OH$ to $>C-H$	(i) concentrated hydriodic acid	(*a*) lactic acid to propionic acid, p. 273, R. 5 (*b*) tartaric acid to succinic acid, p. 299 (*c*) sorbitol to secondary hexyl iodide, p. 339, R. 3
	(ii) hydriodic acid in the presence of phosphorus at 140°	benzyl alcohol to toluene, p. 424
	(iii) a mixture of white phosphorus and iodine in excess, warmed	glycerol to iso-propyl iodide, p. 326, R. 2
	(iv) strongly heated zinc dust	(*a*) phenol to benzene, p. 420, R. 5 (*b*) cresol to toluene, p. 371, R. 4
9. $-C\equiv N$ to 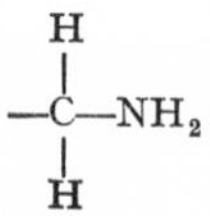 $-\overset{\overset{H}{\|}}{\underset{\underset{H}{\|}}{C}}-NH_2$	(i) sodium and alcohol	(*a*) ethyl cyanide to propylamine, p. 162, R. 1 (*b*) methyl cyanide to ethylamine, p. 184, R. 1
	(ii) zinc and hydrochloric acid	(*a*) methyl cyanide to ethylamine hydrochloride, p. 261

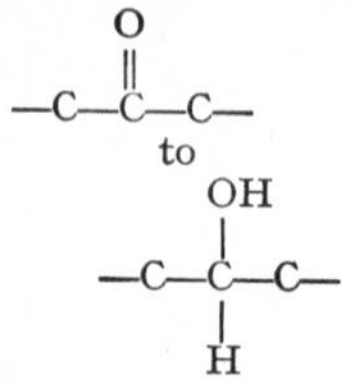

TABLE XVI—*continued*

Type of reaction	Reducing agent	Exemplified by the reduction of
10. —NO$_2$* to NH$_2$	(i) zinc and hydrochloric acid	nitroethane to ethylamine hydrochloride, p. 184, R. 1
	(ii) stannous chloride and hydrochloric acid	(*a*) nitroethane to ethylamine hydrochloride, p. 184, R. 1 (*b*) nitrobenzene to aniline, p. 381, R. 1 (*c*) *m*-dinitrobenzene to *m*-nitroaniline, p. 384
	(iii) a warm alcoholic solution of ammonium sulphide, or a warm aqueous solution of sodium disulphide	*m*-dinitrobenzene to *m*-nitroaniline, p. 384
11. Fission of the benzene nucleus	sodium and boiling amyl alcohol	salicylic acid to pimelic acid, p. 436

HYDROLYSIS

Hydrolysis is chemical decomposition brought about by water. In organic chemistry hydrolytic reactions are met with more frequently than reactions of any other type. The hydrolysis of an organic compound is usually brought about only very slowly by the action of pure water. Solutions of acid or alkalis, which catalyse hydrolytic reactions, are generally used, therefore, as hydrolytic agents. The principal hydrolytic agents, and examples of their use, are given in Table XVII. The alkaline hydrolytic agent most generally used is a ten per cent. aqueous solution of sodium hydroxide. This solution is used for the hydrolysis of alkyl halides to the corresponding alcohols, esters to the corresponding alcohols and the sodium salts of the acids, alkyl cyanides to ammonia and the sodium salt of the corresponding fatty acid, and acyl chlorides and acid anhydrides to the sodium salt of the parent acid. It is also used for the hydrolysis of acetyl derivatives such as aspirin, and of amides and imides.

Sodium hydroxide in aqueous solution may react with halogen derivatives of certain compounds to form unsaturated compounds. Such reactions are particularly liable to take place during the hydrolysis of the halogen derivatives of the higher paraffins. The formation of unsaturated compounds during alkaline hydrolysis may be prevented, either by using the weakly alkaline hydrolytic

* The formation of azoxybenzene, azobenzene, and hydrazobenzene by the reduction of nitrobenzene are important specific reactions and are mentioned on p. 380.

agents moist silver oxide or moist lead monoxide, or by first replacing the halogen atom in the molecule of the compound to be hydrolysed by the acetate group, and then hydrolysing the ester so obtained, p. 148. If it is desired to promote the formation of an unsaturated compound during hydrolysis, as for example in the preparation of propylene by the hydrolysis of propyl bromide, an alcoholic solution of potassium hydroxide is used as the hydrolytic agent.

All organic compounds which undergo hydrolysis in alkaline conditions contain in the molecule a carbon atom which is attached either to a halogen atom, or a doubly-linked oxygen atom, or a triply-linked nitrogen atom. An explanation of the mechanism of alkaline hydrolysis may, therefore, be based on the assumption that there is a displacement of electrons from this carbon atom to the halogen atom, the oxygen atom or the nitrogen atom, which leaves the carbon atom with a positive charge. The molecule of ethyl acetate,

$$CH_3-\overset{\overset{O}{\|}}{C}-OC_2H_5,$$

for example, by electron displacement acquires the constitution,

$$CH_3-\overset{\overset{\uparrow\;O}{\|}}{C}-OC_2H_5.$$

This modified molecule then attracts a negatively charged hydroxyl ion present in the alkaline solution,

$$CH_3-\overset{\overset{\uparrow\;O}{\|}}{C}-OC_2H_5\;+\;OH^-\;=\;CH_3-\overset{\overset{O^-}{|}}{\underset{OH}{C}}-OC_2H_5,$$

and two further changes then occur, leading to the formation of acetic acid and ethyl alcohol,

$$CH_3-\overset{\overset{O^-}{|}}{\underset{OH}{C}}-OC_2H_5\;=\;CH_3-C\overset{\diagup O}{\diagdown OH}\;+\;OC_2H_5^-.$$

$$OC_2H_5^-\;+\;H_2O\;=\;HOC_2H_5\;+\;OH^-.$$

The mechanism of other alkaline hydrolyses may be explained in a parallel manner.

70 per cent. sulphuric acid and concentrated hydrochloric acid are employed for the hydrolysis of many compounds containing a nitrogen atom in the molecule. As a result of hydrolysis this nitrogen atom is usually converted to the group $-NH_2$. For example, ethyl isocyanide is converted to ethylamine hydrochloride according to the equation,

$$C_2H_5\overset{+}{N}\equiv\overset{-}{C}\;+\;2H_2O\;+\;HCl\;=\;C_2H_5NH_2.HCl\;+\;HCOOH.$$

It might be inferred that the essential step in acid hydrolysis is the attraction of hydrogen ions in the acid solution to the nitrogen atom in the molecule of the compound undergoing hydrolysis. There is experimental evidence, however, that this step does not take place, and a comprehensive explanation of acid hydrolysis has yet to be put forward.

The compounds which are hydrolysed by dilute sulphuric acid usually consist only of carbon, hydrogen and oxygen, and frequently the portions of the molecule which become separated by hydrolysis were originally linked together by oxygen atoms. Many of the chemical reactions occurring in fermentation and in the metabolism of living organisms are hydrolyses. Each of these reactions is catalysed by a specific substance known as an enzyme. A few examples of these hydrolyses, and the names of the enzymes which bring them about, are collected in Section 11 of Table XVII.

TABLE XVII

Type of reaction	Hydrolytic agent	Exemplified by the hydrolysis of
1. Replacement of a halogen atom in a molecule by the group —OH	(i) a 10 per cent. aqueous solution of sodium hydroxide	(a) ethyl bromide to ethyl alcohol and potassium bromide, p. 140, R. 2 (b) ethylidene dibromide to acetaldehyde and potassium bromide, p. 131 (c) monochloroacetic acid to sodium glycollate and sodium chloride, p. 266 (d) acetyl chloride to sodium acetate and sodium chloride, p. 248, R. 2
	(ii) silver oxide moistened with water	(a) propyl iodide to propyl alcohol and silver iodide, p. 171 (b) α-chloropropionic acid to lactic acid and silver chloride, p. 271 (c) β-chloropropionic acid to hydracrylic acid and silver chloride, p. 275 (d) dibromosuccinic acid to tartaric acid and silver bromide, p. 297 (e) tetraethyl ammonium iodide to tetraethyl ammonium hydroxide, p. 194
	(iii) lead monoxide moistened with water	ethylidene dibromide to acetaldehyde, p. 199
	(iv) an alcoholic solution of potassium hydroxide	chloroform to potassium formate and potassium chloride, p. 154, R. 2

TABLE XVII—*continued*

Type of reaction	Hydrolytic agent	Exemplified by the hydrolysis of
2. (i) H hal. $\mid$ $\mid$ —C—C— to $\mid$ $\mid$ $\quad$ C=C	an alcoholic solution of potassium hydroxide	iso-propyl bromide to propylene and potassium bromide, p. 148
(ii) H hal. $\mid$ $\mid$ C=C to —C≡C— $\mid$ $\mid$		ethylene dibromide and ethylidene dibromide to acetylene and potassium dibromide, p. 128
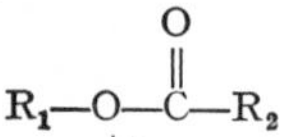 3. $\quad$ O $\quad$ $\parallel$ R_1—O—C—R_2 to R_1OH and R_2COOH	a 10 per cent. aqueous solution of sodium hydroxide	(*a*) ethyl acetate to ethyl alcohol and sodium acetate, p. 259, R. 1 (*b*) acetyl salicylic acid (aspirin) to sodium salicylate and sodium acetate, p. 438
4. 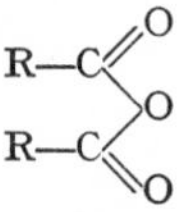 R—C$\langle$ ^{O} $\quad$ ^{O} R—C$\langle$ ^{O} $\quad$ ^{O} to $\quad$ R—COOH $\quad$ R—COOH	a 10 per cent. aqueous solution of sodium hydroxide	(*a*) acetic anhydride to sodium acetate, p. 252, R. 2 (*b*) succinic anhydride, p. 296, and phthalic anhydryde, p. 420, yield sodium succinate and sodium phthalate respectively.
5. 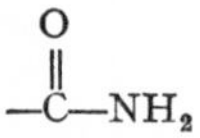 $\quad$ O $\quad$ $\parallel$ —C—NH$_2$ to —COOH	a 10 per cent. aqueous solution of sodium hydroxide	(*a*) acetamide to sodium acetate and ammonia, p. 255, R. 1 (*b*) oxamide to sodium oxalate and ammonia, p. 293
6. —C≡N to —COOH	(i) a 10 per cent. aqueous solution of sodium hydroxide, *or* 70 per cent. sulphuric acid	acetonitrile to acetic acid, p. 230, R. 1 and p. 260
	(ii) concentrated hydrochloric acid	(*a*) ethylene cyanhydrin to hydracrylic acid and ammonium chloride, p. 276 (*b*) sodium cyanoacetate to malonic acid, p. 294 (*c*) ethylene dicyanide to succinic acid and ammonium chloride, p. 295

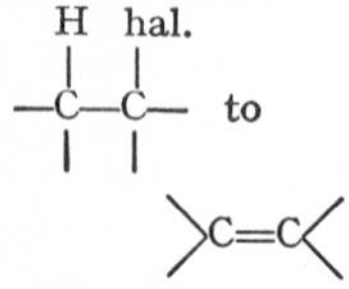

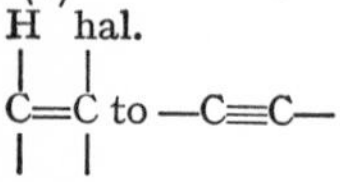

TABLE XVII—continued

Type of reaction	Hydrolytic agent	Exemplified by the hydrolysis of
7. $\begin{array}{c}\text{O}\\ \parallel\\ -\text{C}\\ \phantom{-\text{C}}\diagdown\text{NX}\\ -\text{C}\diagup\\ \parallel\\ \text{O}\end{array}$ to NH$_2$X X is a hydrogen atom or an organic radical	(i) a 10 per cent. aqueous solution of sodium hydroxide (ii) concentrated hydrochloric acid	succinimide to ammonia and sodium succinate, p. 296 (a) ethyl phthalimide to ethylamine hydrochloride and phthalic acid, p. 185, R. 2(c) (b) phthalimide derivative to glycine hydrochloride and phthalic acid, p. 279, R. 3
8. (i) $\begin{array}{c}\text{X}\diagdown\quad\text{O}\\ \diagdown\;\parallel\\ \text{N}-\text{C}-\text{CH}_3\\ \text{X}\diagup\end{array}$ to NHX$_2$	70 per cent. sulphuric acid	(a) acetanilide to aniline hydrogen sulphate and acetic acid, p. 231, R. 2 (b) chloroacetotoluide to chlorotoluidine, p. 413
(ii) $\begin{array}{c}\text{X}\diagdown\\ \diagdown\\ \text{N}-\text{SO}_2\text{C}_6\text{H}_5\\ \text{X}\diagup\end{array}$ to NHX$_2$	70 per cent. sulphuric acid	sulphonyl ethylamine and sulphonyl diethylamine to ethylamine sulphate and diethylamine sulphate, p. 198
(iii) $\begin{array}{c}\text{X}\diagdown\quad\text{O}\\ \diagdown\;\parallel\\ \text{N}-\text{C}-\text{C}_6\text{H}_5\\ \text{X}\diagup\end{array}$ to NHX$_2$	concentrated hydrochloric acid	hippuric acid to glycine hydrochloride, p. 279, R. 2
(iv) $\begin{array}{c}\text{X}\diagdown\\ \diagdown\\ \text{N}-\text{NO to}\\ \text{X}\diagup\\ \text{NHX}_2\end{array}$	concentrated hydrochloric acid	diethylnitrosoamine to diethylamine hydrochloride and nitrous acid, p. 192, R. 2
9. $\begin{array}{c}\text{H}\\ \mid\\ \text{R}_1-\text{C}=\text{N}-\text{R}_2\end{array}$ to $\begin{array}{c}\text{H}\\ \mid\\ \text{R}_1-\text{C}=\text{O}\end{array}$	concentrated hydrochloric acid	(a) acetaldehyde phenyl hydrazone to acetaldehyde and phenyl hydrazine hydrochloride, p. 205, R. 11 (b) phenyl glucosazone to glucosone and phenyl hydrazine hydrochloride, p. 340 (c) acetaldoxime to acetaldehyde and hydroxylamine hydrochloride, p. 204, R. 10

TABLE XVII—*continued*

Type of reaction	Hydrolytic agent	Exemplified by the hydrolysis of
10. The reversal of certain condensations, and the hydrolysis of carbohydrates	Dilute sulphuric acid	(i) methylal to methyl alcohol and formaldehyde, p. 211, R. 3
		(ii) paraldehyde and metaldehyde to acetaldehyde, p. 206, R. 14 and 15
		(iii) mesityl oxide and phorone to acetone, p. 226, R. 12
		(iv) starch and sucrose to monosaccharides, p. 337, R. 1
		(v) cellulose to glucose, p. 356
		(vi) hexamethylene tetramine to formaldehyde and ammonium sulphate, p. 212, R. 4
11. Enzyme reactions		(i) sucrose to invert sugar by invertase, p. 353, R. 4
		(ii) glycogen to maltose by glycogenase or ptyalin, p. 354
		(iii) starch or glycogen to maltose by diastase, p. 351
		(iv) starch to dextrin and maltose by diastase, p. 355
		(v) glucose to alcohol by zymase, p. 339
		(vi) urea to ammonium carbonate by urease, p. 285, R. 3, and p. 287

ACETYLATION

Acetylation is the replacement of the hydrogen atom in a hydroxyl group, or in a primary or secondary amino group, by the acetyl group, $CH_3CO—$. A compound undergoes acetylation only if it contains a hydroxyl group or an amino group. Acetylation is important as the first step in the procedure for estimating the number of hydroxyl groups in the molecule of a hydroxy compound, p. 98. Acetylation is also used for converting the $—NH_2$ group, which is rapidly chlorinated by chlorine, or oxidised by nitric acid, into the group, $NH.CH_3CO$, which is attacked by neither of these reagents. If an organic compound with an —NH$_2$ group in the molecule is to be chlorinated or nitrated, this group is first protected by acetylation, after which chlorination or nitration can be carried out in the normal manner. When the process is completed the —NH.CH$_3$CO group is converted back again to —NH$_2$ by hydrolysis. An example of the use of acetylation to protect an amino group during chlorination is mentioned on p. 413. Certain organic compounds may be identified by the determination of the melting-points of their acetyl derivatives. Many acetyl derivatives, however, are soluble in water which makes their isolation difficult, and the preparation and examination of the benzoyl derivatives is generally a more satisfactory means of identifying the original compounds.

The available acetylating agents are acetyl chloride, acetic anhydride and ethyl acetate ; in ordinary laboratory technique ethyl acetate is rarely used. Acetic anhydride is more convenient to handle than acetyl chloride ; its action is moderated if it is diluted with glacial acetic acid, or promoted if zinc chloride or anhydrous sodium acetate is present to act as a catalyst. The acetylation of organic compounds (with the exception of phenols) must be carried out in anhydrous conditions. Examples of acetylation are collected in Table XVIII.

TABLE XVIII

Type of reaction	Acetylating agent	Exemplified by the acetylation of
1. 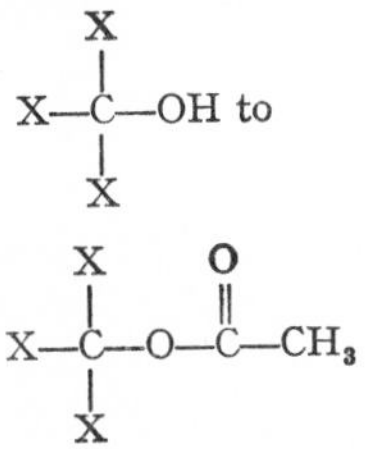 X | X—C—OH to | X X O | ‖ X—C—O—C—CH$_3$ | X	(i) acetyl chloride or acetic anhydride	(a) ethyl alcohol to yield ethyl acetate, p. 257, R. 2, p. 252, R. 4 (b) glycerol to yield glyceryl triacetate, p. 249, R. 4, p. 326, R. 3 (c) phenol to yield phenyl acetate, p. 419, R. 3 (d) salicylic acid to yield aspirin, p. 437
The carbon atom in the hydroxy compound may be part of a benzene ring. X is either a hydrogen atom, or another carbon atom	(ii) acetic anhydride	(a) glucose to yield the pentacetyl derivative, p. 339, R. 4 (b) cellulose to yield cellulose acetate, p. 356

TABLE XVIII—*continued*

Type of reaction	Acetylating agent	Exemplified by the Acetylation of
2. R—N⟨ H / H to R—N⟨ H / C—CH₃ ‖ O R is an alkyl or aryl group	(i) either ethyl acetate, or acetyl chloride, or acetic anhydride	ethylamine to yield ethyl acetamide, p. 188, R. 5 and 6
	(ii) either acetyl chloride, or acetic anhydride	aniline to yield acetanilide, p. 391
3. R\ / N—H to R/ R\ / N—C—CH₃ ‖ R/ O R is an alkyl or aryl group	either ethyl acetate, or acetyl chloride, or acetic anhydride	diethylamine to yield diethyl acetamide, p. 193, R. 3

BENZOYLATION

Benzoylation is the replacement of the hydrogen atom in a hydroxyl group, or in a primary or secondary amino group, by the benzoyl group, $C_6H_5.CO—$. Benzoylation is important because the benzoyl derivative of a compound is often more readily purified and crystallised than the original compound. It is therefore easier to isolate than the compound itself, and a determination of the melting-point of the benzoyl derivative furnishes a reliable means of identifying the original compound. Thus the processes of benzoylation and acetylation may each be used for the identification of certain classes of organic compounds. In most instances benzoylation is preferable to acetylation because :

(i) the benzoylating agent, benzoyl chloride, is much less rapidly hydrolysed by water than either of the acetylating agents acetic anhydride or acetyl chloride ; benzoylation may be carried out in the presence of aqueous solutions, but (with the exception of the acetylation of phenol) all the acetylations mentioned in Table XVIII must be carried out in anhydrous conditions ;

(ii) all benzoyl compounds are insoluble in water, and the crude product is therefore readily separated from the reaction mixture in which it has been prepared ;

(iii) benzoyl derivatives are less soluble in organic solvents than the corresponding acetyl derivatives, and are therefore more easily crystallised ;

(iv) the melting-points of benzoyl derivatives are higher than those of the corresponding acetyl derivatives.

Benzoylation is carried out by means of the Schotten-Baumann reaction. Phenol, for example, is dissolved in excess of a dilute aqueous solution of sodium hydroxide. Benzoyl chloride is added to the solution, and the mixture of liquids is shaken vigorously for several minutes (p. 419). Under these conditions reaction occurs between benzoyl chloride and sodium phenate with the formation of phenyl benzoate which separates as an insoluble solid. When the reaction is over the excess of benzoyl chloride is hydrolysed to sodium benzoate by the sodium hydroxide,

$$C_6H_5COCl + 2NaOH = NaCl + C_6H_5COONa + H_2O.$$

The phenyl benzoate is recrystallised from methylated spirit so that any traces of benzoyl chloride which may contaminate it are removed by reaction with the ethyl alcohol. The benzoylation of aniline, p. 391, and of other amino compounds, is carried out similarly.

SULPHONYLATION

Sulphonylation is the replacement of a hydrogen atom in a hydroxyl group, or in a primary or secondary amino group, by the sulphonyl group, $C_6H_5.SO_2$—. Sulphonylation may be used, like benzoylation, to obtain crystalline derivatives of hydroxy and amino compounds. The sulphonyl derivatives of primary amines are acid, and those of secondary amines are neutral. This difference is made use of in Hinsberg's method for separating a primary from a secondary amine. Sulphonylation is carried out by the Schotten-Baumann technique already described, using benzene sulphonyl chloride, $C_6H_5.SO_2Cl$, instead of benzoyl chloride. The sulphonylation of ethylamine and diethylamine are mentioned on pp. 189 and 193, and Hinsberg's method for the separation of these amines by making use of the acidic properties of sulphonyl ethylamine is described on p. 197.

ESTERIFICATION

Esterification is the process by which an alcohol and an acid are converted to an ester. Esterification may be carried out by the four methods described below.

1. The action of the acid on the alcohol in the presence of sulphuric acid. This method is exemplified by the formation of ethyl acetate from ethyl alcohol and acetic acid. In the absence of sulphuric acid the equilibrium is slowly set up :

$$CH_3.COOH + C_2H_5OH \rightleftharpoons CH_3COOC_2H_5 + H_2O.$$

In the presence of sulphuric acid, under the appropriate experimental conditions (p. 258) the formation of the ester takes place rapidly, and the ester and water distil together from the reaction vessel.

The mechanism of the reaction has not been finally elucidated. According to the older view, ethyl acetate is produced by the alternate formation and decomposition of ethyl hydrogen sulphate, as explained on p. 257. According to the electron-displacement theories of chemical change which are in favour at the present time, the formation of ethyl acetate is explained by the following sequence of reactions.

(*a*) The sulphuric acid furnishes H⁺ ions with which the acetic acid combines, thus :

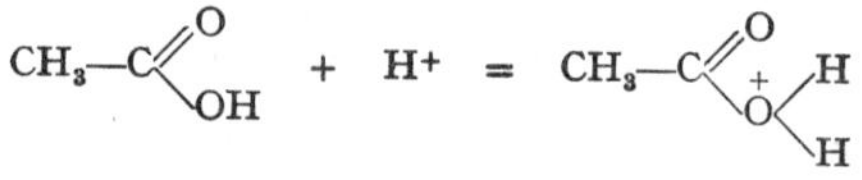

$$CH_3-C{\overset{O}{\underset{OH}{\big<}}} + H^+ = CH_3-C{\overset{O}{\underset{\overset{+}{O}-H}{\big<}}}H$$

and the resulting complex loses a molecule of water to form a positive ion, thus :

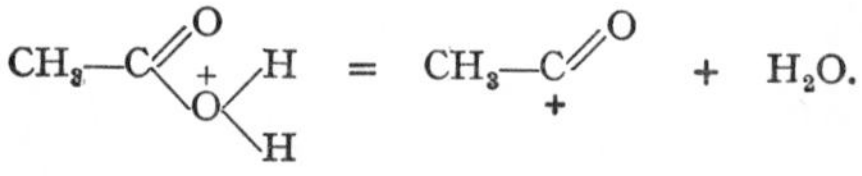

$$CH_3-C{\overset{O}{\underset{\overset{+}{O}-H}{\big<}}}H = CH_3-\overset{+}{C}{\overset{O}{\big/}} + H_2O.$$

(*b*) This positive ion and ethyl alcohol react to yield ethyl acetate and H⁺ ions :

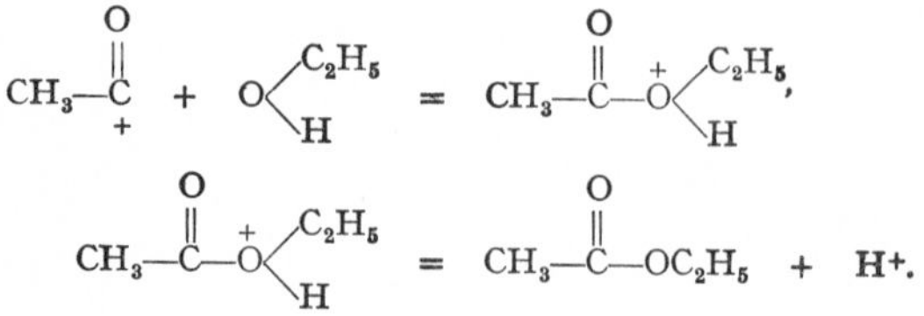

$$CH_3-\overset{\overset{O}{\|}}{\underset{+}{C}} + O{\overset{C_2H_5}{\underset{H}{\big<}}} = CH_3-\overset{\overset{O}{\|}}{C}-\overset{+}{O}{\overset{C_2H_5}{\underset{H}{\big<}}},$$

$$CH_3-\overset{\overset{O}{\|}}{C}-\overset{+}{O}{\overset{C_2H_5}{\underset{H}{\big<}}} = CH_3-\overset{\overset{O}{\|}}{C}-OC_2H_5 + H^+.$$

This scheme of reactions accounts for the fact that the oxygen atom in the molecule of water formed during the esterification comes from the acid and not from the alcohol,* but it appears to overlook the fact that under the usual experimental conditions (p. 258) the

---

* This has been proved by carrying out the reaction with alcohol in which the " oxygen " is a heavy isotope of oxygen. At the end of the experiment none of the heavy oxygen was present in the water.

alcohol and the sulphuric acid must be present largely as ethyl hydrogen sulphate.

The use of sulphuric acid as a catalyst in esterification has the disadvantages :

(i) some ether is invariably formed, according to the equation given on p. 177, Reaction 1 ;

(ii) if the alcohol or the acid contains an unsaturated linking, an additive compound with the sulphuric acid is formed ;

(iii) if the alcohol or the acid contains an amino group, the resulting ester is in the form of a sulphate, which is difficult to separate from the excess of sulphuric which is present ;

(iv) if the alcohol or the acid is an aromatic compound, sulphonation may occur.

2. The action of the acid on the alcohol in the presence of hydrogen chloride. The Fischer-Speier method. The use of this method for the preparation of ethyl acetate is mentioned on p. 257. It is probable that the hydrogen chloride furnishes H^+ ions which catalyse the reaction in the manner suggested under Method 1. The use of hydrogen chloride as a catalyst avoids all the difficulties which may be met when sulphuric acid is used, but it introduces difficulties of manipulation because hydrogen chloride is a gas.

3. The action of an acid chloride or an acidic anhydride on the alcohol. The formation of ethyl acetate by this method is mentioned on p. 257.

4. The action of an alkyl halide on the silver salt of the acid. This method, which is described for the preparation of ethyl acetate on p. 257, is valuable when only a small quantity of an acid is available for esterification.

DE-CARBOXYLATION

When a mixture of sodium acetate and soda-lime is heated, methane and sodium carbonate are formed,

$$CH_3.COONa + NaOH = CH_4 + Na_2CO_3.$$

By means of this reaction the carboxyl group in the molecule of acetic acid has been replaced by an atom of hydrogen. This reaction has many parallels in both aliphatic and aromatic chemistry. By heating with soda-lime it is possible to convert sodium propionate and sodium succinate to ethane, p. 109, sodium benzoate to benzene, p. 363, sodium methyl benzoate to toluene, p. 369, sodium chlorobenzoate to chlorobenzene, p. 405, and sodium salicylate to phenol,

p. 418. Sodium formate when heated with soda-lime yields hydrogen, p. 243.

It is not always necessary to employ such a powerful reagent as hot soda-lime. Malonic acid is changed to acetic acid by heat alone ; other dibasic acids in which two carboxyl groups are attached to one and the same carbon atom behave similarly, p. 295. Glycine is converted to methylamine when heated with barium hydroxide, p. 280. Sodium trichloroacetate is converted to chloroform by warming with an aqueous solution of sodium hydroxide, p. 153. The reaction of potassium monochloroacetate with potassium nitrite in hot aqueous solution to yield nitromethane, p. 267, is also an example of decarboxylation.

The processes of halogenation (pp. 112, 265, and Chapter XXVI), sulphonation and nitration (Chapter XXIII), and diazotization (Chapter XXV), are defined and described in the chapters mentioned.

CERTAIN NAMED REACTIONS

1. The Cannizzaro reaction is the condensation of benzaldehyde in the presence of potassium hydroxide solution to yield a mixture of benzyl alcohol and potassium benzoate, p. 433.

2. The Claisen reaction is the condensation of an aldehyde with either (a) another aldehyde, or (b) a ketone, with the elimination of water. The condensations of benzaldehyde with acetaldehyde, or with acetone, in the presence of dilute sodium hydroxide solution, to yield cinnamic aldehyde or dibenzal acetone respectively, p. 429, are examples of the Claisen reaction.

3. The Claisen condensation is the condensation, in the presence of sodium ethoxide or metallic sodium, of two molecules of an ester, or of one molecule of an ester with one molecule of (a) another ester, (b) a ketone, (c) a nitrile, with the elimination of an alcohol. The condensation occurs only if the second reagent possesses the formula, $R_1H_2C.COOR_2$, $R_1H_2C.COR_2$, or $R_1H_2C.CN$ respectively, where R_1 is either an alkyl group or a hydrogen atom, and R_2 is an alkyl group.

One of the most important examples of the Claisen condensation is the formation of ethyl acetoacetate from ethyl acetate which is described on p. 260. There is no generally accepted explanation of the mechanism of this reaction. A scheme of reactions was suggested by Claisen. This scheme takes into account the facts that the reaction does not proceed unless (a) at least a trace of ethyl alcohol is present, (b) there are at least two hydrogen atoms attached to the α-carbon atom in the molecule of the second reagent. Claisen's scheme is explained by the following sequence of equations :

$$Na + C_2H_5OH = C_2H_5ONa + \tfrac{1}{2}H_2$$

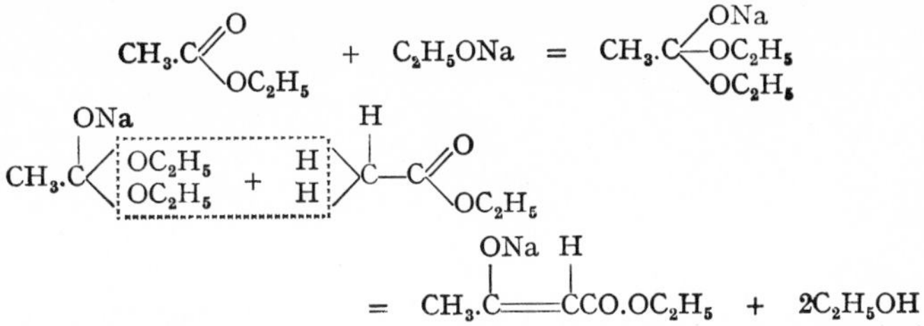

$$CH_3.C{\overset{\text{O}}{\underset{\text{OC}_2\text{H}_5}{\diagdown}}} + C_2H_5ONa = CH_3.C{\overset{\text{ONa}}{\underset{\text{OC}_2\text{H}_5}{\diagdown}}}OC_2H_5$$

$$CH_3.C{\overset{\text{ONa}}{\underset{}{\diagdown}}}{\overset{\text{OC}_2\text{H}_5}{\underset{\text{OC}_2\text{H}_5}{}}} + {\overset{\text{H}}{\underset{\text{H}}{}}}\!\!>\!\!C - C{\overset{\text{O}}{\underset{\text{OC}_2\text{H}_5}{\diagdown}}}$$

$$= CH_3.\overset{\text{ONa}}{\underset{|}{C}}\!\!=\!\!\overset{\text{H}}{\underset{|}{C}}CO.OC_2H_5 + 2C_2H_5OH$$

Another explanation of the mechanism of the condensation may be suggested, based on the present-day concept of electron displacement. The doubly linked oxygen atom in the molecule of ethyl acetate attracts electrons from the carbon atom to which it is attached, and thus (a) leaves this carbon atom positively charged, and (b) imparts a tendency to ionise to the hydrogen atoms of the methyl group. These electron displacements may be represented by arrows (see p. 23) in the molecular formula of ethyl acetate, thus,

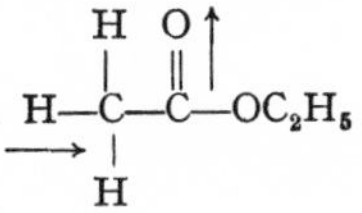

$$\underset{\overset{\longrightarrow}{\underset{\text{H}}{|}}}{\overset{\text{H} \ \ \text{O}\uparrow}{\underset{|}{\text{H}-\text{C}-\text{C}-OC_2H_5}}}$$

The positively charged hydrogen atom unites with a $\overline{O}C_2H_5$ ion (formed by the action of sodium on traces of ethyl alcohol in the ester) and thus liberates the ion

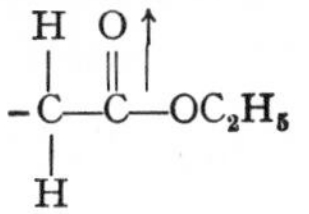

$$\underset{\underset{\text{H}}{|}}{\overset{\text{H} \ \ \text{O}\uparrow}{-\text{C}-\text{C}-OC_2H_5}}$$

This ion then attaches itself to the positively charged carbon atom in another molecule of ethyl acetate, giving the complex,

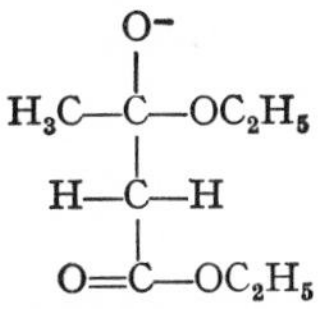

$$\begin{array}{c} \overset{\text{O}^-}{\underset{|}{H_3C-C-OC_2H_5}} \\ H-C-H \\ O=C-OC_2H_5 \end{array}$$

which decomposes to form ethyl acetoacetate

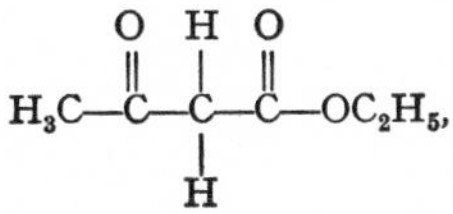

$$\underset{\underset{\text{H}}{|}}{\overset{\text{O} \ \ \text{H} \ \ \text{O}}{H_3C-C-C-C-OC_2H_5}}, \text{ and the ion } OC_2H_5$$

The ion $OC_2H_5^-$, with the Na^+ ion formed at the beginning of the reaction sequence, constitutes sodium ethoxide which reacts with the ethyl acetoacetate to form the sodium derivative and ethyl alcohol,

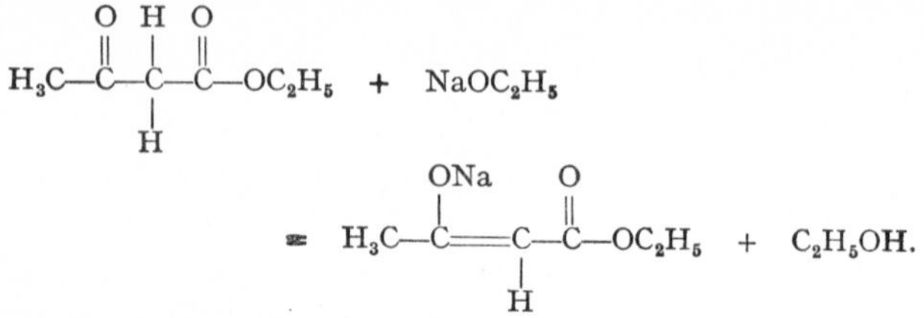

$$H_3C-\overset{\overset{O}{\|}}{C}-\overset{\overset{H}{|}}{\underset{\underset{H}{|}}{C}}-\overset{\overset{O}{\|}}{C}-OC_2H_5 \quad + \quad NaOC_2H_5$$

$$= \quad H_3C-\overset{\overset{ONa}{|}}{C}=\overset{}{\underset{\underset{H}{|}}{C}}-\overset{\overset{O}{\|}}{C}-OC_2H_5 \quad + \quad C_2H_5OH.$$

4. The Friedel-Crafts reaction is the condensation of an alkyl halide with an aromatic hydrocarbon, in the presence of anhydrous aluminium chloride, to yield a higher homologue of the hydrocarbon. The preparation of toluene from benzene by this reaction is described on p. 370. Ketones may be prepared from aromatic hydrocarbons by a modification of the Friedel-Crafts reaction in which an acyl chloride (either aliphatic or aromatic) is used in place of the alkyl halide. The formation of acetophenone from benzene by the action of acetyl chloride in the presence of aluminium chloride is mentioned on p. 249.

The mechanism of the Friedel-Crafts reaction depends on the formation of an ionised intermediate compound of the aromatic hydrocarbon, the alkyl or acyl halide, and aluminium chloride. Benzene, methyl chloride and aluminium chloride, for example, yield the complex

$$(C_6H_6, CH_3)^+ (AlCl_4)^-$$

which subsequently breaks down into $C_6H_5.CH_3$, HCl and $AlCl_3$.

5. The Grignard reactions. Metallic magnesium suspended in dry ether reacts additively with the halogen derivatives of many organic compounds ; the magnesium dissolves and a clear ethereal solution is obtained. If, for example, ethyl bromide is added to a suspension of magnesium turnings in ether, the additive compound magnesium ethyl bromide is formed in solution :

$$Mg + C_2H_5Br = Mg\overset{C_2H_5}{\underset{Br}{\diagdown}}$$

Bromobenzene undergoes a parallel reaction to form

$$Mg\overset{C_6H_5}{\underset{Br}{\diagdown}}$$

Compounds of the type of magnesium ethyl bromide are known as Grignard reagents.

The ethereal solution obtained by allowing magnesium to react with an organic halogen compound, such as ethyl bromide, in the presence of ether, contains three compounds of magnesium: magnesium ethyl bromide, magnesium dibromide, and magnesium diethyl, in chemical equilibrium, thus:

$$2Mg{\Large\langle}\begin{matrix}C_2H_5\\Br\end{matrix} \;\rightleftharpoons\; MgBr_2 \;+\; Mg{\Large\langle}\begin{matrix}C_2H_5\\C_2H_5\end{matrix}$$

It was thought at one time that the ether played some part in the constitution of the Grignard reagents, but it is now accepted that the ether is simply a medium in which the three components of the equilibrium are maintained in homogeneous solution. There is evidence that in the majority of Grignard reactions both the magnesium alkyl halide and the magnesium dialkyl take part to yield identical products. In writing equations, however, it is customary to assume that the Grignard reagent is the magnesium alkyl halide.

Grignard reagents are of great value in the synthesis of various classes of organic compounds. Among the many syntheses in which Grignard reagents are used are the preparations of (i) hydrocarbons, p. 105, R.2 and p. 108, R.2, (ii) primary alcohols from formaldehyde, p. 160, R.5, (iii) secondary alcohols from aldehydes other than formaldehyde, p. 205, R.13 and p. 428, R.9, (iv) tertiary alcohols from ketones, p. 225, R.11, and from esters, p. 259, R.4 and from acid chlorides, p. 250, R.6.

The procedure used in carrying out a Grignard reaction is exemplified by the synthesis of triphenyl carbinol, $(C_6H_5)_3COH$, from ethyl benzoate and phenyl magnesium bromide, which is described on p. 408.

6. The Hofmann reaction. Hofmann's name is given to two reactions.

(i) *The action of a mixture of chloroform * and alcoholic potassium hydroxide solution on a primary amine, or amino compound, to yield an isocyanide (carbylamine)*: this is sometimes known as the carbylamine reaction. The preparations of ethyl isocyanide from ethylamine, and of phenyl isocyanide from aniline, by means of this reaction are mentioned on p. 188 and 391 respectively.

(ii) *The action of bromine and aqueous potassium hydroxide solution on the amide of a fatty acid to yield a primary amine.* The equations for the preparation of ethylamine from propionamide by this reaction are given on p. 185. This reaction is of theoretical importance

---

* Iodoform may be used in place of chloroform.

because it furnishes a method for the descent of a homologous series, p. 255.

7. The Perkin reaction is the action of a mixture of the anhydride of an aliphatic acid and the sodium salt of the acid on an aromatic aldehyde to yield the sodium salt of an unsaturated aromatic acid. The preparation of cinnamic acid from benzaldehyde by the Perkin reaction is described on p. 429. The Perkin reaction is of general application and is frequently used in organic syntheses.

8. The Reimer-Tiemann reaction is the action of chloroform on a phenol in the presence of concentrated potassium hydroxide solution to yield an aromatic hydroxy aldehyde. The preparation of salicyl aldehyde by this reaction is mentioned on p. 154. The potassium derivative of the phenol reacts with the chloroform to give a dichloro-derivative, thus,

which is hydrolysed to the aldehyde,

In accordance with the rule on p. 360, the aldehyde group is introduced into the nucleus in the o- or p-position with regard to the hydroxyl group. The principal product is usually the o-compound.

By an extension of the Reimer-Tiemann reaction, using carbon tetrachloride in place of chloroform, phenolic acids may be prepared. Salicylic acid is prepared in the laboratory by this method as described on p. 434.

THE USE OF ETHYL ACETOACETATE IN ORGANIC SYNTHESIS

Ethyl acetoacetate is used in the synthesis of ketones of the general formula $CH_3CO.CHR^1R^2$, or of acids of the general formula $R^1R^2HC.COOH$, where R^1 and R^2 represent either hydrogen atoms, or identical or different alkyl groups. The use of ethyl acetoacetate as a synthetic agent depends on (i) its property of reacting with sodium or sodium ethoxide to yield a sodium derivative, (ii) the ability of the sodium derivative to react with an alkyl halide to yield an alkyl derivative of the original ester, (iii) the ability of the alkyl derivative to undergo hydrolysis, under controlled conditions, to yield either a ketone or the potassium salt of an acid.

PRINCIPAL REACTIONS IN ORGANIC CHEMISTRY 461

(i) *Formation of the sodium derivative of ethyl acetoacetate.* Ethyl acetoacetate is a well-established example of a tautomeric compound. A *tautomeric compound* consists of two isomeric forms in dynamic equilibrium. The two tautomeric forms of ethyl acetoacetate are the enol form and the keto form,

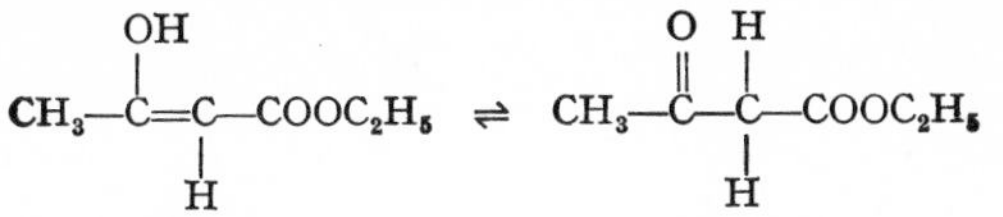

$$CH_3-\underset{H}{\overset{OH}{C}}=C-COOC_2H_5 \rightleftharpoons CH_3-\overset{O}{C}-\underset{H}{\overset{H}{C}}-COOC_2H_5$$

enol form   keto form

At 20° the pure ester consists of 7 per cent. of the enol form and 93 per cent. of the keto form. The proportions vary with the temperature and with the nature of the solvent in which the ester may be dissolved.

The enolic form of the ester reacts with metallic sodium or with sodium ethoxide, to form a sodium derivative,

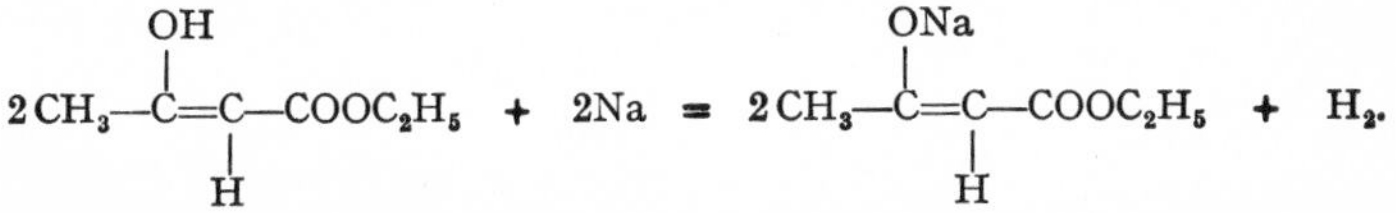

$$2CH_3-\underset{H}{\overset{OH}{C}}=C-COOC_2H_5 + 2Na = 2CH_3-\underset{H}{\overset{ONa}{C}}=C-COOC_2H_5 + H_2.$$

As soon as the enolic modification in the tautomeric mixture is converted to the sodium derivative, some of the ketonic form reverts to the enolic form to preserve the dynamic equilibrium between the two modifications. This process continues until the *whole* of the ester is changed to the sodium derivative.

(ii) *Production of alkyl derivatives of ethyl acetoacetate from the sodium derivative.* The sodium derivative of ethyl acetoacetate reacts with an alkyl halide, R^1I, to produce an alkyl derivative, probably according to the equation,

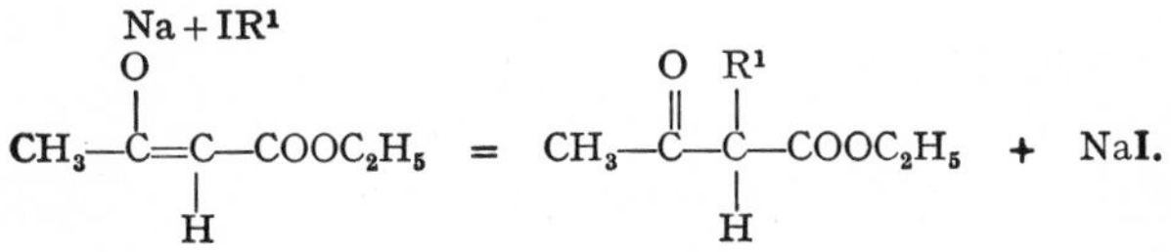

$$CH_3-\overset{Na+IR^1}{\underset{H}{\overset{O}{C}}}=C-COOC_2H_5 = CH_3-\overset{O}{C}-\underset{H}{\overset{R^1}{C}}-COOC_2H_5 + NaI.$$

The alkyl derivative of ethyl acetoacetate also shows tautomerism,

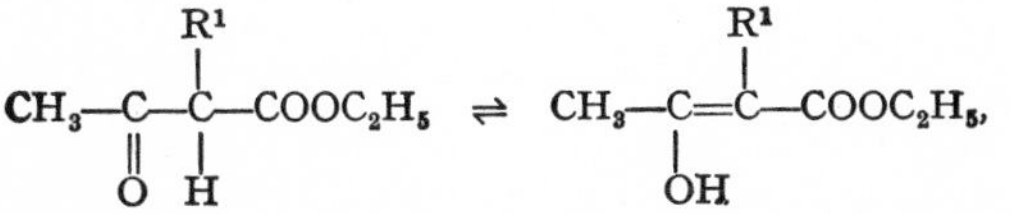

$$CH_3-\underset{\overset{||}{O}\,\,H}{C}-C-COOC_2H_5 \rightleftharpoons CH_3-\underset{OH}{\overset{R^1}{C}}=C-COOC_2H_5,$$

and the enol form yields a sodium derivative which reacts with a second molecule of an alkyl halide, R^2I, to form a dialkyl derivative of the ester having the formula,

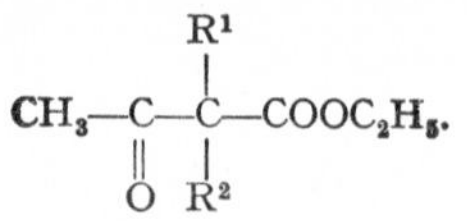

$$CH_3 - C - \underset{\underset{R^2}{|}}{\overset{\overset{R^1}{|}}{C}} - COOC_2H_5.$$
$$\overset{\parallel}{O}$$

This derivative contains no mobile hydrogen atom, and it therefore cannot exist in the enol form, and no further substitution of hydrogen atoms by sodium can take place.

(iii) *Hydrolysis of ethyl acetoacetate and its alkyl derivatives.* Ethyl acetoacetate can be hydrolysed in two ways:

(*a*) with hot dilute alcoholic potassium hydroxide solution to yield acetone, potassium carbonate and ethyl alcohol, thus,

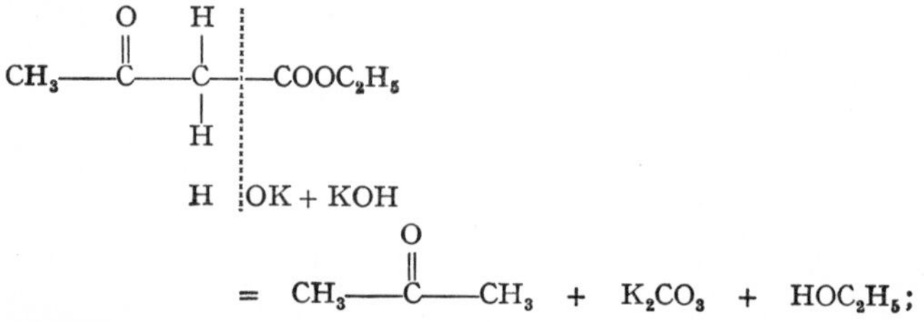

$$CH_3 - \overset{\overset{O}{\parallel}}{C} - \underset{\underset{H}{|}}{\overset{\overset{H}{|}}{C}} - COOC_2H_5$$

$$H \quad OK + KOH$$

$$= CH_3 - \overset{\overset{O}{\parallel}}{C} - CH_3 \; + \; K_2CO_3 \; + \; HOC_2H_5;$$

this mode of hydrolysis, which yields a ketone, is referred to as the *ketonic hydrolysis*;

(*b*) with hot concentrated alcoholic potassium hydroxide solution to yield potassium acetate and ethyl alcohol,

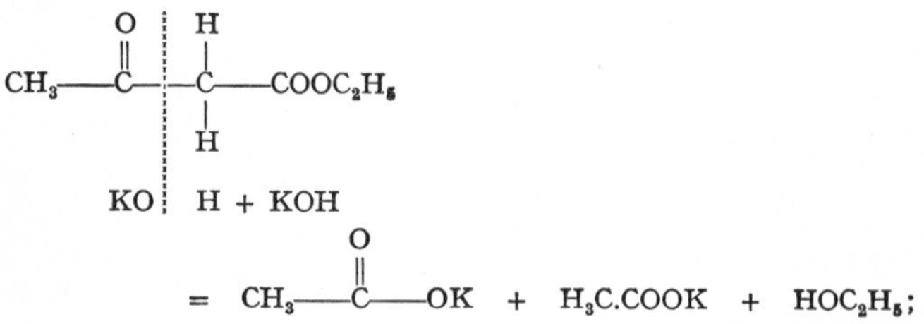

$$CH_3 - \overset{\overset{O}{\parallel}}{C} - \underset{\underset{H}{|}}{\overset{\overset{H}{|}}{C}} - COOC_2H_5$$

$$KO \quad H + KOH$$

$$= CH_3 - \overset{\overset{O}{\parallel}}{C} - OK \; + \; H_3C.COOK \; + \; HOC_2H_5;$$

this mode of hydrolysis, which yields the potassium salt of an acid, is referred to as the *acid hydrolysis*, although it is brought about by the action of a concentrated alkali.

The alkyl derivatives of ethyl acetoacetate undergo ketonic and acid hydrolysis in a precisely parallel manner to yield alkyl derivatives of acetone or acetic acid.

(iv) *Examples of the use of ethyl acetoacetate for the synthesis of organic compounds.*

(a) *The synthesis of methyl ethyl ketone.* This compound could be made by treating ethyl acetoacetate with sodium and methyl iodide to form the monomethyl derivative of the ester,

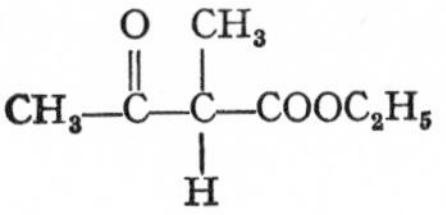

$$CH_3-\overset{\overset{O}{\|}}{C}-\overset{\overset{CH_3}{|}}{\underset{\underset{H}{|}}{C}}-COOC_2H_5$$

which by ketonic hydrolysis with dilute alcoholic potassium hydroxide solution, would yield the required ketone, thus,

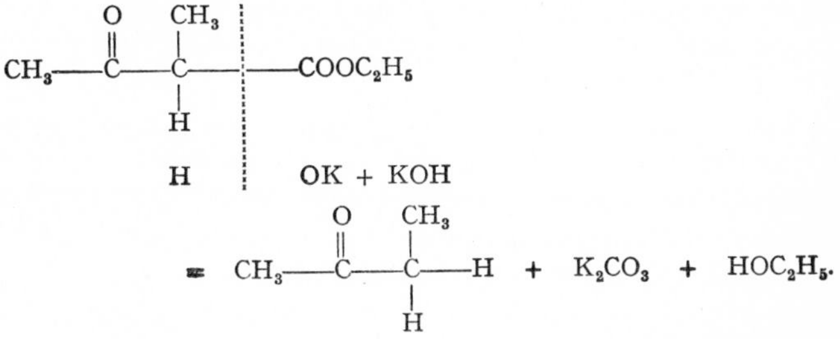

$$CH_3-\overset{\overset{O}{\|}}{C}-\overset{\overset{CH_3}{|}}{\underset{\underset{H}{|}}{C}}-COOC_2H_5$$

$$H \quad OK + KOH$$

$$=\ CH_3-\overset{\overset{O}{\|}}{C}-\overset{\overset{CH_3}{|}}{\underset{\underset{H}{|}}{C}}-H\ +\ K_2CO_3\ +\ HOC_2H_5.$$

(b) *The synthesis of potassium isobutyrate.* This compound could be made by treating ethyl acetoacetate with sodium and methyl iodide in the proportions required to form the dimethyl derivative, and submitting this compound to acid hydrolysis with concentrated alcoholic potassium hydroxide solution,

$$CH_3-\overset{\overset{O}{\|}}{C}-\overset{\overset{H}{|}}{\underset{\underset{H}{|}}{C}}-COOC_2H_5\ +\ 2NaOC_2H_5\ +\ 2CH_3I$$

$$=\ CH_3-\overset{\overset{O}{\|}}{C}-\overset{\overset{CH_3}{|}}{\underset{\underset{CH_3}{|}}{C}}-COOC_2H_5\ +\ 2HOC_2H_5\ +\ 2NaI.$$

$$CH_3-\overset{\overset{O}{\|}}{C}-\overset{\overset{CH_3}{|}}{\underset{\underset{CH_3}{|}}{C}}-COOC_2H_5$$

$$KO\ H + KOH$$

$$=\ CH_3-\overset{\overset{O}{\|}}{C}-OK\ +\ H-\overset{\overset{CH_3}{|}}{\underset{\underset{CH_3}{|}}{C}}-COOK\ +\ HOC_2H_5.$$

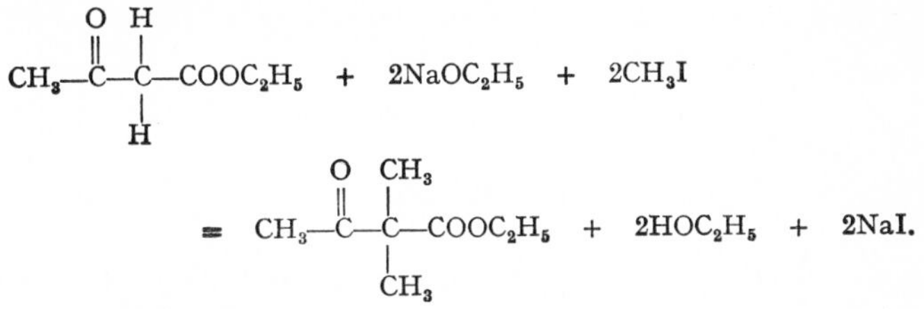

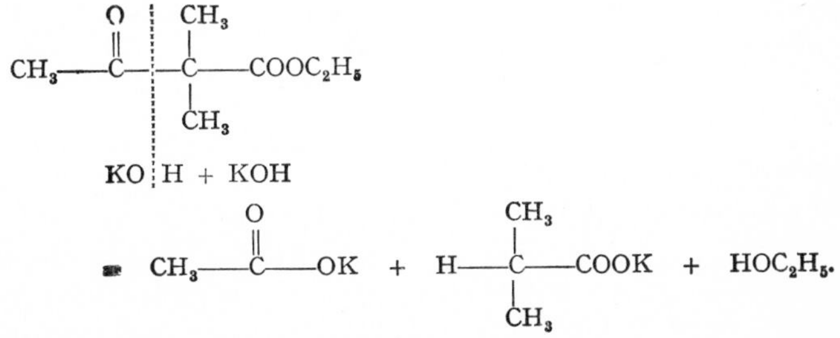

THE USE OF ETHYL MALONATE IN ORGANIC SYNTHESIS

The constitution of ethyl malonate is closely similar to that of ethyl acetoacetate

ethyl malonate   ethyl acetoacetate

Ethyl malonate exists in the tautomeric forms

enol form   keto form

The proportion of the enol form present in the tautomeric mixture of the pure ester at room temperature is, however, very small.

Ethyl malonate reacts with one molecular proportion of sodium ethoxide in alcoholic solution to yield the sodium derivative of the enol form * which, when boiled with an alcoholic solution of an alkyl halide, gives the alkyl derivative of the ester, thus,

By repetition of the treatment with another molecular proportion of sodium ethoxide and an alkyl halide a di-alkyl derivative of the ester, for example ethyl methyl malonic ester,

may be prepared.

* As explained on p. 461, as soon as the small proportion of the enol form in the tautomeric mixture has reacted with sodium the same proportion is regenerated by the conversion of some of the keto form to the enol form. Ultimately, by this process, the whole of the ester is converted to the sodium derivative of the enol form.

Ethyl malonate and its alkyl derivatives may be hydrolysed by boiling with aqueous sodium hydroxide solution to give the sodium salts of the corresponding dicarboxylic acids. If the free acid is prepared from the sodium salt, and heated just above its melting point, it decomposes to a fatty acid with the loss of carbon dioxide, p. 295. For example, methyl propyl acetic acid may be synthesised by :

(i) converting ethyl malonate to the methyl derivative, by reaction with sodium ethoxide and methyl iodide,

$$C_2H_5OOC-CH_2-COOC_2H_5 \rightarrow C_2H_5OOC-\underset{\underset{H}{|}}{\overset{\overset{CH_3}{|}}{C}}-COOC_2H_5$$

(ii) converting the methyl derivative to the methyl propyl derivative by reaction with sodium ethoxide and propyl iodide,

$$C_2H_5OOC-\underset{\underset{H}{|}}{\overset{\overset{CH_3}{|}}{C}}-COOC_2H_5 \rightarrow C_2H_5OOC-\underset{\underset{C_3H_7}{|}}{\overset{\overset{CH_3}{|}}{C}}-COOC_2H_5$$

(iii) hydrolysing the methyl propyl malonic ester to the corresponding derivative of malonic acid, by treating it with sodium hydroxide,

$$C_2H_5OOC-\underset{\underset{C_3H_7}{|}}{\overset{\overset{CH_3}{|}}{C}}-COOC_2H_5 \rightarrow HOOC-\underset{\underset{C_3H_7}{|}}{\overset{\overset{CH_3}{|}}{C}}-COOH$$

(iv) heating the free acid to eliminate carbon dioxide,

$$HOOC-\underset{\underset{C_3H_7}{|}}{\overset{\overset{CH_3}{|}}{C}}-COOH \rightarrow H-\underset{\underset{C_3H_7}{|}}{\overset{\overset{CH_3}{|}}{C}}-COOH$$

Preparation of ethyl malonate. This involves the hydrolysis of sodium cyanoacetate to malonic acid and the esterification of the acid, in a single operation, by the action of a mixture of sulphuric acid and ethyl alcohol. The mixture of potassium chloride and sodium cyanoacetate, obtained as on p. 294, wetted with 20 c.c. of rectified spirit, is placed in a flask fitted with a water reflux condenser. A mixture of 92 gm. of concentrated sulphuric acid and 40 gm. of rectified spirit is added down the condenser in small quantities at a time, and the flask is heated on a boiling water-bath for 1 hour. The contents of the flask are cooled, diluted with 70 c.c. of water, and extracted with ether. The ethereal solution is washed with sodium carbonate solution, and dried over calcium chloride. The ether is removed by distillation, and the ethyl malonate is distilled under reduced pressure. B.P. 198° (with slight decomposition) at 760 mm. ; 93° at 16 mm.

CHART I

SUBSTANCES MANUFACTURED FROM PETROLEUM

Petroleum Deposit

Natural Gas used as a fuel

Oil

Refining and fractionation yields

Petrol ether B.P. 0–40°

Fractionation yields

Butane, iso-butane, pentane and iso-pentane, from which derivatives can be made

Cymogene, B.P. 0°, used in refrigeration, and Rhigoline, B.P. 18°, a local anaesthetic

Gasoline B.P. 40°– 90°

Ligroin, or light petroleum B.P. 90°–120°

Benzoline B.P. 120°– 150°

This fraction constitutes 16·5 per cent. of the crude oil. Used for dry-cleaning and as solvents for fats and oils. The fraction B.P. 70°–140° is suitable for use as motor spirit.

Kerosine B.P. 150°– 300°. This fraction constitutes 54 per cent. of the crude oil. Used in paraffin lamps.

Lubricating oil and Diesel oil. This fraction constitutes 17·5 per cent. of the crude oil. Used in Diesel engines and for steam raising.

Vaseline and paraffin wax

Pitch

Thermal Treatment yields

a mixture of unsaturated hydrocarbons which may be converted to motor-spirit, or from which may be obtained ethylene, propylene, butylene and their derivatives, including glycol, glycol monoethyl ether, and propyl and butyl alcohols, ethers, and acetone.

CHART II

Substances manufactured from Coal

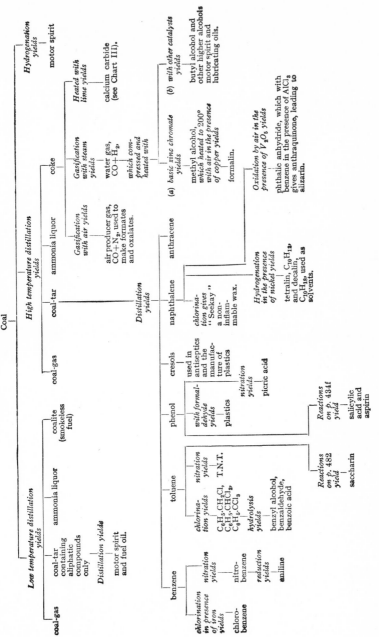

Coal

Low temperature distillation yields

coal-gas

ammonia liquor

coal-tar containing aliphatic compounds only

Distillation yields

motor spirit and fuel oil.

coalite (smokeless fuel)

High temperature distillation yields

coal-gas

coal-tar

Distillation yields

ammonia liquor

Gasification with air yields

air producer gas, CO+N₂, used to make formates and oxalates.

coke

Gasification with steam yields

water gas, CO+H₂,

which compressed and heated with

Heated with lime yields

calcium carbide (see Chart III).

Hydrogenation yields

motor spirit

---

benzene

chlorination in presence of iron yields

chlorobenzene

nitration yields

nitrobenzene

reduction yields

aniline

toluene

chlorination yields

C₆H₅.CH₂Cl, C₆H₅.CHCl₂, C₆H₅.CCl₃

hydrolysis yields

benzyl alcohol, benzaldehyde, benzoic acid

nitration yields

T.N.T.

Reactions on p. 482 yield

saccharin

phenol

with formaldehyde yields

plastics

nitration yields

picric acid

Reactions on p. 434f yield

salicylic acid and aspirin

cresols

used in antiseptics and the manufacture of plastics

naphthalene

chlorination gives "Seekay" a non-inflammable wax.

Hydrogenation in the presence of nickel yields

tetralin, C₁₀H₁₂, and decalin, C₁₀H₁₈, used as solvents.

anthracene

Oxidation by air in the presence of V₂O₅ yields

phthalic anhydride, which with benzene in the presence of AlCl₃ gives anthraquinone, leading to alizarin.

(a) basic zinc chromate yields

methyl alcohol, which heated to 200° with air in the presence of copper yields formalin.

(b) with other catalysts yields

butyl alcohol and other higher alcohols motor spirit and lubricating oils.

CHART III
SUBSTANCES MANUFACTURED FROM CALCIUM CARBIDE

Calcium carbide

Treatment with water yields

acetylene

Chlorination yields

Westron, $C_2H_2Cl_4$, a solvent for rubber and iodine.

Treatment with dilute sulphuric acid and mercuric oxide yields

acetaldehyde

Treatment with acetic acid and mercuric oxide yields

acetic anhydride used in the manufacture of cellulose acetate and aspirin.

Treatment with air in the presence of manganese acetate yields

acetic acid

Chlorination yields

chloroacetic acids.

Passage of vapour over thorium oxide yields

acetone

Reduction yields

iso-propyl alcohol.

Treatment with concentrated hydrochloric acid yields

paraldehyde.

Reduction with hydrogen in the presence of nickel yields

ethyl alcohol

Treatment with aluminium ethylate and aluminium chloride yields

ethyl acetate.

Dehydration yields

ethylene.

Distillation with concentrated sulphuric yields

diethyl ether.

Treatment with alkali and distillation yields

crotonaldehyde

Reduction with hydrogen in the presence of nickel yields

n-butyl alcohol.

CHAPTER XXX

CHEMICAL PRINCIPLES UNDERLYING THE PRODUCTION OF ORGANIC COMPOUNDS FROM NATURAL SOURCES

THERE are four main sources from which organic compounds may be produced on a large scale : (i) carbohydrates, (ii) oils and fats, (iii) coal, (iv) petroleum.

Carbohydrates are formed in plants from the carbon dioxide of the air, which is absorbed by the leaves, and water, which is absorbed by the roots. These simple compounds are elaborated into sugars by a photochemical process in the leaves which utilises the energy of sunlight. The sugars are further elaborated by the plant into starch, which serves as a storage material, and cellulose which is the chief structural material of the plant. Animals use plants as food, and in the animal's body the starch and cellulose are converted partly into oils and fats which serve as storage materials for the animal. Coal is a mineral formed by the modification of carbohydrates deposited in past geological ages ; petroleum is conjectured to be a geological deposit formed by the modification of accumulations of fats and oils.

It is evident that the primary source of all organic compounds is the carbon dioxide in the air, and that it is converted into more complex substances by the utilisation of energy radiated by the sun. The sources of organic materials which are being continually replenished are the carbohydrates and fats and oils. The geological deposits of coal and petroleum have been produced from the same substances accumulated in past ages. When man has consumed these deposits (at the present rate of consumption they will last only for a few hundred years) the only organic substances available for use as food, fuel and as the starting-points in chemical industry will be those elaborated from day to day by living organisms.

It must be remembered that in different countries the choice of processes for the manufacture of a given organic compound is governed as much by economic as by chemical considerations. For example, in Great Britain ethylene is manufactured by the dehydration of ethyl alcohol produced from cane sugar molasses, but in the U.S.A., where ethylene is plentiful as a by-product of petroleum refining, ethyl alcohol is manufactured from ethylene.

Again, in Great Britain acetaldehyde is made by the oxidation of ethyl alcohol, but in Switzerland ethyl alcohol is made by the reduction of acetaldehyde obtained by the hydration of acetylene. The acetylene is made from calcium carbide which can be obtained cheaply with the aid of electricity generated by water power.

In the present chapter outlines are given of the chemistry of the processes by which particular organic compounds are obtained from four sources, petroleum, coal, carbohydrates and fats. It will be observed that a given compound may sometimes be made from more than one source, or by several routes from the same source. The methods of production actually in use vary from one country to another and from year to year, in accordance with the availability of the materials which are used in the processes.

I. *PETROLEUM AND ITS DERIVATIVES*

Mixtures of hydrocarbons occur as natural deposits in many parts of the world. The most important deposits are in the U.S.A. (Pennsylvania), the Caspian Sea district (Baku), Iran, Iraq, S. Persia, Galicia, Roumania, Burmah, Assam, Borneo, Mexico, Trinidad and Japan ; it is noteworthy that there are neither oil-wells nor refineries in Africa or in Australasia. The deposits in Pennsylvania and Persia consist largely of paraffins ; those in the neighbourhood of Baku and in Borneo contain aromatic hydrocarbons, naphthenes and cycloparaffins. There are a few small deposits of hydrocarbons in the United Kingdom ; the shale deposits of the Scottish midlands contain hydrocarbon oils which are isolated by distillation of the powdered shale.

The origin of hydrocarbon deposits remains conjectural. It has been suggested that they may have been formed by the action of steam on metallic carbides in the earth's crust, by the action of heat on fatty substances in the accumulated remains of marine organisms, or on the oils and resins secreted by forests of conifers.

Natural petroleum consists of a dark-coloured, fluorescent oil. It floats on water in which it is insoluble. The deposits of oil are often associated with accumulations of natural gas consisting chiefly of methane mixed with varying proportions of ethane and hydrogen, and also with less volatile hydrocarbons such as butane, iso-butane and pentane. Natural gas is sometimes found in large quantities unassociated with liquid oil. The natural gas at Dexter, U.S.A., is unique and important as it contains 1·84 per cent. of helium, and is the only commercial source of this very light inert gas.

Both natural gas and liquid petroleum have two principal uses, (i) as fuels, and (ii) as sources of chemical substances. Natural gas is principally used as a fuel. Its calorific value is about 1000 B.T.U. per cubic foot, which is twice that of coal-gas. Propane, butane, iso-butane and pentane are extracted from natural gas and used either as the starting-points for the manufacture of other chemical compounds, or for the manufacture of motor spirit by the process of thermal decomposition and polymerisation, (see below).

Liquid petroleum is refined to give a series of products, some of which are used as fuel, and others as starting-points in chemical industry. The trend of modern refinery technique is towards increasing precision in separating petroleum into various constituents so that the most valuable chemical substances may be extracted, and a series of fuels may be produced having predictable graded properties. In the refinery liquid petroleum is distilled, and the distillate is treated with sulphuric acid and sodium hydroxide, or with some absorbent material such as bauxite, to eliminate all compounds more reactive than hydrocarbons. The refined oil is then fractionated to yield the products mentioned in Chart I.

From 1860 until 1914 the most valuable fraction of petroleum was kerosine. Processes were therefore invented by which kerosine could be produced from fractions of higher boiling-point. Since the introduction of the internal combustion engine as the power unit of motor cars, which first became available to the general public about 1914, the distillation products of petroleum with boiling-points between 70° and 140° have been in the greatest demand. Great attention has therefore been paid to the development of methods by which the less valuable fractions of petroleum (including kerosine) may be converted to fractions suitable for use as motor spirit. All the methods which have been devised depend on the chemical reactions which occur when hydrocarbons are subjected to high temperatures in the absence of air. These reactions are divisible into two types :

(i) *thermal decomposition*, in which the original hydrocarbon molecules break down, yielding a mixture of hydrogen, methane, ethane and unsaturated hydrocarbons of low molecular weight ; for example, butane may decompose in three ways, thus :

butane   butylene

$$H-\underset{\underset{H}{|}}{\overset{\overset{H}{|}}{C}}-\underset{\underset{H}{|}}{\overset{\overset{H}{|}}{C}}-\underset{\underset{H}{|}}{\overset{\overset{H}{|}}{C}}-\underset{\underset{H}{|}}{\overset{\overset{H}{|}}{C}}-H \quad = \quad H-\underset{\underset{H}{|}}{\overset{\overset{H}{|}}{C}}-\underset{\underset{H}{|}}{\overset{\overset{H}{|}}{C}}=C\overset{H}{\underset{H}{\big\langle}} \quad + \quad CH_4$$

propylene

$$H-\underset{\underset{H}{|}}{\overset{\overset{H}{|}}{C}}-\underset{\underset{H}{|}}{\overset{\overset{H}{|}}{C}}-\underset{\underset{H}{|}}{\overset{\overset{H}{|}}{C}}-\underset{\underset{H}{|}}{\overset{\overset{H}{|}}{C}}-H \quad = \quad \overset{H}{\underset{H}{\big\rangle}}C=C\overset{H}{\underset{H}{\big\langle}} \quad + \quad C_2H_6$$

ethylene

(ii) *polymerisation*, in which the molecules of the unsaturated hydrocarbons produced by thermal decomposition, react together to give hydrocarbons of higher molecular weight ; propylene, for example, among other polymerisation products, gives hexylene :

$$H-\underset{\underset{H}{|}}{\overset{\overset{H}{|}}{C}}-\underset{H}{\overset{\overset{H}{|}}{C}}=C\overset{H}{\underset{H}{\big\langle}} \quad + \quad \boxed{H}-\underset{\underset{H}{|}}{\overset{\overset{H}{|}}{C}}-\underset{H}{\overset{\overset{H}{|}}{C}}=C\overset{H}{\underset{H}{\big\langle}}$$

$$= \quad H-\underset{\underset{H}{|}}{\overset{\overset{H}{|}}{C}}-\underset{\underset{H}{|}}{\overset{\overset{H}{|}}{C}}-\underset{\underset{H}{|}}{\overset{\overset{H}{|}}{C}}-\underset{\underset{H}{|}}{\overset{\overset{H}{|}}{C}}-\underset{H}{\overset{\overset{H}{|}}{C}}=C\overset{H}{\underset{H}{\big\langle}}$$

The earliest process employed to increase the production of motor spirit from crude petroleum was that of cracking, which was in general use at refineries until 1930. In this process the less volatile fractions of crude petroleum were heated in the absence of air to about 500°. Thermal decomposition and polymerisation took place side by side, and the product was a mixture of hydrogen, methane, hydrocarbons suitable for use as motor spirit, and oils of low volatility and high molecular weight. Pitch and coke were also produced. The gaseous portion of the mixture was burnt as fuel, and the liquid portion was fractionated. The fractions suitable for use as motor spirit were collected and refined ; the less volatile fractions were re-cracked.

Since 1930 new methods have been evolved in which the processes of thermal decomposition and polymerisation are more closely controlled in order to secure the maximum production of hydrocarbons containing eight carbon atoms in the molecule, as these possess high anti-knock values (see below). The details of these modern methods vary from refinery to refinery. In general, the crude petroleum vapour is first heated to 400–700° under a pressure of about 75 atmospheres. The conditions are chosen to ensure that products of cracking contain a high proportion of hydrocarbons containing four atoms of carbon in the molecule. The products of the process which are liquid at room temperature are condensed ; the volatile products are heated to about 250° under a pressure of 13 atmospheres in the presence of a catalyst such as phosphoric acid. Further thermal decomposition occurs followed by polymerisation. Iso-butane, for example, yields isobutylene,

$$\underset{H_3C}{\overset{H_3C}{>}}C\underset{H}{\overset{CH_3}{<}} = \underset{H_3C}{\overset{H_3C}{>}}C=C\underset{H}{\overset{H}{<}} + H_2$$

Two molecules of iso-butylene condense thus,

$$\underset{H_3C}{\overset{H_3C}{>}}C=C\underset{H}{\overset{H}{<}} + \underset{H\ \ CH_3}{\overset{H}{\underset{|}{H-C-C=CH_2}}} = \underset{CH_3\ H\ CH_3}{\overset{CH_3\ H}{\underset{|\ \ |\ \ |}{H_3C-C-C-C=CH_2.}}}$$

and the product combines with hydrogen to yield the paraffin iso-octane,

$$\underset{CH_3\ H\ CH_3}{\overset{CH_3\ H}{\underset{|\ \ |\ \ |}{H_3C-C-C-C=CH_2}}} + H_2 = \underset{CH_3\ H\ CH_3}{\overset{CH_3\ H\ H}{\underset{|\ \ |\ \ |}{H_3C-C-C-C-CH_3.}}}$$

MOTOR SPIRIT

When motor spirit * is used as a fuel in an internal combustion engine it is volatilised, and a mixture of the vapour and air is compressed in the cylinder of the engine and exploded by means of an electric spark. For efficient running the explosion must take place smoothly (it must give the piston a steady push and not a knock) and it must be delayed until the spark is passed. Explosions which occur prematurely while the mixture is being compressed cause " pinking " or " knocking ". Knocking is deleterious to the efficiency and life of the engine, and especially in aeroplane engines it is essential to use fuels of high anti-knock value.

The anti-knock value of a fuel is indicated by its *octane number*. The octane number is expressed on an arbitrary scale on which normal heptane (C_7H_{16}) (which knocks badly) is given an anti-knock value of zero, and iso-octane (p. 474) is given a value of 100. The anti-knock value of any given motor fuel is determined by comparing, in a specially constructed engine, the intensity of knocking produced by the fuel with that of a series of mixtures of heptane and octane of known composition. If, say, an equal intensity of knocking is produced by the given fuel and by a mixture of 20 volumes of heptane

* The term *motor spirit* used in this paragraph means any mixture of hydro-carbons which can be used in an internal combustion engine in which the ignition of the explosion mixture is brought about by an electric spark.

with 80 volumes of iso-octane, the octane number of the fuel is 80. The higher the octane number of a fuel the less is its tendency to knock.

The universal demand for a cheap, fairly efficient motor spirit could not be met by the comparatively costly process of manufacturing pure hydrocarbons of high anti-knock value. Motor spirit in general use is a mixture of the products obtained by (i) the distillation of crude petroleum, (ii) the process of thermal decomposition and polymerisation described on p. 472. The anti-knock value of this spirit is increased by the addition of small quantities of aromatic hydrocarbons, or iso-octane or similar hydrocarbons of high anti-knock value, or lead tetraethyl, $Pb(C_2H_5)_4$.

ORGANIC COMPOUNDS ISOLATED OR MANUFACTURED FROM PETROLEUM

Certain hydrocarbons formed at various stages of the cracking and polymerisation processes are isolated and used for the preparation of pure chemical compounds. Some of the more important compounds obtained directly or indirectly from natural gas or crude petroleum are mentioned below.

1. Propane, butane and iso-butane, pentane and iso-pentane. These hydrocarbons are isolated from natural gas by fractionation under pressure. Iso-butane is one of the sources from which iso-octane is prepared. The pentanes are converted into chlorine derivatives, amyl alcohol, and other amyl compounds. A mixture of 95 per cent. of butane and iso-butane with 5 per cent. of propane is compressed and liquefied, and sold in steel cylinders for use as a fuel under the name of " calor gas ".

2. Iso-octane. Iso-octane is made by allowing iso-butylene to combine with iso-butane at 30° in the presence of sulphuric acid,

$$
\begin{array}{ccc}
\text{CH}_2 \leftarrow\cdots\cdots & \text{H H} & \text{CH}_3 \text{ H H} \\
\| & | \ | & | \ | \ | \\
\text{H}_3\text{C}-\text{C} \quad + \quad & \text{H}-\text{C}-\text{C}-\text{CH}_3 \quad = \quad & \text{H}_3\text{C}-\text{C}-----\text{C}-\text{C}-\text{CH}_3 \\
| & | \ | & | \quad\ \ | \ | \\
\text{CH}_3 & \text{H CH}_3 & \text{CH}_3 \text{ H CH}_3
\end{array}
$$

The yield obtained by this method is 90 per cent. It may also be made by the polymerisation of iso-butylene under pressure at moderate temperatures in the presence of phosphoric acid, followed by hydrogenation, p. 473. Iso-octane is one of the most important materials used for blending with motor spirit to increase the octane number, p. 473.

3. Ethylene, propylene, iso-butylene, butylene : ethyl alcohol, iso-propyl alcohol, secondary butyl alcohol, tertiary butyl alcohol : acetone, iso-propyl ether. The olefines produced by the cracking of crude petroleum are extracted from the gaseous mixture by absorption in sulphuric acid to form the corresponding alkyl hydrogen sulphates, Reaction 5, p. 120. By the use of sulphuric acid of different strengths at different temperatures, it is possible to arrange for the successive absorption of iso-butylene, normal butylene, propylene and ethylene.

The free unsaturated hydrocarbons may be re-generated by heating the solutions of the alkyl hydrogen sulphates in sulphuric acid. By modifying the conditions of temperature, pressure and the degree of dilution of the sulphuric acid, the alkyl hydrogen sulphate solution may be made to yield, instead of an unsaturated hydrocarbon, either an alcohol or an ether. For example, ethyl alcohol is made in the U.S.A. by heating the solution obtained by the absorption of ethylene in sulphuric acid. Tertiary butyl alcohol * is made by diluting and heating the solution of butyl hydrogen sulphate obtained by the absorption of iso-butylene in sulphuric acid,

$$(CH_3)_3C.O.SO_2.OH + H_2O = (CH_3)_3C.OH + H_2SO_4,$$

and iso-propyl ether is made by heating a solution of iso-propyl hydrogen sulphate obtained by the absorption of propylene in sulphuric acid,

$$
\begin{array}{ccccc}
CH_3 & & & & CH_3 \\
| & & & & | \\
H-C-O.SO_2.OH & + & HOH & + & HO.SO_2.O-C-H \\
| & & & & | \\
CH_3 & & & & CH_3
\end{array}
$$

$$
\begin{array}{cc}
& CH_3 \quad CH_3 \\
& | \quad\quad | \\
= & H-C-O-C-H \quad + \quad 2H_2SO_4 \\
& | \quad\quad | \\
& CH_3 \quad CH_3
\end{array}
$$

Acetone is made from iso-propyl alcohol by the method mentioned on p. 221.

Ethylene isolated from cracked petroleum is used as the source of ethylene dichloride, $CH_2Cl.CH_2Cl$ (used as a solvent and for ripening grain), ethylene glycol, $CH_2OH.CH_2OH$, ethylene chlorohydrin, $CH_2Cl.CH_2OH$ (used in the preparation of novacaine, procaine and indigo), ethylene oxide $\begin{array}{c}CH_2\\ | \\ CH_2\end{array}\!\!\big\rangle O$, from which is obtained glycol monoethyl ether $\begin{array}{c}CH_2OC_2H_5\\ | \\ CH_2OH\end{array}$, used as a solvent for cellulose acetate.

4. Acetylene. The refinery gas may be partly converted to

* It follows from Markownikoff's rule, p. 124, that *n*-butyl alcohol cannot be made by heating the solution obtained by the absorption of butylene or iso-butylene in sulphuric acid.

acetylene by exposure to an electric arc struck between iron electrodes. In Germany during the war refinery gases were thus made to yield lamp-black and a mixture of gases containing 50 per cent. hydrogen, 25 per cent. methane and 16 per cent. acetylene. The acetylene was extracted by solution in water at 18 atmospheres pressure, and after purification was used for the manufacture of several important compounds, p. 490.

5. Nitromethane, nitroethane, 1-nitropropane, 2-nitropropane. These compounds are made by the vapour phase nitration of the hydrocarbons, p. 112. They are powerful solvents for many organic compounds, and they are useful because of their low toxicity and low inflammability.

II. *COAL AND ITS DERIVATIVES*

Coal, a product of the action of heat and pressure on vegetable matter accumulated in previous geological ages, occurs in large deposits in many parts of the world. It is a complex mixture of organic compounds which contain a very high proportion of carbon, and smaller proportions of hydrogen and oxygen and sometimes nitrogen and sulphur. The composition and properties of coal vary from deposit to deposit.

Coal is utilised in the following four different ways.

(i) It is burnt under boilers for steam raising, and in open fires and furnaces for heating.

(ii) It is distilled at high temperatures (1100–1300°) for the production of coal-gas and coke. Besides coal-gas and coke, ammonia and coal-tar are obtained as by-products. High-temperature coal-tar is the source of many aromatic compounds, including benzene, toluene, phenol, and naphthalene.

(iii) It is distilled at low temperatures (about 600°) for the production of smokeless fuel such as " coalite ". The by-products are coal-gas, ammonia, and a tar consisting of aliphatic compounds.

(iv) It is treated with hydrogen under pressure to obtain motor spirit.

I. HIGH TEMPERATURE DISTILLATION OF COAL

The coal is distilled in fireclay retorts. The volatile products are led through condensers where the coal-tar and ammonia liquor separate, through scrubbers where the remainder of the ammonia is extracted, and through purifiers where the sulphuretted hydrogen and certain nitrogenous compounds are removed. The gaseous product thus purified is coal-gas. The non-volatile residue of the coal which remains in the retorts is coke.

Coal-gas.* An average value for the composition of coal-gas is

Hydrogen	50	per cent. by volume
Methane	30	,,
Ethylene and its homologues	3	,,
Carbon monoxide	9	,,
Carbon dioxide	1	,,
Nitrogen	6	,,
Oxygen	1	,,

Coal-gas also contains benzene and toluene vapour which contribute greatly to its illuminating power. These hydrocarbons may be extracted from coal-gas by scrubbing it with creosote oil (see below); at most gas-works, however, they are allowed to remain in the gas. Coal-gas is usually burnt as a fuel, and is not used as a source of chemical substances.

Distillation of coal-tar. Coal-tar is the principal source of benzene, toluene, phenol, cresol, naphthalene and anthracene. 1 ton of coal yields 10–12 gallons of tar, from which may be extracted about $3\frac{1}{2}$ lb. of benzene and toluene, $1\frac{1}{4}$ lb. of phenol, 6 lb. of cresol, 5–20 lb. of naphthalene, and $\frac{3}{4}$ lb. of anthracene.

The tar is separated from water, which would cause bumping during the early stages of distillation, and distilled. The simplest type of still is an iron cylinder of 15–20 tons capacity. It is charged with the crude tar, and the temperature is gradually raised. The following fractions are collected.

Name of fraction	Temperature of distillation	Wt. per cent. of original tar	Principal constituents
1. Light oil	up to 170°	2–8	Benzene, toluene, xylene
2. Middle oil or carbolic oil	170–230°	8–10	Naphthalene, phenol
3. Heavy oil or creosote oil	230–270°	8–10	Naphthalene, naphthol
4. Green oil or anthracene oil	270–400°	16–20	Anthracene
5. Pitch	non-volatile and remains in the still	50	

* The gas supplied through mains by gas companies is a mixture of coal-gas and water-gas, p. 488

When the temperature of the still reaches 270°, steam is blown in to assist the distillation.

ISOLATION OR MANUFACTURE OF COMPOUNDS FROM COAL-TAR

Isolation of benzene, toluene and xylene from light oil. The light oil is redistilled, and the residue remaining when the temperature reaches 170° is added to the middle oil. The distillate is agitated with 5 per cent. of concentrated sulphuric acid which dissolves ammonia, pyridine, ethylene derivatives, some sulphur compounds and phenol. The mixture is allowed to stand, when it separates into two layers, the aqueous layer * and the purified oil. The oil is separated from the aqueous layer and washed with water and dilute sodium hydroxide solution to remove excess acid and phenol. It is then dried and fractionated. Three fractions are collected :

Name of fraction	Temperature of distillation	Principal constituents
1. 90 per cent. benzol	up to 110°	Benzene and toluene
2. 50 per cent. benzol	110–140°	Benzene, toluene, and xylene
3.	140–170°	Xylene, solvent naphtha, pseudocumene, mesitylene.

The residue is added to the middle oil.

The 90 per cent. and the 50 per cent. benzol are then fractionated again to yield benzene, B.P. 80°, toluene, B.P. 110°, and xylene, B.P. 140°. The benzene may be further purified by crystallisation. It is cooled in a freezing mixture, the crystals (M.P. 5·5°) are quickly filtered from the mother liquor, melted, and the process is repeated. Toluene crystallises at a much lower temperature, − 94°, and cannot conveniently be purified by a parallel process.†

* The aqueous layer contains quinoline and pyridine, which may be liberated by neutralising the acid solution with ammonia.

† Benzene and toluene thus purified still contain the compounds :

```
    H—C—C—H              H—C—C—H
      ‖  ‖                  ‖  ‖
    H—C  C—H             H—C  C—CH₃
        \ /                  \ /
         S                    S
     thiophene    and      thiotolene
```

The presence of thiophene or thiotolene in benzene or toluene is detected by the indophenin reaction. The hydrocarbon is shaken with a solution of a crystal

Isolation of phenol and naphthalene from middle oil. The middle oil is treated with 10 per cent. sodium hydroxide solution, in which the phenol dissolves as sodium phenate :

$$C_6H_5OH \ + \ NaOH \ = \ C_6H_5ONa \ + \ H_2O.$$

The aqueous layer is separated from the residue of middle oil and concentrated by evaporation of some of the water. Carbon dioxide is passed into the solution and phenol is liberated,

$$2C_6H_5ONa \ + \ CO_2 \ = \ 2C_6H_5OH \ + \ Na_2CO_3.$$

It is separated from the sodium carbonate solution and distilled, using zinc or silver condensing coils. The phenol crystallises out as the distillate cools, and the crystals are centrifuged to separate them from the still fluid cresols.

The residue of the middle oil which is separated from the sodium phenate solution is allowed to stand. The naphthalene crystallises out, and is isolated from the mother liquor by centrifuging and pressing. The crystals are melted and agitated successively with concentrated sulphuric acid and sodium hydroxide solution. The naphthalene is purified by distillation or sublimation.

Isolation of anthracene from green oil. Impure crystals of anthracene separate as the oil cools. The crystals are centrifuged and pressed at 200–300 atmospheres while heated to 100°, and washed with solvent naphtha. The product is 90 per cent. pure, and is used for making alizarin dyes. It may be further purified by distillation, washing with carbon disulphide, and sublimation.

ORGANIC COMPOUNDS MANUFACTURED FROM BENZENE

Chlorobenzene is manufactured by the method outlined on p. 406, and by the first stage of Raschig's process, p. 481.

Nitrobenzene is manufactured by the method outlined on p. 380.

Aniline is manufactured by warming a mixture of nitrobenzene, iron borings, and a relatively small quantity of concentrated hydrochloric acid. The amount of hydrochloric acid necessary for the reaction is only about one-fortieth of that indicated by the equation :

$$C_6H_5NO_2 \ + \ 2Fe \ + \ 6HCl \ = \ C_6H_5NH_2 \ + \ 2FeCl_3 \ + \ 2H_2O.$$

of isatin in cold concentrated sulphuric acid. If thiophene or thiotolene is present the acid layer is coloured dark blue. These compounds are more readily sulphonated than the hydrocarbons. If benzene or toluene is repeatedly shaken with small quantities of cold concentrated sulphuric acid, thiophene and thiotolene sulphonates are formed and dissolve in the acid. The elimination of the sulphur compounds is completed as soon as the sulphuric acid ceases to darken when shaken with the hydrocarbon.

The reduction of nitrobenzene must, therefore, be brought about by the action of metallic iron, probably according to a scheme of reactions represented by the equations :

$$C_6H_5NO_2 + 3Fe + 6HCl = C_6H_5NH_2 + 3FeCl_2 + 2H_2O$$
$$C_6H_5NO_2 + 6FeCl_2 + 4H_2O = C_6H_5NH_2 + 6Fe(OH)Cl_2$$
$$8Fe(OH)Cl_2 + 3Fe = Fe_3O_4 + 8FeCl_2 + 4H_2O.$$

It should be noted that, in contrast to the laboratory preparation of aniline, p. 388, by the reduction of nitrobenzene with tin and hydrochloric acid which yields aniline stannic chloride, the industrial reduction of nitrobenzene with iron leads directly to the formation of free aniline. When the reduction is complete a little lime is added to ensure that the mixture of aniline and iron compounds is alkaline. The mixture is then steam-distilled, and the aniline is collected, with water, in the distillate. The aniline is separated from the water and dried.

Benzaldehyde is manufactured from benzene by Gattermann's reaction. Hydrogen chloride and carbon monoxide are passed into benzene containing anhydrous cuprous chloride and anhydrous aluminium chloride. The action probably takes place in two stages represented by the equations

$$CO + HCl = H-C{\overset{O}{\underset{Cl}{}}}$$

$$H-C{\overset{O}{\underset{Cl}{}}} + C_6H_6 = C_6H_5CHO + HCl$$

Benzaldehyde is also produced commercially by the oxidation of toluene, and by the hydrolysis of benzal chloride. These methods are described under " Toluene " on p. 481.

Phenol. The quantity of phenol obtained from the middle oil distilled from coal-tar is insufficient to meet the industrial demand for phenol for the manufacture of dyes, drugs and plastics. Phenol is therefore manufactured from benzene by several methods. Two of the most important are mentioned below.

(i) Benzene is treated with fuming sulphuric acid, by which it is converted to benzene sulphonic acid :

$$\bigcirc + \underset{HO}{\overset{HO}{\underset{}{S}}}{\overset{O}{\underset{O}{}}} = \bigcirc-S{\overset{O}{\underset{OH}{\overset{O}{}}}} + H_2O$$

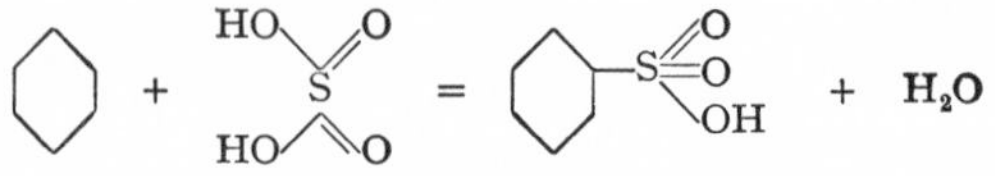

The sodium salt of benzene sulphonic acid is fused with dry sodium hydroxide for 2 or 3 hours in nickel or iron pots at a temperature of 300–350°. Sodium phenate is formed according to the equation :

$$\text{C}_6\text{H}_5\text{—S} \overset{\overset{\displaystyle O}{\parallel}}{\underset{\displaystyle OH}{\parallel}} \text{O} \quad + \quad 3\text{NaOH} \quad = \quad \text{C}_6\text{H}_5\text{—ONa} \quad + \quad \text{Na}_2\text{SO}_3 \quad + \quad 2\text{H}_2\text{O}$$

The melt is cooled and extracted with water in which the sodium phenate is much more soluble than the sodium sulphite. The solution of sodium phenate is acidified with sulphuric acid, and the oily phenol is separated and distilled.

(ii) Raschig's process. A mixture of benzene vapour, hydrogen chloride and oxygen is treated with a catalyst at 230°,

$$\text{C}_6\text{H}_6 \quad + \quad \text{HCl} \quad + \quad \tfrac{1}{2}\text{O}_2 \quad = \quad \text{C}_6\text{H}_5\text{Cl} \quad + \quad \text{H}_2\text{O}.$$

The mixture of chlorobenzene and steam thus obtained is passed over another catalyst at 425°, when phenol is formed and hydrogen chloride is regenerated,

$$\text{C}_6\text{H}_5\text{Cl} \quad + \quad \text{H}_2\text{O} \quad = \quad \text{C}_6\text{H}_5\text{OH} \quad + \quad \text{HCl}.$$

Both reactions are carried out at atmospheric pressure. The hydrogen chloride produced in the second reaction is recovered, and hence, in effect, the phenol is obtained by the oxidation of benzene.

ORGANIC COMPOUNDS MANUFACTURED FROM TOLUENE

Benzyl chloride, $\text{C}_6\text{H}_5\text{.CH}_2\text{Cl}$, benzal chloride, $\text{C}_6\text{H}_5\text{.CHCl}_2$, and benzotrichloride, $\text{C}_6\text{H}_5\text{.CCl}_3$. These compounds, derived from toluene by the replacement of hydrogen atoms in the side-chain by chlorine atoms, are made by passing chlorine into boiling toluene. Chlorine carriers, which promote substitution in the benzene nucleus, must be absent. The reactions may be represented by equations of the type,

$$\text{C}_6\text{H}_5\text{—CH}_3 \quad + \quad \text{Cl}_2 \quad = \quad \text{C}_6\text{H}_5\text{—CH}_2\text{Cl} \quad + \quad \text{HCl}$$

The chloro-derivatives of toluene are separated from one another, and from unchanged toluene, by fractionation.

Benzyl alcohol, $\text{C}_6\text{H}_5\text{.CH}_2\text{OH}$, is made by boiling benzyl chloride with milk of lime, or with a solution of sodium carbonate :

$$2\text{C}_6\text{H}_5\text{.CH}_2\text{Cl} \quad + \quad \text{Ca(OH)}_2 \quad = \quad 2\text{C}_6\text{H}_5\text{.CH}_2\text{OH} \quad + \quad \text{CaCl}_2.$$

It is also manufactured from benzaldehyde (see below) by Cannizzaro's reaction, p. 423.

Benzaldehyde, $\text{C}_6\text{H}_5\text{.CHO}$, is manufactured from toluene, (*a*) by direct oxidation, and (*b*) indirectly by the hydrolysis of benzal chloride.

Q   **D.C.**

Toluene is oxidised to benzaldehyde on an industrial scale by the action of a mixture of precipitated manganese dioxide and 65 per cent. sulphuric acid at 40°.

Benzal chloride is hydrolysed to benzaldehyde by the action of water in the presence of a small quantity of iron powder. The benzal chloride, warmed to 30°, is mixed with 0·3 per cent. of iron powder. After half an hour 15 per cent. of water is added, and the temperature is raised. Hydrolysis of the benzal chloride then takes place in accordance with the equation :

$$C_6H_5.CHCl_2 \ + \ H_2O \ = \ C_6H_5.CHO \ + \ 2HCl.$$

The hydrochloric acid, together with any benzoic acid which may have been formed from benzotrichloride present as an impurity in the original benzal chloride, is neutralised with milk of lime, and the mixture is steam distilled. The benzaldehyde in the distillate is shaken with 35 per cent. sodium bisulphite solution. The precipitated benzaldehyde-sodium bisulphite compound is decomposed by warming with sodium carbonate, and the benzaldehyde is purified by distillation.

Benzaldehyde is also made from benzene by Gattermann's reaction, p. 480.

Benzoic acid, $C_6H_5.COOH$, is made by the hydrolysis of benzotrichloride mentioned on p. 416.

Trinitrotoluene, $C_6H_2.CH_3.(NO_2)_3$, is made by the nitration of toluene. Toluene is first treated in the cold with a mixture of nitric acid and sulphuric acid to give mononitrotoluene,

$$C_6H_5.CH_3 \ + \ HNO_3 \ = \ C_6H_4.CH_3.NO_2 \ + \ H_2O$$

and the mononitrotoluene is then heated with a more concentrated mixture of the same acids to yield the solid trinitrotoluene,

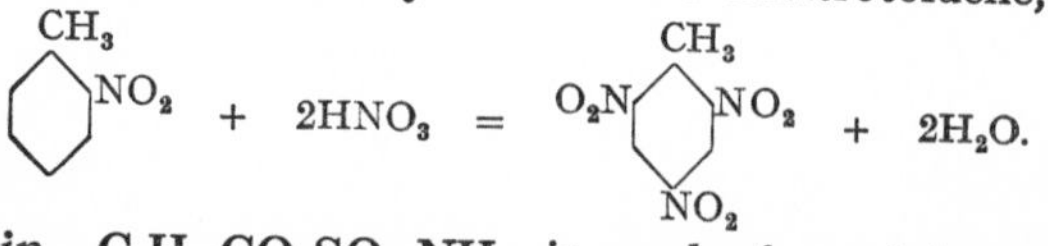

Saccharin, $C_6H_4.CO.SO_2.NH$, is made from toluene by the following sequence of reactions. Toluene is first treated with chlorosulphonic acid, when o-toluene sulphonyl chloride and some p-toluene sulphonyl chloride are formed. The solid p-compound (M.P. 69°) is separated from the liquid o-compound by freezing,

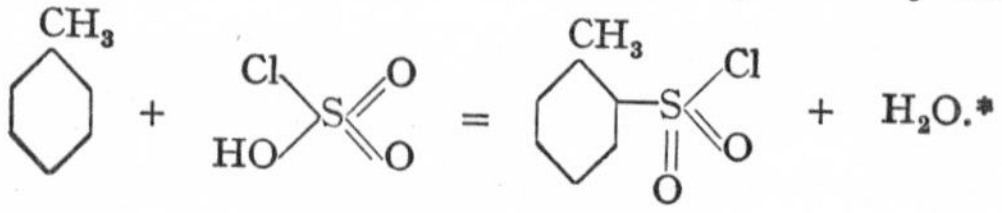

* See footnote on p. 374.

The o-toluene sulphonyl chloride is converted to the amide by the action of ammonia,

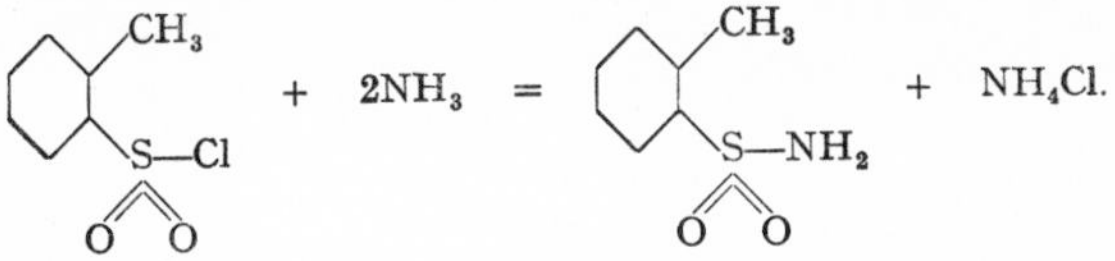

By the oxidation of this compound with alkaline potassium permanganate solution, the methyl group is converted to the carboxyl group, which reacts with the alkali present to yield the sodium salt of benzoic acid o-sulphonamide,

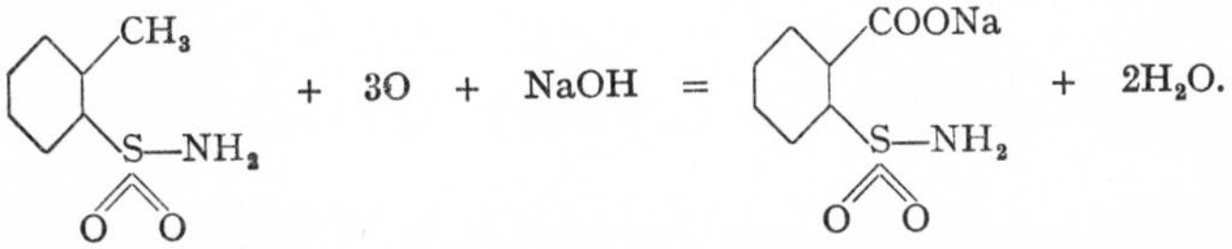

This salt is treated with hydrochloric acid to liberate the free acid, which by the loss of a molecule of water spontaneously yields saccharin, the imide of benzoic acid o-sulphonic acid,

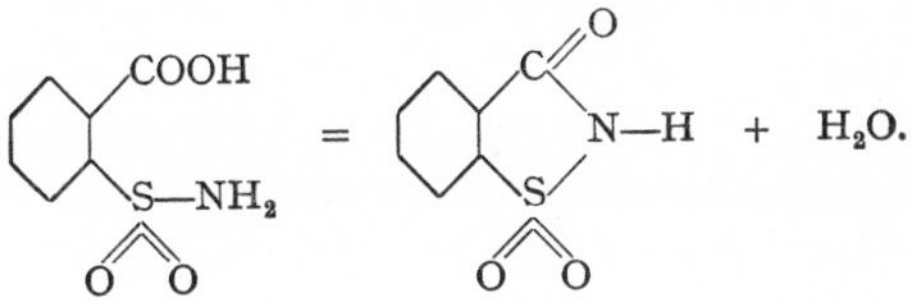

Saccharin is 500 times sweeter than cane sugar : the sodium derivative

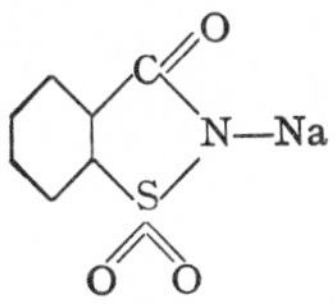

is more soluble in water than saccharin, but is only 400 times sweeter than cane sugar.

ORGANIC COMPOUNDS MANUFACTURED FROM PHENOL

Phenol is obtained either from the middle oil of coal-tar, or from benzene by the processes described on p. 480.

Picric acid, trinitrophenol, $C_6H_2(NO_2)_3.OH$, is manufactured by the nitration of phenol, p. 421. Phenol is dissolved in 55 per cent. sulphuric acid to give phenol p-sulphonic acid. Concentrated nitric acid is added which converts the sulphonic acid to picric acid by a strongly exothermic reaction. On cooling, the picric acid crystallises. It is filtered from the mother liquor, washed, and re-crystallised from hot water. Picric acid is used as a yellow dye, and as a high explosive under the names lyddite or melinite.

Salicylic acid, $C_6H_4.OH.COOH$, is manufactured by heating sodium phenate with carbon dioxide under pressure. The chemistry of the process is described on p. 435. It is a widely used antiseptic, and is the starting-point for the manufacture of aspirin.

Aspirin, the acetyl derivative of salicylic acid, is made by the process described on p. 437.

ORGANIC COMPOUNDS MANUFACTURED FROM NAPHTHALENE

Naphthalene is an aromatic compound with a molecular structure consisting of two condensed benzene rings, thus :

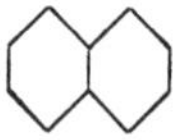

Naphthalene melts at 80°, and boils at 218°, but it is very volatile and it sublimes readily. It is insoluble in water, and its general chemical properties resemble those of benzene. It is used as a fuel in fire-lighters, and as an insecticide. It is the starting-point for the manufacture of many important compounds.

Tetralin, $C_{10}H_{12}$, and **decalin, $C_{10}H_{18}$,** are made by the hydro-genation of naphthalene. Naphthalene vapour and hydrogen are passed over nickel at 150°. An addition reaction occurs, for example,

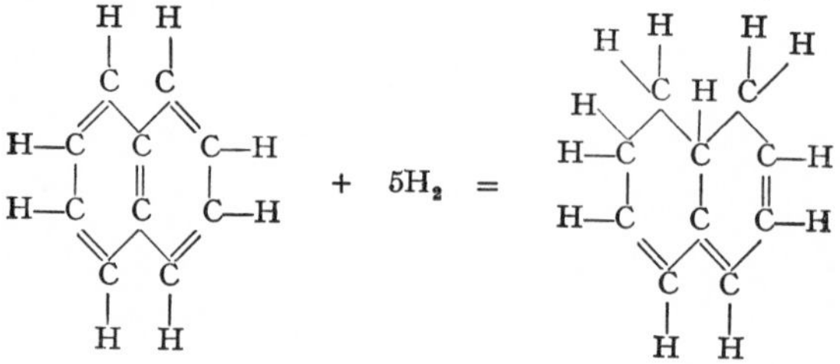

Tetralin and decalin are liquids having B.P. about 200°, and are used as solvents.

Phthalic anhydride is obtained by passing naphthalene vapour mixed with oxygen over vanadium pentoxide at a temperature of about 330°. The reaction which occurs is shown by the equation

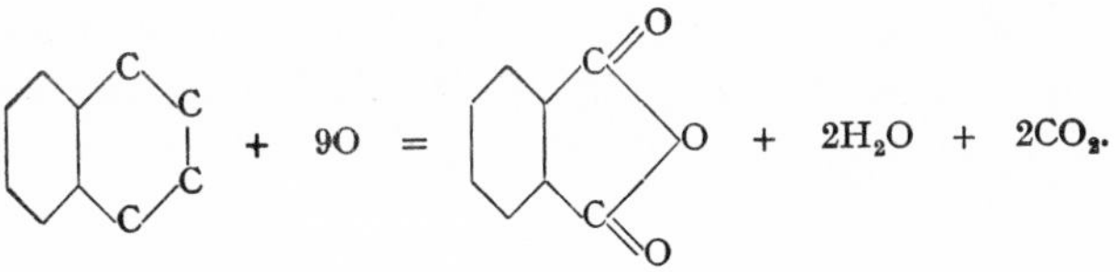

$$+ \quad 9O \quad = \quad \cdots \cdots O \quad + \quad 2H_2O \quad + \quad 2CO_2.$$

Phthalic anhydride forms colourless needles, M.P. 131°, which readily sublime. It is used in the preparation of certain dyestuffs, and also of dibutyl phthalate which is an important solvent or " plasticiser " in the plastics industry.

Anthraquinone was at one time made by the oxidation of anthracene by means of sodium dichromate and sulphuric acid. It is now prepared, however, from the more plentiful naphthalene. The naphthalene is first converted to phthalic anhydride by the process described above. A solution of phthalic anhydride in benzene is then treated with aluminium chloride. The phthalic anhydride and benzene condense according to the equation :

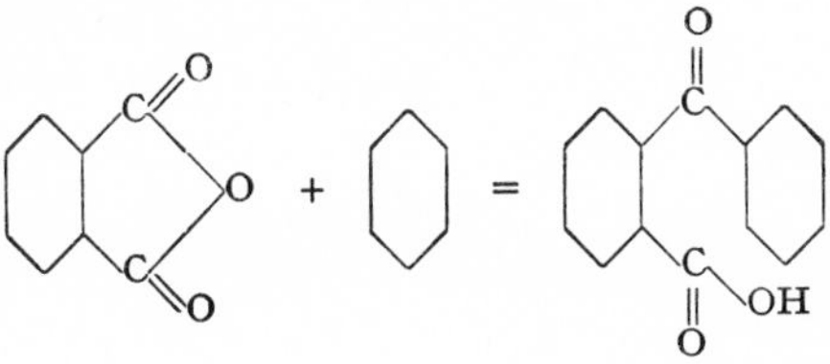

to yield o-benzoyl benzoic acid. When this compound is heated with sulphuric acid at 150° it is converted into anthraquinone, thus :

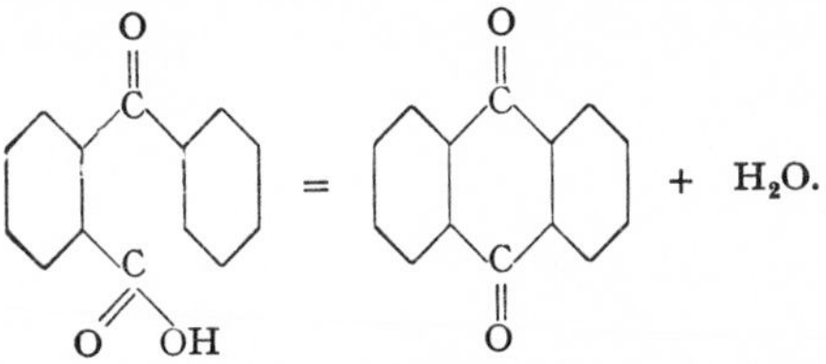

$$= \quad \cdots \cdots \quad + \quad H_2O.$$

Anthraquinone is a stable compound which forms pale-yellow needles, M.P. 285°. When heated with sulphuric acid and sulphur trioxide at 160° it forms anthraquinone monosulphonic acid,

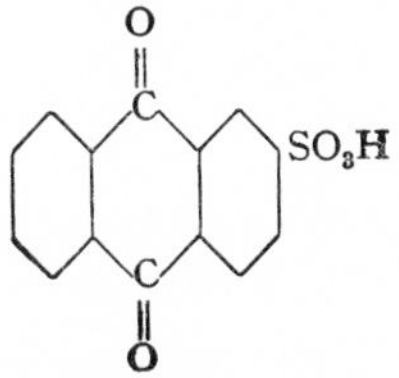

By fusing the sodium salt of this acid with sodium hydroxide mixed with a little potassium chlorate the important dye, *alizarin*, is obtained,

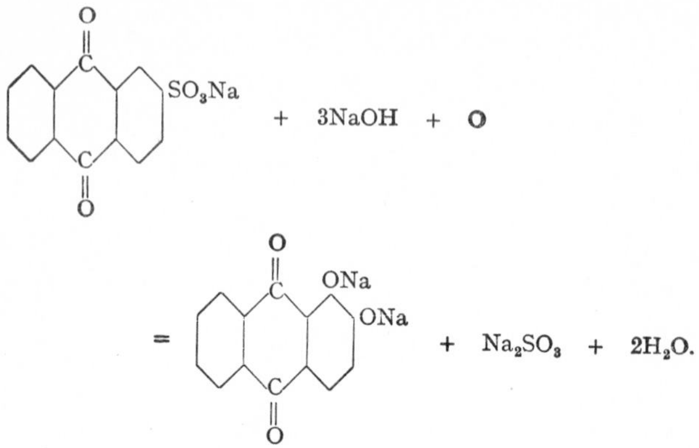

$$+ \ 3NaOH \ + \ \mathbf{O}$$

$$= \qquad\qquad + \ Na_2SO_3 \ + \ 2H_2O.$$

alizarin

2. LOW TEMPERATURE DISTILLATION OF COAL

The low temperature distillation of coal is carried out to produce a fuel which burns brightly in an open grate without the production of smoke. The distillation of coal at 600° also yields a large amount of coal-gas (the yield is about 50 per cent. greater than that produced by high-temperature distillation), ammonia, a volatile oil and a coal-tar which consists almost entirely of aliphatic compounds. This tar, therefore, cannot be used in place of high temperature coal-tar as a source of aromatic compounds. The volatile oil, after being refined, is a highly satisfactory fuel for aeroplane engines.

3. HYDROGENATION OF COAL

Coal is treated with hydrogen under pressure at moderately high temperatures in order to obtain motor-spirit. The coal is ground, mixed with a small quantity of alkaline iron oxide to act as a catalyst, and made into a paste with oil. The paste is injected into a converter where it meets with hydrogen at a pressure of 200 atmospheres and a temperature of 400–500°. The reaction is exothermic and maintains its own temperature without external heating. The product is a mixture of gaseous hydrocarbons and a liquid oil. The gases are used as fuel, and in the production of hydrogen for the process by the methane-steam reaction. The oil is distilled to yield petrol, middle oil and heavy oil. The heavy oil is used for making the coal paste. The middle oil is further hydrogenated by passing the vapour mixed with hydrogen under pressure through heated tubes containing molybdenum sulphide to act as a catalyst. The product of this second hydrogenation is distilled, and the volatile fractions are mixed with the petrol obtained in the first hydrogenation to give a motor-spirit with an octane number of 71–73. 3·65 tons of coal (which includes the coal required for steam-raising, power generation and the manufacture of hydrogen) produce 1 ton of motor-spirit.

4. GASIFICATION OF COKE

(a) Producer gas from coke

If coke is burnt in excess of air, and the temperature of the coke is not allowed to rise above about 1000°, the coke is oxidised to carbon dioxide. If air is passed through a bed of hot coke at least three feet thick, and the temperature is allowed to rise above 1000°, the coke is oxidised to carbon monoxide. Since air contains four-fifths of its volume of nitrogen, and one-fifth of its volume of oxygen, the product of the reaction is a mixture of 2 volumes of carbon monoxide and 4 volumes of nitrogen.

$$4N_2 + O_2 + 2C = 4N_2 + 2CO.$$

This mixture is known as " producer gas ". It is used as a fuel, and for chemical reactions in industry which require carbon monoxide and which are not affected by the presence of the nitrogen. Producer gas is used for the manufacture of sodium formate from which sodium oxalate is made.

Sodium formate is made by treating soda-lime with air producer gas at about 40 atmospheres pressure, and a temperature of about 200°. The reaction proceeds according to the equation,

$$NaOH + CO = HCOONa.$$

Sodium oxalate is made by heating sodium formate to 350–400° in the presence of a small quantity of sodium hydroxide or sodium carbonate which acts as a catalyst. The decomposition of the sodium formate is described by the equation,

$$2H.COONa = H_2 + COONa.COONa.$$

The sodium oxalate is crystallised from water. To obtain **oxalic acid** the sodium oxalate is dissolved in water and the solution is boiled with lime. Calcium oxalate is precipitated. It is filtered off, washed with water, and treated with dilute sulphuric acid,

$$Ca(COO)_2 + H_2SO_4 = CaSO_4 + (COOH)_2.$$

The insoluble calcium sulphate is removed by filtration. The solution of oxalic acid is evaporated to crystallising point.

Sodium oxalate used to be made by heating sawdust with sodium hydroxide to about 350°, but this method is now obsolete.

(b) Water-gas from coke

By treatment with steam at 1200°, coke, produced by the high-temperature distillation of coal, is converted to water-gas, which is a mixture of carbon monoxide and hydrogen. The reaction is represented by the equation,

$$C \ + \ H_2O \ = \ CO \ + \ H_2 \qquad -29,000 \text{ calories.}$$

If the temperature falls below 1000° the reaction becomes very slow, and carbon dioxide is formed according to the equation,

$$C \ + \ 2H_2O \ = \ CO_2 \ + \ 2H_2 \qquad -19,000 \text{ calories.}$$

It is not practicable to maintain the coke at the necessary high temperature by external heating, and therefore water-gas is manufactured by an intermittent process. A bed of red-hot coke, 3 ft. deep, is contained in a producer about 14 ft. high and 12 ft. in diameter. A powerful blast of air is passed through the hot coke for about 1 minute. Part of the coke burns, chiefly to carbon dioxide, and its temperature is raised to about 1500°. All the products of combustion go to waste. Superheated steam at 10 atmospheres pressure is then passed through the bed of coke for 4 minutes, and the water-gas generated is collected. When the coke has cooled to about 1100° the air blast is then turned on again, and the cycle of operations is repeated.

The water-gas is freed from tar and sulphuretted hydrogen by the processes used for the purification of coal-gas. The composition of purified water-gas is approximately

H_2	CO	CH_4	CO_2	N_2	
50	42	1	3	4	per cent. by volume.

Water-gas has many uses. Ordinary town-gas is a mixture of coal-gas and water-gas. Water-gas is used in the refining of nickel, and in the preparation of hydrogen in the Bosch process and the Lane process. If water-gas is heated to 350–400° and compressed to 150–200 atmospheres in the presence of certain substances which act as catalysts, the carbon monoxide and hydrogen react to yield a variety of products. The nature of the product is governed by the catalyst which is employed. The principal substances which may be obtained from water-gas are methane, methyl alcohol, butyl alcohol, motor-spirit and lubricating oil. The conditions leading to the formation of each of these substances are set out below.

Products obtained by reaction between carbon monoxide and hydrogen.

Principal product	Temperature of reaction	Pressure in atmospheres	Catalyst
1. Methane	350–400°	200	nickel, iron or cobalt
2. Methyl alcohol	225–400°	200–600	basic zinc chromate
3. A mixture of higher alcohols from which butyl alcohol may be separated	400–500°	200	partially reduced ferric oxide impregnated with sodium carbonate
4. A mixture of volatile hydrocarbons suitable for use as motor-spirit	200°	200	A mixture of cobalt and thorium
5. Lubricating oil	200°	200	Aluminium chloride

Methyl alcohol is one of the most important compounds manufactured from water-gas. When water-gas enriched with hydrogen is subjected to the conditions mentioned above, a reaction occurs according to the equation :

$$CO \quad + \quad 2H_2 \quad = \quad CH_3OH \quad + 27,000 \text{ cal.}$$

The reaction is strongly exothermic, and external heat is necessary only to start it. Methyl alcohol is used for the preparation of formaldehyde, and in the manufacture of methyl methacrylate used to make the plastics " perspex " and " diakon ".

Formaldehyde, HCHO, is manufactured by passing a mixture of methyl alcohol vapour and air over copper at a temperature of about 200°. Oxidation of the alcohol proceeds according to the equation :

$$2CH_3OH \quad + \quad O_2 \quad = \quad 2CH_2O \quad + \quad 2H_2O.$$

The products of the reaction are condensed to yield an aqueous solution known as " formalin " containing about 40 per cent. of formaldehyde and 15 per cent. of methyl alcohol. Formalin is used in the manufacture of casein plastics, bakelite plastics, and urea and thiourea plastics. It is also used for hardening gelatine, and as a disinfectant. It is used as a methylating agent in the preparation of methyl aniline, and of methylamine.

5. CALCIUM CARBIDE AND ITS DERIVATIVES

Coke is heated with lime in an electric furnace to yield calcium carbide and carbon monoxide, according to the equation,

$$3C \quad + \quad CaO \quad = \quad CaC_2 \quad + \quad CO.$$

The reaction requires an estimated temperature of 3000°. The furnace, therefore, demands a heavy current, and the process is practicable only where electricity is cheaply generated.

Calcium carbide is used for the manufacture of acetylene, which in turn is used for the manufacture of acetaldehyde and other compounds mentioned below. The acetylene generated by the action of

Q2   D.C.

water on calcium carbide is passed over some absorbent material, such as ferric oxychloride, which extracts the impurities phosphine and hydrogen sulphide. The purified gas is dried, and stored in solution in acetone under a pressure of 10 atmospheres.

COMPOUNDS MANUFACTURED FROM ACETYLENE

Acetaldehyde, $CH_3.CHO$, is made by passing acetylene into dilute sulphuric acid containing small quantities of mercuric and ferric sulphates. The mixture is mechanically stirred and maintained at 60–65°, mainly by the heat of the reaction. The excess of acetylene carries away the acetaldehyde, which is condensed and collected.

In Great Britain acetaldehyde is also made by the oxidation of ethyl alcohol, p. 495.

Acetic anhydride, $(CH_3.CO)_2O$, is made by passing acetylene into anhydrous acetic acid mixed with a small quantity of mercuric acetate and sulphuric acid. Ethylidene di-acetate is first formed according to the equations,

$$HC\!:\!CH \ + \ 2HOH \ = \ CH_3.C\!\!\begin{array}{c}\diagup OH \\ \!\!-\!OH \\ \diagdown H\end{array}$$

$$CH_3.C\!\!\begin{array}{c}\diagup OH \\ \!\!-\!OH \\ \diagdown H\end{array} \ + \ 2CH_3.COOH \ = \ CH_3.C\!\!\begin{array}{c}\diagup O.COCH_3 \\ \!\!-\!O.COCH_3 \\ \diagdown H\end{array} \ + \ 2H_2O.$$

The ethylidene di-acetate is then warmed to 80° under pressure in the presence of a catalyst such as zinc chloride, when it decomposes to yield acetic anhydride and acetaldehyde,

$$CH_3.CH.(CH_3.COO)_2 \ = \ CH_3.CHO \ + \ (CH_3.CO)_2O.$$

Acetic Acid, $CH_3.COOH$, is made by the oxidation of acetaldehyde with air, in the presence of the catalyst manganese acetate. Acetaldehyde combines with the oxygen of the air to yield acetyl peroxide, thus:

$$CH_3.CHO \ + \ O_2 \ = \ CH_3.C\!\!\begin{array}{c}\diagup O \\ \diagdown O\!-\!O\!-\!H\end{array}$$

The acetyl peroxide may accumulate and decompose suddenly, giving rise to a dangerous explosion. The presence of the manganese acetate ensures that the acetyl peroxide decomposes smoothly by combination with acetaldehyde according to the equation,

$$CH_3.CHO \ + \ CH_3.COOOH \ = \ 2CH_3.COOH.$$

In practice 1000 gallons of acetaldehyde mixed with 0·5 per cent. of manganese acetate are charged into a closed vessel lined with aluminium. The vessel is warmed to 25°, and air is pumped in. The pressure rises to 5 atmospheres, and the temperature to 65°. The residual nitrogen is collected. The reaction is complete in about 12 hours. The acetic acid is distilled to yield a product of 98–99 per cent. purity.

Acetone. The preparation of acetone from acetylene is outlined on p. 220.

Paraldehyde, $(CH_3.CHO)_3$, is made by polymerising acetaldehyde. Acetaldehyde is agitated in a closed vessel with successive additions of a few drops of concentrated hydrochloric acid, until no further heat is evolved. The hydrochloric acid is then neutralised with sodium bicarbonate, and the mixture is distilled. Unchanged acetaldehyde is first evolved, and is recovered. The paraldehyde distils at 124°. It is used as a sleep inducer and sedative.

Metaldehyde, which is produced by the polymerisation of acetaldehyde in the presence of an acid at low temperatures, is used as a solid fuel for small lamps, under the name, " Meta Fuel ".

n-Butyl alcohol, $CH_3.CH_2.CH_2.CH_2OH$, is made from acetaldehyde by a series of reactions in which aldol and crotonaldehyde are formed intermediately, p. 207. Aldol is produced by the polymerisation of acetaldehyde in the presence of strontia, $Sr(OH)_2$. The aldol is distilled in a current of inert gas, when it breaks down into steam and crotonaldehyde. The vapour of crotonaldehyde is then passed with hydrogen over heated nickel, and n-butyl alcohol is formed,

$$CH_3.CH{=}CH.CHO \ + \ 2H_2 \ = \ CH_3.CH_2.CH_2.CH_2OH.$$

It is used as a solvent for lacquers and spirit varnishes. Butyl alcohol is also made from water-gas, p. 489, and by the fermentation of starch, p. 221.

Westron (tetrachloroethane, $C_2H_2Cl_4$, B.P. 147°) is made by distilling the compound formed by passing acetylene into excess of antimony pentachloride, p. 132. It is used as a solvent for oils, fats, resins and cellulose acetate, and also for sulphur and phosphorus. It is toxic, and is used as an insecticide. *Westrol* (trichloroethylene, $CCl_2 : CHCl$, B.P. 88°) is made by treating tetrachloroethane with milk of lime. It is less toxic than Westron and is used as a solvent. In Germany during the war many important substances, including *vinyl ether, vinyl acetate* used in the manufacture of plastics, and *vinyl pyrrolidon* used in the manufacture of artificial blood plasma, were synthesised from acetylene compressed to about 20 atmospheres.

III. *THE CARBOHYDRATES AND THEIR DERIVATIVES*

Three carbohydrates, sucrose (cane sugar), starch and cellulose are produced on a very large scale. Sucrose is obtained from the sugar cane and the sugar beet, starch from potatoes and grain, cellulose from the cotton plant and from wood.

1. SUCROSE

The *sugar cane* is grown in sub-tropical climates in southern U.S.A., Cuba and Mexico. The sugar cane (*Saccharum Officinaram*) is a grass which grows 15–16 ft. high. It contains about 12–20 per cent. of its weight of sugar, and the yield of sugar is 4–5 tons per acre.

The juice containing the sugar is expressed from the canes by crushing them between rollers. The residual vegetable material is used as fuel. The expressed juice is a dark grey unfilterable liquid which, in addition to sucrose, contains reducing sugars and many salts.

The juice is submitted to a process known as defecation. 1–1·5 per cent. of lime is mixed with the juice, and a current of carbon dioxide is passed through the mixture. The lime is converted to a precipitate of calcium carbonate which carries down many of the suspended impurities. The clarified liquid is filtered, evaporated, and allowed to crystallise. The crystals of sugar are separated from the mother liquor by centrifuging. The mother liquor, known as molasses, still contains about 50 per cent. of sucrose which is prevented from crystallising by the presence of invert sugar in it. The sucrose in molasses may be precipitated as the sparingly soluble $C_{12}H_{22}O_{11}.2SrO$ by adding strontia to the molasses. The precipitate is filtered off from the solution, which contains the invert sugar, and decomposed with carbon dioxide. The strontium carbonate is removed by filtration, and the sucrose is crystallised. Molasses may be refined to give treacle or golden syrup, or fermented to yield ethyl alcohol.

The sucrose obtained by the above methods still needs further refining. It is dissolved in water and treated with lime and phosphoric acid, so that the voluminous precipitate of calcium phosphate carries down gummy impurities. The solution is filtered and the filtrate is passed through animal charcoal. The clear colourless filtrate is then evaporated and crystallised, and the crystals are separated by centrifuging.

The *sugar beet* grows in temperate climates. It contains about 17 per cent. of sucrose and yields about 1½ tons of sucrose per acre. The sugar beet is grown in England, but its cultivation is not economic, and the industry has to be subsidised by the State.

Sucrose is extracted from beet, not by crushing, but by a process of solution. The beets are topped, washed and dried, and cut into thin slices. These are then heated with warm water at 70–80°. The cell walls of the plant act as dialysing membranes through which the sucrose passes while the protein remains behind. The crude sucrose solution thus obtained is defecated with lime and carbon dioxide. The filtered solution is concentrated, evaporated and allowed to crystallise. The crystals are centrifuged and dried. The mother liquor, beet molasses, contains sucrose. Beet molasses does not yield edible products, but it may be fermented to yield alcohol, acetone, and glycerol.

Sucrose is used as a food. Invert sugar, a mixture of equimolecular proportions of glucose and fructose, used in the manufacture of confectionery and preserves, is obtained from sucrose by hydrolysis, p. 337.

ETHYL ALCOHOL

Cane-sugar molasses is the principal source from which ethyl alcohol is manufactured in Great Britain.

The molasses, which contain about 50 per cent. of fermentable sugar, are diluted with water, acidified with sulphuric acid until the free acid content is 0·1 per cent., and warmed to 26°. The solution is placed in fermentation tanks, each of which holds 75,000 gallons, and yeast is added. As the yeast grows fermentation occurs, and the temperature is allowed to rise to 36°. The yeast contains two enzymes which bring about the decomposition of sucrose. Invertase converts sucrose to a mixture of glucose and fructose,

$$\underset{\text{sucrose}}{C_{12}H_{22}O_{11}} \ + \ H_2O \ = \ \underset{\text{glucose}}{C_6H_{12}O_6} \ + \ \underset{\text{fructose,}}{C_6H_{12}O_6}$$

and zymase converts the glucose and fructose to ethyl alcohol and carbon dioxide,

$$C_6H_{12}O_6 \ = \ 2C_2H_5OH \ + \ 2CO_2.$$

The carbon dioxide is collected and solidified.

The aqueous solution of alcohol obtained by fermentation, known as " wash ", contains 7–15 per cent. of ethyl alcohol, and also furfuraldehyde, and a mixture of butyl alcohol and amyl alcohol called " fusel oil ". The wash is fractionated in a continuous still. Since ethyl alcohol and water form a minimum boiling-point mixture (p. 63), the product of fractionation is this mixture, which contains 95·6 per cent. of alcohol. This product is known as " raw spirit ". Raw spirit still contains fusel oil. This is removed by diluting it with water, treating the solution with charcoal and redistilling. The distillate is rectified spirit.

Ethyl alcohol is also manufactured from starch (p. 496), from cellulose (p. 498), and, in America, from ethylene, and in Switzerland from acetylene. It might also be made from water-gas.

Absolute alcohol is manufactured from rectified spirit by fractionating a mixture of rectified spirit and benzene, p. 161.

Methylated spirit is a mixture containing about 90 per cent. of raw spirit, 10 per cent. of methyl alcohol, and small quantities of paraffin oil, pyridine and dyes. The mixture is offensive and unfit for drinking, and yet retains almost as much value as a solvent as rectified spirit. There is no simple process by which the adulterants can be removed to yield pure alcohol.

Uses of ethyl alcohol. Ethyl alcohol is a useful solvent for gums and resins and many other organic substances. It is used as a solvent in the preparation of tinctures, varnishes, perfumes and plastics. It is used on the industrial scale to convert aniline to monoethyl aniline and diethyl aniline. It may be used as a fuel in internal-combustion engines ; it is the fuel used in spirit-lamps. A mixture of alcohol and liquid oxygen is used as a fuel for propelling rockets.

ORGANIC COMPOUNDS MANUFACTURED FROM ETHYL ALCOHOL

Ethylene, $CH_2 : CH_2$, is manufactured in Great Britain by passing ethyl alcohol vapour over alumina, or over phosphoric acid supported on pumice, at a temperature of 200°. Dehydration of the alcohol occurs according to the equation,

$$CH_3.CH_2OH = CH_2 : CH_2 + H_2O.$$

Chloral, $CCl_3.CHO$, is made by the action of chlorine on ethyl alcohol. Chlorine is passed, for several days, into absolute alcohol containing ferric chloride as a catalyst. The reaction mixture is at first cooled, and later is heated to 100°.

The initial product of the reaction of chlorine on ethyl alcohol is hypochlorous ester, C_2H_5OCl :

$$C_2H_5OH + Cl_2 = C_2H_5OCl + HCl.$$

This compound reacts with alcohol to yield acetaldehyde, thus

$$C_2H_5OCl + HOC_2H_5 = C_2H_5—O—O—C_2H_5 + HCl$$
$$C_2H_5—O—O—C_2H_5 = CH_3.CHO + C_2H_5OH.$$

The acetaldehyde then condenses with alcohol to yield acetal,

$$CH_3.CHO + 2HOC_2H_5 = CH_3—\overset{\displaystyle H}{\underset{\displaystyle OC_2H_5}{C}}—OC_2H_5 + H_2O$$

and the acetal, by a two-stage process, yields chloral alcoholate,

$$CH_3\overset{\overset{\displaystyle H}{|}}{\underset{\underset{\displaystyle OC_2H_5}{|}}{C}}OC_2H_5 \ + \ 3Cl_2 \ = \ CCl_3\overset{\overset{\displaystyle H}{|}}{\underset{\underset{\displaystyle OC_2H_5}{|}}{C}}OC_2H_5 \ + \ 3HCl$$

$$Cl_3C.CH.(OC_2H_5)_2 \ + \ HCl \ = \ Cl_3.CCH.OH.OC_2H_5 \ + \ C_2H_5Cl.$$

The chloral alcoholate solidifies as a white mass when the mixture is cooled at the conclusion of the reaction. It is mixed with concentrated sulphuric acid and distilled. Chloral is liberated and is purified by re-distillation,

$$Cl_3C\overset{\overset{\displaystyle H}{|}}{\underset{\underset{\displaystyle OC_2H_5}{|}}{C}}OH \ + \ H_2SO_4 \ = \ CCl_3-C{\overset{\displaystyle H}{\underset{\displaystyle O}{\diagdown}}} \ + \ C_2H_5HSO_4 \ + \ H_2O.$$

Chloroform, $CHCl_3$, is made by decomposing chloral with warm sodium hydroxide solution. The equation for this reaction is given on p. 153.

Acetaldehyde, $CH_3.CHO$, is made by passing the vapour of ethyl alcohol mixed with air over a catalyst consisting of metallic silver, maintained at a dull red heat by the heat of the reaction,

$$CH_3.CH_2OH \ + \ O \ = \ CH_3.CHO \ + \ H_2O.$$

The product is cooled to separate the excess of alcohol; the more volatile acetaldehyde is condensed and collected. It is purified by distillation.

Acetaldehyde is also made from acetylene, p. 490.

Diethyl ether and **ethyl esters** are made from ethyl alcohol by the methods described on pp. 178 and 258 respectively.

2. STARCH

Starch is present in the grain of rice, barley, wheat and maize, and in the tubers of potatoes and arrowroot. Starch is obtained from these sources by processes of maceration and washing which remove the cellulose and other unwanted material, and leave the starch as a white, soft, insoluble powder.

The grain is soaked in warm water, crushed and allowed to undergo lactic fermentation which converts the sugars into acids, and renders the gluten less sticky. The product is filtered, and the starch is washed by decantation and dried.

The potatoes are washed, crushed and macerated with water in fine sieves. Cellulose and other substances remain in the sieve, while the suspension of starch passes through. The starch settles in the form of a paste, which is washed by decantation and dried.

ORGANIC COMPOUNDS MANUFACTURED FROM STARCH

Dextrin is made by heating starch to 120° *in vacuo* from which water vapour is removed by the presence of phosphorus pentoxide. Dextrin is a colourless soluble powder. The aqueous solution is known as " British gum " and is used as an adhesive on stamps and envelopes.

Glucose is made by heating starch with very dilute (0·5 per cent.) sulphuric acid at 120° under a pressure of 2 or 3 atmospheres. The resulting solution is neutralised with calcium carbonate, and the precipitated calcium salts are filtered off. The filtrate is decolorised by boiling with animal charcoal, and evaporated under reduced pressure and crystallised.

Butyl alcohol, $CH_3.(CH_2)_2.CH_2OH$, and acetone are made by the fermentation of starch under the conditions mentioned on p. 221, Reaction 4.

Butyl alcohol is also made from acetaldehyde, p. 491, and from water-gas, p. 489.

Ethyl alcohol is made from starch by means of enzyme reactions. By means of the enzyme diastase the starch is first broken down to the sugar maltose, and to dextrin,

$$(C_6H_{10}O_5)_n + H_2O = C_{12}H_{22}O_{11} + (C_6H_{10}O_5)_{n-2}.$$

By further action of the diastase, the dextrin is also broken down to maltose. The maltose is hydrolysed by the enzyme maltase to glucose,

$$C_{12}H_{22}O_{11} + H_2O = 2C_6H_{12}O_6,$$

and the glucose is converted to ethyl alcohol and carbon dioxide by the enzyme zymase :

$$C_6H_{12}O_6 = 2C_2H_5OH + 2CO_2.$$

These reactions are the basis of two important processes for converting starch to ethyl alcohol which may be referred to as the British process, and the Continental process.

The British process. The diastase is obtained from barley. Barley grains are soaked in water and allowed to germinate. During the germination diastase is produced in the grain as a necessary preliminary to the process of growth. After some days the sprouting barley, called " malt " is dried in a kiln. The malt is crushed and added to a warm mash of the raw grain or potato which is to be converted to alcohol. The temperature is maintained between 40° and 60° for some time, and the starch is slowly changed to maltose. The sugary solution which is produced is known as "wort". The enzymes, maltase and zymase, are found in the yeast plant (*Saccharomyces*). Yeast is introduced into the wort. The cells multiply and the enzymes produced convert the maltose into glucose, and the glucose into alcohol.

The Continental process. The diastase is obtained from a mould. either *Rhizopus Delemar* or *Mucor Boulard*. The raw starch is gelatinised by agitation with very dilute hydrochloric acid solution. The mash is boiled to sterilise it and cooled to 40°. Spores of the mould are then added and in about 15 hours the mycelium of the mould has grown throughout the mash. Yeast is added to furnish maltase and zymase and the mixture is allowed to stand for four days, after which the conversion to alcohol is complete. 1 gm. of mould is sufficient to convert 30,000 gallons of starch solution to alcohol.

Both these processes yield a dilute solution of alcohol in water known as " wash " from which alcohol is extracted by the procedure outlined on p. 493.

3. CELLULOSE

Cellulose of the highest quality is obtained from the hairy material covering the seeds of the cotton plant (*Gossypium*). Less pure cellulose is manufactured in large quantities from wood, straw, and from various grasses, especially esparto grass.

The crude cellulose from the cotton seeds is treated with alkalis, bleaching agents and acids. It is then washed with water and dried.

Wood shavings or sawdust are boiled under pressure with a solution of calcium bisulphite (made by saturating a suspension of lime with sulphur dioxide). The lignone and resins which are present with cellulose in wood are thus destroyed, and the cellulose separates as insoluble fibres which are thoroughly washed with water. The cellulose thus obtained is known as " wood pulp ". The residual sulphite liquor contains glucose which may be fermented to give alcohol.

Cellulose fibres are used in the manufacture of paper, and in the manufacture of the important compounds cellulose nitrate and cellulose acetate. These manufacturing processes are briefly decribed on the following page. Artificial silk is made from cellulose.

In countries where wood is plentiful, for example Sweden, cellulose is the starting-point for the manufacture of alcohol.

Cellulose acetate. Cellulose acetate is manufactured by treating cotton at 0° with a mixture of acetic acid, acetic anhydride and concentrated sulphuric acid. The reaction is exothermic, and the reaction mixture must be cooled. When the cotton has dissolved completely to form a syrupy solution the acid is neutralised with lime, and the cellulose acetate is precipitated as an opaque white solid by the addition of excess water. It is washed with water and dried. The cellulose acetate thus made contains some unacetylated hydroxyl groups. It differs from the completely acetylated tri-acetate in being soluble in acetone.

Cellulose acetate is used in the manufacture of plastics, dopes and artificial silk (celanese).

Cellulose nitrate. Cellulose nitrate is manufactured by adding cotton linters to a carefully controlled mixture of concentrated nitric acid, concentrated sulphuric acid and water, contained in stainless steel vessels. The mixture is stirred for $2\frac{1}{2}$ hours, and the excess acid is then removed by centrifuging. The fibrous cake of cellulose nitrate, which does not differ greatly in appearance from the original cotton, is washed with a large quantity of water, first cold and then hot, and is partly dried by spinning in a centrifuge. The damp, fibrous cake which is obtained is safe for handling and transport.

The degree of nitration of the cellulose is governed by the strength of the nitrating acid mixture. If the acids are highly concentrated, all the hydroxyl groups in cellulose are replaced by nitro groups, and the product is gun-cotton, which has the empirical formula $C_6H_7O_2(O.NO_2)_3$. It is soluble neither in water nor in a mixture of alcohol and ether. If less concentrated acids are employed, some of the hydroxyl groups in cellulose escape nitration, and the product known as collodion cotton is obtained. It has the approximate empirical composition $C_6H_7O_2.OH.(O.NO_2)_2$, and contains between 10·8 and 11·9 per cent. of nitrogen. It is soluble in acetone and in ether-alcohol mixtures. It is used in the manufacture of celluloid and collodion.

Manufacture of ethyl alcohol from cellulose. If cellulose is digested with dilute sulphuric acid and steam at a pressure of 6 to 7 atmospheres it is rapidly hydrolysed to glucose. During the conversion of wood to wood-pulp (p. 497), some of the cellulose is hydrolysed to glucose. The glucose thus obtained is fermented by yeast to give alcohol by a process similar to that described on p. 493.

IV. *FATS AND VEGETABLE OILS*

Fats are secreted in the bodies of animals as a reserve supply of energy-yielding material. Vegetable oils are found in the seeds of certain plants. Among the most important are olive oil, linseed oil, soya-bean oil and groundnut oil.

The fat from beef or mutton suet, after separation from membranous tissue by kneading with hot water and filtering through muslin, is known as *tallow* ; the fat similarly obtained from pig suet is *lard*.

The principal constituents of fats and oils are esters of glycerol with stearic acid, palmitic acid and oleic acid. All three hydroxyl groups in the glycerol molecule are esterified. The formula of the simple esters would be :

$$
\begin{array}{lll}
H_2C\text{—}O.OC.C_{17}H_{35} & H_2C\text{—}O.OC.C_{15}H_{31} & H_2C\text{—}O.OC.C_{17}H_{33} \\
| & | & | \\
HC\text{—}O.OC.C_{17}H_{35} & HC\text{—}O.OC.C_{15}H_{31} & HC\text{—}O.OC.C_{17}H_{33} \\
| & | & | \\
H_2C\text{—}O.OC.C_{17}H_{35} & H_2C\text{—}O.OC.C_{15}H_{31} & H_2C\text{—}O.OC.C_{17}H_{33}
\end{array}
$$

| tristearin (glyceryl tristearate) | tripalmitin (glyceryl tripalmitate) | triolein (glyceryl trioleate) |

It has been shown, however, that natural fats and oils usually consist of mixed esters, in which one glycerol residue is combined with the acid radicals of two or three different acids. Tristearin and tripalmitin are solids at room temperature, whereas triolein is a liquid. Fats such as tallow and lard, which contain a high proportion of stearic and palmitic acid radicals are, therefore, solid at room temperature, and others such as olive oil, which contain a high proportion of the oleic acid radical, are liquid. Stearic acid, $C_{17}H_{35}COOH$, and palmitic acid, $C_{15}H_{31}COOH$, are fatty acids with unbranched chains of carbon atoms in the molecule. Oleic acid also has an unbranched chain in the molecule, but two of the carbon atoms in the chain are linked by a double bond. Its constitution is $CH_3(CH_2)_7.CH\text{=}CH.(CH_2)_7.COOH$.

Fats are hydrolysed, (i) by sodium hydroxide solution to yield glycerol and the sodium salt of the constituent acid

$$
\begin{array}{l}
H_2C\text{—}O.OC.C_{17}H_{35} \\
| \\
HC\text{—}O.OC.C_{17}H_{35} \quad + \quad 3NaOH \quad = \quad \\
| \\
H_2C\text{—}O.OC.C_{17}H_{35} \\
\text{tristearin}
\end{array}
\qquad
\begin{array}{l}
H_2C\text{—}OH \\
| \\
HC\text{—}OH \quad + \quad 3C_{17}H_{35}COONa \\
| \\
H_2C\text{—}OH \\
\text{glycerol} \qquad \text{sodium stearate}
\end{array}
$$

(the sodium salt of the acid is a member of the class of compounds known as *soaps*), (ii) by treatment with water under pressure at 150° in the presence of small quantities of a catalyst, which may be lime or magnesium oxide, or dilute sulphuric acid, to yield glycerol and the free acid,

$$
\begin{array}{ccccc}
H_2C-O.OC.C_{17}H_{35} & & H_2C-OH & & \\
| & & | & & \\
HC-O.OC.C_{17}H_{35} & + \; 3H_2O \; = & HC-OH & + \; 3C_{17}H_{35}COOH \\
| & & | & & \\
H_2C-O.OC.C_{17}H_{35} & & H_2C-OH & & \\
& & \text{glycerol} & & \text{stearic acid}
\end{array}
$$

SUBSTANCES MANUFACTURED FROM FATS

Soap is manufactured by boiling a mixture of fats, such as tallow and palm oil, with the calculated quantity of an aqueous solution of sodium hydroxide. A homogeneous solution is obtained, which contains glycerol and the sodium salts of the acids originally present in the fats. Common salt is added to the solution, and the soap, which is insoluble in salt water, is precipitated as a curd. The glycerol, salt and any excess of sodium hydroxide remain in solution. The curd is removed, dissolved in water, and again precipitated with salt. This treatment is repeated, and finally the purified curd is dissolved in hot water. On cooling, the solution solidifies to yield *hard soap*, which consists of sodium salts of the fatty acids, water and a small quantity of glycerol ; it is free from alkali. The soap thus obtained is " genuine soap ". It is mixed with fillers such as sodium silicate, and is coloured and perfumed before it is put on the market.

If a fat is hydrolysed with potassium hydroxide instead of sodium hydroxide, a solution is obtained which, on cooling, sets to a jelly known as *soft soap*. Soft soap contains glycerol as well as the potassium salts of the acids originally present in the fat.

Stearin is a mixture consisting principally of stearic acid and palmitic acid, obtained by hydrolysing tallow with water under pressure in the presence of lime or dilute sulphuric acid. The paste of insoluble acids is separated from the aqueous layer which contains glycerol, and pressed between warm plates to remove the liquid oleic acid. The remaining waxy solid is stearin. It is used, admixed with paraffin, for the manufacture of candles.

Glycerol is a by-product in the manufacture of hard soap and stearin. The aqueous solution of glycerol and salt which remains after the soap or stearin has been removed is filtered, concentrated and distilled as described on p. 324.

—

HARDENING OF FATS

The fats, tristearin and tripalmitin, which are solid at room temperature, have a wider range of usefulness than liquid fats, and they are therefore of greater commercial value. The fatty oils are glyceryl esters of unsaturated acids such as oleic acid, $C_{17}H_{33}.COOH$, and linoleic acid, $C_{17}H_{31}.COOH$. If each of these acids is made to combine additively with hydrogen, the double linkages in the molecules are saturated (p. 118), and stearic acid, $C_{17}H_{35}.COOH$, is obtained. If the corresponding chemical change is carried out on the glyceryl esters triolein and trilinolein, the solid fat, tristearin, is obtained.

The conversion of fatty oils to solid fats is carried out commercially on a very large scale. Oils such as olive oil, soya-bean oil, groundnut oil and whale oil, after clarification, are mixed with a small quantity of reduced nickel, heated to 180°, and treated with hydrogen under a pressure of 3–5 atmospheres. The product of the reaction is a fat, solid at room temperature, which is used in the manufacture of soap, candles, and margarine. A liquid fat which is converted to a solid fat by catalytic hydrogenation is said to be *hardened*.

Margarine is manufactured by churning a mixture of fats and oils with milk. The fats employed may be tallow, lard or the products obtained by hardening whale oil or vegetable oils such as soya-bean oil, coconut oil, groundnut oil or palm-kernel oil. A butter flavour is secured by bacterial treatment of the milk. Vitamins A and D are added to bring the nutritional value of the margarine up to that of butter.

Appendix

Use of lithium aluminium hydride, LiAlH₄ as a reducing agent

The reagent is prepared by the action of lithium hydride on an ethereal solution of aluminium chloride,

$$4LiH + AlCl_3 = LiAlH_4 + 3LiCl.$$

The technique employed is similar to that used in the preparation of a Grignard reagent. The solution is stable at room temperature. It reduces acids, esters, acyl halides, acid anhydrides, ketones and aldehydes, to *alcohols*, for example,

$$4C_2H_5.CO.OH + 3LiAlH_4 = (C_2H_5.CH_2.O)_4 LiAl. + 2LiAlO_2 + 4H_2,$$

$$(C_2H_5.CH_2.O)_4LiAl + 2H_2O = 4C_2H_5.CH_2.OH + LiAlO_2.$$

Amides and nitriles are reduced to *amines*. The olefinic double link is usually unaffected.

QUESTIONS

SECTION I

MANIPULATION AND ANALYSIS

Chapter III (p. 53) and Chapter IV (p. 77)

1. Describe how *one* constituent in each of the following mixtures may be obtained in a pure condition : (*a*) acetanilide and salicylic acid, (*b*) ethyl alcohol and water, (*c*) phenol and benzene. (Cambridge 1st M.B.)

2. Describe how you would separate in a pure condition each component of a mixture of ethyl alcohol, benzoic acid and acetanilide. (Cambridge 1st M.B.)

3. " Distillation is one of the most valuable methods at the disposal of the organic chemist." Discuss this statement with respect to fractional distillation and distillation in steam. Explain the principles underlying these processes, and describe in detail apparatus necessary for efficiency. (J.M.B.)

4. The isolation of organic compounds is sometimes effected by distillation in steam, sometimes by extraction with a suitable solvent. Describe how each of these processes is employed, giving one example of each. Write a short account of the physical principles on which they depend for their success. (Oxford H.S.C.)

5. Give the details of the tests used in the laboratory for identifying the elements present in an organic substance. Write equations wherever possible. (University of Melbourne.)

6. Describe with all essential practical details how you would test an organic substance for the presence of (*a*) halogens, (*b*) nitrogen. Give equations for each stage of the work. (J.M.B.)

7. Explain the principles underlying the estimation of nitrogen by Dumas' and Kjeldahl's methods, and describe one of them. (University of Calcutta.)

8. 0·2316 gm. of an organic substance containing carbon, hydrogen and nitrogen, but no other element, yielded 0·5584 gm. of carbon dioxide and 0·3141 gm. of water on combustion. Its vapour density was found to be between 35 and 40. Calculate the empirical formula of the substance. What isomers having this formula should exist? (J.M.B.)

9. 0·15 gm. of an organic compound containing only carbon, hydrogen and oxygen gave on combustion 0·33 gm. of carbon dioxide and 0·18 gm. of water. Its vapour density was 30. What is the molecular formula of the compound? What structural formulae might it possess, and how would you know which was correct? (London H.S.C.)

10. On combustion 0·1579 gm. of an organic compound gave 0·2254 gm. of carbon dioxide, and 0·0769 gm. of water. The same weight of the original compound, on treatment with silver nitrate and nitric acid, yielded 0·2450 gm. of silver chloride. The vapour density of the compound was approximately 46. Calculate its molecular formula. (J.M.B.)

11. What methods are available for the quantitative determination of nitrogen in an organic compound? 0·2853 gm. of an organic compound containing nitrogen was heated with 10 c.c. of concentrated sulphuric acid until the liquid was practically colourless. It was then diluted, rendered alkaline, and distilled into 50 c.c. of 0·98 N/10 hydrochloric acid. After the distillation was complete, the excess hydrochloric acid in the absorption vessel required 34·33 c.c. of 1·04 N/10 sodium hydroxide for neutralisation. Calculate the percentage of nitrogen in the original compound. (London Inter. B.Sc.)

12. A white crystalline solid gave the following results on analysis. 0·3170 gm. gave 0·2325 gm. carbon dioxide, and 0·1902 gm. of water. 0·3170 gm. when treated by Kjeldahl's method yielded sufficient ammonia to neutralise 52·8 c.c. of N/5 sulphuric acid. 0·250 gm. dissolved in 15 gm. of water gave a solution freezing at − 0·524° C. Calculate the molecular formula of the substance, and write two possible structural formulae for it. The molecular freezing point constant for 100 gm. of water is 18·6. (J.M.B.)

13. A mixture of 4 c.c. of a gaseous hydrocarbon with 50 c.c. of oxygen was exploded. On treatment of the resulting mixture with potassium hydroxide solution a contraction in volume of 16 c.c. occurred, and the volume of residual oxygen was 24 c.c. Deduce the molecular formula of the hydrocarbon. (All measurements were made at atmospheric temperature and pressure.) (Cambridge 1st M.B.)

14. 10 c.c. of a mixture of carbon monoxide, methane, hydrogen and nitrogen were mixed with 15 c.c. of oxygen and then exploded. After cooling, the residual gas occupied 12 c.c., of which 5 c.c. were absorbed by potassium hydroxide, and a further 6 c.c. by alkaline pyrogallol. Calculate the composition of the original mixture. (Oxford H.S.C.)

Numerical problems which require for solution a knowledge of the chemical properties of the compounds concerned are included in Section XIX.

SECTION II

Aliphatic Hydrocarbons

Chapter V (p. 104), Chapter VI (p. 115) and Chapter VII (p. 128)

15. Outline three methods of preparing ethane. How may ethane be distinguished from methane? Write down the structural formulae of the isomeric pentanes. (Cambridge H.S.C.)

16. Give three general methods for the preparation of the hydrocarbons of the paraffin series of the general formula C_nH_{2n+2}. Give the structural formulae of the two isomeric butanes. What reaction would you expect to result from gently heating paraffin wax with bromine? (London Inter. B.Sc.)

17. Explain what is meant by the term " chain isomerism " as applied to aliphatic hydrocarbons, and show by means of planar formulae how it is that only one propane (C_3H_8) exists, but two butanes (C_4H_{10}) are known. Give their structural formulae and names. If you were provided with methane and ethane, by what reactions would you prepare propane from them? (London Inter. B.Sc.)

18. Describe briefly two methods by which paraffins can be prepared. After 10 c.c. of a gaseous hydrocarbon had been exploded with 60 c.c. of oxygen, the volume of the remaining gas was 45 c.c. ; 20 c.c. of this were absorbed by potash solution. Calculate the molecular formula of the hydrocarbon. (All volumes were measured at room temperature and pressure.) (Cambridge H.S.C.)

19. How is ethylene prepared? From ethylene how are the following substances obtained : (*a*) glycol, (*b*) acetylene, (*c*) tartaric acid, (*d*) nitroethane? (Cambridge 1st M.B.)

20. Describe the preparation of ethylene and its conversion to ethylene dibromide. When ethylene dibromide is treated with potassium cyanide under certain conditions, a crystalline solid of composition C 60·0 per cent., H 5·0 per cent. and N 35·0 per cent. is produced. Give the structural formula of the compound, and write down the equation for its reaction with dilute sulphuric acid. (Cambridge H.S.C.)

21. Describe the general methods for the preparation of hydrocarbons of (*a*) the paraffin, (*b*) the olefine series. 10 c.c. of a certain gaseous hydrocarbon were exploded with 100 c.c. of oxygen. The volume after explosion was 85 c.c., and this was reduced to 55 c.c. by treatment with aqueous potassium hydroxide. Find the molecular formula of the gas. All volumes were measured at 15° C. and 755 mm. (O. and C. H.S.C.)

22. Compare and contrast the properties of a typical paraffin such as ethane with those of a typical olefine such as ethylene. 10 c.c. of a gaseous hydrocarbon were exploded with 70 c.c. (excess) of oxygen. After explosion the residual gases occupied 50 c.c., and this volume was reduced to 20 c.c. on addition of potassium hydroxide. From these data identify the hydrocarbon. (All measurements were made at N.T.P.) (J.M.B.)

23. What is meant by unsaturation? Describe two methods of preparing ethylene and give three characteristic reactions of unsaturated compounds. (London H.S.C.)

24. Describe the preparation of acetylene. How may acetylene be converted into (*a*) ethane, (*b*) acetaldehyde, (*c*) ethylidene bromide, (*d*) copper acetylide? (Cambridge 1st M.B.)

25. Outline the reactions by which the following compounds may be prepared from acetylene : (*a*) acetic acid, (*b*) ethylene, (*c*) benzene, (*d*) ethylidene bromide, (*e*) copper acetylide, (*f*) acetone.

(Cambridge 1st M.B.)

26. Compare the reactions of ethane, ethylene and acetylene. How may acetic acid be prepared from acetylene? (Cambridge 1st M.B.)

SECTION III

Halogen Derivatives of the Paraffins

Chapter VIII (p. 136)

27. Describe how you would prepare a specimen of ethyl bromide from ethyl alcohol. How may ethyl bromide be converted into (*a*) ethane, (*b*) ethylene, (*c*) normal butane? (London Inter. B.Sc.)

28. Describe a laboratory method for the preparation of ethyl iodide. Explain briefly how, starting from ethyl iodide, you can obtain specimens of (a) diethyl ether, (b) ethylene, (c) ethyl alcohol, (d) ethane.

(J.M.B.)

29. Describe how you would prepare and purify ethyl iodide. How does this substance react with the following : (a) an alcoholic solution of potassium hydroxide, (b) an alcoholic solution of ammonia, (c) silver acetate, (d) sodium ethylate? By what reactions could ethyl iodide be converted into (i) propane, (ii) propionic acid? (Oxford H.S.C.)

30. Describe in detail the preparation of *either* ethyl bromide *or* ethyl iodide. By what reactions can one or other of these compounds be converted into (a) ethane, (b) ethylene, (c) acetylene? (Oxford H.S.C.)

31. Describe with experimental details how you could prepare a pure specimen of ethyl bromide in the laboratory. What is the action of ethyl bromide on (a) ammonia, (b) sodium ethoxide, (c) caustic potash, (d) aluminium mercury couple and alcohol? (London H.S.C.)

32. Give an account of the general methods of preparation of the halogen substitution products of the paraffin hydrocarbons. Indicate their importance in organic synthesis. (University of Bombay.)

33. How is the percentage of chlorine in an organic compound determined? Outline the reactions whereby the chlorine atom in an alkyl chloride may be replaced by (a) —H, (b) —COOH, (c) —OH, (d) —CH$_3$. (Oxford H.S.C.)

34. Write the structural formulae of the compounds which may be produced by the replacement of 1 or 2 hydrogen atoms in the molecule of ethane by chlorine. Give an account of the reactions of these chlorine derivatives with potassium hydroxide in aqueous solution and in alcoholic solution. (All reactions should be illustrated with structural equations.) (Cambridge H.S.C.)

35. Describe the reactions of compounds of the general formula C$_n$H$_{2n+1}$Cl, and C$_n$H$_{2n}$Cl$_2$ with (a) dilute aqueous alkali, (b) concentrated alcoholic alkali. Name the substances which you would choose as examples, and illustrate their behaviour by means of structural formulae. (London Inter. B.Sc.)

36. Describe the preparation from ethyl alcohol of (a) ethyl iodide, (b) iodoform. How and under what conditions do ethyl iodide and iodoform react with potassium hydroxide? (London Inter. B.Sc.)

37. Describe the preparation of a specimen of chloroform. What reactions take place during the preparation? How does chloroform behave on treatment with (a) sodium hydroxide, (b) aniline and sodium hydroxide? How would you test for the purity of chloroform?

(London 2nd M.B.)

38. Describe the preparation and properties of chloroform. What are its likely impurities, and how would you detect them?

(University of Calcutta.)

39. Describe the preparation of (a) chloral hydrate, (b) chloroform. How does chloroform react with (a) alcoholic potash, (b) alcoholic potash and aniline, (c) nascent hydrogen? (Cambridge 1st M.B.)

SECTION IV

ALIPHATIC ALCOHOLS AND ETHERS

Chapter IX (p. 158) and Chapter X (p. 176)

40. How is ethyl alcohol obtained commercially? How is it purified? Explain carefully the evidence upon which the formula CH_3CH_2OH is assigned to the molecule of this compound. (J.M.B.)

41. How would you prepare a small quantity of absolute alcohol from sugar? What evidence can you bring forward in support of the structural formula which is adopted for ethyl alcohol? (Oxford H.S.C.)

42. Describe the reactions by which ethyl alcohol is obtained from starch, indicating the enzymes concerned with each stage. Starting with ethyl alcohol, outline the reactions by which the following may be obtained : (a) ethyl chloride, (b) ether, (c) chloroform.

(Cambridge 1st M.B.)

43. Outline (without giving experimental details) the stages by which the following substances could be obtained from ethyl alcohol : chloroacetic acid, acetyl chloride, ethylidene dichloride, ethylene dichloride. (Cambridge H.S.C.)

44. Outline the methods by which the following might be prepared starting from ethyl alcohol : ethyl acetate, ethylene, acetylene, acetaldehyde, acetone. (Cambridge H.S.C.)

45. Name, and write the formulae of, the three different products that may be obtained by the action of concentrated sulphuric acid on ethyl alcohol under different experimental conditions. Describe these conditions, and in each case state the class of organic compound to which the product belongs. Describe, with a diagram, the laboratory preparation of one of the products. (London Inter. B.Sc.)

46. In what different ways and under what conditions does ethyl alcohol react with sulphuric acid? Describe how you would prepare a pure specimen of ethylene dibromide from ethyl alcohol. How can the elements bromine and nitrogen be detected when present in the same organic compound? (Oxford H.S.C.)

47. Specify the reactions it would be necessary to carry out in order to demonstrate the constitution of ethyl alcohol. How would you confirm the constitution by synthesis? By what reactions could you convert ethyl alcohol into (a) acetaldehyde, (b) acetic acid, (c) ethyl acetate? (London Inter. B.Sc.)

48. Describe the behaviour of primary, secondary and tertiary monohydric alcohols on oxidation. A compound containing 62·1 per cent. of carbon, 10·35 per cent. of hydrogen, and no other element except oxygen, gave on oxidation an acid containing 48·6 per cent. of carbon and 8·1 per cent. of hydrogen. The vapour density of the original compound was 29. Write structural formulae for both compounds.
(J.M.B.)

49. Write structural formulae for the three isomeric pentanes. By replacing one hydrogen atom by a hydroxyl group in different positions on these formulae, arrive at the structural formulae of the eight amyl

QUESTIONS

alcohols. How might these isomeric alcohols be distinguished from one another? (University of Melbourne.)

50. Describe how (a) diethyl ether, (b) ethyl acetate, (c) ethylene may be prepared from ethyl alcohol. Outline the evidence which establishes the constitutional formula of diethyl ether as $C_2H_5.O.C_2H_5$. (London Inter. B.Sc.)

51. Mention the chemical changes that take place in alcoholic fermentation. How would you estimate the percentage of alcohol in a sample of wine? (University of Calcutta.)

SECTION V

ALIPHATIC AMINES. Chapter XI (p. 182)

52. How may ethylamine be prepared from (a) acetaldehyde, (b) propionamide? How does ethylamine react with (i) ethyl iodide, (ii) hydrochloric acid, (iii) sodium nitrite and hydrochloric acid, (iv) chloroform and alcoholic potash? (Cambridge 1st M.B.)

53. Give the constitutional formulae for a primary, a secondary, and a tertiary amine. By what tests would you distinguish between these substances? Describe three methods by which methylamine can be prepared. (London Inter. B.Sc.)

54. How are the amines classified? Indicate how they may be distinguished from one another. (University of Calcutta.)

55. Classify, and write general formulae for, the alkyl derivatives of ammonia. Name the compounds in which the alkyl group is CH_3, and state how these compounds exhibit (a) similarities, (b) differences.
(London Inter. B.Sc.)

56. Write down the structural formulae and give the names of four amines having the molecular formula C_3H_9N, and describe how any one of them may be prepared. By what reactions could they be distinguished? (Cambridge 1st M.B.)

57. Two isomeric substances A and B gave the following results on analysis. 0·197 gm. gave 0·293 gm. carbon dioxide and 0·150 gm. water. By the Kjeldahl method, 0·59 gm. required 10·0 c.c. of N sulphuric acid for neutralisation of the ammonia. The substance A, when boiled with caustic soda, evolved ammonia, and the dry residue, heated with soda lime, gave off methane. The substance B on reduction gave ethylamine. Give the structural formulae of the two substances.
(University of Bombay.)

58. A simple aliphatic amine contained 61·02 per cent. C, 15·25 per cent. H, and 23·73 per cent. N. By treatment with excess methyl iodide, a quaternary ammonium iodide was formed, 0·3015 gm. of which gave 0·3525 gm. of AgI. What was the structural formula of the amine? What other structures will give the same percentage composition? (University of Melbourne.)

SECTION VI

ALIPHATIC ALDEHYDES AND KETONES

Chapter XII (p. 199) and Chapter XIII (p. 220)

59. What is the effect of heat on (*a*) calcium acetate, (*b*) a mixture of calcium acetate and calcium formate? Compare and contrast the properties of the organic substances thus obtained. (Cambridge H.S.C.)

60. Describe two methods by which acetaldehyde may be prepared in the laboratory. State the properties of this substance, and indicate how they differ from those of formaldehyde. (London Inter. B.Sc.)

61. Describe the preparation of acetaldehyde from ethyl alcohol. On what grounds is it thought that the molecule of acetaldehyde contains the group —CHO? Show that the chemical properties of acetaldehyde and formaldehyde are not always similar by contrasting their reactions with one chosen reagent. (London Inter. B.Sc.)

62. Describe briefly the preparation of acetaldehyde. With the aid of formulae (no experimental details are required) show how acetaldehyde might be converted into (*a*) ethyl bromide, (*b*) acetic acid, (*c*) acetyl chloride, (*d*) acetone. (Cambridge H.S.C.)

63. Briefly describe how crude acetaldehyde is prepared from ethyl alcohol, and state how it may be obtained from sodium or calcium acetate, writing the equation for this reaction. How does acetaldehyde react with (*a*) sodium hydrogen sulphite, (*b*) phosphorus pentachloride, (*c*) ammonia? Name the organic products and give their structural formulae. Quote three simple chemical tests for acetaldehyde.

(Oxford H.S.C.)

64. Give the evidence on which the structural formula of acetaldehyde is based. Make a brief survey, comparing the reactions of acetaldehyde with those of acetone. (London Inter. B.Sc.)

65. Give one example in each case of polymerisation, addition and condensation reactions as shown by aldehydes. Show how, in the case of one of these reactions, the product may be used to identify an aldehyde, and in another case, to purify an aldehyde. (London Inter. B.Sc.)

66. The reaction of a solution of hydrogen peroxide on an alkaline solution of formaldehyde liberates hydrogen and also produces formic acid. How would you propose to determine the weights of each product and each reactant concerned in the reaction? (J.M.B.)

67. How is acetone prepared on a large scale? How does acetone react with (*a*) reducing agents, (*b*) phenylhydrazine, (*c*) bleaching powder, (*d*) phosphorus pentachloride? (Cambridge 1st M.B.)

68. Describe (*a*) a large scale and (*b*) a laboratory process for the production of acetone. How would you detect the presence of acetone in a dilute aqueous solution? By what arguments would you prove that the formula contains a carbonyl group? (Oxford H.S.C.)

69. Indicate by means of equations three reactions common to aldehydes and ketones. How is acetaldehyde prepared (*a*) in the laboratory, (*b*) commercially? How would you distinguish between an aldehyde and a ketone? (London H.S.C.)

70. Starting from acetic acid, outline the methods you would use to prepare (a) methane, (b) acetone, (c) acetaldehyde. Give two reactions in which acetone and acetaldehyde behave similarly, and two in which their behaviour differs. (London H.S.C.)

71. By what reactions can the constitution of acetone be established? Name and formulate the compounds obtained from acetone and acetaldehyde respectively with hydrogen cyanide. In the latter case name and give the formula of the substance which results on hydrolysis.
(London Inter. B.Sc.)

72. Give the names and structural formulae of two isomers with the formula C_3H_6O, neither of which contains a hydroxyl group. State two methods of preparing each of these substances, and by means of equations indicate how they react with (a) sodium hydrogen sulphite, (b) phosphorus pentachloride, (c) phenyl hydrazine. Name the organic products. In what respects do the two isomers differ from each other chemically? (Oxford H.S.C.)

73. Give the constitutional formulae for a primary, a secondary, and a tertiary alcohol. How do normal propyl alcohol, $CH_3.CH_2.CH_2OH$, and iso-propyl alcohol $(CH_3)_2.CH.OH$, react when oxidised with chromic acid? In the case of iso-propyl alcohol, state how you would obtain, purify, and identify the principal product, and describe its behaviour (a) when heated with an aqueous solution of hydroxylamine, (b) when reduced with sodium amalgam. (London Inter. B.Sc.)

SECTION VII

FATTY ACIDS. Chapter XIV (p. 229)

74. Indicate the stages by which acetic acid is obtained commercially from calcium carbide. State how you could obtain from glacial acetic acid (a) acetyl chloride, (b) acetamide, (c) acetone, (d) methyl cyanide. Summarise the evidence which justifies the conclusion that acetic acid contains a methyl group. (Oxford H.S.C.)

75. Describe in outline how acetic acid may be prepared using calcium carbide. Starting with acetic acid, how can (a) methylamine, (b) ethylamine, (c) chloroform be prepared? (Cambridge H.S.C.)

76. What is the evidence for the constitutional formula of acetic acid? How may acetic acid be converted into (a) methane, (b) acetone, (c) acetamide, (d) monochloroacetic acid? (London Inter. B.Sc.)

77. Explain carefully the way in which the structural formulae of (a) acetic acid, (b) acetone have been established. (J.M.B.)

78. Show, by means of properly balanced equations only, how the following substances may be obtained, starting from acetic acid : (a) methane, (b) ethane, (c) monochloroacetic acid, (d) acetyl chloride, (e) acetic anhydride, (f) acetone, (g) aminoacetic acid, (h) acetaldehyde, (i) methyl cyanide (acetonitrile). (J.M.B.)

79. Describe in outline the reactions whereby acetic acid may be converted into (a) acetic anhydride, (b) acetone, (c) acetamide, (d) ethylamine, (e) acetonitrile (methyl cyanide). (Oxford H.S.C.)

80. Starting from acetic acid, how may (a) ethane, (b) acetonitrile, (c) propionic acid be prepared? How may acetic acid be obtained from each of these three compounds? (Cambridge 1st M.B.)

81. How would you prepare a specimen of formic acid in the laboratory? State the chemical properties of the acid and show that they agree with the formula usually assigned to it. (London H.S.C.)

82. State briefly how formic acid (or one of its salts) can be produced from (a) carbon monoxide, (b) chloroform, (c) hydrogen cyanide. How do formates react with (i) concentrated sulphuric acid, (ii) silver nitrate solution, (iii) acidified potassium permanganate solution?

(Oxford H.S.C.)

83. Describe the preparation of anhydrous formic acid from oxalic acid. How may formic acid be converted into (a) oxalic acid, (b) formamide, (c) formaldehyde? (Cambridge 1st M.B.)

84. Give an account of the properties of formic acid and of any two of its salts with which you are familiar. If formic acid vapour be passed through a hot tube, it is decomposed in the following ways :

(a) $H.COOH = H_2O + CO$, (b) $H.COOH = H_2 + CO_2$.

Describe briefly the experiments you would carry out to find the relative proportions in which these two reactions had taken place. (Cambridge H.S.C.)

85. Explain what you understand by the terms " carbonyl group " and " carboxyl group ". Give an account of the principal reactions of acetone, acetaldehyde, and acetic acid. Do these reactions provide evidence that a carbonyl group is present in acetic acid?

(Cambridge H.S.C.)

SECTION VIII

Acid Chlorides, Anhydrides, Amides, Esters and Nitriles of the Fatty Acids, and the Isonitriles. Chapter XV (p. 246)

86. Starting from acetic acid, outline the preparation of acetyl chloride and of acetic anhydride. How do these substances react with (a) ethyl alcohol, (b) ammonia, (c) water? (Cambridge H.S.C.)

87. Describe the preparation of acetamide from ammonium acetate. How, and under what conditions, does acetamide react with (a) sodium hydroxide, (b) sulphuric acid? (Cambridge H.S.C.)

88. Describe two methods for the preparation of acetamide. What is the action on acetamide of (a) nitrous acid, (b) bromine and sodium hydroxide, (c) phosphorus pentoxide? (Cambridge 1st M.B.)

89. Compare the properties of methylamine and acetamide. Describe the test you would make to show the presence of nitrogen in acetamide, and indicate, by means of equations, the reactions involved in this test. (Cambridge H.S.C.)

90. What classes of substances are obtained when the hydroxyl group in (a) a primary monohydric alcohol, and (b) a monobasic organic acid is replaced by the group NH_2? Name, and give a brief account of the preparation (not necessarily in the pure state) of the NH_2 compounds from any such alcohol and acid you may choose. (London Inter. B.Sc.)

91. Describe the laboratory preparation of ethyl acetate. Discuss the reaction involved from the standpoint of chemical equilibrium, and indicate to what extent your method of preparation realises the optimum conditions for the reaction. (Cambridge H.S.C.)

92. Starting from ethyl alcohol and acetic acid, describe how you would prepare a pure sample of ethyl acetate. Give two methods by which you would demonstrate the purity of your product. (London 2nd M.B.)

93. Describe two methods for preparing esters. How do esters react with (a) water, (b) aqueous caustic soda, (c) concentrated ammonia? (London Inter. B.Sc.)

94. Describe in detail the preparation and purification of ethyl acetate. Indicate briefly how the hydrolysis of ethyl acetate may be used to determine the molecular weight of acetic acid, given that this acid is monobasic. (Cambridge H.S.C.)

95. What is an ester? Give three methods for the preparation of esters. On boiling 0·277 gm. of an ester with 50 c.c. of decinormal sodium hydroxide until the reaction was complete, the resulting liquid required 18·5 c.c. of decinormal hydrochloric acid for neutralisation. If the ester were derived from a monobasic acid and a monohydric alcohol, what would be its molecular weight? (J.M.B.)

96. State how you would obtain (a) ethyl propionate from a silver salt, (b) methyl acetate from an acid chloride. Write equations for the reactions. Outline the preparation and purification of ethyl acetate. What are the functions of sulphuric acid in the preparation? Indicate how you could obtain glacial acetic acid from ethyl acetate.
(Oxford H.S.C.)

97. What is meant by (a) an amine, (b) an amide? Give two examples of each class. What reactions have amines and amides in common, and in what respects do they differ? Describe the preparation of acetamide from acetic acid. (Oxford H.S.C.)

98. What is (a) an amide, (b) a primary amine? Write the structural formulae of oxamide and ethylamine. Given a supply of glacial acetic acid and 0·880 ammonia, describe how you would obtain a specimen of acetamide. State how acetamide reacts with (a) sodium hydroxide, (b) nitrous acid, (d) phosphorus pentoxide. (Oxford H.S.C.)

99. By what reactions are nitriles distinguished from isocyanides? How may nitriles be utilized in order to convert (a) methyl alcohol into acetic acid, (b) acetic acid into ethylamine. Mention two methods of preparing isocyanides? (Oxford H.S.C.)

100. Outline one method for the preparation of methylamine free from other amines. How may methylamine be converted to methyl isocyanide? Write equations describing how methyl cyanide and iso-cyanide behave on reduction and on hydrolysis. What evidence do these reactions provide for the structural formulae of these compounds?
(Cambridge H.S.C.)

101. Describe briefly, with the aid of formulae, the preparation of two substances of molecular formula C_2H_3N from hydrocyanic acid, and state one other method for the preparation of each. Give an account of the reactions of these two substances which prove the structures assigned to them. Explain their relationships to hydro-cyanic acid. (Cambridge H.S.C. (A).)

SECTION IX

Chloro-, Hydroxy-, and Amino-fatty Acids.

Chapter XVI (p. 264)

102. How is monochloroacetic acid prepared? How does it react with (a) alkali, (b) potassium phthalimide, (c) phosphorus pentachloride? (Cambridge 1st M.B.)

103. Outline the evidence which establishes the formula of acetic acid as $CH_3.COOH$. Describe the preparation from acetic acid of (a) acetyl chloride, (b) monochloroacetic acid. How would you show that the chlorine atoms in these two substances have entered different positions in the acetic acid molecule? (London Inter. B.Sc.)

104. Describe the synthesis of lactic acid. Give an account of the reactions of this acid which throw light upon its constitution. (Cambridge 1st M.B.)

105. How is lactic acid usually prepared? By what reactions has the formula of lactic acid been proved? Explain the existence of the different varieties of lactic acid, and how they can be separated. (London 2nd M.B.)

106. Write equations showing how lactic acid may be prepared in the laboratory from (a) propionic acid, (b) acetaldehyde. In what important respect would the synthetic lactic acid differ from the lactic acid present in fatigued muscle? Give an explanation of this difference. (London 2nd M.B.)

107. Describe the preparation of glycine from monochloroacetic acid. How does glycine react with (a) soda-lime, (b) sodium hydroxide solution, (c) ethyl alcohol and hydrogen chloride, (d) sodium nitrite and hydrochloric acid? (Cambridge 1st M.B.)

108. Describe the preparation of amino-acetic acid. Compare and contrast its properties with those of (a) methylamine, (b) acetic acid. (Cambridge 1st M.B.)

109. Briefly describe the preparation of amino-acetic acid, acetamide, and methylamine from acetic acid. What is the action of nitrous acid on these three substances? (London Inter. B.Sc.)

110. What characteristic properties are conferred on a molecule by the presence of the group NH_2? Illustrate your answer by reference to ethylamine, amino-acetic acid, and acetamide. Outline the steps by which amino-acetic acid and acetamide might be obtained from ethylamine. (Cambridge H.S.C.)

111. Why is it impossible to titrate an amino-acid directly against an alkali? What method is employed to overcome this difficulty? Give reasons why the method you describe is satisfactory. (University of Cape Town.)

SECTION X

Aliphatic Dibasic Acids. Chapter XVII (p. 282)

112. Give in outline an account of the properties, constitution, and the basis of two methods of estimation of urea. (London 2nd M.B.)

113. Give an account of the constitution and distinguishing properties of urea. How could you prepare a specimen of this substance (a) synthetically, (b) from a natural source? (London 2nd M.B.)

114. Describe Wöhler's synthesis of urea. How may urea be prepared on a large scale? State what reactions occur when urea is (a) heated, (b) boiled with aqueous sodium hydroxide, (c) heated with sodium nitrite and dilute hydrochloric acid. (London Inter. B.Sc.)

115. How did Wöhler synthesise urea? Why was this synthesis a landmark in the history of chemistry? How does urea react with (a) nitric acid, (b) caustic soda, (c) nitrous acid, (d) a mixture of bromine and caustic soda? (Oxford H.S.C.)

116. Outline a method for the preparation of oxalic acid on a large scale. Starting from oxalic acid how would you prepare (a) ethyl oxalate, (b) formic acid, (c) oxamide? (University of Calcutta.)

117. How is oxalic acid obtained from carbon monoxide? How may oxalic acid be converted into (a) formic acid, (b) carbon monoxide, (c) cyanogen, (d) dimethyl oxalate? (Cambridge 1st M.B.)

118. How would you prepare a crystalline specimen of oxalic acid in the laboratory? Give details of one method of manufacturing this acid. Briefly describe how ethyl oxalate is prepared. What is the effect of (a) adding a concentrated solution of ammonia to this ester, (b) distilling the solid product of (a) with phosphorus pentoxide? (Oxford H.S.C.)

119. Describe in detail the preparation of acetamide from acetic acid. In what respects do acetamide, oxamide, and urea resemble each other? By what chemical tests would you distinguish between them? (Oxford H.S.C.)

120. Give an account of the preparation of methyl oxalate from oxalic acid. How can methyl oxalate be converted into oxamide and the latter into cyanogen? (Cambridge 1st M.B.)

SECTION XI

ISOMERISM. Chapter XVIII (p. 302)

121. What is meant by isomerism? Write the structural formulae of two isomers containing chlorine, of two containing nitrogen, and of two isomeric esters. Describe one chemical method of distinguishing between each pair of isomers. Describe briefly the isomerism of the tartaric acids. (Oxford H.S.C.)

122. Define the terms " structural isomerism " and " stereoisomerism ", and illustrate each of these types of isomerism by two examples. Explain why (a) racemic acid, and (b) mesotartaric acid are optically inactive, and indicate briefly how one of these substances can be resolved into optically active forms. (London Inter. B.Sc.)

123. What do you understand by the terms (a) structural isomerism, (b) geometrical isomerism, (c) optical isomerism? Illustrate your answer by means of two pairs of isomerides in each class. How is it possible to separate the components of a mixture of optical isomerides? (London Inter. B.Sc.)

R   D.C.

124. Discuss two cases of isomerism of carbon compounds, in one of which a three-dimensional formula is necessary to account for the isomerism. (Cambridge H.S.C.)

125. Write an account of the various types of isomerism encountered in organic chemistry. (London 2nd M.B.)

126. Write an account of the isomerism exhibited by lactic acid.
(London H.S.C.)

127. Explain how acetaldehyde may be converted to lactic acid, and discuss briefly the constitution of this acid. How many modifications of lactic acid are known, and how is their isomerism explained?
(Cambridge H.S.C.)

128. Write equations for a series of reactions by which lactic acid might be prepared from ethyl alcohol. What evidence goes to show that lactic acid contains (*a*) a hydroxyl group, (*b*) a carboxyl group? Explain how a study of the isomerism of lactic acid leads on to a knowledge of the directions of the four valencies of the carbon atom.
(London Inter. B.Sc.)

129. Explain what is meant by (*a*) structural isomerism, illustrating your answer by reference to compounds of molecular formula C_3H_8O; and (*b*) stereoisomerism, illustrating your answer with an account of the lactic acids. In each case point out where the physical and chemical properties of the isomers are similar and where they are different.
(Cambridge H.S.C.)

130. How may tartaric acid be synthesised from ethylene? Give an account of the optical isomerism of tartaric acid. (Cambridge 1st M.B.)

131. Outline a series of reactions whereby *either* lactic acid *or* tartaric acid may be synthesised from carbon. Write an account of the particular type of isomerism shown by these acids. (Oxford H.S.C.)

132. Describe the isomerism shown by:

    (*a*) chlorides of the molecular formula $C_2H_4Cl_2$,
    (*b*) esters of the molecular formula $C_3H_6O_2$,
    (*c*) acids of the molecular formula $C_3H_6O_3$.

Indicate in each case how the different isomers may be distinguished. (Cambridge H.S.C.)

133. An optically active compound had C 40·4 per cent., H 7·85 per cent., N 15·75 per cent., and a molecular weight of about 90. It was treated in aqueous solution with hydrochloric acid and sodium nitrite; nitrogen was evolved and an optically active acid A, having C 40·0 per cent., H 6·67 per cent., was produced. Write structural formulae for these compounds, and an equation for the reaction involved. How might an inactive compound isomeric with A be synthesised?
(O. and C. H.S.C.)

134. Explain the terms (*a*) asymmetric synthesis; (*b*) optical inactivity due to internal compensation. Write structural formulae of all the optical isomers of the following:

$$CH_3—CHBr—CHOH—COOH;$$
$$(CH_3)_2=CH—CO—COOH.$$

(University of Melbourne.)

SECTION XII

POLYHYDRIC ALCOHOLS AND THE CARBOHYDRATES.

Chapter XIX (p. 320) and Chapter XX (p. 332)

135. Give two ways in which glycol may be obtained from ethylene. Describe the reactions by which the following may be obtained from glycol : (a) oxalic acid, (b) succinic acid, (c) acetylene, (d) ethylene chlorohydrin. (Cambridge 1st M.B.)

136. What do you understand by the term " polyhydric alcohol "? Name, and give the formulae of, two such substances. In one case describe how the substance may be prepared in the laboratory, and state what happens when it reacts with hydrogen chloride.
(London Inter. B.Sc.)

137. Describe one method by which glycerol is manufactured. Describe an experiment by which it may be proved that glycerol contains three hydroxyl groups. (Cambridge H.S.C.)

138. Give an account of the process and of the reactions involved in the production of ethyl alcohol and of glycerol from a suitable carbohydrate. (London 2nd M.B.)

139. What are the chief sources of glycerol? How is it obtained pure from any of these sources? State the action of (a) nitric acid, and (b) oxalic acid on glycerol. (University of Calcutta.)

140. How is glucose manufactured? Discuss its constitution. How is fructose converted into glucose? (University of Bombay.)

141. How does glucose react with (a) phenylhydrazine, (b) acetic anhydride, (c) reducing agents, (d) oxidising agents? What conclusions concerning the structure of glucose can be drawn from these reactions?
(Cambridge 1st M.B.)

142. How is fructose prepared? How would you convert fructose into (a) glucose, (b) n-hexyl iodide, (c) glucosone, (d) penta-acetyl fructose? (Cambridge 1st M.B.)

143. How may (a) glucose, (b) fructose be obtained from cane sugar? How does fructose react with (a) phenylhydrazine, (b) acetic anhydride, (c) oxidising agents, (d) reducing agents? (Cambridge 1st M.B.)

144. Compare and contrast the properties of glucose and fructose. What do you know about the structures of these sugars and their chemical significance? (London 2nd M.B.)

145. Give an outline of the evidence by which the constitutional formula of glucose has been established. How is glucose related to sucrose and lactose? (London 2nd M.B.)

146. Give an example of a reducing sugar. Discuss its structure in relation to its physical and chemical properties. (London 2nd M.B.)

147. Mention two disaccharides and their characteristic properties. What are the different methods by which they can be hydrolysed?
(University of Calcutta.)

148. Write a short account of the polysaccharides. (University of Cape Town.)

149. What is a polysaccharide? Name the polysaccharides which yield only glucose on hydrolysis. How is starch prepared and what are the intermediate products formed during its hydrolysis?
(University of Calcutta.)

SECTION XIII

AROMATIC HYDROCARBONS AND CERTAIN OF THEIR
DERIVATIVES

Chapter XXI (p. 357), Chapter XXII (p. 362), Chapter XXIII (p. 374)

150. If you were given a liquid hydrocarbon, what experiments would you make to decide whether it was aliphatic or aromatic? Starting from benzene, how would you prepare specimens of (a) toluene, (b) phenol, (c) benzoic acid?   (J.M.B.)

151. How may benzene be converted into toluene, and thence into benzaldehyde? How, and under what conditions, does toluene react with (a) chlorine, (b) nitric acid?   (Oxford H.S.C.)

152. How may benzene be converted into (a) salicylic acid, (b) benzoic acid, (c) chlorobenzene, (d) benzaldehyde?   (Cambridge 1st M.B.)

153. How may benzene be converted into (a) iodobenzene, (b) benzene sulphonamide, (c) salicylic acid, (d) benzamide?

(Cambridge 1st M.B.)

154. Compare the chemical properties of the paraffins, the olefines, and the aromatic hydrocarbons, illustrating your answer by reference to methane, ethylene and benzene.   (Cambridge H.S.C.)

155. State and explain how ethane, ethylene, and benzene react (if at all) in the presence of chlorine, hydrogen chloride, sulphuric acid, nitric acid, and ozone. What evidence is given by these reactions of the constitutional formulae of these hydrocarbons?   (Cambridge H.S.C.)

156. Summarise the evidence upon which the ring structure for benzene is based.   (Cambridge H.S.C.)

157. Discuss briefly the structure of benzene. The introduction of a phenyl group into a compound tends to make it more acidic, while the introduction of an alkyl group has the opposite effect. Comment on this statement with reference to ammonia, aniline, methylamine, and any other compounds which illustrate this effect.

(Cambridge H.S.C.)

158. How may sodium benzene sulphonate be prepared from benzene? How, and under what conditions, does this compound react with (a) sodium hydroxide, (b) potassium cyanide?

(Cambridge 1st M.B.)

159. Benzene reacts with sulphuric acid to give a compound having an acid reaction, and so does ethylene. Describe the reactions, and discuss the constitutions of the two substances produced. In what other way may the compound obtained from ethylene be prepared?

(J.M.B.)

160. Describe the preparation from benzene of (a) nitrobenzene, (b) m-dinitrobenzene.

SECTION XIV

ANILINE AND THE DIAZO-COMPOUNDS

Chapter XXIV (p. 387) and Chapter XXV (p. 396)

161. Describe the preparation of aniline from nitrobenzene, and explain the principle of the process used to isolate it from the reaction mixture. (Oxford H.S.C.)

162. How would you prepare a sample of aniline from benzene? What reactions occur when aniline is treated with (*a*) acetic anhydride, (*b*) hydrochloric acid, (*c*) nitrous acid? (London 2nd M.B.)

163. Describe the preparation of aniline from benzene. How may aniline be converted into benzanilide, (*b*) benzylamine, (*c*) phenylhydrazine, (*d*) benzene? (Cambridge 1st M.B.)

164. Describe how aniline is prepared in the laboratory. How does it react with (*a*) hydrochloric acid, (*b*) sodium nitrite and hydrochloric acid, (*c*) chloroform and potassium hydroxide, (*d*) acetic acid?
(O. and C. H.S.C.)

165. Outline the steps in the production of pure benzene from coal tar. Starting from benzene, describe how aniline is prepared in the laboratory. Write equations for the different reactions, and name the intermediate compounds produced. Quote two chemical tests for aniline. (Oxford H.S.C.)

166. Describe the preparation of an aqueous solution of phenyl diazonium chloride. How can the following be obtained from the solution : (*a*) phenylhydrazine, (*b*) benzylamine, (*c*) iodobenzene, (*d*) phenol, (*e*) benzene? (Cambridge 1st M.B.)

167. What is meant by diazotisation? Describe how you would carry out the process in any one case. How is it utilized in producing substitution derivatives of benzene? (Oxford H.S.C.)

168. What is meant by diazotisation? Describe briefly the diazotisation of aniline, and show by means of equations the principal types of reaction into which diazonium salts may enter. (J.M.B.)

169. What are diazo-compounds? Indicate their importance in organic synthesis. (University of Bombay.)

SECTION XV

PHENOLS.   Chapter XXVII (p. 417)

170. Describe in outline two methods by which phenol can be obtained from benzene. In one case indicate how you would purify the product. (Cambridge H.S.C.)

171. Describe two methods by which phenol may be prepared from benzene. How may phenol be converted into (*a*) phenyl acetate, (*b*) benzene, (*c*) aspirin? (Cambridge 1st M.B.)

172. How may phenol be obtained from aniline? Give an account of the properties and the chief reactions of phenol. How would you separate a mixture of phenol and benzoic acid? (Cambridge H.S.C.)

173. What is the reaction of phenol with (a) sodium hydroxide solution, (b) bromine water, (c) ferric chloride solution, (d) benzoyl chloride and sodium hydroxide solution? (J.M.B.)

174. Give in outline two methods by means of which phenol can be prepared from benzene. What happens when phenol is treated with (a) aqueous ferric chloride, (b) bromine water, (c) caustic soda, (d) aqueous sodium carbonate? (O. and C. H.S.C.)

175. How is phenol obtained commercially? Describe its chief physical and chemical properties, pointing out in what respects it (a) resembles, (b) differs from an alcohol. By what tests would you recognise phenol? (J.M.B.)

176. Give an account of the properties of the —OH group in organic compounds, illustrating your answer by reference to ethyl alcohol, acetic acid, and phenol. (Cambridge H.S.C.)

SECTION XVI

Benzyl Alcohol, Benzaldehyde, Benzoic Acid and Salicylic Acid

Chapter XXVIII (p. 423)

177. Describe the preparation of (a) phenol from benzene, (b) benzyl alcohol from toluene. By what chemical tests could you distinguish phenol from benzyl alcohol? (Cambridge 1st M.B.)

178. How would you prepare benzaldehyde? Describe how you would prepare and isolate a characteristic derivative of benzaldehyde.
(O. and C. H.S.C.)

179. Outline two methods by which benzaldehyde may be prepared from toluene. Compare and contrast the properties of benzaldehyde and acetaldehyde with reference to their reactions with sodium hydroxide, sodium cyanide, Fehling's solution, and ammonia.
(Cambridge H.S.C.)

180. Describe one method for the preparation of benzaldehyde. Compare and contrast its properties with those of acetaldehyde.
(J.M.B.)

181. Starting with toluene, outline the laboratory preparation of pure benzaldehyde. Write equations for the reactions of benzaldehyde with (a) phenylhydrazine, (b) phosphorus pentachloride, (c) sodium hydrogen sulphite. Name the organic products. What are the chemical differences between acetaldehyde and benzaldehyde? (Oxford H.S.C.)

182. Briefly discuss each of the following :

(a) the action of hot concentrated alkali on (i) benzaldehyde, (ii) acetaldehyde ;

(b) the action of a mixture of sodium acetate and acetic anhydride on benzaldehyde ; what would be the product with sodium propionate and propionic anhydride?

(c) the reaction of benzaldehyde with itself in the presence of potassium cyanide ;

(d) the mechanism of the addition reaction between sodium bisulphite and benzaldehyde. (University of Melbourne.)

183. Give two ways by which benzoic acid may be prepared from benzene. Describe the reactions by which the following may be obtained from benzoic acid : (a) benzamide, (b) ethyl benzoate, (c) silver benzoate, (d) benzonitrile. (Cambridge 1st M.B.)

184. Give two methods by which benzoic acid may be prepared from toluene. How may benzoic acid be converted into (a) benzene, (b) ethyl benzoate, (c) benzoyl chloride, (d) silver benzoate? (Cambridge 1st M.B.)

185. How may benzaldehyde and benzoic acid be obtained from toluene? Compare and contrast the properties of (a) benzaldehyde and acetaldehyde, and (b) benzoic acid and acetic acid? (London 2nd M.B.)

186. Assuming that benzene can be represented as

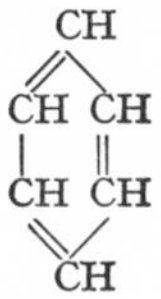

$$CH$$
$$CH\quad CH$$
$$CH\quad CH$$
$$CH$$

discuss the evidence in support of the formula

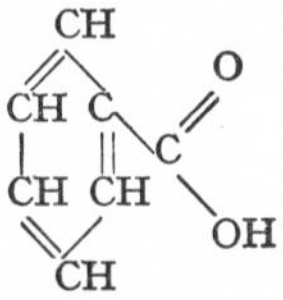

$$CH$$
$$CH\quad C\diagdown O$$
$$CH\quad CH \diagdown C$$
$$CH\qquad OH$$

for benzoic acid. Suggest two ways in which benzoic acid could be made from toluene. Name, and distinguish between the substances represented by the formulae $C_6H_5.CO.O.CH_3$ and $C_6H_5.O.CO.CH_3$.
(Cambridge H.S.C. (A).)

187. Describe the preparation of benzoyl chloride from benzoic acid. How does benzoyl chloride react with (a) water, (b) ammonia, (c) sodium hydroxide, (d) glycine? (Cambridge 1st M.B.)

188. Describe the preparation of (a) phenol from benzene, (b) salicylic acid from phenol. How may salicylic acid be converted into phenol? (Cambridge 1st M.B.)

189. Write short notes on salicylic acid and its derivatives, indicating chiefly their structural formulae and physiological properties and uses.
(University of Cape Town.)

190. A colourless organic liquid A was heated with an excess of potassium hydroxide until no further action took place, and the volatile distillate was collected. The latter was a neutral aqueous solution which gave the iodoform reaction, and yielded a volatile aldehyde on oxidation. When the residual alkaline solution was acidified, a colourless crystalline precipitate was obtained. When this precipitate was heated with calcium oxide, phenol was produced, and like the original substance A, the colourless crystalline precipitate gave a violet colour with ferric chloride. The saponification value of A was approximately 337.* What conclusions can you draw as to the nature of A? As far as possible give equations representing the above reactions.

* The saponification value of a fat is the number of milligrams of potassium hydroxide required to hydrolyse completely 1 gram of the fat.

SECTION XVII
GENERAL REACTIONS. Chapter XXIX (p. 439)

191. What is the effect of heat on : (*a*) calcium acetate, (*b*) calcium formate, (*c*) a mixture of calcium acetate and calcium formate? How do calcium acetate and calcium formate react with sulphuric acid? Name three other reactions in organic chemistry in which sulphuric acid acts as a dehydrating agent. (London Inter. B.Sc.)

192. Give an account of the action of heat on the following : (*a*) calcium acetate, (*b*) urea, (*c*) a mixture of aniline, chloroform and alcoholic sodium hydroxide, (*d*) a mixture of ammonium acetate and phosphorus pentoxide, (*e*) a freshly-prepared solution of sucrose in dilute hydrochloric acid. (Cambridge H.S.C. (A).)

193. Explain what is meant by hydrolysis in organic chemistry. Name the products of the hydrolysis of each of the following substances, and write equations for the reactions : (*a*) chloral, (*b*) benzyl chloride, (*c*) methyl cyanide, (*d*) methyl isocyanide, (*e*) sucrose, (*f*) benzonitrile. State briefly the conditions under which the hydrolysis is effected in each case. (Cambridge H.S.C. (A).)

194. Compare the action of an alcoholic solution of potassium hydroxide and an aqueous solution of potassium hydroxide on each of the following : (*a*) ethyl chloride, (*b*) ethylene dibromide. What is the effect of warming (i) a mixture of aniline and chloroform in an alcoholic solution of potassium hydroxide, (ii) a mixture of acetaldehyde and an aqueous solution of potassium hydroxide? (Cambridge H.S.C.)

195. Indicate nature of any change which occurs when sodium hydroxide is brought into contact with the following compounds : (*a*) ethylamine, (*b*) acetamide, (*c*) ammonium acetate, (*d*) acetonitrile (methyl cyanide), (*e*) chlorobenzene, (*f*) benzoyl chloride, (*g*) acetyl chloride, (*h*) ethyl ether, (*i*) ethyl acetate. Give balanced equations for the reactions described. (J.M.B.)

196. What do you understand by the term " hydrolysis "? Give, with equations, six examples of hydrolysis of naturally occurring compounds of different chemical groups. What chemical reagents are used to promote hydrolysis? (London 2nd M.B.)

197. Describe the reaction (if any) of sodium hydroxide solution on each of the following : acetamide, chloral hydrate, ethyl salicylate, aniline, phenyl cyanide, a fat. (Cambridge 1st M.B.)

198. Some organic compounds are reducing agents. With particular reference to their reducing action, give an account of two organic compounds not belonging to the same class. How may reducing power be estimated? (London 2nd M.B.)

199. Discuss the conditions employed, and name the products, when the following are reduced : ethyl iodide, ethyl nitrile, nitrobenzene, ethyl cyanide, phenyl diazonium chloride. (Cambridge 1st M.B.)

200. What products are formed by the action of acetic anhydride on (*a*) aniline, (*b*) salicylic acid, (*c*) glycerol, (*d*) diethylamine? In the case of one of these reactions, outline the method of isolation and purification of the final product. (Cambridge 1st M.B.)

201. What is meant by acetylation, and how is the process carried out? Write down the products of acetylation (if any) of the following compounds : $C_6H_5.NH.CH_3$, $C_6H_5CH_2NH_2$, $HOOC.COOH$,

$C_6H_4(OH)COOH$.

(Cambridge 1st M.B.)

202. Describe the action of sulphuric acid on each of the following : (a) ethyl alcohol, (b) benzene, (c) oxalic acid, (d) aniline, (e) sucrose.

(Cambridge 1st M.B.)

203. How and under what conditions does sulphuric acid react with four of the following : (a) oxalic acid, (b) ethyl alcohol, (c) benzene, (d) aniline, (e) acetamide? (Cambridge 1st M.B.)

204. What are Grignard Reagents, and how are they prepared? Show how they may be used to synthesise primary, secondary and tertiary alcohols. (University of Sydney.)

205. Give one example of the use of each of the following reagents in the preparation of an organic compound : (a) bleaching powder, (b) sodium, (c) nitric acid, (d) bromine and sodium hydroxide, (e) phosphorus trichloride, (f) acidified potassium dichromate. Experimental details are not required. (Cambridge H.S.C.)

206. Give a full account of the uses of each of the following in organic chemistry : sodium acetate, an alcoholic solution of potassium hydroxide, metallic sodium. (Cambridge H.S.C.)

207. Making use of two examples in each case, discuss the use of the following reagents in organic chemistry : benzoyl chloride, phenylhydrazine, potassium permanganate. Starting from benzene outline a method for preparing (a) benzoyl chloride, and (b) phenylhydrazine.

(London 2nd M.B.)

208. Give one example in each case of the use of the following reagents in organic chemistry, and write the structural formulae of the organic substances concerned : (a) nitrous acid, (b) sulphuric acid, (c) metallic sodium, (d) nitric acid, (e) zinc copper couple, (f) phosphorus trichloride. (J.M.B.)

209. Give one instance of the use of each of the following reagents in organic chemistry : (a) hydroxylamine, (b) phenylhydrazine, (c) silver oxide, (d) potassium permanganate, (e) fuming sulphuric acid. Include in your answer complete equations. (J.M.B.)

210. How are (a) phenylhydrazine, (b) formaldehyde, (c) acetic anhydride obtained? For what purposes are these substances used as reagents? (London 2nd M.B.)

211. Describe the preparation of acetoacetic ester. How may this compound be converted into (a) methyl ethyl ketone, (b) n-butyric acid? (Cambridge 1st M.B.)

212. Describe the preparation of diethyl malonate from acetic acid. How may this compound be used for the synthesis of (a) n-butyric acid, (b) iso-butyric acid? (Cambridge 1st M.B.)

213. Describe the preparation of diethyl malonate from chloroacetic acid. How may this compound be used for the synthesis of (a) propionic acid, (b) iso-butyric acid? (Cambridge 1st M.B.)

214. Explain and illustrate the meaning of any five of the following terms : (a) Williamson's continuous etherification process, (b) Wurtz's synthesis of paraffins, (c) Hofmann's reaction for preparing primary amines, (d) Schiff's reagent, (e) Grignard's reagent, (f) Fehling's solution.   (London Inter. B.Sc.)

215. What classes of compounds may be (a) brominated, (b) acetylated, (c) hydrolysed? Illustrate your answer with formulae wherever possible. (London 2nd M.B.)

216. Compare the action of (a) water, (b) aqueous caustic soda, (c) ammonia, (d) aqueous silver nitrate, on the following : (i) acetyl chloride, (ii) ethyl chloride, (iii) ethylamine hydrochloride.
(Cambridge H.S.C.)

217. Comment on the following suggested syntheses, pointing out any stages which are either inefficient or impossible, and also drawing attention to those which might be expected to work well. Insert the formulae of the reagents used where these are omitted. Suggest better ways of obtaining the final product in (a) and (b), either from the suggested starting material or from any other suitable substance.

(a) $CH_3.CH_3 \xrightarrow{Br_2} CH_3.CH_2Br \rightarrow CH_3.CH_2ONa \xrightarrow{CH_3.CH_2Br} (CH_3.CH_2)_2O$.

(b) $CH_3.CH_2.CO.OC_2H_5 \xrightarrow{NH_3} CH_3.CH_2.CO.NH_2 \xrightarrow{NHO_2} CH_3.CH_2.CO.OH$.

(c) $CH_3.Br \rightarrow CH_3CN \rightarrow CH_3.CO.OH \rightarrow CH_3.CH_2OH$.

(d) $CH_3.CO.CH_3 \xrightarrow{Cl_2} CH_3.CO.CCl_3 \xrightarrow{\text{aqueous NaOH}} CH_3.CO.CO.OH$.

(e) $CH_3.CH_2.CH.CH_3 \xrightarrow{\text{dehydrate}} CH_3.CH:CH.CH_3$.
$\quad\quad\quad\quad |$
$\quad\quad\quad OH$

(Cambridge H.S.C. (A).)

218. Describe in each case two reactions associated with the presence of the following groups in the molecules of organic compounds :

$\quad$ —$CH_2.OH$ $\quad\quad\quad$ =C=O $\quad\quad\quad$ —$CONH_2$

$\quad$ —C=O
$\quad\quad |$ $\quad\quad\quad\quad\quad\quad$ —$CH_2.NH_2$
$\quad\quad$ H

(J.M.B.)

219. Write short notes on any three of the following : (a) acetoacetic ester, (b) diazotisation, (c) Friedel and Crafts' reaction, (d) Perkin's reaction. (University of Bombay.)

220. Write notes on : (a) aldol condensation, (b) Claisen's reaction, (c) Perkin's reaction, (d) Cannizzaro's reaction, (e) Reimer-Tiemann reaction. (University of Bombay.)

SECTION XVIII

INDUSTRIAL ORGANIC CHEMISTRY.   Chapter XXX (p. 469)

221. Give a short account of the distillation of coal tar. Mention particularly three typical products (two hydrocarbons and one non-hydrocarbon), and state how you might obtain a specimen of each kind in a state of purity. (J.M.B.)

222. Briefly describe how benzene, toluene, and phenol are isolated from coal tar. Outline the reactions whereby (a) toluene and (b) phenol may be obtained from benzene. (Oxford H.S.C.)

223. Write an account of the methods used to produce other fuels, both liquid and gaseous, from coal. (Oxford H.S.C.)

224. Write a short account of the following : (a) the importance of water gas in industrial chemistry, (b) the reactions involved in the production of one azo-dye from benzene. (Oxford H.S.C. (A).)

225. Describe the preparation on a large scale of (a) methyl alcohol, (b) formaldehyde, (c) acetone. What are the uses of these substances? (Cambridge 1st M.B.)

226. How is calcium carbide manufactured? Why has its production been neglected in this country? Give some account of its increasing importance as the starting point for the preparation of many organic compounds. (Oxford H.S.C. (A).)

227. Discuss the synthesis of at least seven important organic chemicals, starting from lime and coke as essential raw materials. Indicate clearly the nature of the organic reactions involved, and the reagents required for carrying out these reactions.
(University of Sydney.)

228. What is the action of sodium hydroxide on a fat? Describe in detail the method of isolating the resulting products. What is meant by the hardening of fats? (Cambridge 1st M.B.)

229. State what you know of the composition of fats. How are fats converted into their constituents? By what reactions are fats identified? (London 2nd M.B.)

230. Mutton fat is a hard fat ; butter fat and beef fat are soft fats ; olive oil is a liquid. Discuss the factors which account for the differences in the physical properties of these fats. What methods would you use to demonstrate chemically the differences in composition of these fats? (London 2nd M.B.)

231. Write a short account of one of the following : (a) the nature of high explosives in general, with special reference to one derived from toluene and one from glycerine, (b) the nature of flame, with special reference to coal gas flames. (Oxford H.S.C.)

232. Outline two ways in which (a) methyl alcohol, (b) ethyl alcohol may be prepared on a large scale. Indicate briefly any points of chemical interest in the methods you describe. (O. and C. H.S.C.)

233. Write short notes on the chemical nature of the following common substances, and state what you know of their sources : (a) paraffin oil, (b) petrol, (c) paraffin wax, (d) carbolic acid, (e) soap, (f) animal fat, (g) coal gas, (h) natural gas, (i) methylated spirit.
(J.M.B.)

SECTION XIX

Questions demanding a General Knowledge of Organic Chemistry

(i) Preparations and properties of organic compounds

234. Describe how you would separate the following mixtures, and obtain each ingredient in a pure condition : (a) phenol and nitrobenzene, (b) toluene and benzoic acid, (c) nitrobenzene and aniline, (d) benzoic acid and phenol. (J.M.B.)

235. Describe the actions of sodium hydroxide, hydrochloric acid,

and nitrous acid on (a) urea, (b) glycine, stating the conditions under which the reactions take place. Do you consider that methylamine hydrochloride or methyl ammonium chloride is the more correct name for the substance obtained when hydrochloric acid reacts with methylamine? Give your reasons. (Cambridge H.S.C. (A).)

236. Certain classes of simple organic substances yield ammonia when boiled with sodium hydroxide solution. Give the structural formulae of *one* example of *each of three* such classes. Explain how you would distinguish between them, and show how each class of compound may be converted into the others. Give properly balanced equations where possible. (J.M.B.)

237. Write the structural formulae of (a) acetoacetic acid, (b) lactic acid, (c) hippuric acid, (d) glucose, (e) salicylic acid. Describe the chief chemical properties of any *two* of these compounds. (London 2nd M.B.)

238. How would you prepare ethyl acetate in the laboratory? By means of what reactions would you attempt to identify the following compounds : (a) sodium formate, (b) methylamine hydrochloride, (c) benzoic acid? (Cambridge H.S.C.)

239. Starting from benzene, how would you prepare specimens of (a) sodium benzene sulphonate, (b) aniline, (c) monochlorobenzene. (Give only *essential* practical details.) State in outline how each of the above substances could be reconverted into benzene. (J.M.B.)

240. Describe the preparation from benzene of (a) pure bromobenzene, (b) pure sodium benzene sulphonate. How would you show that the sulphonate contains the element sulphur? What is (i) a sulphonic chloride, (ii) a sulphonamide? (Oxford H.S.C.)

241. Some ammonium acetate was heated in a sealed tube, and a white crystalline substance A was obtained. On treatment with bromine and caustic potash solution, A produced a colourless gas B with a fishy ammoniacal smell. On dissolving B in water and adding nitrous acid, nitrogen was given off, and on fractional distillation the residual liquid gave a colourless volatile inflammable liquid C. On passing the vapour of C mixed with air over a heated copper spiral, a pungent gas D was formed which reduced Fehling's solution and ammoniacal silver nitrate. Identify A, B, C and D, write their formulae, and give equations for the changes in which they were formed. For what purposes are C and D used in everyday life? (J.M.B.)

242. How and under what conditions does sulphuric acid react with (a) chloral hydrate, (b) ethyl alcohol, (c) benzene, (d) acetamide?
(London Inter. B.Sc.)

243. Briefly describe the way in which toluene is produced commercially. Outline *one* method in each case for effecting the following changes : (a) toluene to benzoic acid, (b) benzoic acid to benzene, (c) phenol to benzene, (d) benzene to phenol. (Cambridge H.S.C.)

244. Identify the substances A, B, C, D in the following equations and write a short note on each of these reactions :

$$A + 3I_2 + 4KOH = CHI_3 + CH_3COOK + 3KI + H_2O.$$
$$B + HCl + 2H_2O = CH_3.CH(OH).COOH + NH_4Cl.$$
$$C + Br_2 + 4KOH = CH_3NH_2 + 2KBr + K_2CO_3 + 2H_2O.$$
$$D + NaOH \text{ (soda-lime)} = CH_3NH_2 + Na_2CO_3.$$

(Cambridge H.S.C. (A).)

245. In what ways does sulphuric acid act on organic compounds? Illustrate your answer by reference to its behaviour with (a) ethyl alcohol, (b) acetone, (c) acetaldehyde, (d) benzene. (Cambridge H.S.C.)

246. Describe the preparation of nitrobenzene in the laboratory. Compare the behaviour of the aromatic and aliphatic series as illustrated by the following reactions : (a) the action of bromine on benzene and ethylene, (b) the action of nitrous acid on aniline and ethylamine.
(Cambridge H.S.C.)

247. What general methods are available for the preparation of (a) aldehydes, (b) nitriles, (c) alkyl chlorides? (O. and C. H.S.C.)

248. Describe and write equations representing the reactions (if any) which occur between phosphorus pentachloride, and (a) ethyl alcohol, (b) acetaldehyde, (c) acetone, (d) ethyl ether, and (e) acetic acid.
(London Inter. B.Sc.)

249. Describe briefly how you would prepare any *five* of the following : (a) formic acid from glycerol, (b) ethyl mercaptan from ethyl iodide, (c) acetylene from ethylene, (d) chloroform from acetone, (e) glucose from maltose, (f) phenol from benzene. (London Inter. B.Sc.)

(ii) *Identification and estimation of organic substances*

250. Give an account of *three* of the following : (a) the estimation of nitrogen in an organic compound, (b) the estimation of urea in urine, (c) the detection of sulphur in an organic compound, (d) the acetylation of aniline. (Cambridge 1st M.B.)

251. How may the following substances be distinguished : (a) phenol and salicylic acid, (b) benzyl chloride and chlorobenzene, (c) methylamine and dimethylamine, (d) tartaric acid and citric acid, (e) glucose and cane sugar? (Cambridge 1st M.B.)

252. By what simple laboratory tests could you distinguish between the following : the ammonium salt of an organic acid : an amide ; a primary alkylamine : a primary arylamine? Give equations for the tests you would employ. (London 2nd M.B.)

253. How would you distinguish chemically between (a) chloroform and carbon tetrachloride, (b) formic and acetic acid, (c) benzyl chloride and chlorobenzene, (d) urea and oxamide? In the case of each pair of compounds give two tests, and state the effect of applying the test to both substances. (Oxford H.S.C. (A).)

254. How would you detect the presence in benzene of the following impurities, not more than one being present at a time : (a) phenol, (b) benzoic acid, (c) aniline, (d) nitrobenzene? How might any *two* of these impurities be separated in a pure state? (J.M.B.)

255. How would you distinguish between (a) chloroform and benzyl chloride, (b) phenol and benzoic acid, (c) aniline and ethylamine, (d) benzyl alcohol and phenol? Describe and explain *two* methods of differentiation in each case. (J.M.B.)

256. Give one reaction which can be used generally to distinguish between (a) aldehydes and ketones, (b) primary alcohols and tertiary alcohols, (c) aliphatic primary amines and secondary amines, (d) paraffins and olefines, (e) alkyl chlorides and acyl chlorides.
(University of Sydney.)

257. Give chemical equations to show what reactions take place in

the following cases, and give the names of the products formed : (*a*) iodoform is prepared from ethyl alcohol, (*b*) acetylene is passed into a dilute solution of sulphuric acid containing a little mercuric salt ; the product is treated with hydrogen cyanide and then hydrolysed, (*c*) 3-hexanol is cautiously oxidised, and the product somewhat more vigorously oxidised. (University of Cape Town.)

258. How would you distinguish in the laboratory between solutions of acetaldehyde, ethyl alcohol, methyl alcohol, and glucose?

(University of Cape Town.)

259. State briefly how you would attempt to distinguish in the laboratory between (*a*) sucrose, fructose and glucose, (*b*) acetaldehyde and propionaldehyde, (*c*) ethyl alcohol and isopropyl alcohol.

(University of Cape Town.)

(iii) *Constitution of organic compounds*

260. **Give a** brief account of the reactions on which the structural formulae of the following are based : (*a*) ethylene, (*b*) ethyl nitrite, (*c*) ethyl cyanide. (Cambridge 1st M.B.)

261. What evidence can you bring forward in support of the structural formula assigned to (*a*) acetic acid, (*b*) the two compounds having the formula $C_2H_4Cl_2$? (Oxford H.S.C. (A).)

262. How may the constitutional formulae of *three* of the following be established : (*a*) acetone, (*b*) methyl ethyl ether, (*c*) benzoic acid, (*d*) urea? (O. and C. H.S.C.)

263. Write the constitutional formulae of the following compounds : acetone, acetic anhydride, ethyl formate, methyl cyanide, acetamide. Describe (*a*) the laboratory preparation of any *one* of the above compounds, and (*b*) the chemical properties of any *two* of the compounds.

(Cambridge H.S.C.)

264. Describe one method of determining the percentage of nitrogen in an organic compound. Write the structural formulae of *four* nitrogenous organic compounds, other than ammonium salts, belonging to different classes, and mention *one* typical reaction of each compound.

(Oxford H.S.C.)

265. Give a clear account, by reference to the structural formulae and to *one* distinctive chemical reaction in each case, of the difference between (*a*) a chloro-acid and an acid chloride, (*b*) a primary amine and a secondary amine, (*c*) a primary amine and an acid amide, (*d*) an acid amide and a nitrile, (*e*) an ester and an ether, (*f*) a phenol and a primary alcohol. (J.M.B.)

266. Select four of the following, and for each of those you select, give the class of compounds to which it belongs, substances from which it can be made, and one reason why it is of medical interest : (*a*) chloroform, (*b*) mandelic acid, (*c*) paraldehyde, (*d*) barbituric acid, (*e*) amyl nitrite, (*f*) hippuric acid. (University of Cape Town.)

267. Give complete graphic formulae for the following substances, and state to which class of organic compounds each belongs : phosgene, formaldehyde, acetone, acetamide, isobutyl-*n*-propylamine, ethyl acetoacetate. (University of Cape Town.)

268. What do you understand by the term isomerism? Give **exa**mples and clear definitions of each of the following kinds of isomer-

ism : (a) nuclear isomerism, (b) position isomerism, (c) geometrical isomerism, (d) stereoisomerism.

How many isomers would you expect to be theoretically possible for each of the following : (a) aromatic substances of the formula $C_6H_4Br_2$, (b) hydrocarbons of the formula C_4H_8, (c) carboxylic acids of the formula $C_2H_2O_2ClI$?   (University of Sydney.)

269. Describe one commercial preparation of acetic acid. Give a full account of the reason for assigning the formula $CH_3.COOH$ to this substance.   (J.M.B.)

270. What are the constitutional conditions necessary for a compound (a) to be capable of existing in optically active forms, (b) to be capable of yielding an acetyl derivative, (c) to yield derivatives by the direct addition of suitable reagents, (d) to be a reducing agent?   Illustrate your answer by reference to two typical substances in each case.
(London 2nd M.B.)

271. Write an account of (a) the type of isomerism exhibited by the di-substitution derivatives of benzene, and (b) the type of isomerism exhibited by lactic acid.   (Oxford H.S.C. (A).)

(iv) *Synthesis of organic compounds*

272. How would you effect the following changes : (a) benzene to salicylic acid, (b) ethyl alcohol to lactic acid, (c) methyl iodide to ethylamine, (d) ethyl acetoacetate to

$$CH_3.CO.CH{\Large\langle}\begin{matrix}CH_3\\C_2H_5\end{matrix} \quad ?$$

(Cambridge 1st M.B.)

273. How may the following changes be effected : (a) acetic acid to ethyl alcohol, (b) glucose to fructose, (c) toluene to benzene, (d) benzene to iodobenzene, (e) methyl alcohol to acetic acid?   (Cambridge 1st M.B.)

274. How may the following changes be effected :
   (a) $CH_3.CH_2OH \rightarrow CH_3.CH_2.CH_2OH$,
   (b) $CH_3.CH_2OH \rightarrow CH_3.CH(OH).CH_3$,
   (c) $CH_3.CH_2OH \rightarrow CH_3.CH_2.O.CH_2.CH_3$,
   (d) $CH_3.CHO \quad \rightarrow CH_3.CH(OH).COOH$,
   (e) $C_2H_5.COOH \rightarrow CH_3.COOH$?

(Cambridge 1st M.B.)

275. How would you convert : (a) acetone to acetic acid, (b) ethyl alcohol to n-butyl alcohol, (c) ethylene to ethyl cyanide, (d) ethyl alcohol to diethylamine, (e) nitrobenzene to phenol?
(University of Sydney.)

276. Suggest methods for the preparation of any five of the following, starting in each case from ethyl alcohol : (a) ethyl bromide, (b) n-butane, (c) ethylidene chloride, (d) paraldehyde, (e) ethylene glycol, (f) acetal, (g) ethylene dichloride.   (University of Sydney.)

277. How may the following changes be effected :
   (a) $CH_3.COOH \rightarrow CH_3.CHO$,
   (b) $H.COOH \quad \rightarrow HOOC.COOH$,
   (c) $CH_2=CH_2 \rightarrow CH\equiv CH$?

(Cambridge 1st M.B.)

278. Using suitable examples in each case, give an account of the use of the following reagents in organic chemistry : (a) acetic anhydride, (b) phenyl hydrazine, (c) nitrous acid. (London 2nd M.B.)

279. Show by means of properly balanced equations how the following series of changes might be brought about : (a) acetamide→methyl-amine→methyl alcohol→methyl iodide→methyl cyanide→acetic acid →acetamide. Describe briefly the conditions under which those reactions occur. (J.M.B.)

280. Give chemical equations to indicate what takes place in the following : (a) urea is treated with an alkaline solution of sodium hypobromite, (b) acetaldehyde is treated with hydrogen cyanide, and the product is hydrolysed by boiling with dilute hydrochloric acid, (c) secondary n-butyl alcohol is oxidised, and the product obtained is strongly oxidised, (d) lactic acid is prepared from propionic acid. (University of Cape Town.)

281. Show by equations how four of the following preparations may be carried out : (a) mandelic acid from benzaldehyde, (b) picric acid from phenol, (c) alanine from propionic acid, (d) n-butyraldehyde from n-butyric acid, (e) ethylamine from methyl alcohol, (f) toluene from benzene, (g) acetamide from acetic acid. (University of Cape Town.)

(v) *The properties of groups and radicals*

282. Indicate briefly the reactions characteristic of the primary and secondary alcoholic groups, the carboxyl group, and the primary amino group. (London H.S.C.)

283. Compare and contrast the general properties of aromatic substances with those of the corresponding aliphatic compounds. (J.M.B.)

284. Describe *two* methods by which each of the following groups may be introduced into the benzene nucleus : (a) —COOH, (b) —OH, (c) —CH$_3$. (J.M.B.)

285. Give two reactions in each case to show the difference in properties exhibited by (a) the —OH group in alcohols as compared with the —OH group in acids, (b) the —NH$_2$ group in amines as compared with the —NH$_1$ group in amides. (London Inter. B.Sc.)

286. What general properties are associated with the groups :

$$—CONH_2, \quad —COOH, \quad >O?$$

(Cambridge 1st M.B.)

287. Select three of the following and give for each of those selected one reaction (with equations) which can be used to prove the presence of that group or bond : (a) hydroxyl group, (b) carbonyl group, (c) secondary amino group, (d) unsaturated bond.

(University of Cape Town.)

(vi) *Definitions*

288. Explain, with examples, the following terms : (a) isonitrile, (b) osazone, (c) biuret reaction, (d) secondary alcohol, (e) amino-acid. (Cambridge 1st M.B.)

289. Write short notes on : (a) mutarotation, (b) tautomerism, (c) unsaturation, (d) homologous series. Give one example of each. (London 2nd M.B.)

290. Give one illustration with any necessary brief explanation of each of the following : (a) homologous series, (b) isomerism, (c) stereo-isomerism not associated with optical activity, (d) tautomerism or dynamic isomerism, (e) saponification value. (London 2nd M.B.)

291. Explain with examples the meaning of the following : (a) a fat, (b) a nitrile, (c) a disaccharide, (d) the biuret reaction, (e) a quaternary ammonium salt, (f) a sulphonic acid. (Cambridge 1st M.B.)

292. What do you understand by the following terms : (a) homologous series, (b) polymerisation, (c) hydrolysis, (d) substitution, (e) nitration, (f) unsaturated hydrocarbon? Illustrate each term by one example. (Oxford H.S.C.)

293. Explain what is meant by (a) an ester, (b) a nitrile, (c) a ketone. Describe, with essential practical details, the preparation of *one* compound belonging to each class. By what tests would you identify the ester the preparation of which you have described? (J.M.B.)

294. What do you understand by (a) an unsaturated substance, (b) isomeric substances? Give *two* examples in each case, and describe and explain the experimental evidence relating to each of the examples chosen. (J.M.B.)

295. Explain the meaning of the following terms and give suitable examples : (a) isomerism, (b) unsaturated compounds, (c) homologous series, (d) esterification. (J.M.B.)

296. Define carefully any five of the following, illustrating your answers with specific examples : (a) polymerisation, (b) aromatic hydrocarbon, (c) Wurtz reaction, (d) acid anhydride, (e) fat, (f) monosaccharide, (g) sulphonation. (University of Sydney.)

297. Explain, giving one example of each, the meaning of the terms : alkyl radical ; enol form ; monosaccharide ; nitrile ; enzyme.
(University of Cape Town.)

298. Explain, with the help of one illustrative example in each case, what is meant by four of the following : (a) saponification, (b) the diazo reaction, (c) Cannizzaro's reaction, (d) the aldol condensation, (f) polymerisation, (e) tautomerism. (University of Cape Town.)

299. Explain and exemplify what you understand by the following terms : homologous series, secondary amine, asymmetric carbon atom, condensation, isomerism. (London Inter. B.Sc.)

(vii) *Calculations*

300. 0·6 gm. of a simple triglyceride was found to require 16·5 c.c. of N/2 potassium hydroxide for complete hydrolysis. Calculate the molecular weight of the triglyceride. The potassium salt of the monobasic acid obtained on hydrolysis was converted into the silver salt, which was found to contain 64·6 per cent. of silver. What is the molecular weight of the acid? $Ag = 108$, $K = 39$.
(Cambridge 1st M.B.)

301. A neutral organic liquid A, $C_9H_{14}O_6$, yields sodium acetate when it is boiled with sodium hydroxide solution ; and when 3·27 gm. of A are boiled with 50·0 c.c. of normal sodium hydroxide, 5·0 c.c. of normal sulphuric acid are required to neutralise the excess sodium hydroxide.

The other product resulting from this reaction is a syrupy hygroscopic liquid B, which is soluble in water; and 0·92 gm. of B yield 336 c.c. of hydrogen (measured at N.T.P.) when treated with sodium. Suggest structures for A and B, and explain these reactions. $C = 12$, $H = 1$, $O = 16$. (Cambridge H.S.C. (A).)

302. 0·500 gm. of an organic compound (containing C, H, and O only) gave 0·892 gm. CO_2, and 0·365 gm. H_2O on combustion. Its vapour density was 37. Give two of the possible structural formulae for the compound, and say how you would distinguish between the compounds with these formulae. $C = 12$, $O = 16$, $H = 1$.

(Cambridge H.S.C.)

303. 0·15 gm. of an organic compound dissolved in 80 c.c. of water lowered the freezing point by 0·059° C. The substance contained 40·7 per cent. of carbon, 23·7 per cent. of nitrogen, and 27·1 per cent. of oxygen, and also hydrogen. With nitrous acid it yielded a monobasic acid. Give the structure which is suggested by these results for the original substance, and explain how it will behave when treated with bromine and caustic soda.

Also calculate the weight of silver obtained on igniting 1 gm. of the silver salt of the monobasic acid. ($C = 12$, $N = 14$, $O = 16$, $H = 1$, $Ag = 108$. 1 gm.-molecule of a solute depresses the freezing point of 1,000 c.c. of water by 1·86.) (London H.S.C.)

304. 0·164 gm. of an organic compound gave on combustion 0·352 gm. of CO_2, and 0·108 gm. of H_2O. On heating 1 gm. with sodium hydroxide and absorbing the ammonia produced in 50 c.c. of N hydrochloric acid the resulting solution required 25·6 c.c. of N sodium hydroxide to neutralise it. The sodium salt produced by hydrolysis of the compound with sodium hydroxide, when heated with solid sodium hydroxide gave methane. Give the structural formula of the compound, suggest how it could be prepared, and represent by equations the action of sodium hydroxide on the compound. (London H.S.C.)

305. When the vapour of acetic acid is passed over heated alumina a liquid is obtained which :

(a) contains 62·07 per cent. of carbon ($C = 12$), and 10·34 per cent. of hydrogen,

(b) has vapour density 29,

(c) gives the " iodoform " reaction with iodine and an alkali,

(d) forms a crystalline compound with sodium bisulphite,

(e) does not reduce ammoniacal silver nitrate solution.

Identify the liquid, giving your reasons, and write the equations for its production by this method. (Oxford H.S.C.)

306. A colourless fuming liquid A containing oxygen was found on analysis to contain 59·79 per cent. of carbon, 3·56 per cent. of hydrogen, and 25·27 per cent. of chlorine. The density of its vapour was 0·0063 gm. per c.c. at N.T.P. When treated with ammonia it yielded a substance B, which when boiled with caustic soda gave off ammonia, leaving a residue of the sodium salt of a monobasic acid C. The molecular weight of C was 122. Identify the compounds A, B, and C. Write their structural formulae, and explain the reactions referred to. ($H = 1$, $C = 12$ $O = 16$, $Cl = 35·5$, 1 litre of hydrogen at N.T.P. weighs 0·09 gm.)

(Oxford H.S.C.)

307. What is (a) an ether, (b) an ester? Explain the meaning of the term isomerism : illustrate by reference to two ethers. On complete combustion 0·55 gm. of an ester gave 1·10 gm. of carbon dioxide and 0·45 gm. of water. The vapour density of the ester was 44. Find the molecular formula of this compound, and give the names and constitutional formulae of *three* esters to which it might apply. Indicate briefly a method of distinguishing between these esters chemically.

(Oxford H.S.C.)

308. A solid organic acid contains 19·05 per cent. of carbon and 4·75 per cent. of hydrogen. The usual tests for other elements give negative results, but on heating the acid at 100° C. water is given off. The vapour density of the ethyl ester of this acid is 73. What is the acid? By what tests would you confirm your deductions? How, and under what conditions, does this acid react with glycerol?

(Oxford H.S.C. (A).)

309. A compound A has the following composition : $C = 40·7\%$, $H = 8·5\%$, $N = 23·7\%$, $O = 27·1\%$. When A is refluxed with hydrochloric acid a compound B containing $40·0\%$ C, and belonging to a series with the general formula $C_nH_{2n}O_2$ is produced. Identify the compounds A and B. Indicate how methylamine hydrochloride can be obtained from A, and give an account of the properties of methylamine. ($C = 12$, $N = 14$.) (Oxford H.S.C.)

310. On treatment with hydroxylamine a colourless volatile liquid A yielded a white crystalline solid B, which contained 19·18 per cent. of nitrogen. A did not reduce Fehling's solution or ammoniacal silver nitrate. Its vapour density was 29. Identify A and B, and state how A might be prepared in the laboratory. ($H = 1$, $C = 12$, $O = 16$, $N = 14$.) (J.M.B.)

311. A mixture of propane, C_3H_8, with a gaseous hydrocarbon of the olefine series occupied 24 c.c. To burn the mixture completely 114 c.c. of oxygen were required and after the combustion 72 c.c. of carbon dioxide were left. Calculate (a) the formula of the olefine, (b) the composition of the mixture by volume. All volumes were measured at the same temperature and pressure. (J.M.B.)

312. A colourless solid A dissolves in water to form a solution which is neutral to litmus. When heated, A loses water to form another colourless neutral solid B which is also soluble in water. The substance A yields ammonia on treatment with cold sodium hydroxide solution, while B yields ammonia only on boiling with sodium hydroxide. When A is distilled with sulphuric acid, an acid distillate C is formed. C can be neutralised by treatment with calcium carbonate, and evaporation to dryness then leaves a solid residue D. When D is heated it decomposes yielding a volatile liquid C_3H_6O. Write down possible formulae for A, B, C and D, and give the structures of the substance C_3H_6O. Explain the reactions described above. What would happen if B were heated with phosphorus pentoxide? (Cambridge H.S.C. (A).)

313. A crystalline organic compound was found to contain : 27·3 per cent. carbon, 4·55 per cent. hydrogen, 31·8 per cent. nitrogen. When the compound was boiled with aqueous NaOH ammonia was slowly evolved. The aqueous solution, when evaporated to dryness and heated with concentrated H_2SO_4, gave off equal volumes of CO and CO_2. When it was heated with ethyl alcohol and H_2SO_4, the compound gave

an ester having a vapour density of 73 (H = 1), and ammonium sulphate was left in the reaction mixture. Deduce the molecular formula of the original compound, and follow out the above reactions.

(Cambridge H.S.C.)

314. An organic compound contains 40·0 per cent. carbon and 6·7 per cent. of hydrogen, and has a vapour density 30. Find its molecular formula, and suggest two possible structural formulae, and show clearly how to distinguish experimentally the two compounds you have specified. Write down a third possible structural formula corresponding to the molecular formula you have obtained. (O = 16, C = 12, H = 1.) (Cambridge H.S.C.)

315. An organic compound has the composition C 64·8 per cent., H 13·6 per cent., O 21·6 per cent. Calculate the empirical formula. Assuming this to be the molecular formula, give the possible constitutional formulae, and write down the equation for the action of phosphorus pentachloride on each isomer. (H = 1·01, C = 12·0, O = 16·0.) (Cambridge H.S.C.)

ANSWERS TO NUMERICAL QUESTIONS

8. NC_4H_{11}.   9. C_3H_8O.   10. C_3H_5ClO.   11. 6·53.

12. CON_2H_4.   13. C_4H_{10}.

14. CO, 2 c.c. ; CH_4, 3 c.c. ; H_2, 4 c.c. ; N_2, 1 c.c.

18. C_2H_6.   20. $C_4H_4N_2$.   21. C_3H_6.   22. C_3H_8.

48. C_2H_5CHO ; C_2H_5COOH.

58. $(CH_3)_3N$. $C_2H_5.CH_3.NH$; $CH_3.CH_2.CH_2.NH_2$; $(CH_3)_2CH.NH_2$.

95. 88.   133. $CH_3.CHOH.COOH$.   300. 218, 60·2.

302. Empirical formula $C_3H_6O_2$.   303. $CH_3.CO.NH_2$.   0·647 gm.

304. $CH_3.CN$.   306. A is C_6H_5COCl.   307. $C_4H_8O_2$.

308. $(COOH)_2$, $2H_2O$.   309. A is $CH_3.CO.NH_2$.

310. A is acetone.

311. C_3H_6.   50 per cent. each of propane and propylene.

313. $(CONH_2)_2$.   314. $C_2H_4O_2$.   315. $C_4H_{10}O$.

INDEX

The alphabetical order is decided without reference to the subdivision of the items into words, e.g. " Acetylation " precedes " Acetyl chloride ". Important references are printed in heavy type. Index references frequently lead to cross-references in the text. These should be consulted ; they are not normally repeated in the index.

Urea oxalate, 283, 285
Urease, 285, 287
Ureides, 286

Valency, *see* " Bond "
Vanadium pentoxide, 201, 484
Verdigris, 238
Veronal, 286
Vicinal additive compound, 126
Victor Meyer's method, 175
Vinegar, 164, 231
Vinyl acetate, 491
Vinyl chloride, 128
Vinyl ether, 491
Vinyl pyrrolidon, 491
Vital force, 29

Water gas, 167, 488 f.
Water molecule, structure of, 14
Westrol, 491

Westron, 132, 265, 491
Williamson's continuous etherification process, 177, 178 f.
Williamson's synthesis of ether, 140 f., 177
Wintergreen, oil of, 170, 434
Wöhler's synthesis of urea, 284
Wood pulp, 497
Wort, 497
Wurtz's reaction, 109, 111, 141

Xylene, 478

Yeast, 339, 353, 493, 497

Zinc-copper couple, 150, 140, 106
Zinc dust, 371, 363
Zinc lactate, 273, 309
Zymase, 339, 353, 493, 496